PRINCIPLES OF
Electricity

PRINCIPLES OF

Electricity

An Intermediate Text in Electricity and Magnetism

BY

LEIGH PAGE, Ph.D., 1884-

Late Professor of Mathematical Physics
Yale University

AND

NORMAN ILSLEY ADAMS, Jr., Ph.D.

Emeritus Professor of Physics
Yale University

FOURTH EDITION

D. VAN NOSTRAND COMPANY, Inc.

PRINCETON, NEW JERSEY

TORONTO   LONDON

MELBOURNE

[1969]

Van Nostrand Regional Offices: *New York, Chicago, San Francisco*

D. Van Nostrand Company, Ltd., *London*

D. Van Nostrand Company (Canada), Ltd., *Toronto*

D. Van Nostrand Australia Pty. Ltd., *Melbourne*

Published simultaneously in Canada by
D. Van Nostrand Company (Canada), Ltd.

Library of Congress Catalog Card No. 58-7963

PRINTED IN THE UNITED STATES OF AMERICA

PREFACE

The purpose of this book is to provide a comprehensive intermediate text suitable for college undergraduates who have completed general courses in physics and in the calculus.

Considerable space is devoted to the theory of electrical measurements in the belief that a didactic course should be accompanied by practice in the laboratory. Nevertheless, the main emphasis is placed not on applications of the theory, but on instilling correct concepts in the mind of the reader. While the relativity principle—so intimately connected with electromagnetism—is mentioned only incidentally, the point of view of that theory is maintained throughout. The electron theory of matter is adopted from the beginning and every effort is made to develop the material in a logical manner. Carefully selected problems are appended to most of the articles.

There are two approaches to the theory of magnetism. The traditional approach based on the magnetic pole concept is adopted in the body of the text, as it depends on easily observed quantities and it is especially convenient in the discussion of forces on magnets. However, the more fundamental but somewhat more difficult approach based on the interaction of current elements is preferred by some. Hence, this is given in Appendix A, so arranged that it can be presented in conjunction with Chapter VII.

Although there has been no change in point of view, the book has been brought up to date in the successive editions by the addition of new topics and by the omission of topics of diminishing interest. Material has been rearranged and clarified where experience has shown this to be desirable. The general treatment of units has been expanded and improved. Throughout the present edition m.k.s. practical units are employed, rather than the somewhat more fundamental c.g.s. units, in accordance with the modern trend. However, basic laws are expressed in appropriate c.g.s. units, as well as in m.k.s. practical units, to give the reader some familiarity with c.g.s. systems and with the relations between them and the m.k.s. practical system.

N. I. A., Jr.

CONTENTS

CHAPTER I

FUNDAMENTAL LAWS OF ELECTROSTATICS

CHAPTER II

DIELECTRICS AND CONDUCTORS

CHAPTER III

SOLUTION OF ELECTROSTATIC PROBLEMS

CONTENTS

CONTENTS

CHAPTER VII

MAGNETIC FIELD OF A CURRENT

CHAPTER VIII

MOTION OF IONS IN ELECTRIC AND MAGNETIC FIELDS

CHAPTER IX

ELECTROMAGNETIC INDUCTION

CHAPTER X

INTERACTION OF CURRENTS AND FIELDS

CHAPTER XI

FLUX MEASUREMENTS

CHAPTER XII

ABSOLUTE STANDARDS AND UNITS

CHAPTER XIII

ALTERNATING CURRENTS

CHAPTER XIV

MEASUREMENTS WITH VARYING CURRENTS

CHAPTER XV

COUPLED CIRCUITS, FILTERS AND LINES

CHAPTER XVI

ELECTROMAGNETIC WAVES

APPENDIX A

ALTERNATIVE DEVELOPMENT OF MAGNETIC THEORY

APPENDIX B

VALUES OF PHYSICAL CONSTANTS AND ATOMIC WEIGHTS

CONVERSION TABLE OF ELECTRIC AND MAGNETIC QUANTITIES

As throughout the book, symbols without special subscript are used to represent quantities in m.k.s. practical units (pr.u.). Subscripts g, h, e, m indicate Gaussian units (g.u.), Heaviside-Lorentz units (h.l.u.), electrostatic units (e.s.u.), electromagnetic units (e.m.u.), respectively. Each symbol is followed in parentheses by the name of its unit, if the unit has a name. The use of the conversion relations contained in the table is explained and illustrated in art. 50. Any factor 3 appearing in the conversion relations is, of course, more accurately 2.998.

QUANTITY	PR.U.	G.U.	H.L.U.	E.S.U.	E.M.U.
Length	l (meter)	$= (10)^{-2} l_g$ (cm)	$= (10)^{-2} l_h$ (cm)	$= (10)^{-2} l_e$ (cm)	$= (10)^{-2} l_m$ (cm)
Mass	m (kilogram)	$= (10)^{-3} m_g$ (gm)	$= (10)^{-3} m_h$ (gm)	$= (10)^{-3} m_e$ (gm)	$= (10)^{-3} m_m$ (gm)
Force	$\mathfrak{F}$ (newton)	$= (10)^{-5} \mathfrak{F}_g$ (dyne)	$= (10)^{-5} \mathfrak{F}_h$ (dyne)	$= (10)^{-5} \mathfrak{F}_e$ (dyne)	$= (10)^{-5} \mathfrak{F}_m$ (dyne)
Force/Area	$\mathfrak{F}_s$ (n/meter^2)	$= (10)^{-1} \mathfrak{F}_{sg}$ (d/cm^2)	$= (10)^{-1} \mathfrak{F}_{sh}$ (d/cm^2)	$= (10)^{-1} \mathfrak{F}_{se}$ (d/cm^2)	$= (10)^{-1} \mathfrak{F}_{sm}$ (d/cm^2)
Force/Volume	$\mathfrak{F}_\tau$ (n/meter^3)	$= (10) \mathfrak{F}_{\tau g}$ (d/cm^3)	$= (10) \mathfrak{F}_{\tau h}$ (d/cm^3)	$= (10) \mathfrak{F}_{\tau e}$ (d/cm^3)	$= (10) \mathfrak{F}_{\tau m}$ (d/cm^3)
Energy or Work	U (joule)	$= (10)^{-7} U_g$ (erg)	$= (10)^{-7} U_h$ (erg)	$= (10)^{-7} U_e$ (erg)	$= (10)^{-7} U_m$ (erg)
Power	$\mathcal{P}$ (watt)	$= (10)^{-7} \mathcal{P}_g$ (erg/sec)	$= (10)^{-7} \mathcal{P}_h$ (erg/sec)	$= (10)^{-7} \mathcal{P}_e$ (erg/sec)	$= (10)^{-7} \mathcal{P}_m$ (erg/sec)
Charge	Q (coulomb)	$= \frac{1}{3}(10)^{-9} Q_g$	$= \frac{1}{3\sqrt{4\pi}}(10)^{-9} Q_h$	$= \frac{1}{3}(10)^{-9} Q_e$	$= (10) Q_m$
Charge/Area	σ (c/meter^2)	$= \frac{1}{3}(10)^{-5} \sigma_g$	$= \frac{1}{3\sqrt{4\pi}}(10)^{-5} \sigma_h$	$= \frac{1}{3}(10)^{-5} \sigma_e$	$= (10)^5 \sigma_m$
Charge/Volume	ρ (c/meter^3)	$= \frac{1}{3}(10)^{-3} \rho_g$	$= \frac{1}{3\sqrt{4\pi}}(10)^{-3} \rho_h$	$= \frac{1}{3}(10)^{-3} \rho_e$	$= (10)^7 \rho_m$
Elec. Intensity	E (volt/meter)	$= 3(10)^4 E_g$	$= 3\sqrt{4\pi}(10)^4 E_h$	$= 3(10)^4 E_e$	$= (10)^{-6} E_m$
Polarization	P	$= \frac{1}{3}(10)^{-5} P_g$	$= \frac{1}{3\sqrt{4\pi}}(10)^{-5} P_h$	$= \frac{1}{3}(10)^{-5} P_e$	$= (10)^5 P_m$
Elec. Displacement	D	$= \frac{1}{12\pi}(10)^{-5} D_g$	$= \frac{1}{3\sqrt{4\pi}}(10)^{-5} D_h$	$= \frac{1}{12\pi}(10)^{-5} D_e$	$= \frac{1}{4\pi}(10)^5 D_m$
Elec. Susceptibility	ϵ	$= 4\pi\epsilon_g$	$= \epsilon_h$	$= 4\pi\epsilon_e$	$= 4\pi\epsilon_m$
Flux of Displacement	N	$= \frac{1}{12\pi}(10)^{-9} N_g$	$= \frac{1}{3\sqrt{4\pi}}(10)^{-9} N_h$	$= \frac{1}{12\pi}(10)^{-9} N_e$	$= \frac{1}{4\pi}(10) N_m$
E.m.f. or Elec. Potential	$\mathcal{E}$ (volt)	$= 3(10)^2 \mathcal{E}_g$	$= 3\sqrt{4\pi}(10)^2 \mathcal{E}_h$	$= 3(10)^2 \mathcal{E}_e$	$= (10)^{-8} \mathcal{E}_m$
Current	i (ampere)	$= \frac{1}{3}(10)^{-9} i_g$	$= \frac{1}{3\sqrt{4\pi}}(10)^{-9} i_h$	$= \frac{1}{3}(10)^{-9} i_e$	$= (10)^{-1} i_m$

Quantity	Symbol (unit)				
Current/Area	j (amp/meter²)	$= \frac{1}{3}(10)^{-5}j_g$	$= \frac{1}{3\sqrt{4\pi}}(10)^{-5}j_h$	$= \frac{1}{3}(10)^{-5}j_e$	$= (10)^5 j_m$
Conductivity	γ	$= \frac{1}{9}(10)^{-9}\gamma_g$	$= \frac{1}{36\pi}(10)^{-9}\gamma_h$	$= \frac{1}{9}(10)^{-9}\gamma_e$	$= (10)^{11}\gamma_m$
Resistivity	ρ (ohm meter)	$= 9(10)^9\rho_g$	$= 36\pi(10)^9\rho_h$	$= 9(10)^9\rho_e$	$= (10)^{-11}\rho_m$
Resistance	R (ohm)	$= 9(10)^{11}R_g$	$= 36\pi(10)^{11}R_h$	$= 9(10)^{11}R_e$	$= (10)^{-9}R_m$
Inductance	L (henry)	$= 9(10)^{11}L_g$	$= 36\pi(10)^{11}L_h$	$= 9(10)^{11}L_e$	$= (10)^{-9}L_m$
Capacitance	C (farad)	$= \frac{1}{9}(10)^{-11}C_g$	$= \frac{1}{36\pi}(10)^{-11}C_h$	$= \frac{1}{9}(10)^{-11}C_e$	$= (10)^9 C_m$
Pole-Strength	m	$= 4\pi(10)^{-8}m_g$	$= \sqrt{4\pi}(10)^{-8}m_h$	$= 12\pi(10)^2 m_e$	$= 4\pi(10)^{-8}m_m$
Pole-Str./Area	σ	$= 4\pi(10)^{-4}\sigma_g$	$= \sqrt{4\pi}(10)^{-4}\sigma_h$	$= 12\pi(10)^6\sigma_e$	$= 4\pi(10)^{-4}\sigma_m$
Mag. Mom./Area	Φ	$= 4\pi(10)^{-6}\Phi_g$	$= \sqrt{4\pi}(10)^{-6}\Phi_h$	$= 12\pi(10)^4\Phi_e$	$= 4\pi(10)^{-6}\Phi_m$
Mag. Intensity	H (amp/meter)	$= \frac{1}{4\pi}(10)^3 H_g$ (oersted)	$= \frac{1}{\sqrt{4\pi}}(10)^3 H_h$	$= \frac{1}{12\pi}(10)^{-7}H_e$	$= \frac{1}{4\pi}(10)^3 H_m$ (oersted)
Magnetization	I	$= 4\pi(10)^{-4}I_g$	$= \sqrt{4\pi}(10)^{-4}I_h$	$= 12\pi(10)^6 I_e$	$= 4\pi(10)^{-4}I_m$
Mag. Induction	B (web/meter²)	$= (10)^{-4}B_g$ (gauss)	$= \sqrt{4\pi}(10)^{-4}B_h$	$= 3(10)^6 B_e$	$= (10)^{-4}B_m$ (gauss)
Mag. Susceptibility	χ	$= 4\pi\chi_g$	$= \chi_h$	$= 4\pi\chi_e$	$= 4\pi\chi_m$
Flux of Induction	N (weber)	$= (10)^{-8}N_g$ (maxwell)	$= \sqrt{4\pi}(10)^{-8}N_h$	$= 3(10)^2 N_e$	$= (10)^{-8}N_m$ (maxwell)
M.m.f. or Mag. Pot.	$\mathcal{C}$ (ampere)	$= \frac{1}{4\pi}(10)\mathcal{C}_g$ (gilbert)	$= \frac{1}{\sqrt{4\pi}}(10)\mathcal{C}_h$	$= \frac{1}{12\pi}(10)^{-9}\mathcal{C}_e$	$= \frac{1}{4\pi}(10)\mathcal{C}_m$ (gilbert)
Reluctance	$\mathfrak{R}$	$= \frac{1}{4\pi}(10)^9\mathfrak{R}_g$	$= \frac{1}{4\pi}(10)^9\mathfrak{R}_h$	$= \frac{1}{36\pi}(10)^{-11}\mathfrak{R}_e$	$= \frac{1}{4\pi}(10)^9\mathfrak{R}_m$

The constants κ and μ are the same for all units and do not require distinguishing subscripts. A complete set of transformations of Faraday's law (86-1) is shown below as an example. The first transformation is

$$3(10)^2\mathcal{E}_g = -(10)^{-8}\frac{dN_g}{dt}, \qquad \mathcal{E}_g = -\frac{1}{3(10)^{10}}\left(\frac{dN_g}{dt}\right),$$

in which the dimensional constant $3(10)^{10}$ is recognized as c_g, the velocity of light (in g.u.). The second transformation is similar and the other two can be written directly from the table, giving

$$\mathcal{E}_g = -\frac{1}{c_g}\left(\frac{dN_g}{dt}\right), \quad \mathcal{E}_h = -\frac{1}{c_h}\left(\frac{dN_h}{dt}\right), \quad \mathcal{E}_e = -\frac{dN_e}{dt}, \quad \mathcal{E}_m = -\frac{dN_m}{dt}.$$

xiii

Chapter I

FUNDAMENTAL LAWS OF ELECTROSTATICS

1. Attraction and Repulsion. The discovery of electrification, which appears to have been made by the Greeks about 600 B.C., consisted in the observation that a piece of amber which has been rubbed acquires the property of attracting light bodies to itself. It was not until 1600 that it was noticed that electrified bodies may repel as well as attract, and du Fay, about 1733, was the first to appreciate the fact that there are two distinct kinds of electricity.

These two kinds of electricity are called *positive* and *negative*. When a glass rod is rubbed with silk, the glass acquires a positive (*vitreous*) charge of electricity and the silk a negative charge. Conversely, when an ebonite rod is rubbed with fur, the ebonite obtains a negative (*resinous*) charge and the fur a positive charge. The recognition of two kinds of electricity rests upon the observation that two electrified glass rods, or two electrified ebonite rods, repel each other, whereas an electrified glass rod attracts an electrified ebonite rod. The results of early experiments may be embodied in the following qualitative laws:

(I) *Like charges repel, unlike charges attract.*

(II) *The force between two charges decreases as the distance between them is increased.*

We have noted that when a glass rod is rubbed with silk, the silk is electrified as well as the glass, and with a charge of opposite sign to that on the glass. This fact suggests that electrification consists in the *separation* of equal charges of opposite sign rather than in the creation of charges. In more detail it indicates that the glass and the silk in their original unelectrified condition each contains equal amounts of positive and negative electricity, the attraction of the one just sufficing to neutralize the repulsion of the other on any third charge, and that when the two are rubbed together negative electricity is transferred from the glass to the silk, or positive electricity from the silk to the glass, or both. If, now, we keep the silk tightly wound around the glass rod after the two have been rubbed together, we find that the combination exhibits no evidence of electrification, showing that the negative charge

1

on the former neutralizes the positive charge on the latter and therefore is equal to it in magnitude.   Thus we confirm our surmise that electrification consists in a separation and not in a creation of charges.

While ideally we might suppose that continued rubbing of glass with silk would result in a transfer of all the positive electricity in the combination to the glass and of all the negative electricity to the silk, it is found that this limiting state is far from being reached by any methods available in the laboratory.   In fact our present knowledge of the constitution of matter indicates that the most intense electrification obtainable in gross matter represents the transfer of a very minute portion of the electricity originally contained in the bodies concerned.

Furthermore, as will appear from the results of experiments to be described later, electricity is not infinitely divisible, but consists of small discrete entities.   The elementary negatively charged particle, known as the *electron*, has a charge $-1.60(10)^{-19}$ coulomb and a mass $9.11(10)^{-31}$ kilogram.   All negative charges consist of an integral number of electrons.   The charge of the electron is so small, however, that ordinary electrical experiments fail to reveal the fact that the least amount by which two negative charges may differ is the charge of a single electron.

The elementary positively charged particle is known as the *proton*. It has a charge $1.60(10)^{-19}$ coulomb and a mass $1.67(10)^{-27}$ kilogram. The charge of the proton is equal in magnitude and opposite in sign to that of the electron, but its mass, which is substantially the same as that of the hydrogen atom, is 1836 times greater.   Therefore, the proton is much less mobile than the electron.   In addition to the electron and the proton, a third elementary particle, known as the *neutron*, has been isolated.   This particle has no resultant charge, although it exhibits a magnetic moment.   Its mass is effectively the same as that of the proton.

A normal atom consists of a positively charged nucleus, built up of protons and neutrons, with which are associated electrons sufficient in number to make the atom as a whole electrically neutral.   The number of protons in the nucleus is equal to the atomic number of the element (the ordinal number specifying its position in the periodic table), and the number of neutrons is equal to the excess of the atomic weight over the atomic number.   Thus the hydrogen nucleus consists of a single proton and the helium nucleus of two protons and two neutrons.

The fact that the electron is much lighter and therefore much more mobile than the proton indicates that electrification consists solely in the transfer of negative electricity.   So great is the evidence supporting this view that we may conceive of the positive atomic nuclei as fixed in the bodies of which they are constituents, and of electrification as due to an excess or defect of electrons.   Thus when glass is rubbed with silk the contact of the two dissimilar substances results in the detachment of electrons from surface atoms in the glass and their attachment to surface atoms in the silk. The glass becomes positively charged as a result of the subtraction of electrons, and the silk negatively charged in consequence of the addition of electrons.

2. Insulators and Conductors. With respect to their electrical properties solids may be classified as *insulators* or *conductors*. The electrons in the former are so tightly attached to the atoms that only on the surface can they be torn loose and here only by relatively large forces. Insulators, or *dielectrics* as we shall more frequently call them, are characterized by the fact that thin sheets are transparent or at least translucent to light. If we electrify a dielectric, such as a glass rod, by tearing off electrons from a few spots on the surface, the remaining electrons in the rod are unable to redistribute themselves under the action of the electrical forces to which the electrification gives rise. Therefore, the charges remain at the spots on the surface at which they have been produced. Nevertheless a dielectric does not remain altogether uninfluenced by electrical forces. Even though the electrons in each atom cannot easily be detached completely from the atom, they suffer a small displacement from their equilibrium positions under the action of electrical forces. Although the displacement of the electrons in a single atom is too small to produce noticeable effects, a displacement of the electrons in all the atoms of an insulator in the same direction gives rise to pronounced effects which are of great importance in many electrostatic phenomena.

In conductors, on the other hand, the outer electrons normally present in each atom become loosened from the atom and are free to wander through the solid under the influence of electrical forces. Therefore, if a charge is produced on the surface of a conductor by rubbing, these *free electrons* redistribute themselves under the forces of electrical attraction and repulsion with the result that the charge does not necessarily remain localized in its original situation. As the human body is a fair conductor, charges produced on a conducting rod held in the hand do not remain on the rod, but run over to the hand and through the experimenter's body to earth. If it is desired to retain the charge on the conducting rod it must be supported by an insulating handle. As a class, conductors are opaque to light except in the very thinnest sheets. Metals are the best conductors of electricity, particularly such metals as copper and silver. As will be shown later, good conductors of electricity generally are good conductors of heat also.

If two conductors are placed in contact, the free electrons in the one have no great difficulty in passing across the boundary surface into the other.   On the other hand, electrons do not easily escape through the surface of a conductor into an adjacent gas or vacuum.   Only under special conditions, such as when enormous electric fields are applied or high temperatures used, or when ultra-violet light or X-rays are allowed to impinge on a metal, are electrons emitted from its surface into the surrounding space.

Next we must mention an important class of liquid conductors known as *electrolytes*.   In these the charged particles which are free to move under the influence of the electrical forces are not electrons but charged atoms or groups of atoms, known as *ions*.   The carriers of electricity are of both signs, the positive ions moving in one direction under the action of electrical forces and the negative ions in the opposite.   The most important electrolytes are solutions of salts or acids in water.

Finally, a gas may be made conducting by the passage through it of X-rays or rays from radioactive substances, or by high temperature such as exists in a flame.   Under these conditions electrons are torn loose from normally uncharged atoms or molecules and either move freely or attach themselves to other molecules.   We have present in the gas, therefore, ions of both signs which move in opposite directions under the influence of electrical forces until they become neutralized by recombination or reach a metal electrode.

3. Electrification by Induction.   Once a positive charge has been produced on the end of a glass rod by rubbing it with silk, any number of additional charges can be produced on near-by conductors by the process of *induction*.   Consider the uncharged metal rod *AB* (Fig. 1) with rounded ends supported by the insulating stand *C*.   If the charged end *G* of the glass rod is brought near the end *A* of the metal, the electrons in the conductor are attracted to *A*, giving rise to a negative charge on this end of the metal rod and leaving the end *B* positively charged.   The charges so produced are said to be *induced*.   On removal of the glass rod the metal resumes its original unelectrified condition. If, however, the experimenter touches the metal rod at *B* while *G* is held in the position indicated in the figure, additional electrons pass up from the ground through the observer's body to *AB* under the attraction of the positive charge on the glass rod.   If, now, the experimenter removes his finger from contact with *B* while still keeping *G* close to *A*, the metal rod retains the excess electrons, thus acquiring a net negative charge.   On final removal of the glass rod this negative charge spreads over the whole of the surface of *AB*.

By a slight modification of this procedure charges of both signs can be induced.   All that is necessary is to replace the metal rod by two uncharged metal spheres *A* and *B* (Fig. 2) suspended by insulating silk threads. The spheres are held in contact with each other and the positively electrified glass rod G is brought near A. Under the attraction of the charge on G, electrons pass from B to A. If, now, A and B are separated before G is removed, the first is left with a negative charge and the second with an *equal* positive charge. Note that in the former experiment the conductor consisting of the observer's body and the earth took the place of the sphere B and was left with a positive charge at the end of the process.

Electrostatic induction is responsible for the attraction exerted by a charge on uncharged bodies. On account of its closer proximity to G, the negative charge on the end A of the metal rod in Fig. 1 is attracted by the positive charge on the glass rod more than the equal positive charge at B is repelled. Consequently, the rod AB, if free to move, would be drawn toward G. If the rod AB were a dielectric instead of a conductor, the electrons bound to the atoms of which it is composed

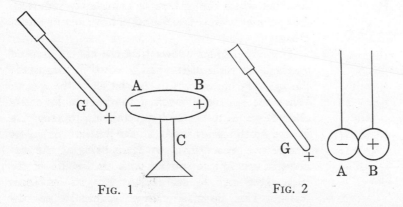

FIG. 1   FIG. 2

would be slightly displaced to the left by the attraction of the charge at G, giving rise to a negative charge on the end A and a positive charge on the end B. As the electrons are tightly fastened to the atoms in this case, the charge cannot be altered to any considerable extent by touching the rod with the finger, but the rod is attracted by the charge at G for precisely the same reason as in the case of a conductor.

Problem 3. Does it matter if the experimenter touches A rather than B in inducing a charge on the metal rod of Fig. 1? Give reasons.

4. The Electroscope. This simple instrument is very useful in investigating electrostatic phenomena in a qualitative manner, and when calibrated it can be used for quantitative measurements. Many forms of electroscope have been designed, but we shall describe only the simplest type consisting of a pair of gold leaves G, G (Fig. 3) suspended from a metal rod R which supports a conducting disk D on its upper end.   The metal parts are insulated from the ground by the glass bottle B through the neck of which the rod R projects.   On the disk D may be placed a metal pail P.

With this instrument Faraday performed the famous "ice-pail" experiment, so named because he used a common metal ice-pail for P. Lowering a positively charged metal sphere into P without touching it to the sides or bottom of the pail, electrons were attracted to the inner surface of P by the positive charge on the sphere, leaving the gold leaves positively electrified.   Having like charges the gold leaves repelled each other and therefore diverged.   The following phenomena were noted:

(*a*) Provided the sphere is well below the mouth of the pail the degree of divergence of the gold leaves is independent of its position.

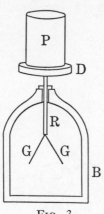

FIG. 3

(*b*) If the charged sphere is brought into contact with the bottom of the pail the divergence of the gold leaves remains unchanged, and does not decrease when the sphere is completely removed. The sphere, however, is found to have lost its entire charge.

This experiment shows that the charge induced on the inner walls of the pail is equal in magnitude though opposite in sign to the charge on the sphere. When the sphere is touched to the pail its entire charge escapes to the pail, neutralizing the negative charge on the inner walls of the latter.   Since no charge can be acquired by again bringing the discharged sphere into contact with the inside of the pail, there can be no charge left on its inner walls.   The positive charge originally on the sphere now resides entirely on the gold leaves, rod and outer walls of the pail.

If the electroscope is charged positively, the introduction of a positive charge into the pail P causes the divergence of the gold leaves to increase, for electrons are attracted to the inner surface of the pail, leaving the leaves with an increased positive charge.   On the other hand, the introduction of a negative charge into the pail causes electrons to be repelled from the pail to the gold leaves, diminishing the positive charge on the latter and decreasing the divergence.   If the negative charge introduced into the pail is large enough, sufficient electrons may be repelled to the leaves to cause them to collapse as the charge approaches the pail and then to diverge again with a negative charge.   In this way the electroscope may be used to determine the sign of the charge on an electrified body, or the sign of the charge on the gold leaves may be ascertained if that of the charge on the body introduced into the pail is known.

If two uncharged rods, one of glass and the other of ebonite, are introduced into the pail of an uncharged electroscope and rubbed together inside the pail, no divergence of the gold leaves is noted. If either rod is removed, however, the gold leaves diverge with a charge of the same sign as that of the rod remaining in the pail. This experiment constitutes a more precise method than that previously described of showing that the negative charge acquired by the one rod is exactly equal to the positive charge obtained by the other and therefore that electrification consists solely in the separation of charges already in existence.

The experiments described above enable us to draw the following conclusions regarding the relative magnitudes of charges:

(*a*) Two charges of opposite sign are of the same magnitude if they produce no effect on the gold leaves when they are placed together inside the pail of the electroscope.

(*b*) Two charges, *A* and *B*, of like sign are of equal magnitude if the one produces the same effect on the gold leaves as the other when introduced into the pail.

(*c*) A charge *C* has twice the magnitude of *A* if it produces the same effect on the gold leaves as *A* and *B* together.

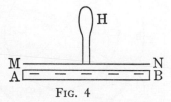

Fig. 4

5. Induction Machines. The simplest type of induction machine is the *electrophorus*. It consists of a disk of sealing wax *AB* (Fig. 4), the upper surface of which has been charged negatively by being rubbed with fur. Above the sealing wax base is a metal disk *MN* of the same area supported by an insulating handle *H*. If the experimenter's finger is touched for a moment to *MN* while in the position indicated in the figure, electrons are repelled from this conductor through the observer's body to earth, leaving it positively charged. So long as *MN* remains close to *AB*, the repulsion of the negative charge on the insulating base prevents electrons passing to *MN* from any other conductor which may be brought into contact with it. If, however, the metal disk is carried to a distance from *AB* by means of the insulating handle and the observer's finger is brought near to the edge *N*, the attraction of the positive charge on the disk for the electrons in the finger may be great enough to cause a small spark to pass to *MN*. Since the positive charge on the metal disk is held in position by the attraction of the negative charge on the wax base when the two are close together, the positive charge is said to be *bound* under these conditions. On the other hand, when the metal disk is removed to such a distance that the force due to the charge on the base becomes negligible, the charge on the disk becomes *free* and is shared with any conductor with which the disk is brought into contact.   In the first position the metal disk may be laid on top of the base, for the two come into actual contact at only a few spots, and since the base is an insulator no appreciable part of the negative charge on its surface passes to the disk.

By repeating the process of charging the metal disk of the electrophorus by induction and then transporting it to a distant conductor a large charge may be imparted to the latter.   Various machines have been devised to do this automatically.   The *Wimshurst machine*, which

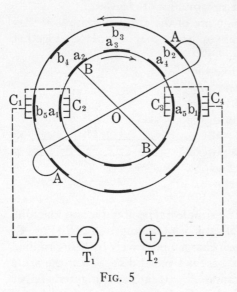

FIG. 5

is illustrated diagrammatically in Fig. 5, consists of two sets of metal carriers, indicated by thick lines, which are mounted on glass disks and revolved in opposite senses about an axis through O perpendicular to the plane of the figure.   The stationary wire connectors AA and BB, provided with brushes to make contact with the carriers, may, for convenience, be connected to earth, although it is not necessary that they should be.   Suppose that the carrier at a_4 has been given a positive charge by contact with an electrified glass rod.   It induces a negative charge on the carrier at b_2 which is carried around to b_4 and there induces a positive charge on the carrier then at a_2.   The carrier at b_4 then moves on to b_5, where it shares its charge with the collector C_1, which is provided with points to facilitate the transfer.   The operation of these points is discussed in art. 11.   From C_1 the charge travels along the wire represented by the broken line to the terminal T_1.

In the meanwhile the carrier at a_2 carries the positive charge which has been induced on it to a_4, where it induces a negative charge on the carrier then at b_2, and proceeding to a_5 shares its charge with the collector C_3 and the terminal T_2.   On the lower halves of the disks the signs of the charges on the two sets of carriers are reversed.   In this way a positive charge is built up on T_2 and a negative charge on T_1, and if the terminals are not too far apart a spark eventually passes across the gap between them. The capacity of the terminals for accumulating electricity may be greatly increased by connecting them to the two plates of a device for storing charge known as a *capacitor*. In this case discharges across the gap take place less frequently but with much greater intensity.

6. Coulomb's Law. Before stating the law of attraction and repulsion between electric charges in quantitative form we must be careful to specify precisely the reference system or set of axes relative to which the quantities involved are to be measured. Consider a set of axes which is fixed relative to the average positions of the fixed stars. This set of axes, and in addition all sets of non-rotating axes which are in motion relative to it with constant velocities, are known as *inertial systems*. We shall suppose that the observer who is measuring the quantities involved in any of the laws of electromagnetism taken up in this book is permanently at rest in an inertial system to which we shall refer as the *observer's inertial system*. It is immaterial which one of the infinity of possible inertial systems we select wherein to locate the observer. But in all cases the quantities to which we shall have occasion to refer are those measured relative to the particular set of axes chosen. The laws of electromagnetism that we are going to develop are valid relative to any inertial system in which the observer may happen to be located. When we pass from one inertial system to another the laws remain unchanged, although the values of the quantities involved may be quite different when determined by one observer from what they are when determined by another observer who is moving relative to the first. Thus one observer may conclude that there are electric forces in his vicinity but no magnetic forces, while another observer, located at the same spot as the first but moving relative to him, is aware of magnetic as well as of electric forces. The nature of an electromagnetic field—that is, a region in which electric and magnetic forces are present—is as much dependent upon the state of motion of the observer as upon the distribution of charged bodies and magnets. Lack of recognition of this fact has led to much confusion in the solution of problems involving rotating magnets and the like.

In electrostatics we limit ourselves to the study of the forces between charges which are all at rest in the observer's inertial system. Suppose, now, that we have two *point charges* q and q' a distance r apart. By point charges we mean charges of linear dimensions very small compared with the distance between them. If we double the charge q we find that the force on q' becomes twice as great, since each half of the doubled charge exerts the same force on q' as that exerted by the original charge. Therefore, the force between the two charges, that is, the force exerted by either on the other, is proportional to q. In the same way we see that it is proportional to q'. Consequently, *the force between two charges is proportional to the product of their magnitudes.*

To find how the force varies with the distance between two point charges Coulomb performed the following experiment in 1785. A charge is placed on a small conducting sphere B (Fig. 6) attached to the end of the insulating horizontal arm AB of a torsion balance. This arm is suspended at its center of mass from the drum D by means of the torsion fibre F. The torsion fibre is rigidly fastened to the drum at its upper end and to the horizontal arm at its lower end, so that if the drum is held fixed the arm cannot rotate about the fibre as axis without twisting it.

A second charge is placed on the small conducting sphere C supported on the insulating handle H. We shall suppose this charge to be of the same sign as the charge already on B. If, now, C is brought up to a point at a pre-determined distance in front of the original position of B, the charge on B is repelled and moves backward in the direction of the arrow, turning the arm AB and twisting the fibre F. Next the experimenter rotates the drum in the opposite sense until B is restored to the position originally occupied. The angle through which it has been turned is equal to the twist now present in the fibre and, therefore, is proportional to the force on B. By placing C at various distances in front of B Coulomb found that *the force between two charges is inversely proportional to the square of the distance between them.*

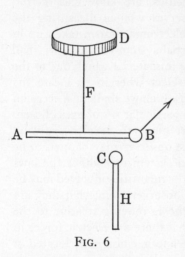

FIG. 6

In analytical form Coulomb's law for the force between two point charges must contain a constant of proportionality. However, since no unit of charge has as yet been defined, the constant may be taken equal to unity for the sake of simplicity. In this case it is customary to employ c.g.s. (centimeter gram second) units, here indicated by subscript e, and we have

$$\mathscr{F}_e = \frac{q_e q_e'}{r_e^2}. \tag{6-1}$$

If q_e and q_e' have the same sign, $\mathscr{F}_e$ is positive, whereas, if they have opposite signs, $\mathscr{F}_e$ is negative. Consequently, a positive value of the force indicates repulsion, a negative value attraction. As we shall see later, the force between two charges is diminished by the presence of a dielectric between them. While the effect of air on the magnitude of the force is very small, the expression (6-1) applies exactly only to the case of charges *in vacuo*. Evidently (6-1) defines, implicitly, *a unit charge as one which repels a like equal charge placed at a distance 1 cm in vacuo with a force 1 dyne*. Putting 1 cm gm sec^{-2} for $\mathscr{F}_e$ and 1 cm for r_e and solving for $q_e = q_e'$, we find that this c.g.s. unit charge is 1 cm$^{3/2}$ gm$^{1/2}$ sec^{-1}. This unit, and all other c.g.s. units based on Coulomb's law of force (6-1), are known as *electrostatic units* and are designated by the abbreviation e.s.u.

Although the electrostatic unit charge itself is of suitable magnitude for most purposes, the electrostatic system as a whole proves to be inconvenient in practice. Hence, let us express Coulomb's law in the form

$$\mathscr{F} = \frac{qq'}{4\pi\kappa_0 r^2}, \tag{6-2}$$

where now m.k.s. (meter kilogram second) units are used and $\kappa_0 \equiv [1/4\pi c^2](10)^7$, c representing the velocity of light, as usual. The presently accepted value of c is $2.997925(10)^8$ meter sec^{-1}, but ordinarily we shall use the approximate value $3(10)^8$ meter sec^{-1} or, when more accuracy is required, the closer value $2.998(10)^8$ meter sec^{-1}. Thus, $\kappa_0 = [1/36\pi](10)^{-9}$ meter^{-2} sec^2 and (6-2) defines *a unit charge as one which repels a like equal charge placed at a distance 1 meter in vacuo with a force $9(10)^9$ newtons*. Since the newton is $(10)^5$ dynes, this m.k.s. unit charge, named the *coulomb*, has the magnitude of $3(10)^9$ electrostatic units. Putting $9(10)^9$ meter kg sec^{-2} for $\mathscr{F}$ and 1 meter for r and solving for $q = q'$, we find that the coulomb is 1 meter$^{1/2}$ kg$^{1/2}$. The coulomb and all following m.k.s. units are known as *practical units* and are designated by the abbreviation pr.u.

The quantity κ_0 is called the *permittivity of free space*. The reasons for choosing it as we do and for including the factor 4π in the denominator of (6-2) are made clear in Chapter XII, where all common systems of units are described and the relations between them are analyzed. As m.k.s. practical units are now generally accepted and widely used, we shall employ them as primary units throughout this book. However, c.g.s. units are preferred by some writers and they appear, almost exclusively, in the older literature. Hence, we shall express important relations, such as fundamental laws, in terms of appropriate c.g.s. units as well as in terms of m.k.s. units, in order that the reader may become familiar with both types and be able to change from one to the other. Conversion of units and transformation of formulas are discussed in art. 25 and art. 50.   In addition, a general conversion table is provided immediately preceding art. 1.

Problem 6a.   Two particles are suspended by strings of the same length l from the same point.   Each has a mass m and a charge q.   Show that the angle θ which each string makes with the vertical is given by

$$16\pi\kappa_0 mgl^2 \sin^3\theta = q^2\cos\theta.$$

Problem 6b.   A small positively charged conducting sphere is brought into contact with an identical uncharged sphere.   When separated by 10 cm, the repulsion between them is $9(10)^{-3}$ newton.   Find the original charge on the first sphere.   Ans. $2(10)^{-7}$ coulomb.

Problem 6c.   Two small identical conducting spheres with charges $5(10)^{-7}$ coulomb and $-1(10)^{-7}$ coulomb, respectively, are 30 cm apart.   What is the force between them?   What will be the force if they are brought into contact and then separated by the same distance as before?   Ans. $-5(10)^{-3}$ newton, $4(10)^{-3}$ newton.

7. Electric Intensity and Potential.

A region in which electric forces are acting is called an *electric field*.   In order to explore the field we may carry a unit positive charge of very small dimensions around the field, being careful to keep all the charges producing the field fixed in position so that the field shall not be changed by the attractions or repulsions exerted by the test charge.   The force experienced by the unit test charge when at rest relative to the observer at any point in the field is known as the *electric intensity* or the *electric field strength E* at that point.   Basically, the unit of electric intensity is the *newton per coulomb* or, in terms of the fundamental units, 1 meter$^{1/2}$ kg$^{1/2}$ sec^{-2}. However, a newton meter is a joule, the m.k.s. unit of work, and a joule per coulomb is a *volt*, by definition.   Hence, the practical unit of electric intensity is commonly called the *volt per meter*.   Since the electric intensity is a force, it is a vector and has direction as well as magnitude.   In expressing vector relations we shall represent vectors by letters printed in **black face** type, using the same letters in *italics* to represent their scalar magnitudes.   Thus the equation

$$\mathbf{C} = \mathbf{A} + \mathbf{B}$$

signifies that the vector **C** is the *vector sum* or *resultant* of the two vectors **A** and **B** as indicated in Fig. 7.   The corresponding scalar relation is $C^2 = A^2 + 2AB\cos\alpha + B^2$, where α is the angle between the positive directions of A and B.

Evidently the force $\mathscr{F}$ on a charge q placed at a point where the electric intensity is E is

$$\mathscr{F} = qE.$$

If q is positive $\mathscr{F}$ has the direction of E, otherwise the opposite direction. The complete relationship between these quantities is expressed by the vector equation

$$\mathscr{F} = q\mathbf{E}. \tag{7-1}$$

It is clear from this equation that if the electric intensity is known at every point in the field the force on a charge of any magnitude placed at any point can be computed at once, provided the charges producing the field are held rigidly in position so that the field remains unaltered by the introduction of the charge on which the force is to be determined.

The electric intensity at a distance r from a point charge q is obtained at once from Coulomb's law by making q' equal to unity.   It is

$$E = \frac{q}{4\pi\kappa_0 r^2} \tag{7-2}$$

in the direction of the radius vector drawn from q.   Since any field may be considered to be due to a number of point charges, the resultant electric intensity at a point may be calculated by finding the vector sum of the electric intensities due to the individual charges.   Except in the simplest cases such a procedure is difficult to carry out, however, and simpler methods depending on the concept of potential are employed instead.

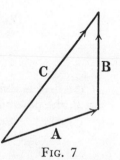

Fig. 7

The *potential V* at a point in an electrostatic field is the work necessary to bring a unit positive charge from infinity, that is, from outside the field, up to the point in question, the charges producing the field being held rigidly in position during the process. Physically it represents the potential energy of a unit charge placed at the given point.   Its unit is the *joule per coulomb*, that is, the *volt*.   For future reference we note that the volt is 1 meter$^{3/2}$ kg$^{1/2}$ sec^{-2}. Evidently V is also the work done *by* the field on the unit positive charge as the latter moves *from* the given point to infinity.   As it represents work per unit charge, potential is a scalar quantity.

Let us calculate the potential due to a point charge q placed at O (Fig. 8).   To find the potential at a point P distant r_P from q, we shall compute the work done by the field on a unit charge as it moves from P to infinity.   Let PQ be the path followed.   The electric intensity at Q_1 is

$$E = \frac{q}{4\pi\kappa_0 r^2}$$

in the direction of the radius vector r, and the work done by the field in moving the unit charge the distance dl from Q_1 to Q_2 is

$$\frac{q}{4\pi\kappa_0 r^2}\, dl \cos\alpha = \frac{q}{4\pi\kappa_0 r^2}\, dr$$

where α is the angle between E and dl.   Integrating from r_P to infinity,

$$V = \frac{q}{4\pi\kappa_0}\int_{r_P}^{\infty}\frac{dr}{r^2} = \frac{q}{4\pi\kappa_0 r_P}, \tag{7-3}$$

showing that the value of the potential depends only upon the coordinates of the point P and is independent of the path followed by the unit positive charge.

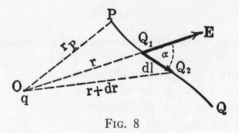

FIG. 8

If the field is due to point charges q_1, q_2, $\cdots$ at distances r_1, r_2, $\cdots$ from P, the potential at P is the scalar sum

$$V = \frac{q_1}{4\pi\kappa_0 r_1} + \frac{q_2}{4\pi\kappa_0 r_2} + \cdots = \frac{1}{4\pi\kappa_0}\sum\frac{q}{r}, \tag{7-4}$$

and in the case of a continuous distribution of electricity consisting of ρ units of charge per unit volume occupying a volume τ and σ units of charge per unit area distributed over a surface s

$$V = \frac{1}{4\pi\kappa_0}\int_{\tau}\frac{\rho d\tau}{r} + \frac{1}{4\pi\kappa_0}\int_{s}\frac{\sigma ds}{r}, \tag{7-5}$$

the distance r now being measured from P.

As is evident from the forms of these expressions, *the electrostatic potential in all cases is a function only of the coordinates of the point P at which it is to be evaluated and is independent of the path along which the unit charge moves.*   It is this property which makes the concept of potential important.   In fact, we say that a field of force possesses a potential only in regions where these conditions are fulfilled.

Evidently the drop in potential when we pass from a point A to a point B is equal to the work done by the field on a unit positive charge as it moves from the first point to the second, all paths between the two points being equivalent.   The work, then, performed on a charge q as it moves by any path from a point A where the potential is V_A to a point B where the potential is V_B is $q(V_A - V_B)$.   If the charge moves around a closed curve, the two ends of the path coincide.   Therefore, $V_B = V_A$ and the net work done is zero.

Consider two near-by points P and Q (Fig. 9) a distance dl apart and denote the potentials at P and Q by V and $V + dV$ respectively.   As the force on a unit positive charge is the electric intensity E, the drop in potential in going from P to Q is the work done by the electric intensity. Therefore,

$$V_P - V_Q \equiv -dV = E \cos \alpha dl.$$

Hence the component of E in the direction of the displacement PQ is

$$E_l = E \cos \alpha = -\frac{\partial V}{\partial l}, \qquad (7\text{-}6)$$

equal to the space rate of decrease of potential in the direction PQ. The left-hand side of this equation is greatest for α equal to zero. Therefore, the potential decreases most rapidly in the direction of the electric intensity.

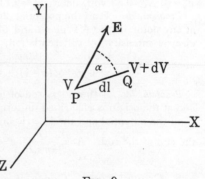

FIG. 9

If dl is parallel to the X axis, it becomes dx and $E \cos \alpha$ becomes E_x, the X component of the electric intensity.   Consequently,

$$E_x = -\frac{\partial V}{\partial x}.$$

Similar expressions hold for the Y and Z components of E.   So if V is expressed as a function of the coordinates x, y, z,

$$E_x = -\frac{\partial V}{\partial x}, \qquad E_y = -\frac{\partial V}{\partial y}, \qquad E_z = -\frac{\partial V}{\partial z}. \qquad (7\text{-}7)$$

By means of these relations we can obtain the electric intensity if the potential function is known.   As the electric intensity is equal to the space rate of decrease of potential, it follows that a positive charge placed in an electric field experiences a force urging it from regions of higher to regions of lower potential while a negative charge tends to move from regions of lower to regions of higher potential.

If the potential V is expressed as a function of the spherical co-ordinates r, θ, ϕ, where r represents the radius vector, θ the polar angle and ϕ the azimuth, the space rates of decrease of potential and therefore the components of electric intensity in the directions of increasing r, θ, ϕ are respectively

$$E_r = -\frac{\partial V}{\partial r}, \qquad E_\theta = -\frac{\partial V}{r\partial\theta}, \qquad E_\phi = -\frac{\partial V}{r\sin\theta\partial\phi}. \qquad (7\text{-}8)$$

Similarly, if V is expressed as a function of the cylindrical coordinates r, θ, z, where now r represents the distance from the Z axis and θ the azimuth measured around this axis, the components of electric intensity in the directions of increasing r, θ, z are respectively

$$E_r = -\frac{\partial V}{\partial r}, \qquad E_\theta = -\frac{\partial V}{r\partial\theta}, \qquad E_z = -\frac{\partial V}{\partial z}. \qquad (7\text{-}9)$$

Problem 7a.   Charges $2(10)^{-7}$ coulomb and $-1(10)^{-7}$ coulomb, respectively, are placed at the points $(0, 0)$ and $(1 \text{ meter}, 0)$ in the XY plane. Find the components of electric intensity at the points $(10 \text{ meter}, 0)$ and $(0, 10 \text{ meter})$ and find a point on the X axis where the field vanishes. Ans. $E_x = 6.89$ volt/meter, $E_y = 0$; $E_x = 0.89$ volt/meter, $E_y = 9.13$ volt/meter; $x = 3.41$ meter.

Problem 7b.   Find the potential due to the charges in the preceding problem at any point in the XY plane and obtain the rectangular components of the electric intensity by differentiation, checking the numerical values obtained above.   Ans. $\dfrac{1800}{\sqrt{x^2+y^2}} - \dfrac{900}{\sqrt{(x-1)^2+y^2}}$.

Problem 7c.   A thin glass rod of length l placed along the X axis with one end at the origin is electrified uniformly along its length with a total charge Q. Find the potential and the electric intensity at any point on the X axis beyond the end of the rod.   Ans. $\dfrac{Q}{4\pi\kappa_0 l}\log\dfrac{x}{x-l}$, $\dfrac{Q}{4\pi\kappa_0 x(x-l)}$.

8. Gauss' Law.

Consider an element of surface ds at a point in an electric field at which the electric intensity is E. If α is the angle between the direction of E and that of the normal to the surface, the product $E\cos\alpha\, ds$ of the component of E perpendicular to the surface by the area of the surface is called the *electric flux* through the surface ds. The sign of the electric flux depends upon which side of the surface is chosen as positive, that is to say, upon whether the normal is drawn perpendicular to the surface on the one side or the other.   The following conventions are employed to determine the positive sense of the normal:

(*a*) If the surface is closed, the outward drawn normal is taken as positive.

(*b*) If the surface is open, the positive sense of the normal is related to the sense in which the periphery is described by the rule that a right-handed screw with its axis perpendicular to the surface advances in the direction of the normal when rotated in the sense in which the periphery is described.   This rule determines the positive sense of the normal only if the positive sense of describing the periphery is specified, or, vice versa, it prescribes the positive sense in which the periphery is to be described if the positive side of the surface is given.

Take first the case of a point charge q (Fig. 10) inside a closed surface s. If n represents the normal to the surface at P, the electric flux dF through the element AB of area ds due to q is

$$dF = E \cos \alpha ds = \frac{q ds \cos \alpha}{4\pi \kappa_0 r^2},$$

where r is the distance of P from the charge.

If we draw straight lines from all points on the periphery of the surface element AB to q, the cone so described is said to define a *conical angle* or *solid angle*.   The solid angle is measured by the area intercepted on the surface of a sphere of unit radius having the vertex of the cone as center.   Since the area of a sphere is proportional to the square of its radius, the magnitude of a solid angle is also equal to the area intercepted on the surface of any sphere with center at the vertex of the angle divided by the square of its radius.   Furthermore, as the superficial area of a sphere of radius r is $4\pi r^2$, the solid angle subtended at q by a surface such as s entirely surrounding it is 4π.

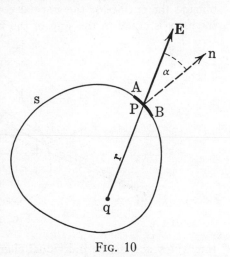

Fig. 10

Now $ds \cos \alpha$ is the projection of the area AB perpendicular to the radius vector r, and this projection divided by r^2 is the solid angle $d\Omega$ subtended by AB at q.   Hence $dF = q d\Omega / 4\pi\kappa_0$ and if we integrate over the entire surface, the total outward flux is seen to be

$$F = \frac{q}{\kappa_0}. \tag{8-1}$$

Consider now a charge q (Fig. 11) lying outside the closed surface. With q as vertex describe a cone of angular aperture $d\Omega$.   Let ds_1 be the area of the surface intercepted at P_1 and ds_2 that at P_2.   The projections of these surfaces perpendicular to the radius vector are $ds_1 \cos \alpha_1$ and $ds_2 \cos \alpha_2$, and

$$d\Omega = \frac{ds_1 \cos \alpha_1}{r_1^2} = \frac{ds_2 \cos \alpha_2}{r_2^2}.$$

Since the angle $\pi - \alpha_1$ between the directions of E_1 and n_1 is obtuse, the flux through ds_1 is negative, signifying that it is directed inward through the closed surface instead of outward. Taking ds_1 and ds_2 together, the outward flux is

$$- E_1 \cos \alpha_1 ds_1 + E_2 \cos \alpha_2 ds_2 = - \frac{q ds_1 \cos \alpha_1}{4\pi \kappa_0 r_1^2} + \frac{q ds_2 \cos \alpha_2}{4\pi \kappa_0 r_2^2}.$$

But the geometrical relation above shows that this expression vanishes. Hence, as the whole surface s can be divided into pairs of elements subtending the same solid angle at q such that the inward flux through one annuls outward flux through the other, the net outward flux through the entire surface due to a charge outside is zero.

If a number of point charges are present, some inside and others outside the surface s, the normal component of the resultant electric intensity is equal to the sum of the normal components of the electric

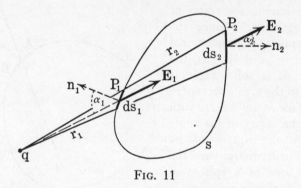

Fig. 11

intensities due to the individual charges. Therefore, if q_1, q_2, q_3, $\cdots$ are the point charges lying *inside* the surface, the entire outward flux through the surface is

$$F = \frac{q_1}{\kappa_0} + \frac{q_2}{\kappa_0} + \frac{q_3}{\kappa_0} + \cdots = \frac{\Sigma q}{\kappa_0}, \tag{8-2}$$

since the charges *outside* make no contribution. If charge is distributed continuously with density ρ units of charge per unit volume,

$$F = \frac{1}{\kappa_0} \int_\tau \rho d\tau, \tag{8-3}$$

where the integral is taken through the volume τ enclosed by the surface s.

Equations (8-2) and (8-3) are equivalent statements of *Gauss' law*. In words this law states that the net outward electric flux through any closed surface is equal to $1/\kappa_0$ times the total charge contained within that surface. It is important to note that the deduction of this law depends only upon the fact that electrical forces vary inversely with the square of the distances between charges. Therefore, it is valid for a gravitational field as well as for an electrostatic field.

If we write for F the surface integral of the normal component of the electric intensity in accord with the definition of electric flux, (8-2) and (8-3) take the forms

$$\int_s E \cos \alpha ds = \frac{\Sigma q}{\kappa_0}, \tag{8-4}$$

and

$$\int_s E \cos \alpha ds = \frac{1}{\kappa_0} \int_\tau \rho d\tau. \tag{8-5}$$

In the first of these Σq represents the sum of all the charges contained in the closed surface s, and in the second the volume integral is to be taken over the entire volume τ surrounded by s.

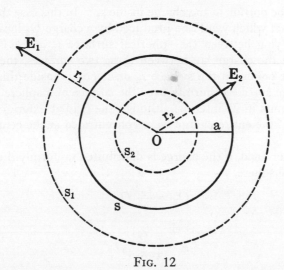

FIG. 12

9. Applications of Gauss' Law. Gauss' law constitutes a powerful tool for finding the electric intensity in fields of such symmetry that we can draw surfaces everywhere normal to E at all points of which the magnitude of the electric intensity is the same.

Consider, for instance, a sphere s (Fig. 12) of radius a inside of which electric charge is so distributed that the charge density ρ is a function of the radius vector r alone. Describe a concentric spherical surface s_1 of radius r_1 greater than a. It is clear from symmetry that the electric intensity is everywhere normal to s_1 and has the same magnitude E_1 at all points of this surface. Therefore, the total flux through s_1 is $4\pi r_1{}^2 E_1$, and Gauss' law requires that $4\pi r_1{}^2 E_1 = Q/\kappa_0$, where Q represents the entire charge inside s, or

$$E_1 = \frac{Q}{4\pi\kappa_0 r_1{}^2}. \tag{9-1}$$

This is just the expression we should have found if all the charge had been concentrated at the center O of the sphere s. Therefore, any distribution of charge in which the density is a function of the radius vector only, such as that on an isolated charged conducting sphere, produces the same field at exterior points as if the entire charge were located at the central point.

If we apply Gauss' law to the spherical surface s_2 of radius r_2 less than a, we find in the same way

$$E_2 = \frac{Q_2}{4\pi\kappa_0 r_2{}^2}$$

where Q_2 is the portion of the charge inside s_2. In this case the electric intensity is that which would be produced by a charge Q_2 located at O. The charge lying between the spherical surfaces s_2 and s is without effect. If all the charge lay between these two surfaces, there would be no field at points on the surface s_2 or at points inside this surface. Thus a charge spread uniformly over the surface of a sphere produces no field at points in its interior, although the field at exterior points is the same as if the entire charge were concentrated at the center of the sphere.

On the other hand, if the charge is distributed uniformly through the volume of the sphere,

$$Q_2 = \frac{r_2{}^3}{a^3} Q,$$

and

$$E_2 = \frac{Q}{4\pi\kappa_0 a^3} r_2 \tag{9-2}$$

in the interior of the sphere.

Suppose we wish to find the force between two spherical charges Q_1 and Q_2 in each of which the charge density ρ is a function of the distance from the center only. Denote the centers of the two spheres by O_1 and O_2 and the distance between centers by R. Replace the second spherical distribution by a point charge Q_2 located at O_2. The electric intensity at O_2 due to the first sphere is

$$E_1 = \frac{Q_1}{4\pi\kappa_0 R^2},$$

as proved above, and therefore the force on the point charge Q_2 at O_2 due to Q_1 is

$$\mathscr{F} = \frac{Q_1 Q_2}{4\pi\kappa_0 R^2} = Q_1 E_2,$$

where E_2 is the electric intensity at O_1 due to Q_2.

But the law of action and reaction requires that this expression should also represent the force exerted by Q_2 on Q_1. If now the point charge at O_2 is replaced by the spherical distribution originally assumed, the field due to Q_2 and therefore the force exerted by it on Q_1 remain unchanged. Consequently the force between the two spherical charges is the same as if each were a point charge located at its geometrical center. It is of interest to note that in order to deduce this result, which follows so simply from Gauss' law, for the corresponding case of gravitational attraction, Newton delayed publication of the law of gravitation for twenty years.

Next consider a uniformly charged plane MN (Fig. 13) of very great

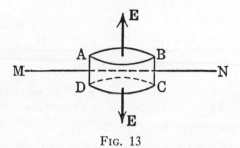

Fig. 13

(strictly infinite) extent. Let σ be the charge per unit area of the surface. From symmetry it is clear that the electric intensity is perpendicular to the plane, being directed upward above the plane and downward below if the charge is positive. Describe a pill-box shaped surface $ABCD$, the flat bases AB and DC of the box lying parallel to and equidistant from the plane MN. If Δs is the area of one of the bases, the flux through the surface of the pill-box is $2E\Delta s$ and the charge enclosed is $\sigma\Delta s$. Therefore Gauss' law takes the form $2E\Delta s = \sigma\Delta s/\kappa_0$, giving

$$E = \frac{\sigma}{2\kappa_0}. \tag{9-3}$$

Consequently, the field is uniform on each side of the plane, the magnitude of E being independent of the distance from the plane.

Finally consider the field due to two parallel conducting plates AB

and CD (Fig. 14) of very great extent, the lower of which has a (uniform) positive charge density σ and the upper of which has an equal negative charge density.   At a point P between the plates the electric intensity due to AB is $\sigma/2\kappa_0$ upward and that due to CD is also $\sigma/2\kappa_0$ upward. Therefore, the total field is

$$E = \frac{\sigma}{\kappa_0} \qquad (9\text{-}4)$$

upward, everywhere between the plates.   The electric intensity at a point Q outside the plates, on the other hand, is $\sigma/2\kappa_0$ upward due to AB and $\sigma/2\kappa_0$ downward due to CD.   Hence the field outside the plates vanishes.   These results apply, of course, regardless of the way in which the charge densities divide between the inside and outside surfaces of their respective plates.   However, as is shown in art. 11, there can be no field within the plates themselves and this requires that the charge densities be confined to the inside surfaces.

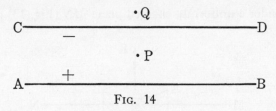

$$\cdot Q$$

C————————————————————D

$$-$$

$$\cdot P$$

A————+————————————B

Fig. 14

Problem 9a.   What is the potential due to a uniformly charged spherical shell of radius a at a point (a) outside, (b) on the surface, (c) in the interior of the shell?   Ans. (a) $\dfrac{Q}{4\pi\kappa_0 r}$,   (b) $\dfrac{Q}{4\pi\kappa_0 a}$,   (c) $\dfrac{Q}{4\pi\kappa_0 a}$.

Problem 9b.   The plane of Fig. 13 is replaced by a slab of thickness t, the charge being uniformly distributed throughout its volume.   Find the electric intensity at a distance y from the median plane of the slab less than one-half t.

Ans. $\dfrac{\sigma}{\kappa_0 t}\, y$.

Problem 9c.   Find the field at a distance r greater than a from the axis of an infinitely long straight cylindrical rod of radius a whose charge per unit length is λ.   Find the field inside the rod (a) if the charge is distributed uniformly over the surface of the cylinder, (b) if the charge is distributed uniformly throughout its volume.   Ans. $\dfrac{\lambda}{2\pi\kappa_0 r}$,   (a) 0,   (b) $\dfrac{\lambda}{2\pi\kappa_0 a^2}\, r$.

Problem 9d.   Prove that the electric intensity outside a uniformly charged spherical shell is the same as if the charge were concentrated at the center of the shell in accord with (9-1), using (7-5) and (7-6) instead of Gauss' law.

10. Lines and Tubes of Force.

A *line of force* in an electric field is a curve so drawn as to have everywhere the direction of the electric intensity, the sense in which the line is described being indicated on diagrams by an arrowhead.   Free positive charges, therefore, tend to move along lines of force in the forward sense and free negative charges in the backward sense. A bundle of M lines of force, where M is a large integer arbitrarily chosen but fixed in value, is known as a *tube of force*. Lines of force are drawn in such density that the number of tubes of force per unit cross section is everywhere equal to the magnitude of the electric intensity. By selecting a large enough number for M the representation of an electric field by lines of force may be made as nearly continuous as desired, even in regions where the electric intensity is very small.

Consider a small surface AB (Fig. 15) of area ds through which dT_F tubes of force pass at an angle α with the normal n. The cross section of this group of tubes is the projection of ds on a plane perpendicular

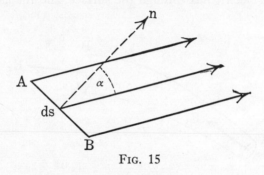

Fig. 15

to E, that is, $ds \cos \alpha$. Therefore, in accordance with the convention for drawing lines of force,

$$E = \frac{dT_F}{ds \cos \alpha},$$

or

$$dT_F = E \cos \alpha \, ds. \qquad (10\text{-}1)$$

But the right-hand side of this equation represents the electric flux through ds. Therefore, *the number of tubes of force passing through any surface is equal to the electric flux through that surface.*

We shall now prove two fundamental theorems regarding tubes of force.

THEOREM I. *Tubes of force are continuous in regions containing no charge.*

To prove this theorem let us examine the closed surface AB (Fig. 16) which is bounded on the sides by lines of force and terminated by the cross sections s_1 and s_2. The flux through the tubular portion vanishes because the electric intensity is everywhere parallel to the surface.

Therefore, the total flux is that through the ends and as there is no charge inside the surface, Gauss' law requires that the inward flux through s_1 should equal the outward flux through s_2. But the flux through a surface has been shown to be equal to the number of tubes of force passing through the surface. Therefore, as many tubes of force pass out through s_2 as come in through s_1. Consequently, tubes of force are continuous in the region under consideration and hence in any region containing no charge. The same conclusion applies, of course, to the lines of which the tubes are composed.

THEOREM II. *The number of tubes of force diverging from a positive charge q or converging on a negative charge $-q$ is q/κ_0.*

This theorem follows at once from Gauss' law. For the number of tubes of force passing through any closed surface surrounding a charge q is equal to the electric flux through the surface, and the latter is equal

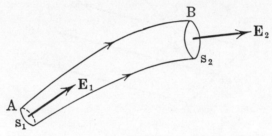

FIG. 16

to q/κ_0. Each tube starts on a positive charge of magnitude κ_0 and ends on an equal negative charge.

In Fig. 17 the lines of force are shown for the fields due to (a) two equal point charges of the same sign, (b) two equal point charges of opposite sign, (c) two oppositely charged parallel conducting plates, (d) a point charge near an earthed conducting plate.

An important theorem due to Earnshaw states that no charge can be in stable equilibrium in an electrostatic field under the influence of electrical forces alone. The proof of this theorem is very simple if we make use of the properties of tubes of force which we have just developed. Assume that O (Fig. 18) is a point at which a positive test charge would find itself in stable equilibrium in the field under consideration. Then in whatever direction the test charge is displaced from O the force due to the field must urge it back toward O. Consequently, tubes of force must converge at O. But this would require the presence of a negative charge. Therefore, there can be no point of stable equilibrium in an electrostatic field. A point of unstable equilibrium may exist, such as the point of zero field in problem 7a, where displacements of a positive charge along the X axis tend to increase

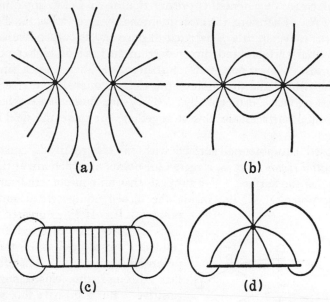

(a)   (b)

(c)   (d)

Fig. 17

whereas those in the plane at right angles give rise to restoring forces directed toward the point of equilibrium.

11. Equipotential Surfaces and Regions. An *equipotential surface* is a surface all points of which are at the same potential. No two different equipotential surfaces can intersect, for if they did the potential along the curve of intersection would have more than one value. Equipotential surfaces are drawn for equal increments of potential, for example, for the potentials 0, 5, 10, 15, 20, · · · . As the electric intensity is equal to the space rate of decrease of potential, the field is most intense where the equipotential surfaces are most closely crowded together and least intense

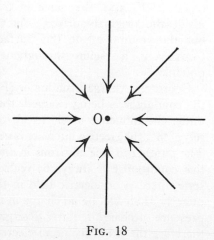

Fig. 18

where they are farthest apart.   Let AB and CD (Fig. 19) be two adjacent equipotential surfaces, AB being the surface of higher potential.   If we pass from AB to CD along the normal PQ the space rate of decrease of potential is greater than if we follow any other path such as PR.   Therefore, the electric intensity, since it has the direction of the greatest space rate of decrease of potential, is perpendicular to the equipotential surfaces and directed from surfaces of higher potential toward those of lower potential.   Furthermore, lines of force, since they have everywhere the direction of the electric intensity, intersect equipotential surfaces orthogonally.   They are most dense where the equipotential surfaces are closest together, for there the field is most intense.

A closed equipotential surface with no charge inside encloses an *equipotential region*, that is, a region all points of which are at the same potential as the surface.   For suppose that an equipotential surface of different potential V' lies inside the closed equipotential surface of potential V.   If V' is greater than V lines of force are directed from V' toward V at all points of the equipotential surface V'.   Therefore the flux through this closed surface is positive.   But a positive flux requires a positive charge inside the surface V'.   Consequently, V' cannot be greater than V.   A similar line of

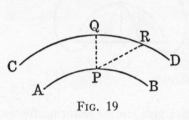

Fig. 19

reasoning shows that V' cannot be less than V.   Therefore, V' is equal to V, and the same is true of the potential at all points inside the original surface.   As the potential is uniform throughout the volume inside this surface, no field can be present there. Conversely, a region throughout which no field exists is equipotential.

Consider a charged conductor (Fig. 20) with a cavity inside.   While the conductor is being charged, the free electrons in its interior move under the influence of electrical forces until they so distribute themselves that the electric intensity is zero everywhere inside the conductor. The number of free electrons in any metallic conductor is so great that this condition can always be realized.   Therefore, in the equilibrium state, there is no electric field in the body of the conductor.   Consequently, there can be no charge in the interior of the conductor, for the presence of charge requires diverging or converging tubes of force and therefore the existence of an electric field.   So all the charge must be located on the surface of the conductor.   Finally, the absence of an electric field in the body of the conductor means that the potential is everywhere the same. The outer surface and the surface of the cavity are equipotential surfaces of the same potential.

If the cavity is empty, it is, of course, an equipotential region at the same potential as the conductor. On the other hand, if it contains a charge, a field is present, and the cavity is no longer an equipotential region. Since the tubes of force originating on the charge must end on the surface of the cavity, a charge of equal magnitude and opposite sign is induced there. This releases to the outer surface of the conductor an equal charge of the same sign as that introduced into the cavity. The phenomena observed in the Faraday "ice-pail" experiment (art. 4) are thus explained.

If the force between charges did not vary inversely with the square of the distance, the field inside a cavity in a charged conductor would

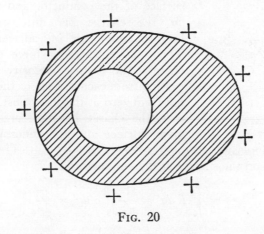

Fig. 20

not vanish. Cavendish and, later, Maxwell attempted to detect the presence of electrical forces in such a cavity with null results. So sensitive is this method of showing that the force varies inversely with the square of the distance that Maxwell calculated that if the exponent differed from 2 by as much as one part in 21,600 evidence of a field would have been found.

Next let us calculate the field just outside the conductor in terms of the charge density σ on its surface. As lines of force are perpendicular to equipotential surfaces, the electric intensity just outside a conductor must be at right angles to its surface. Therefore, the flux through the pill-box shaped surface $ABCD$ (Fig. 21) enclosing a small area Δs of the surface consists entirely of that through the base AB, the flux through CD being zero since there is no field in the body of the conductor.   Consequently, Gauss' law gives $E\Delta s = \sigma \Delta s / \kappa_0$, that is,

$$E = \frac{\sigma}{\kappa_0}. \tag{11-1}$$

It follows from this equation that no charge can reside on the surface of a conductor outside of which the field vanishes.   This is the case, for example, at the outside surfaces of the parallel conducting plates of Fig. 14.

Finally, we shall calculate the stress $\mathscr{F}_s$ on the surface of the conductor due to the action of the field outside on the charge located on the surface.   Strictly speaking the charge density σ does not lie on a mathematical surface but occupies a thin layer extending a short distance into the conductor.   Let us describe in this layer a number of surfaces parallel to the surface of the conductor and designate by $d\sigma'$ the charge per unit area included between any pair of adjacent surfaces. Then, since tubes of force originate on charges, the electric intensity increases in passing from each surface to the next, starting from zero at the innermost surface.   If σ' is the charge per unit area between a given surface and the innermost surface, the electric intensity at the former is $E' = \sigma' / \kappa_0$.   Therefore, the tension stress on the surface of the conductor is

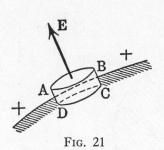

FIG. 21

$$\mathscr{F}_s = \int_0^\sigma E' d\sigma' = \frac{1}{\kappa_0} \int_0^\sigma \sigma' d\sigma' = \frac{\sigma^2}{2\kappa_0}. \tag{11-2}$$

Since σ appears as a square in this expression the stress on the surface is always a tension, no matter whether the charge is positive or negative. In terms of the electric intensity $E = \sigma / \kappa_0$ just outside the surface of the conductor, the tension is

$$\mathscr{F}_s = \frac{\kappa_0}{2} E^2. \tag{11-3}$$

Faraday and Maxwell conceived a tension of this amount as existing everywhere along the tubes of force.   On this representation the tubes of force may be thought of as having the properties of stretched elastic bands tending to draw together the positive charges on which they originate and the negative charges on which they end.   With this conception in mind mere inspection of the fields illustrated in Fig. 17 reveals the direction in which each of the charges or conductors depicted there tends to move under the action of the electrical forces operating on it.

Let us examine qualitatively the field between two oppositely charged parallel conducting planes *AB* and *CD* (Fig. 22), the latter of which is provided with a rounded protuberance *M* and a point *P*. The lines of force are represented by full lines while the traces of the equipotential surfaces are shown by broken lines. While the field is somewhat increased in the neighborhood of *M*, it is seen to be very intense close to *P*. Therefore, air molecules in the vicinity of the point are strongly attracted to it. On reaching *P* they acquire some of the charge on the point and are then repelled to *AB*. In this way the plate *CD* loses its charge to *AB* through the agency of the point. This action is made use of in transferring the charge from the carriers to the collectors of an induction machine such as was described in art. 5.

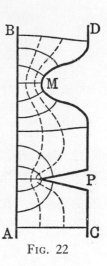

Fig. 22

Problem 11a. Construct roughly the lines of force and the equipotential surfaces in the field of the two charges of problem 7*b*.

Problem 11b. Two concentric spherical metal shells of radii 2 cm and 8 cm have charges of $1(10)^{-9}$ coulomb and $50(10)^{-9}$ coulomb, respectively. Find the stress on each.   Ans. $2.24(10)^{-3}$ newton/meter², $22.7(10)^{-3}$ newton/meter².

Problem 11c. Referring to the preceding problem, find the stresses if one of the positive charges is replaced by a negative charge of the same magnitude. Ans. $2.24(10)^{-3}$ newton/meter², $21.0(10)^{-3}$ newton/meter².

REFERENCES

Duckworth, *Electricity and Magnetism* (Holt, Rinehart and Winston, 1960).   Pp. 1–25, 43–48.

Kip, *Electricity and Magnetism* (McGraw-Hill, 1962).   Chap. 1–2, pp. 44–54.

Winch, *Electricity and Magnetism* (Prentice-Hall, 1963).   Chap. IX, pp. 229–248.

Chapter II

DIELECTRICS AND CONDUCTORS

12. Electric Dipoles.   If two equal point charges of opposite sign are located at the same point, the field of the one will exactly annul that of the other so that the pair will give rise to no electrical forces on a third charge.   If, however, one of the two charges is displaced a small distance relative to the other, the fields of the two will no longer quite

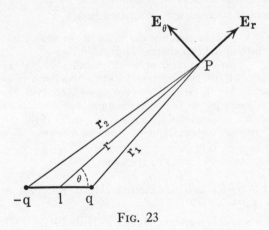

Fig. 23

compensate.   Such a combination is known as an *electric dipole*.   We have already made note of the fact that when a dielectric is subjected to electrical forces the bound electrons in each atom suffer a small displacement.   Therefore, each atom becomes an electric dipole, or more accurately a group of electric dipoles each one of which may be supposed to consist of one electron and one proton.   Under such circumstances the dielectric is said to be *polarized*.

Let l be the distance (Fig. 23) between the two charges q and $-q$ constituting a dipole.   We shall calculate the potential and the components of electric intensity at a point P at a distance r from the center

of the dipole large compared with its length l.   The potential at P due
to the two charges q and $-q$ is

$$V = \frac{q}{4\pi\kappa_0 r_1} - \frac{q}{4\pi\kappa_0 r_2} = \frac{1}{4\pi\kappa_0}\left[\frac{q}{r-\dfrac{l}{2}\cos\theta} - \frac{q}{r+\dfrac{l}{2}\cos\theta}\right]$$

$$= \frac{1}{4\pi\kappa_0}\left[\frac{ql\cos\theta}{r^2-\dfrac{l^2}{4}\cos^2\theta}\right] = \frac{ql\cos\theta}{4\pi\kappa_0 r^2},$$

as l^2 is negligible compared with r^2.   The product ql is known as the
electric moment of the dipole and is designated by p.   Evidently the
electric moment is a vector having the direction of the axis of the dipole.
We shall take its positive sense to be that of the line from $-q$ to q.
Then the numerator of the expression for the potential is just the
component of the electric moment in the direction of the radius vector r
and we can write

$$V = \frac{p\cos\theta}{4\pi\kappa_0 r^2}. \tag{12-1}$$

If a number of dipoles are located in a small region, the potential at

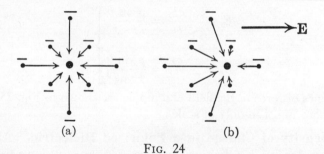

(a)   (b)

FIG. 24

a distant point is given by the same expression, provided that we understand by p the magnitude of the vector sum of the electric moments of
all the dipoles and by θ the angle which the resultant electric moment
makes with the radius vector r.   In the case of a normal atom (Fig. 24a)
the electrons may be considered to be distributed symmetrically about
the protons in the nucleus, and if we pair off each electron with a
proton we have a number of dipoles the moments of which are represented by arrows in the figure.   Clearly the resultant moment is zero
and therefore the potential vanishes at distant points.   If the atom is
placed in an electric field, however, the electrons are displaced relative

to the nucleus in a direction opposite to that of the electric intensity E (Fig. 24b). Evidently in this case the atom has a resultant electric moment which has the same direction as the field if the atom is isotropic.

Differentiating the expression (12-1) for the potential, we find for the

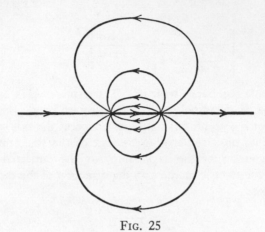

FIG. 25

components E_r and E_θ of the electric intensity in the directions of increasing r and increasing θ, respectively,

$$\left.\begin{aligned} E_r &= -\frac{\partial V}{\partial r} = \frac{p \cos \theta}{2\pi\kappa_0 r^3}, \\[2mm] E_\theta &= -\frac{\partial V}{r\partial \theta} = \frac{p \sin \theta}{4\pi\kappa_0 r^3}. \end{aligned}\right\} \tag{12-2}$$

The lines of force in the field of a dipole are shown in Fig. 25, which differs from Fig. 17b only in scale.

13. Density of Charge in a Polarized Dielectric. Although the charge density in a dielectric changes very greatly as we pass from proton to electron in an atom, ordinary electrical instruments are unable to measure fluctuations which occur in so short a distance. The measurements we make have to do rather with the *mean* values of the charge averaged over regions containing many thousands of atoms. Therefore, we shall replace the distribution of charge actually present by a smoothed distribution and understand henceforth by the charge density in a dielectric that obtained by averaging the actual charge density over a volume $\Delta\tau$ which is small by usual standards but large enough to contain a great many atoms. As a consequence, we must understand by the electric field in the medium the smooth field to which the smooth charge density gives rise.

We shall now calculate the average density of charge in the small volume $\Delta\tau = \Delta x \Delta y \Delta z$ (Fig. 26). Evidently this charge density vanishes if the medium is unpolarized, so our problem is to calculate the excess of the charge entering $\Delta\tau$ over that leaving this volume when the bound electrons in each atom become displaced by an impressed electric field. As the effect we are investigating is due to the displacement of charge of one sign relative to that of the other, the analysis is simplified without in any way limiting the generality of the result by assuming that the negative electricity remains fixed and that the electric moment of each atom is due to a displacement R of the positive electricity. If $ABCD$ represents a face $\Delta y \Delta z$ of the volume $\Delta\tau$, the positive charge passing through this face when the medium is polarized is that contained in the narrow prism $ABCDEFGH$ whose slant height is R. Denoting the X

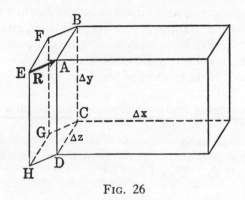

FIG. 26

component of the displacement by R_x, the volume of the prism $ABCDEFGH$ is $R_x \Delta y \Delta z$ and the positive electricity contained in it is

$$\rho' R_x \Delta y \Delta z,$$

where ρ' represents the aggregate positive charge per unit volume. This expression, then, gives the charge passing into $\Delta\tau$ through the left-hand boundary when the medium is polarized. That passing out through the right-hand boundary is

$$\left\{ \rho' R_x + \frac{\partial}{\partial x}(\rho' R_x)\Delta x \right\}\Delta y \Delta z,$$

where ρ' as well as R_x may have different values at the two boundaries. Subtracting the second of these expressions from the first we find for the net charge entering $\Delta\tau$ through the two faces perpendicular to the X axis the quantity,

$$-\frac{\partial}{\partial x}(\rho' R_x)\Delta x \Delta y \Delta z.$$

Now $\rho'R$ is the electric moment per unit volume. This quantity is called the *polarization* and is denoted by P. It is a vector having the direction of the displacement R. Adding to the expression above corresponding expressions for the charge entering $\Delta\tau$ through the pairs of boundary surfaces perpendicular to the Y and Z axes, and dividing by the volume $\Delta x \Delta y \Delta z$ of the region, the net volume charge density ρ_P produced by the polarization of the medium is seen to be

$$\rho_P = -\left(\frac{\partial P_x}{\partial x}+\frac{\partial P_y}{\partial y}+\frac{\partial P_z}{\partial z}\right). \tag{13-1}$$

If the polarization is constant throughout the medium the charge per unit volume in its interior is zero since each of the derivatives in (13-1) vanishes. In this case as much charge passes out of one face of a volume $\Delta\tau$ situated entirely inside the dielectric as passes in through the opposite one, and the only charges are those produced on the surface of the medium.

The surface charge is easily calculated in the case of a bar of length l and cross section A polarized uniformly along its axis. Denoting the charge per unit area on the two ends of the bar by σ_P and $-\sigma_P$, respectively, the electric moment of the bar is $\sigma_P A l$, and the electric moment per unit volume is σ_P. Therefore,

$$\sigma_P = P. \tag{13-2}$$

We can express the charge passing into any volume τ when the dielectric is polarized as a surface integral. For if β (Fig. 27) is the angle between R and the outward drawn normal n to the surface s bounding τ, the charge entering τ through the surface element ds is that contained in the prism $ABCD$ of volume $-R\cos\beta ds$, that is, a charge $-\rho'R\cos\beta ds$. Therefore, the total charge entering τ when the medium is polarized is

$$Q_P = -\int_s P\cos\beta ds, \tag{13-3}$$

where the surface integral is taken over the closed surface s which surrounds the volume τ.

We can use this formula to obtain a general expression for the density of charge on the surface of a dielectric. Let $ABCD$ (Fig. 28) be a pill-box shaped surface enclosing an area Δs of the surface of the dielectric, the altitude BC of the pill-box being very small compared with the diameter of the base. Applying (13-3) to the surface of the pill-box, the value of the integral over AB vanishes since this base of the pill-box lies outside the dielectric where the polarization is zero, and the area of the cylindrical portion of the pill-box is so small that the integral over this portion of the surface is negligible. So the right-hand side of (13-3) reduces to the integral over the base CD of the pill-box which lies inside the dielectric. If, then, σ_P is the charge per unit area on the surface of the dielectric,

$$\sigma_P \Delta s = -P \cos \beta \Delta s = P \cos \gamma \Delta s,$$

since γ is the supplement of the angle β between P and the normal n

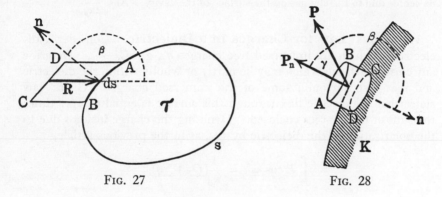

Fig. 27   Fig. 28

to CD. But $P \cos \gamma$ is the component P_n of the polarization at right angles to the surface of the dielectric. Therefore

$$\sigma_P = P_n \tag{13-4}$$

is the charge per unit area on the surface. This expression evidently reduces to (13-2) for the special case considered there. If the polarization of the medium is not uniform the surface charge is accompanied by a volume distribution of charge in the interior of the dielectric given by (13-1). To find the mean electric field in the vicinity of a dielectric— whether outside or inside the medium—we must add to the impressed electric intensity due to outside charges that produced by the surface charge (13-4) on the surface of the dielectric and that produced by the volume charge (13-1) in the interior of the dielectric.

Problem 13a. A sphere of radius a is polarized along the radius vector so that $P = kr$. Find the volume and surface charge densities and show that the total charge is zero. Ans. $-3k$, ka.

Problem 13b. A thin rod of cross section A and length l lies on the X axis with its nearer end at a distance b from the origin. The polarization is kx parallel to the X axis. Find the charge at each end and the volume density of charge in the interior of the rod, and show that the total charge is zero. Also find the potential at the origin due to the rod. Ans. $-kAb$, $kA(b+l)$, $-k$,

$$-\frac{kA}{4\pi\kappa_0} \log\left(1+\frac{l}{b}\right).$$

Problem 13c. The following cavities are cut in a dielectric in which the polarization P is uniform and fixed; (a) a narrow slit at right angles to the polarization, (b) a sphere, (c) a long needle-like cavity with its axis parallel to the polarization. Find the electric intensity at the center of each due to the charge produced on the surface of the cavity. Ans. (a) $\frac{P}{\kappa_0}$, (b) $\frac{P}{3\kappa_0}$, (c) 0.

Problem 13d. A long cylindrical cavity at right angles to the polarization is cut in the dielectric of the preceding problem. Find the electric intensity at its center due to the charges on the surface of the cavity. Ans. $\frac{P}{2\kappa_0}$.

14. Gauss' Law for Charges in a Dielectric.

Consider a dielectric in which are immersed free charges q_1, q_2, q_3, $\cdots$. Describe any closed surface s which may lie partly or wholly within the dielectric and may also surround some of the immersed charges. Gauss' law states that the electric flux through this surface is equal to $1/\kappa_0$ times the sum of the charges enclosed. Denoting the charge inside s due to the polarization of the dielectric by Q_P, as in the previous article,

$$\int_s E \cos \alpha ds = \frac{1}{\kappa_0}(Q_P + \Sigma q),$$

where α is the angle between E and the outward drawn normal to the surface and Σq represents the sum of the free charges inside.

Replacing Q_P by the right-hand side of (13-3) and rearranging terms so as to combine the two surface integrals,

$$\int_s (\kappa_0 E \cos \alpha + P \cos \beta)ds = \Sigma q, \tag{14-1}$$

where β is the angle between P and the outward drawn normal to the surface.

Using vector notation, we define the *electric displacement* **D** as the vector sum of κ_0**E** and **P**, that is,

$$\mathbf{D} \equiv \kappa_0\mathbf{E} + \mathbf{P}. \tag{14-2}$$

It is clear from (14-1) that $\kappa_0 E$ and P and, consequently, D have the same physical dimensions. All three, therefore, may be expressed in the same unit, namely, the *coulomb per meter*^{2}. This is 1 meter$^{-3/2}$ kg$^{1/2}$ in terms of the fundamental units.

If, now, γ is the angle between D and the normal n to the surface s,

$$D \cos \gamma = \kappa_0 E \cos \alpha + P \cos \beta,$$

as is evident from Fig. 29.   Therefore Gauss' law (14-1) becomes

$$\int_s D \cos \gamma ds = \Sigma q, \tag{14-3}$$

or, for a continuous distribution of free charge of volume density ρ,

$$\int_s D \cos \gamma ds = \int_\tau \rho d\tau, \tag{14-4}$$

the volume integral being taken over the entire volume τ enclosed by the surface s.

It is only in an anisotropic dielectric, such as crystalline quartz, that $\mathbf{P}$ and $\kappa_0\mathbf{E}$ have different directions.   In the case of isotropic media, such as glass or paraffin, $\mathbf{P}$ and $\kappa_0\mathbf{E}$, and therefore $\mathbf{D}$, have the same direction.   Then the three angles α, β and γ in Fig. 29 are equal, and (14–2) may be replaced by the scalar equation $D = \kappa_0 E + P$.

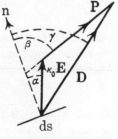

FIG. 29

We define the *flux of displacement* through a surface ds as the product of the component of the displacement D normal to the surface by the area of the surface.   Then the left-hand side of (14-3) or (14-4) represents the outward flux of displacement through the closed surface s and these two equivalent forms of Gauss' law state that the total outward flux of displacement through any closed surface is equal to the sum of the *free charges* enclosed within the surface, that is, of all the charges except those due to the polarization of the medium.   The charges due to polarization are included in the left-hand members of equations (14-3) and (14-4).

Lines of electric displacement may be drawn so as to have everywhere the direction of D and in such density that the number of *tubes of displacement*—defined as bundles of M lines of displacement—per unit cross section is equal to the displacement.   Following the same line of argument as that applied to lines of force in art. 10, it is clear that tubes and lines of displacement are continuous in regions in which no free charges are present, and that each tube of displacement originates on a unit positive free charge and terminates on a unit negative free charge. When we pass from one dielectric to another through the surface separating them, or from a dielectric into empty space, tubes of displacement are continuous provided no free charge resides on the surface. Tubes of force, on the other hand, are not continuous across the boundary, since they end on polarization charge as well as on free charge.

Consider two dielectrics K_1 and K_2 (Fig. 30) in contact. Describe the pill-box shaped surface $ABCD$ about an area Δs of the surface of separation, the height BC of the pill-box being very small compared with the diameter of the bases. Let D_{1n} and D_{2n} be the normal components of the displacement in the two media. Then, as there is no free charge inside the pill-box, Gauss' law requires that

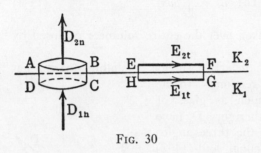

FIG. 30

$$D_{2n}\Delta s - D_{1n}\Delta s = 0,$$

or

$$D_{2n} = D_{1n}. \quad (14\text{-}5)$$

Therefore, the normal component of the displacement is the same on both sides of the surface of separation. Next consider the rectangle $EFGH$ of length Δl and negligible height. Let E_{1t} and E_{2t} be the tangential components of the electric intensity in the two media. Then the work done in taking a unit charge around the rectangle is

$$E_{2t}\Delta l - E_{1t}\Delta l.$$

As this represents the drop in potential around a closed path, it must vanish. Hence

$$E_{2t} = E_{1t}, \quad (14\text{-}6)$$

and the tangential component of the electric intensity is the same on both sides of the surface.

15. Isotropic Dielectrics. Although the basic relations expressed in the preceding article are equally valid for isotropic and for anisotropic dielectrics, we shall confine ourselves hereafter to the more common isotropic case. Here the polarization must be in the direction of the electric field which produces it and, as we should expect, P is found to be proportional to E, at least for ordinary fields. Introducing the factor κ_0 for later convenience, we can write

$$P = \kappa_0 \epsilon E, \quad (15\text{-}1)$$

where ϵ, the *electric susceptibility*, is a numerical constant characteristic of the medium. Hence

$$D = \kappa_0 E + P = \kappa_0(1 + \epsilon)E,$$

and if we put

$$\kappa \equiv 1 + \epsilon, \tag{15-2}$$

the relation between D and E becomes

$$D = \kappa_0 \kappa E. \tag{15-3}$$

The quantity κ is known as the *permittivity of the dielectric*, or the *dielectric constant*. Like ϵ it is a numerical constant characteristic of the medium. Unlike ϵ, however, it has the same value, for a given dielectric, in all systems of units, both m.k.s. and c.g.s. Evidently κ is simply the ratio of the displacement produced in the dielectric to the displacement produced in free space by the same electric field.

In an isotropic dielectric Gauss' law (14-3) takes the form

$$\int_s \kappa E \cos \gamma ds = \frac{\Sigma q}{\kappa_0}, \tag{15-4}$$

and this reduces to

$$\int_s E \cos \gamma ds = \frac{\Sigma q}{\kappa_0 \kappa} \tag{15-5}$$

when the dielectric is homogeneous, since κ then has the same value everywhere.

Remembering that q in these formulas represents free charge, we see from the second that if no free charge is present in the interior of a homogeneous isotropic dielectric the flux of E out of any closed surface lying wholly in the medium is zero. Consequently no polarization charge can be present in the interior of such a dielectric. All charges must reside on its surface.

By means of Gauss' law (15-5) we find at once the electric field in an isotropic dielectric surrounding a spherical charge Q in which the charge density is a function of the distance from the center only. The method is identical with that employed in art. 9 in the case where no dielectric is present. Since Gauss' law (15-5) for charges immersed in a dielectric differs from the corresponding law (8-4) for charges in empty space only in the appearance of the factor κ in the denominator on the right, the expression (9-1) for the electric intensity in empty space must be replaced by

$$E = \frac{Q}{4\pi \kappa_0 \kappa r^2} \tag{15-6}$$

when the charge is immersed in a dielectric.

The reason why the electric intensity is reduced in the ratio 1 to κ

by the dielectric is made clearer if we examine the polarization charges in the medium. Eliminating ϵ from (15-1) and (15-2),

$$P = \kappa_0(\kappa - 1)E, \tag{15-7}$$

and making use of (15-6),

$$P = \left(\frac{\kappa - 1}{\kappa}\right)\frac{Q}{4\pi r^2}.$$

If a is the radius of the charge Q, the polarization charge per unit area of the cavity in the dielectric in which Q lies is

$$\sigma_P = -(P)_{r=a} = -\left(\frac{\kappa - 1}{\kappa}\right)\frac{Q}{4\pi a^2}$$

from (13-4), and the total polarization charge on the surface of the cavity is

$$Q_P = 4\pi a^2 \sigma_P = -\frac{\kappa - 1}{\kappa} Q.$$

The effective charge producing the field is the sum of Q and the polarization charge Q_P, that is,

$$Q - \frac{\kappa - 1}{\kappa} Q = \frac{Q}{\kappa}$$

Consequently the electric intensity in the dielectric is only $1/\kappa$ times that which would be produced by Q alone.

On account of the factor κ in the denominator of (15-6) we must replace the expression (7-4) for the potential due to a number of point charges by

$$V = \frac{1}{4\pi\kappa_0\kappa} \sum \frac{q}{r} \tag{15-8}$$

when the charges are surrounded by a dielectric. Similarly we have for the potential due to a continuous distribution of charge on a surface s immersed in a dielectric

$$V = \frac{1}{4\pi\kappa_0\kappa} \int_s \frac{\sigma ds}{r} \tag{15-9}$$

where σ is the charge per unit area. If this surface is a closed conducting shell, the presence of the dielectric within the shell is of no consequence since no field exists there (art. 11). This means that (15-9) remains valid even if the dielectric in the interior of the shell is partially or wholly replaced by conducting material. Therefore, this expression may be used to calculate the potential due to the surface charges on extended solid conductors immersed in a dielectric.

Furthermore, if the charged surfaces discussed in art. 9 and art. 11 are surrounded by a dielectric, the expressions obtained for the electric intensity at outside points must be modified by the introduction of the factor κ into the denominator of each. Thus (11-1) for the electric intensity just outside a charged conducting surface becomes

$$E = \frac{\sigma}{\kappa_0 \kappa}. \tag{15-10}$$

When two dielectrics are in contact, both lines of force and lines of displacement are bent in passing from the one to the other. To calculate the law of refraction of these lines, we make use of equations (14-5) and (14-6). Designating the angles which the lines of displace-

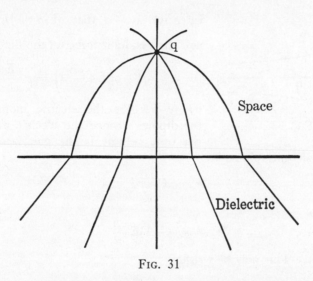

FIG. 31

ment make with the normal to the surface of separation of the two dielectrics of Fig. 30 by θ_1 and θ_2 we have

$$\kappa_2 E_2 \cos \theta_2 = \kappa_1 E_1 \cos \theta_1$$

from (14-5) and (15-3), and

$$E_2 \sin \theta_2 = E_1 \sin \theta_1$$

from (14-6). Dividing the one by the other, we obtain

$$\frac{\tan \theta_1}{\tan \theta_2} = \frac{\kappa_1}{\kappa_2}. \tag{15-11}$$

In passing from empty space into a dielectric, then, the lines of displacement are bent *away* from the normal to the surface, an effect opposite to that which takes place when a ray of light passes into a transparent medium, such as glass.   In Fig. 31 the bending of the lines of displacement is shown for the case of a point charge q placed above a dielectric.

16. Stresses in a Dielectric.   In the last article we investigated the electric field produced by charges immersed in an isotropic dielectric. It remains to find the force experienced by a charge surrounded by a dielectric.   As a first step we must examine the electrical forces on the elements of the dielectric itself.

As the polarization in an isotropic dielectric is parallel to the electric intensity, each atomic dipole may be considered to be lined up with its axis parallel to the lines of force as in Fig. 32.   If, then, E is the electric intensity at $-q$, that at q is $E + \dfrac{\partial E}{\partial l} l$

and the resultant force on the dipole is

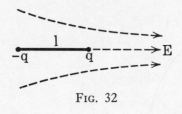

FIG. 32

$$-qE + q\left(E + \frac{\partial E}{\partial l} l\right) = p\,\frac{\partial E}{\partial l},$$

where $p \equiv ql$ is the electric moment of the dipole.   Since the electric moment per unit volume is the polarization P, the force per unit volume is

$$\mathscr{F}_\tau = P\,\frac{\partial E}{\partial l},$$

or

$$\mathscr{F}_\tau = \kappa_0(\kappa - 1)E\,\frac{\partial E}{\partial l} \tag{16-1}$$

from (15-7).   This may be written

$$\mathscr{F}_\tau = \frac{\kappa_0(\kappa - 1)}{2}\,\frac{\partial}{\partial l}(E^2). \tag{16-2}$$

If, now, we designate the pressure in the dielectric by p, we see that the pressure over the right-hand face of the rectangular parallelepiped of unit cross section and thickness dl pictured in Fig. 33 must be greater than that over the left-hand face by an amount just sufficient to balance the electrical force given by (16-2), that is,

$$\frac{\partial p}{\partial l}\,dl = \frac{\kappa_0(\kappa - 1)}{2}\,\frac{\partial}{\partial l}(E^2)dl.$$

Integrating, we have

$$p = \frac{\kappa_0(\kappa - 1)}{2}\,E^2 \tag{16-3}$$

except for a constant of integration which is of no significance since it represents merely a constant pressure which is everywhere the same and therefore gives rise to no tractive forces. Equation (16-3) shows that the pressure in a dielectric is proportional to the square of the electric intensity, being large near charges, where E is great, and small at great distances from charges, where the field is weak.

Stress on Surface of Dielectric. We have seen that a dipole well inside the body of a dielectric is urged by the electrical forces acting on it from the weaker to the stronger parts of the field. The same is true of the dipoles extending into the transition layer at the surface of a dielectric, where the polarization charge resides. However, the field changes so rapidly in this region from the value E in the interior of the dielectric to the value E_o outside, that a special analysis of the forces

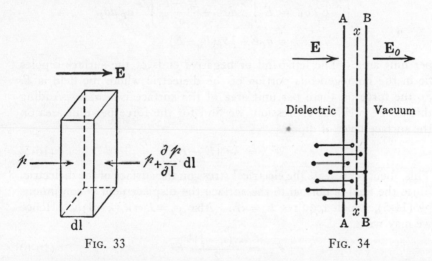

Fig. 33   Fig. 34

is needed. We shall confine our discussion to the case where the field and therefore the polarization are normal to the surface of the dielectric.

Let the region between AA and BB (Fig. 34) be the transition layer at the surface of the dielectric lying to the left. As we pass from AA to BB the polarization charge per unit area increases from zero to its full value σ_P, and the field increases from E to E_o at the same rate. Therefore, if the polarization charge per unit area between AA and any intermediate plane xx is σ_P', the field E' at xx is

$$E' = E + \frac{\sigma_P'}{\sigma_P}(E_o - E). \tag{16-4}$$

Now the existence of the transition layer is due to the fact that the surface of the dielectric is not actually a perfectly smooth surface. At some places the last dipole reaches only as far to the right as AA, at others the last dipole in the dielectric extends well into the region between AA and BB, whereas at still others the last dipole reaches as far as BB. This is illustrated in the lower part of the figure. So the field acting on the right-hand or positive end of a surface dipole may be anything between E and E_o, depending upon how far the dipole under consideration extends into the transition layer. Since the polarization charge is due, however, to the uncompensated charges on the right-hand ends of the surface dipoles, the charge per unit area on the right-hand ends of all the surface dipoles which extend no farther to the right than xx is σ_P'. Hence the force on the right-hand ends of the dipoles with charge $d\sigma_P'$ is $E'd\sigma_P'$ and the force on the right-hand ends of all the surface dipoles is

$$\int_0^{\sigma_P} E'd\sigma_P' = E \int_0^{\sigma_P} d\sigma_P' + \frac{E_o-E}{\sigma_P} \int_0^{\sigma_P} \sigma_P'd\sigma_P'$$

$$= \sigma_P E + \tfrac{1}{2}\sigma_P(E_o-E)$$

per unit area. The left-hand or negative ends of the surface dipoles lie in the homogeneous portion of the dielectric where the field is E. So the force on them per unit area of the surface is $-\sigma_P E$. Adding this to the previous expression, we find for the force per unit area on the surface layer of dipoles

$$\mathscr{F}_s' = \tfrac{1}{2}\sigma_P(E_o-E). \tag{16-5}$$

This, then, represents the electrical stress on the surface of the dielectric. Since the field is normal to the surface the displacement is continuous by (14-5), which requires $E_o=\kappa E$. Also $\sigma_P=P=\kappa_0(\kappa-1)E$. Hence we may write

$$\mathscr{F}_s' = \frac{\kappa_0(\kappa-1)^2}{2} E^2. \tag{16-6}$$

To $\mathscr{F}_s'$ we must add the mechanical pressure (16-3) in the homogeneous body of the dielectric to get the total stress $\mathscr{F}_s''$ on the surface. Thus

$$\mathscr{F}_s'' = \frac{\kappa_0(\kappa-1)^2}{2} E^2 + \frac{\kappa_0(\kappa-1)}{2} E^2$$

$$= \frac{\kappa_0\kappa(\kappa-1)}{2} E^2 = \frac{\kappa_0}{2}\left(\frac{\kappa-1}{\kappa}\right)E_o^2. \tag{16-7}$$

As the expression for the stress involves only the square of the field strength it represents a positive stress or tension whether the electric intensity is directed along the outward normal to the surface, as we have supposed, or in the opposite sense. This tension tends to stretch a solid dielectric in the direction of the lines of force of the field in which it is placed, an effect known as *electrostriction*. Using a liquid dielectric with an air bubble above it, Quincke has verified the formula (16-7) by measuring the increase in pressure of the air as the field is increased.

Stress on Surface of Conductor. Only when a conductor is immersed in a *fluid* dielectric does the total stress on the surface of the conductor have, in general, a unique value. For, when the conductor is located in a cavity in a *solid* dielectric, the stress on any portion of the conductor's surface depends on the completeness of its contact with the surrounding medium and on the elastic properties of the medium. Consequently, we shall confine our analysis to the case of a conductor with a surface charge density σ immersed in a fluid dielectric. The total stress $\mathscr{F}_s$ on the surface of the conductor is the tension $\sigma^2/2\kappa_0$ in empty space, given by (11-2), less the tension on the surface of the dielectric specified by (16-7), since the latter is transmitted to the conductor as a pressure. Hence

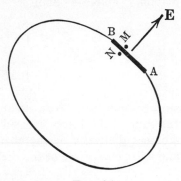

FIG. 35

$$\mathscr{F}_s = \frac{\sigma^2}{2\kappa_0} - \frac{\kappa_0\kappa(\kappa-1)}{2} E^2.$$

Now the free charge density σ on the surface of the conductor may be expressed in terms of the electric intensity E just outside by (15-10), that is, $\sigma = \kappa_0\kappa E$. Hence

$$\mathscr{F}_s = \frac{\kappa_0\kappa}{2} E^2 = \tfrac{1}{2}\sigma E = \frac{\sigma^2}{2\kappa_0\kappa}. \tag{16-8}$$

By integrating this stress over the entire surface of a conductor immersed in a homogeneous fluid dielectric we can find the resultant mechanical force experienced by the conductor.

Force on Conductor. Consider a conductor immersed in a homogeneous fluid dielectric. The field $\mathbf{E}$ at a point M (Fig. 35) in the dielectric just outside the surface element AB of the conductor may be considered as the resultant of three fields: the external field $\mathbf{E}_0$, the field $\mathbf{E}'$ due to the charge densities σ on AB and σ_P on the adjacent surface of the dielectric, and the field $\mathbf{E}''$ due to the charge on the remainder of the conductor and adjacent surface of the dielectric.

Now the field at N due to the charge on the portion AB of the conductor and the adjacent surface of the dielectric is, from symmetry, equal and opposite to that M, that is, equal to $-\mathbf{E}'$. The remainder of the field at N differs, however, only infinitesimally from that at M.

But, as N is inside the conductor, the resultant field vanishes. Hence at N we have

$$\mathbf{E}_0 - \mathbf{E}' + \mathbf{E}'' = 0,$$

whereas at M we have

$$\mathbf{E}_0 + \mathbf{E}' + \mathbf{E}'' = \mathbf{E}.$$

Adding, we find that

$$\mathbf{E}_0 + \mathbf{E}'' = \tfrac{1}{2}\mathbf{E}. \tag{16-9}$$

So the stress given by (16-8) is

$$\mathscr{F}_s = \tfrac{1}{2}\sigma\mathbf{E} = \sigma\mathbf{E}_0 + \sigma\mathbf{E}''.$$

The resultant force $\mathscr{F}$ on the conductor is obtained by integrating the stress $\mathscr{F}_s$ over its surface s, integration of a vector representing vector summation just as integration of a scalar represents scalar summation. Thus we obtain

$$\mathscr{F} = \int_s \sigma\mathbf{E}_0 ds + \int_s \sigma\mathbf{E}'' ds$$

$$= \int_s \sigma\mathbf{E}_0 ds + \kappa\int_s (\sigma + \sigma_P)\mathbf{E}'' ds$$

since $\sigma + \sigma_P = \sigma/\kappa$. Now the second integral must vanish as it represents the sum of the forces exerted on each element of the conductor and adjacent dielectric by the charges on the remainder of the conductor and adjacent surface of the dielectric. Hence we have

$$\mathscr{F} = \int_s \sigma\mathbf{E}_0 ds. \tag{16-10}$$

Therefore the resultant force exerted on a conductor immersed in a fluid dielectric is obtained by multiplying each element of charge by the external electric intensity and summing up over the surface of the conductor. If, for instance, we have two conductors with charges Q_1 and Q_2 at a distance r apart large compared with their linear dimensions, the electric intensity at Q_2 due to Q_1 is

$$E = \frac{Q_1}{4\pi\kappa_0\kappa r^2},$$

and the resultant force on Q_2 is

$$\mathscr{F} = \frac{Q_1 Q_2}{4\pi\kappa_0\kappa r^2}. \tag{16-11}$$

As a charged conductor of very small dimensions is effectively the same thing as a point charge, (16-11) also holds for the force between two point charges immersed in a fluid dielectric.

Of course, the restriction to fluid dielectrics made here applies only to expressions for the *stress* or *force* and not to expressions for the *field* such as given in art. 15.

Problem 16a. Two parallel plates of infinite extent are separated by a slab of solid dielectric of permittivity κ. One plate has a charge density σ and the other a charge density $-\sigma$. What force per unit area is required to pull either plate completely away from the dielectric? What is the stress on the surface of the dielectric after the plate has lost contact with it? Ans. $\frac{\sigma^2}{2\kappa_0}$, $\frac{\sigma^2}{2\kappa_0}\left(\frac{\kappa-1}{\kappa}\right)$.

Problem 16b. The space between two concentric spherical conductors of radius 5 cm and 10 cm, respectively, is filled with a fluid whose permittivity is 5, at atmospheric pressure. The inner conductor is given a charge $(10)^{-7}$ coulomb. Calculate the excess pressure due to the electric field (a) on the inner conductor, (b) in the fluid very close to the inner conductor, (c) on the inner surface of the outer conductor. Ans. (a) -0.115 newton/meter^2, (b) 0.092 newton/meter^2, (c) -0.007 newton/meter^2.

17. Electric Field in a Dielectric. The electric field E_1 which is responsible for the displacement of the bound electrons in the atoms in a small volume $\Delta\tau$ of a dielectric is the resultant of the field due to external sources, including the surface and volume charges in the dielectric calculated in art. 13, and that due to the adjacent polarized atoms. This is not, however, the total field E. The latter is the sum of E_1 and the field E_2 to which the polarization of the region $\Delta\tau$ itself gives rise. In order to find the relation between E_1 and E we shall calculate E_2 and make use of the equation

$$E = E_1 + E_2. \tag{17-1}$$

The field E_2 is, of course, the smooth field in $\Delta\tau$ due to the smooth charge density by which we have replaced the actual charge density, as explained in art. 13. Consequently, in a polarized region, it is the field that would be produced if we take two equal and opposite charges uniformly distributed throughout $\Delta\tau$ with densities ρ' and $-\rho'$, respectively, and displace the positive charge relative to the negative charge the small distance necessary to produce the required uniform polarization. Although the electric intensity E_2 so produced depends to some extent on the shape of the region $\Delta\tau$, we shall take this region to be a sphere on the ground that the distribution of the atoms in an isotropic medium has approximate spherical symmetry.

Let a (Fig. 36) be the radius of either of the two relatively displaced spherical charges, and let $\mathbf{r}'$ and $\mathbf{r}''$ be the vector distances of a point A from the centers of the positive and of the negative spheres, respectively. Written in vector form, the electric fields $\mathbf{E}'$ and $\mathbf{E}''$ at A due to the charges $\frac{4}{3}\pi a^3\rho'$ and $-\frac{4}{3}\pi a^3\rho'$ are

$$\mathbf{E}' = \frac{\rho'\mathbf{r}'}{3\kappa_0}, \quad \mathbf{E}'' = -\frac{\rho'\mathbf{r}''}{3\kappa_0},$$

in accord with (9-2).   Therefore,

$$\mathbf{E}_2 = \mathbf{E}' + \mathbf{E}'' = -\frac{\rho'(\mathbf{r}'' - \mathbf{r}')}{3\kappa_0} = -\frac{\rho'\mathbf{R}}{3\kappa_0},$$

where $\mathbf{R} \equiv \mathbf{r}'' - \mathbf{r}'$ is the vector displacement of the center of the positive charge relative to that of the negative charge.   Since $\rho'\mathbf{R}$ is $\mathbf{P}$ the electric moment per unit volume,

$$\mathbf{E}_2 = -\frac{1}{3\kappa_0}\mathbf{P}. \tag{17-2}$$

Returning to (17-1) we have then

$$E_1 = E + \frac{1}{3\kappa_0}P, \tag{17-3}$$

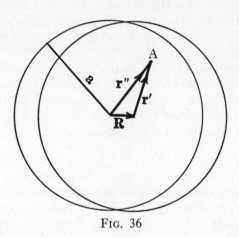

FIG. 36

which shows that the polarizing field in the dielectric is actually greater than the total field.

Evidently P has the same direction as E_1.   In magnitude it is found to be proportional to E_1 and to n the number of atoms per unit volume. Accordingly

$$P = n\alpha E_1, \tag{17-4}$$

where α, the *atomic polarizability*, is a constant characteristic of the type of atom (or atoms) of which the dielectric is composed and independent of the density.

To find the relation between α and κ we note that

$$(\kappa - 1)E = \frac{1}{\kappa_0}P$$

from (15-7), so that (17-3) may be written

$$\frac{1}{3\kappa_0}P = \frac{\kappa-1}{\kappa+2}E_1. \tag{17-5}$$

Comparing this with (17-4), we get

$$\frac{\kappa-1}{\kappa+2} = \frac{n\alpha}{3\kappa_0}. \tag{17-6}$$

Since n represents the number of atoms per unit volume, the right-hand side of this equation is proportional to the density of the dielectric. Therefore, the ratio of $\kappa-1$ to $\kappa+2$ is also proportional to the density. That this is the case has been verified for a number of gases.

18. Capacitance and Capacitors. There is a definite relation between charge and potential in any electrostatic system. Consider first a single conductor with charge Q at potential V, surrounded by an infinite dielectric of permittivity κ. As the charge is located entirely on the surface of the conductor, we have from (15-9)

$$V = \frac{1}{4\pi\kappa_0\kappa}\int_s \frac{\sigma ds}{r}$$

for the potential at any point in space, including, in particular, any point P on the surface of the conductor.

Evidently multiplying every element of charge by any factor multiplies V by the same factor. The surface of the conductor remains equipotential and equilibrium is not disturbed. Hence V is proportional to the total charge Q. If we write

$$Q = CV, \tag{18-1}$$

C is called the *capacitance* of the conductor. It is the charge that can be placed on the conductor per unit potential.

In the case of a uniformly charged sphere of radius a immersed in an infinite dielectric the electric intensity outside the sphere is given by (15-6), that is,

$$E = \frac{Q}{4\pi\kappa_0\kappa r^2},$$

and the potential at the surface of the sphere is

$$V = \frac{Q}{4\pi\kappa_0\kappa}\int_a^\infty \frac{dr}{r^2} = \frac{Q}{4\pi\kappa_0\kappa a}. \tag{18-2}$$

Therefore, from (18-1),

$$C = 4\pi\kappa_0\kappa a. \tag{18-3}$$

Basically, capacitance is measured in coulombs per volt. However, the unit of capacitance is of sufficient importance to be independently named the *farad*. In practice, capacitances usually are measured in *microfarads*, a microfarad being $(10)^{-6}$ farad. In terms of the fundamental units the farad is 1 meter^{-1} sec^2. Referring to (18-3), note that the unit of κ_0 can be called the *farad per meter*.

If several conductors are present there is no definite capacitance associated with each one, since the charge on each depends not only on its potential, but also on the potentials of the other conductors. However, in the special case of *two conductors arranged always to have charges of equal magnitude and opposite sign*, we have as before

$$V_1 = \frac{Q}{C_1}, \quad V_2 = -\frac{Q}{C_2},$$

so that we may write

$$Q = C(V_1 - V_2), \qquad (18\text{-}4)$$

where

$$\frac{1}{C} = \frac{1}{C_1} + \frac{1}{C_2}.$$

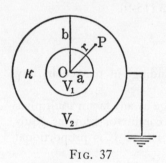

FIG. 37

Such a combination of conductors is called a *capacitor* or *condenser*. It is a device for the storage of charge, the quantity stored being proportional to the potential difference of its elements. The constant C is its *capacitance*.

Concentric spheres with a dielectric between them (Fig. 37) form a simple capacitor. Let the outer sphere be grounded, that is, be at the same potential as the earth, walls of the room, and other near-by objects. Since we are concerned with potential difference alone, it is usually convenient to take the invariable potential of the earth as zero. The electric intensity at a point P between the spheres is $Q/4\pi\kappa_0\kappa r^2$, as the charge $-Q$ on the outer sphere does not produce an electric field inside. Hence

$$V_1 - V_2 = \frac{Q}{4\pi\kappa_0\kappa} \int_a^b \frac{dr}{r^2} = \frac{Q(b-a)}{4\pi\kappa_0\kappa ab},$$

where a is the radius of the inner sphere and b the radius of the inner surface of the outer sphere. Therefore,

$$C = \frac{4\pi\kappa_0\kappa ab}{b-a}, \qquad (18\text{-}5)$$

which may be made much greater than the capacitance (18-3) of an isolated sphere.

In the case just considered the charge on the outer sphere is evidently all on the inner surface. If now we ground the inner sphere instead of the outer, keeping $V_1 - V_2$ unchanged, there will be an additional charge on the outer surface of the outer sphere due to its capacitance relative to surrounding objects. This charge corresponds, approximately at least, to that on a single isolated sphere. So, if b' is the radius of the outer surface, the total charge on the outer sphere is

$$-4\pi\kappa_0\left[\frac{\kappa ab}{b-a}+b'\right](V_1-V_2),$$

and the capacitance is

$$C = 4\pi\kappa_0\left[\frac{\kappa ab}{b-a}+b'\right]. \tag{18-6}$$

It is usually preferable to ground the outer sphere, since then the capacitance is entirely independent of external objects. We have here a simple case of *electric shielding*, discussed in more detail in art. 19.

A very common and convenient type of capacitor consists of two parallel plates separated by a dielectric. If the distance d between the plates is small compared with the dimensions of the plates, the electric intensity is zero outside and constant between the plates, except near the edges. In fact, in the central portion of the capacitor E is perpendicular to the plates and, modifying (9-4) to take account of the dielectric,

$$E = \frac{\sigma}{\kappa_0\kappa}, \tag{18-7}$$

where σ is the charge per unit area. Then

$$V = Ed = \frac{\sigma d}{\kappa_0\kappa}$$

and the capacitance per unit area is given by

$$C_s = \frac{\kappa_0\kappa}{d}. \tag{18-8}$$

With the geometrical limitation mentioned above the *edge effect* is small. That is, if A is the area of either plate, the total charge is approximately $A\sigma$ and the total capacitance is given by

$$C = \frac{\kappa_0\kappa A}{d}. \tag{18-9}$$

To obtain large capacitance without excessive size, capacitors are often composed of a pile of plates separated by thin layers of dielectric such as mica or waxed paper. Alternate plates have the same polarity, so that double use is made of their area. If air is the dielectric, one group of plates may be arranged to move relative to the other, thus making the capacitor *variable*.

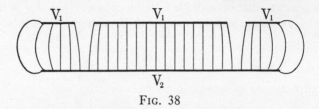

FIG. 38

When it is necessary to calculate capacitance very accurately, in order to establish laboratory standards or to make absolute measurements, the edge effect may be eliminated. Suppose the central portion of one plate of a single parallel plate capacitor is separated from the rest of the plate by a narrow gap (Fig. 38). The outer portion is called a *guard ring* and its use is due to Kelvin. The lines of force remain perpendicular almost to the edge of the guarded plate, and on the lower unguarded plate they are practically undisturbed by the gap. If then A' equals the area A of the guarded plate plus one-half the area of the gap,

$$C = \frac{\kappa_0 \kappa A'}{d} \quad (18\text{-}10)$$

to a high degree of accuracy. Of course, the potential of the ring must be kept exactly equal to that of the plate by some agency independent of that supplying the charge to the plate.

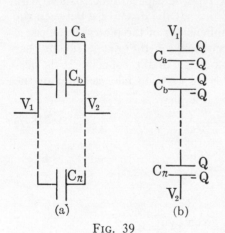

FIG. 39

The capacitance of combinations of capacitors is easily calculated. Suppose we have several capacitances C_a, C_b, $\cdots C_n$ in *parallel* (Fig. 39a). The total charge is given by

$$Q = Q_a + Q_b + \cdots Q_n = (C_a + C_b + \cdots C_n)(V_1 - V_2),$$

so that the resultant capacitance is

$$C = C_a + C_b + \cdots C_n. \quad (18\text{-}11)$$

On the other hand, with capacitances in *series* (Fig. 39b)

$$V_1 - V_2 = \frac{Q}{C_a} + \frac{Q}{C_b} + \cdots \frac{Q}{C_n} = \left(\frac{1}{C_a} + \frac{1}{C_b} + \cdots \frac{1}{C_n} \right) Q.$$

Therefore, in this case

$$\frac{1}{C} = \frac{1}{C_a} + \frac{1}{C_b} + \cdots \frac{1}{C_n}. \tag{18-12}$$

It should be noted that when capacitors are connected in series we actually have a combination of series and parallel capacitances on account of the capacitances of the outsides of the capacitors to one another and to surrounding objects. Generally, however, these stray parallel capacitances are negligible.

Problem 18a. Two infinitely long concentric cylinders, of radii a and b ($b > a$), are separated by a dielectric of permittivity κ. Find the capacitance per unit length when the outer cylinder is grounded. Ans. $\dfrac{2\pi\kappa_0\kappa}{\log\dfrac{b}{a}}$.

Problem 18b. A capacitor known as a *Leyden jar* is formed by coating the inside and outside of a cylindrical bottle (open at the top) with tin foil. The diameter is 10 cm, the height 15 cm, and the thickness 1 mm. If the dielectric constant of the glass is 7, find the capacitance. Ans. 0.0034 microfarad.

Problem 18c. A parallel plate capacitor contains a dielectric slab of permittivity κ whose thickness t is less than the separation of the plates. If the latter quantity is d, find the capacitance per unit area. Ans. $\dfrac{\kappa_0}{\left\{ d - t\left(\dfrac{\kappa - 1}{\kappa} \right) \right\}}$.

Problem 18d. A capacitor is composed of a pile of n plates of alternate polarity, each of area A, separated by thin layers of dielectric of thickness d and dielectric constant κ. Find its capacitance. Ans. $(n-1)\dfrac{\kappa_0\kappa A}{d}$.

Problem 18e. Given two identical spherical air capacitors with radii as shown in Fig. 37. Let the outer sphere of one be connected to the inner sphere of the other, and the outer sphere of the latter connected to ground. Assuming that the spheres are not close to each other or to any other conductors, calculate approximately the total capacitance of the series combination, taking into account all stray capacitance to ground. Ans. $\dfrac{4\pi\kappa_0 ab}{b-a}\left[\dfrac{ab + b'(b-a)}{2ab + b'(b-a)} \right]$.

19. Coefficients of Potential, Capacitance and Induction.

In the case of several charged conductors the relations between charges and potentials are still linear. For simplicity we shall confine the proof to three conductors immersed in a homogeneous medium, but the analysis is applicable to any number of conductors. Let V_1, V_2, V_3 be the potentials for conductors (1), (2), (3) respectively, when we put charges Q_1, Q_2, Q_3 on them, and V_1', V_2', V_3' the potentials when, in place of the previous charges, we put charges Q_1', Q_2', Q_3' on them. Then it follows from (15-9) that if we put charges $Q_1 + Q_1'$ on conductor (1), $Q_2 + Q_2'$ on (2) and $Q_3 + Q_3'$ on (3) the respective potentials are $V_1 + V_1'$, $V_2 + V_2'$ and $V_3 + V_3'$, for we have now just a superposition of the two separate fields.

In the special case that the primed Q's are equal to the unprimed Q's the primed V's are equal to the unprimed V's, showing that the effect of doubling all the charges is to double all the potentials. Hence if we increase the charges on the three conductors in the same ratio, the potentials are also increased in that ratio. Consider now a set of charges Q_1, 0, 0 on the three conductors. As the charges on (2) and (3) are zero, all three potentials must be proportional to Q_1, so that we may write for the potentials of the three conductors $p_{11}Q_1$, $p_{21}Q_1$, $p_{31}Q_1$, respectively, where the p's are constants independent of Q_1. Similarly a set of charges 0, Q_2, 0 results in potentials $p_{12}Q_2$, $p_{22}Q_2$, $p_{32}Q_2$ and a set 0, 0, Q_3 in potentials $p_{13}Q_3$, $p_{23}Q_3$, $p_{33}Q_3$. In view of the conclusions reached in the preceding paragraph, then, the potentials when all three conductors are charged are

$$\left. \begin{array}{l} V_1 = p_{11}Q_1 + p_{12}Q_2 + p_{13}Q_3, \\ V_2 = p_{21}Q_1 + p_{22}Q_2 + p_{23}Q_3, \\ V_3 = p_{31}Q_1 + p_{32}Q_2 + p_{33}Q_3. \end{array} \right\} \quad (19\text{-}1)$$

The p's are known as *coefficients of potential*. Their values depend on the dielectric constant and the geometry of the system. Note that since the Q's represent total algebraic charge, the equations give no information about the distribution of charge on a conductor.

The coefficients are not all independent. Suppose that charges Q_1, Q_2, Q_3 give rise to potentials V_1, V_2, V_3, and that Q_1', Q_2', Q_3' give rise to V_1', V_2', V_3'. Consider first the potential V_1 at a point on conductor (1). Using (15-9), this is given in terms of the charge density σ by

$$V_1 = \frac{1}{4\pi\kappa_0\kappa}\left[\int_{s_1}\frac{\sigma ds}{r_1} + \int_{s_2}\frac{\sigma ds}{r_1} + \int_{s_3}\frac{\sigma ds}{r_1}\right] \equiv \frac{1}{4\pi\kappa_0\kappa}\int_{s_{123}}\frac{\sigma ds}{r_1},$$

where the variable r_1 is the distance from the chosen point on conductor (1) to the surface element ds, and the integrals are taken over the surfaces of the three conductors as indicated by the s-subscripts. Furthermore,

$$Q_1' = \int_{s_1}\sigma' ds',$$

the surface element being written ds' to indicate that here we are dealing with the primed distribution of charge. Consequently,

$$Q_1'V_1 = \frac{1}{4\pi\kappa_0\kappa} \int_{s_1} \sigma'ds' \int_{s_{123}} \frac{\sigma ds}{r_1}.$$

Now, since the potential V_1 is the same at all points of conductor (1),

$$\int_{s_1} \sigma'ds' \int_{s_{123}} \frac{\sigma ds}{r_1} = \int_{s_{123}} \int_{s_1} \frac{\sigma'ds'\sigma ds}{r}$$

where r is the distance from the surface element ds' to the surface element ds. Expressions for the other conductors are similar. Hence

$$Q_1'V_1 + Q_2'V_2 + Q_3'V_3 = \frac{1}{4\pi\kappa_0\kappa} \int_{s_{123}} \int_{s_{123}} \frac{\sigma'ds'\sigma ds}{r}.$$

In the same way, we find

$$Q_1V_1' + Q_2V_2' + Q_3V_3' = \frac{1}{4\pi\kappa_0\kappa} \int_{s_{123}} \int_{s_{123}} \frac{\sigma ds\, \sigma'ds'}{r}.$$

As the integral expressions in the last two equations are equal,

$$Q_1'V_1 + Q_2'V_2 + Q_3'V_3 = Q_1V_1' + Q_2V_2' + Q_3V_3', \qquad (19\text{-}2)$$

a theorem due to Green. If now we take

$$Q_1 = 1, \qquad Q_2 = 0, \qquad Q_3 = 0,$$
$$Q_1' = 0, \qquad Q_2' = 1, \qquad Q_3' = 0,$$

we have at once $V_1' = V_2$, and therefore from (19-1) $p_{12} = p_{21}$. Similarly, in general,

$$p_{ij} = p_{ji}, \qquad (19\text{-}3)$$

a result of some importance. In words it is: *The potential of one conductor due only to a unit charge on another is equal to the potential of the second due only to a unit charge on the first.* For example, a unit charge on a sphere produces a potential $1/4\pi\kappa_0\kappa r$ at an outside point distant r from the center. Hence a unit charge at this point raises the uncharged sphere to a potential $1/4\pi\kappa_0\kappa r$. Another proof of (19-3) will be found in art. 21.

It is often convenient to express the charges in terms of the potentials. The solution of (19-1) for the charges gives

$$\left.\begin{array}{l} Q_1 = c_{11}V_1 + c_{12}V_2 + c_{13}V_3, \\ Q_2 = c_{21}V_1 + c_{22}V_2 + c_{23}V_3, \\ Q_3 = c_{31}V_1 + c_{32}V_2 + c_{33}V_3, \end{array}\right\} \qquad (19\text{-}4)$$

where

$$c_{11} = \frac{p_{22}p_{33}-p_{23}^{2}}{\Delta}, \qquad c_{12} = c_{21} = \frac{p_{23}p_{31}-p_{12}p_{33}}{\Delta},$$

$$c_{22} = \frac{p_{33}p_{11}-p_{31}^{2}}{\Delta}, \qquad c_{23} = c_{32} = \frac{p_{31}p_{12}-p_{23}p_{11}}{\Delta}, \qquad (19\text{-}5)$$

$$c_{33} = \frac{p_{11}p_{22}-p_{12}^{2}}{\Delta}, \qquad c_{31} = c_{13} = \frac{p_{12}p_{23}-p_{31}p_{22}}{\Delta},$$

and

$$\Delta \equiv p_{11}p_{22}p_{33}+2p_{12}p_{23}p_{31}-p_{11}p_{23}^{2}-p_{22}p_{31}^{2}-p_{33}p_{12}^{2}.$$

The quantities c_{11}, c_{22}, c_{33} are called *coefficients of capacitance* and the constants c_{12}, c_{23}, c_{31} *coefficients of induction*. If all conductors but one are kept at zero potential, a positive charge on that one produces a positive potential; so the coefficients of capacitance are all positive. On the other hand, the charges induced on the other conductors are

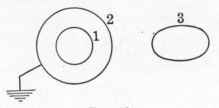

Fig. 40

negative or, in special cases, zero; so the coefficients of induction are negative or zero.

The theory of *electric shielding* follows at once from (19-4). Let conductor (2) (Fig. 40) completely surround (1) and let $V_2=0$. Then

$$Q_1 = c_{11}V_1+c_{13}V_3,$$
$$Q_2 = c_{21}V_1+c_{23}V_3,$$
$$Q_3 = c_{31}V_1+c_{33}V_3.$$

Since $V_1=V_2=0$ if $Q_1=0$ (art. 11) regardless of V_3, it is evident that $c_{13}=0$. In consequence

$$Q_1 = c_{11}V_1, \qquad Q_3 = c_{33}V_3, \qquad (19\text{-}6)$$

so that the electric condition of (1) is entirely independent of (3) and vice versa. Thus a piece of electrostatic apparatus may be protected from external disturbances by enclosing it in a grounded metal box, a matter of great importance in making accurate measurements.

Problem 19a. Show that (a) $c_{11}+c_{12}+c_{13}\geq 0$, (b) all coefficients of potential are positive and $p_{11}-p_{12}\geq 0$.

Problem 19b. By solving (19–4) for the potentials find the p's in terms of the c's.

Problem 19c. Calculate the c's for the concentric spheres shown in Fig. 37. What change will be made by the presence of a third conductor as in Fig. 40?

Ans. $c_{11}=-c_{12}=\dfrac{4\pi\kappa_0\kappa ab}{b-a}$, $c_{22}=4\pi\kappa_0\left[\dfrac{\kappa ab}{b-a}+b'\right]$.

20. Dielectric Absorption.

If dielectrics were perfect insulators, as we have tacitly assumed in the previous article, and if they had no internal resistance to polarization, a capacitor would assume its full charge instantly on the application of a potential difference, and discharge instantly on being short-circuited. But experiment shows that with certain dielectrics a capacitor continues to absorb charge for many minutes, and discharges in a similar manner. In fact, if such a capacitor

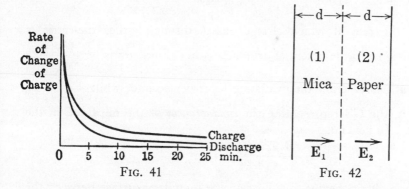

FIG. 41   FIG. 42

is short-circuited at regular intervals, being allowed to stand idle in between, repeated sparks of successively smaller intensity may be drawn from it. In measurement it is the first rush of charge or discharge, completed in a fraction of a second, that determines the *geometric capacitance* of the capacitor.

The behavior of a typical capacitor both while charging and while discharging is illustrated in Fig. 41, the ordinate indicating the rate of increase of charge in the case of the upper curve and the rate of decrease in the case of the lower. The two curves are similar in form, but at any time they differ in value by a small amount. This is due to the dielectric's lack of perfection as an insulator; as long as the charging potential is applied, there is a small but steady passage of electricity through the capacitor. This is not real *absorption* of charge, of course, and on discharge it is not present. With liquid dielectrics or solids that have absorbed moisture the charge and the discharge curves sometimes differ in form as well as in magnitude.

In itself the slight conductivity of the dielectric is usually not important, but Maxwell showed that indirectly it may be responsible for a real absorption of charge, corresponding to the rapidly falling portion of the curves in Fig. 41. Maxwell's theory rests on the assumption that the dielectric layer is not homogeneous. As a very simple case let the insulating layer consist of two different dielectrics, mica and paper, say, of equal thickness (Fig. 42). If E_1 and E_2 represent the fields in the mica and in the paper, respectively, $E_1 d + E_2 d = V_0$, where V_0 is the total potential difference applied to the capacitor. Consider, first, conditions at the moment when V_0 is applied. Indicating initial values of the variables by primes, we have $E_1' d + E_2' d = V_0$ and, by (14-5) and (15-3), $\kappa_1 E_1' = \kappa_2 E_2'$, so that the initial potential drops across the mica and across the paper are

$$E_1'd = \frac{\kappa_2}{\kappa_1 + \kappa_2} V_0, \qquad E_2'd = \frac{\kappa_1}{\kappa_1 + \kappa_2} V_0.$$

Now, the rate at which charge passes through either dielectric is proportional to the potential drop across it. Thus, initially, $\dfrac{G_1 \kappa_2}{\kappa_1 + \kappa_2} V_0$ units of charge enter the insulating layer per second, while $\dfrac{G_2 \kappa_1}{\kappa_1 + \kappa_2} V_0$ leave it, the G's representing the *conductances* of the mica and of the paper. In general,

$$\frac{G_1 \kappa_2 - G_2 \kappa_1}{\kappa_1 + \kappa_2} V_0 \neq 0,$$

so that a charge begins to collect on the boundary surface between the dielectrics. The presence of this charge decreases E_1 and increases E_2, or vice versa, depending on the sign of the charge, until finally there is no further accumulation of charge but only a steady passage through the entire layer, given by

$$G_1 E_1'' d = G_2 E_2'' d = \frac{G_1 G_2}{G_1 + G_2} V_0,$$

where E_1'' and E_2'' are the final values of the fields. When the capacitor is short-circuited, the constant conduction disappears and the process described above is reversed. Thus, we have, qualitatively at least, an explanation of Fig. 41. Of course, in practice we seldom have the ideal double-layer dielectric, but waxed paper approximates it, and any mixed or non-homogeneous dielectric should behave in the same way.

Maxwell's theory receives considerable support from experiment.

Usually mixed dielectrics exhibit absorption whereas pure ones often do not. On the other hand, the absorption curves may not be of the form predicted by the theory, and absorption is found in some pure homogeneous dielectrics. This suggests that there are other possible causes of absorption. One of the most important of these is found to be a viscous resistance to molecular polarizations, that is, polarizations in which molecules possessing permanent electric moments are oriented or displaced as a whole. Mechanisms of absorption and the resulting characteristics of capacitors are described in detail by Brotherton.*

Problem 20. Find the density of charge on both plates of the capacitor shown in Fig. 42 and on the dielectric interface (1) initially and (2) finally.

Ans. (1) $\dfrac{\kappa_0 V_0}{d}\left(\dfrac{\kappa_2\kappa_1}{\kappa_1+\kappa_2}\right)$, $\quad -\dfrac{\kappa_0 V_0}{d}\left(\dfrac{\kappa_1\kappa_2}{\kappa_1+\kappa_2}\right)$, $\quad 0$;

(2) $\dfrac{\kappa_0 V_0}{d}\left(\dfrac{G_2\kappa_1}{G_1+G_2}\right)$, $\quad -\dfrac{\kappa_0 V_0}{d}\left(\dfrac{G_1\kappa_2}{G_1+G_2}\right)$, $\quad \dfrac{\kappa_0 V_0}{d}\left(\dfrac{G_1\kappa_2-G_2\kappa_1}{G_1+G_2}\right)$.

21. Energy of Charged Systems. To charge a system of conductors requires the expenditure of energy. This energy is stored electrostatically and becomes available again when the system is discharged. Let us build up a charge Q on an isolated conductor by bringing up infinitesimal charges dq through the surrounding medium. If q is the charge and v the potential at any time during this process, $q=Cv$ by (18-1). Similarly $Q=CV$, where Q and V represent the final charge and the final potential. Bringing up an infinitesimal charge from infinity does not change the potential by any finite amount; so the amount of work done, that is, the increase in the potential energy of the system during this process, is vdq. The total energy of the charged conductor is therefore given by

$$U = \int_0^Q vdq = \frac{1}{C}\int_0^Q qdq = \frac{1}{2}\frac{Q^2}{C} = \frac{1}{2}QV = \frac{1}{2}CV^2. \quad (21\text{-}1)$$

With a capacitor we may take the elements of charge from the negative to the positive plate and

$$U = \int_0^Q (v_1-v_2)dq = \frac{1}{C}\int_0^Q qdq = \frac{1}{2}\frac{Q^2}{C}$$

$$= \frac{1}{2}Q(V_1-V_2) = \frac{1}{2}C(V_1-V_2)^2. \quad (21\text{-}2)$$

By an extension of the above method we can calculate the energy of any number k of charged conductors (Fig. 43). As before, we build up

* Brotherton, M., *Capacitors*, D. Van Nostrand Co., Inc., 1946.

the charge on each conductor in infinitesimal steps, but in such a way that every charge at any time is the same fraction of its final value.

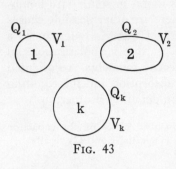

FIG. 43

Thus, at any instant, $q_1 = \alpha Q_1$, $q_2 = \alpha Q_2, \cdots q_k = \alpha Q_k$, where α lies between zero and unity. One step in the charging process must then consist of bringing up from infinity to (1) a charge $dq_1 = Q_1 d\alpha$, to (2) a charge $dq_2 = Q_2 d\alpha$, and so on. When all charges are multiplied by a given factor, the potentials are multiplied by the same factor; so, using the same notation as in (21-1), $v_1 = \alpha V_1$, $v_2 = \alpha V_2, \cdots v_k = \alpha V_k$.

The work done per step is $v_1 dq_1 + v_2 dq_2 + \cdots v_k dq_k$. Therefore

$$U = \int_0^Q (v_1 dq_1 + v_2 dq_2 + \cdots v_k dq_k)$$

$$= (Q_1 V_1 + Q_2 V_2 + \cdots Q_k V_k) \int_0^1 \alpha \, d\alpha = \tfrac{1}{2} \sum_1^k Q_i V_i. \qquad (21\text{-}3)$$

By means of the coefficients introduced in art. 19 the energy may be expressed in terms of the charges or of the potentials. Restricting ourselves again for simplicity to three conductors, we have for the energy in terms of the charges,

$$\left. \begin{aligned} U_Q = \tfrac{1}{2} \{ & p_{11} Q_1{}^2 && + p_{12} Q_1 Q_2 + p_{13} Q_1 Q_3 \\ & + p_{21} Q_2 Q_1 + p_{22} Q_2{}^2 && + p_{23} Q_2 Q_3 \\ & + p_{31} Q_3 Q_1 + p_{32} Q_3 Q_2 + p_{33} Q_3{}^2 \}, \end{aligned} \right\} \qquad (21\text{-}4)$$

and for the energy in terms of the potentials,

$$\left. \begin{aligned} U_V = \tfrac{1}{2} \{ & c_{11} V_1{}^2 && + c_{12} V_1 V_2 + c_{13} V_1 V_3 \\ & + c_{21} V_2 V_1 + c_{22} V_2{}^2 && + c_{23} V_2 V_3 \\ & + c_{31} V_3 V_1 + c_{32} V_3 V_2 + c_{33} V_3{}^2 \}. \end{aligned} \right\} \qquad (21\text{-}5)$$

Now from (21-3)

$$2 dU = (V_1 dQ_1 + V_2 dQ_2 + V_3 dQ_3) + (Q_1 dV_1 + Q_2 dV_2 + Q_3 dV_3).$$

But we know

$$dU = V_1 dQ_1 + V_2 dQ_2 + V_3 dQ_3,$$

so that also

$$dU = Q_1 dV_1 + Q_2 dV_2 + Q_3 dV_3.$$

Thus when the energy is expressed in terms of the Q's,

$$V_1 = \frac{\partial U_Q}{\partial Q_1}, \qquad V_2 = \frac{\partial U_Q}{\partial Q_2}, \qquad V_3 = \frac{\partial U_Q}{\partial Q_3}, \qquad (21\text{-}6)$$

and when in terms of the V's,

$$Q_1 = \frac{\partial U_V}{\partial V_1}, \qquad Q_2 = \frac{\partial U_V}{\partial V_2}, \qquad Q_3 = \frac{\partial U_V}{\partial V_3}. \tag{21-7}$$

These differential relations are often useful. For example, from (21-6),

$$V_1 = p_{11}Q_1 + \tfrac{1}{2}(p_{12}+p_{21})Q_2 + \tfrac{1}{2}(p_{13}+p_{31})Q_3.$$

But

$$V_1 = p_{11}Q_1 + p_{12}Q_2 + p_{13}Q_3,$$

giving $p_{12}=p_{21}$, $p_{13}=p_{31}$; so that we have another proof of (19-3) that $p_{ij}=p_{ji}$. Similarly, using (21-7), we find $c_{ij}=c_{ji}$.

The amount of energy associated with a system of charges having been determined, the question of its location arises. This is evidently a somewhat arbitrary matter, since energy in itself is an intangible thing. When a dielectric is present, at least some of the energy is in the region between the charges, that is, in the field. It seems desirable therefore to distribute all the energy through the field. To see how this may be done, consider a single tube of electric displacement. This will begin on a unit positive free charge and end on a unit negative free charge. If the potentials at the ends of the tube are V_1 and V_2 respectively, the contribution of the two charges to the energy of the entire system is, by (21-3),

$$\tfrac{1}{2}V_1 - \tfrac{1}{2}V_2 = \tfrac{1}{2}(V_1 - V_2) = \tfrac{1}{2}\int_1^2 Edl, \tag{21-8}$$

where dl is an element of the path along the tube from (1) to (2). This energy *of* the tube we may distribute *along* the tube as we please. The simplest way is at the rate of $E/2$ joules per meter at every point along the tube, as this leads directly to (21-8) for the total energy of the tube. Since there are D tubes of displacement per meter² of cross section (art. 14), energy is distributed through the field in the amount of $DE/2$ joules per meter³. Replacing D by $\kappa_0\kappa E$, we have

$$U = \frac{\kappa_0}{2}\int_\tau \kappa E^2 d\tau, \tag{21-9}$$

the volume integral being taken through all space. The arbitrary nature of the distribution is quite evident from (21-9); for we may add to the integrand any quantity whose integral through all space is zero and still obtain the correct result. The distribution here obtained, however, has the advantage of being everywhere positive. As $D = \kappa_0 E + P$, we have

$$\frac{1}{2}DE = \frac{\kappa_0}{2}E^2 + \frac{1}{2}PE, \tag{21-10}$$

the last term being the energy per unit volume assignable to the dielectric proper.

The concept of energy in the field is an illuminating one, particularly in the study of forces on conductors and dielectrics. Use of it will be made in the following article.

Problem 21a. A sphere of radius 2 meters is charged in air to a potential 3000 volts. Find its energy. Ans. 0.001 joule.

Problem 21b. Two capacitances C_1 and C_2 have charges Q_1 and Q_2, respectively. Calculate the amount of energy which disappears when they are connected in parallel and explain how the energy is dissipated.

$$\text{Ans. } \frac{(Q_1C_2 - Q_2C_1)^2}{2C_1C_2(C_1 + C_2)}.$$

Problem 21c. A capacitor composed of concentric spheres ($\kappa = 1$) is so constructed that the outer sphere can be separated and the inner sphere removed without changing the charges on either. The radius of the inner sphere is a, of the outer b, and the charges are Q and $-Q$ respectively. Let the inner sphere be removed, the outer restored to its original form, and the two separated by a great distance. Calculate the increase of energy during this process. What is the source of it? Ans. $\dfrac{Q^2}{4\pi\kappa_0 b}$.

22. Forces and Torques.

When a system changes its configuration under its own forces, work is done, which can only be at the expense of its potential energy if there is no external supply of energy. Thus, let one of the conductors move a distance $d\xi$ under a force whose component in the direction of the displacement is $\mathscr{F}_\xi$, the charges on all conductors in the system being kept constant. Then

$$dU_Q = -\mathscr{F}_\xi\, d\xi,$$

$$\mathscr{F}_\xi = -\frac{\partial U_Q}{\partial \xi}. \tag{22-1}$$

Here we are differentiating the p's in the expression (21-4), the Q's remaining constant.

It often happens that the potentials are constant instead of the charges. For a given configuration of the system the forces are the same, of course, whether charges or potentials are kept constant. However, the work done in a change of configuration no longer comes from the potential energy; so $\mathscr{F}_\xi$ must be calculated differently. For simplicity we limit ourselves to one movable and one fixed conductor, but the number of fixed conductors does not affect the result. We may imagine that the displacement $d\xi$ with constant V's is performed in two steps, a motion with constant Q's, followed by an addition of charges sufficient to restore the potentials to their initial values. If the energy added in the latter step is δU,

$$dU_V = dU_Q + \delta U, \tag{22-2}$$

where dU_V is the desired energy increase due to displacement with the V's constant. During the first step the potentials change by

$$dV_1 = \left(\frac{\partial p_{11}}{\partial \xi} Q_1 + \frac{\partial p_{12}}{\partial \xi} Q_2\right) d\xi,$$

$$dV_2 = \left(\frac{\partial p_{21}}{\partial \xi} Q_1 + \frac{\partial p_{22}}{\partial \xi} Q_2\right) d\xi.$$

Hence in the second step we must add charges dQ_1 and dQ_2 given by

$$p_{11}dQ_1 + p_{12}dQ_2 = -\left(\frac{\partial p_{11}}{\partial \xi} Q_1 + \frac{\partial p_{12}}{\partial \xi} Q_2\right) d\xi,$$

$$p_{21}dQ_1 + p_{22}dQ_2 = -\left(\frac{\partial p_{21}}{\partial \xi} Q_1 + \frac{\partial p_{22}}{\partial \xi} Q_2\right) d\xi,$$

which will cause the energy to increase by

$$\begin{aligned}
\delta U &= V_1 dQ_1 + V_2 dQ_2 \\
&= (p_{11}dQ_1 + p_{21}dQ_2)Q_1 + (p_{12}dQ_1 + p_{22}dQ_2)Q_2 \\
&= -\left(\frac{\partial p_{11}}{\partial \xi}Q_1{}^2 + 2\frac{\partial p_{12}}{\partial \xi}Q_1Q_2 + \frac{\partial p_{22}}{\partial \xi}Q_2{}^2\right) d\xi,
\end{aligned}$$

since $p_{12} = p_{21}$. But

$$U_Q = \tfrac{1}{2}(p_{11}Q_1{}^2 + 2p_{12}Q_1Q_2 + p_{22}Q_2{}^2),$$

and therefore

$$\delta U = -2dU_Q.$$

This gives

$$dU_V = -dU_Q = \mathscr{F}_\xi d\xi,$$

and

$$\mathscr{F}_\xi = \frac{\partial U_V}{\partial \xi}. \tag{22-3}$$

Here we are differentiating the c's in the expression (21-5), the V's being held constant. This is an interesting result; it shows that in motions with constant potentials the potential energy *increases* by an amount exactly equal to the mechanical work done. In other words, the sources of the constant potentials supply double energy to the system.

Torques are calculated by differentiating with respect to an angle. For constant charges the torque about the axis around which the angle θ is measured is given by

$$\mathscr{L}_\theta = -\frac{\partial U_Q}{\partial \theta} \tag{22-4}$$

and for constant potentials by

$$\mathscr{L}_\theta = \frac{\partial U_V}{\partial \theta}. \tag{22-5}$$

A piece of dielectric in an electric field experiences forces, in general, just as a conductor does, and these are calculated according to the same principles. It is usually more convenient, however, to use the distributed energy function (21-9) rather than (21-3). For example, the energy per unit volume may be written $D^2/2\kappa_0\kappa$, and as the tubes of displacement are continuous across the dielectric boundary the potential energy of the system will be least when the greatest possible number of tubes are included in the dielectric. Therefore, the forces on a dielectric are such as to move it from a weaker to a stronger part of the field.

Problem 22. A parallel plate capacitor of length l, width b and plate separation d has the space between the plates filled by a slab of dielectric whose constant is κ. This slab is withdrawn in the direction of its length until only a length x remains between the plates. The potential difference V of the plates is maintained constant. Neglecting edge effects, calculate the force tending to restore the slab to its original position.   Ans. $\dfrac{\kappa_0(\kappa-1)}{2}\left(\dfrac{bV^2}{d}\right)$.

23. Electrostatic Instruments.

Mention has already been made of the electroscope. This is a sensitive instrument but not one adapted to accurate quantitative measurements, except in special cases. There are, however, accurate potential measuring instruments, known as *electrometers*.

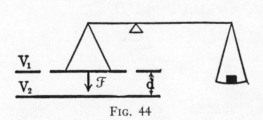

FIG. 44

The Absolute Electrometer. This instrument (Fig. 44) is essentially a parallel plate capacitor with a guard ring, the guarded plate being suspended from a balance arm, so that the force $\mathscr{F}$ on it is measurable in terms of weight. The distance between the plates and the mass in the pan are adjusted until the movable plate hangs exactly in the plane of the guard ring. Then, if A' is the area of the plate plus one-half the gap, as in (18-10),

$$\mathscr{F} = \frac{\sigma^2 A'}{2\kappa_0}.$$

But

$$\frac{V_1 - V_2}{d} = E = \frac{\sigma}{\kappa_0},$$

so that

$$\mathscr{F} = \frac{\kappa_0}{2}\left(\frac{V_1 - V_2}{d}\right)^2 A'$$

and

$$V_1 - V_2 = d\sqrt{\frac{2\mathscr{F}}{\kappa_0 A'}}. \tag{23-1}$$

As $\mathscr{F}$ is known directly in terms of fundamental quantities, the instrument does not require calibration; hence the designation "absolute".

The Quadrant Electrometer. This has been one of the most useful electrostatic instruments. It combines high sensitivity with great accuracy and is adaptable to a great variety of uses. It consists of a small metal pill-box cut into quadrants, shown both in plan and in section in Fig. 45. Within is a metal vane, known as the *needle*, which is suspended by a fine torsion fibre. Opposite quadrants are connected by a wire, the potentials of the two pairs being respectively V_1 and V_2. The needle is maintained at some known potential V_3. If it assumes a position symmetrical with the quadrants when both pairs are at the same potential, it will turn through some angle θ when different potentials are applied to the two. When the constants of the instrument are known, $V_1 - V_2$ may be determined from θ. In practice this angle is determined by means of a small mirror mounted on the needle suspension, and an external telescope and scale. The instrument has a removable metal case which serves as an electrostatic shield. The details of construction are shown in Fig. 46, the case having been removed.

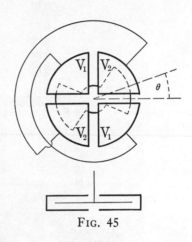

FIG. 45

The complete theory of the quadrant electrometer is somewhat elaborate, but a sufficiently accurate result is obtained by an approximate treatment. Since the quadrants are edge to edge, the direct capacitance between them is small compared with the capacitance between quadrants and needle. Hence the energy of the system may be expressed approximately as

$$U_V = \tfrac{1}{2}C_1(V_3 - V_1)^2 + \tfrac{1}{2}C_2(V_3 - V_2)^2 + U_0, \tag{23-2}$$

where C_1 is the capacitance of quadrants (1) relative to the needle, neglecting the existence of quadrants (2). Similarly C_2 refers to quadrants (2) and the needle, and U_0 is a term independent of the needle, involving the capacitance of the quadrants to ground. Evidently C_1 and C_2 are functions of θ. The torque on the needle is, by (22-5),

$$\mathscr{L}_\theta = \frac{\partial U_V}{\partial \theta} = \frac{1}{2}\frac{\partial C_1}{\partial \theta}(V_3 - V_1)^2 + \frac{1}{2}\frac{\partial C_2}{\partial \theta}(V_3 - V_2)^2.$$

This torque is balanced by that of the fibre, which, as it is proportional

FIG. 46

to θ, may be written $a\theta$. Also, since the needle turns out of one pair of quadrants as much as it turns into the other,

$$-\frac{\partial C_1}{\partial \theta} = \frac{\partial C_2}{\partial \theta} \equiv b,$$

another constant. Therefore

$$a\theta = -\tfrac{1}{2}b(V_3 - V_1)^2 + \tfrac{1}{2}b(V_3 - V_2)^2,$$

or

$$\theta = k(V_1 - V_2)\left\{V_3 - \frac{V_1 + V_2}{2}\right\}, \qquad (23\text{-}3)$$

where $k \equiv b/a$ is a constant to be determined by calibration.

There are two methods of use. In the *heterostatic method* V_3 is large compared with V_1 and V_2 and is held constant. Then (23-3) reduces to

$$\theta = kV_3(V_1 - V_2), \qquad (23\text{-}4)$$

so that the deflection is proportional to $(V_1 - V_2)$.

In the *idiostatic* method the needle is connected to one pair of quadrants, say (1). This gives

$$\theta = \tfrac{1}{2}k(V_1 - V_2)^2. \qquad (23\text{-}5)$$

This method is less sensitive than the first, but it permits the measure-

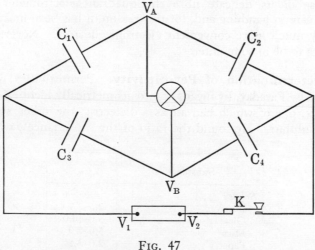

Fig. 47

ment of alternating potentials, since the deflection is always in the same direction.

Although the quadrant electrometer is not an absolute instrument, it is much more sensitive than the absolute electrometer. Used heterostatically it can measure $(10)^{-3}$ volt without difficulty. With special precautions an even greater sensitivity is obtainable. In precise measurements it is customarily used as a *null* instrument. An example of such use is the *capacitance bridge* (Fig. 47), where C_1 is an unknown capacitance and C_2, C_3, C_4 are known. Now C_2, being variable, is adjusted until the electrometer shows no deflection when a potential difference $V_1 - V_2$ is placed across the bridge by closing the key K.

Under this condition the potentials V_A and V_B of the two pairs of quadrants are equal. Hence the quadrants are uncharged, so that C_1 has the same charge Q as C_2, and C_3 the same charge Q' as C_4. Then

$$V_1 - V_A = \frac{Q}{C_1}, \qquad V_A - V_2 = \frac{Q}{C_2},$$

$$V_1 - V_B = \frac{Q'}{C_3}, \qquad V_B - V_2 = \frac{Q'}{C_4}.$$

Therefore

$$C_1(V_1 - V_A) = C_2(V_A - V_2),$$
$$C_3(V_1 - V_B) = C_4(V_B - V_2),$$

and as $V_A = V_B$,

$$\frac{C_1}{C_2} = \frac{C_3}{C_4}. \tag{23-6}$$

Because of its delicate fibre the quadrant electrometer requires unusual care in handling and, for this reason, it has been mostly superseded by much more convenient electronic devices. Nevertheless, it continues to be of some interest.

24. Determination of Permittivity. Permittivities were first measured by Faraday, by means of two geometrically identical spherical capacitors, one of which had air as a dielectric, the other some solid such as sulphur. He found the ratio of the capacitances, which is κ,

Substance	κ
Solids :	
Beeswax . . .	2.5–2.9
Glass	5.0–10.0
Mica	5.0–7.0
Paper	2.0–2.5
Paraffin . . .	2.3
Quartz . . .	4.3
Shellac . . .	3.1–3.7
Sulphur . . .	4.0
Liquids :	
Castor oil . . .	4.7
Kerosene . . .	2.1
Transformer oil . .	2.2
Water	80.4
Gases :	
Air	1.000588
Hydrogen . . .	1.000264
Carbon Dioxide . .	1.000966

by charging one capacitor to a known potential, allowing it to share its charge with the other, and then determining the final potential. Boltzmann later employed a similar scheme using a parallel plate capacitor into which a slab of dielectric could be introduced. These early measurements were all subject to error on account of dielectric absorption (art. 20). This error is now avoided by means of quick-acting switches and other special devices.

A table is included giving values of κ for a few common dielectrics. The gases are at $0°$ C and under a pressure of one atmosphere. It is worthy of note that for practically all solids κ lies between one and ten.

25. Electrostatic Units. From art. 6 we know that the electrostatic unit of charge has the magnitude of $\frac{1}{3}(10)^{-9}$ coulomb. Definitions and magnitudes of a few other common electrostatic units are listed below. The electrostatic unit of

Force	is the *dyne*.	In magnitude it is $(10)^{-5}$ newton.
Energy	*erg*.	$(10)^{-7}$ joule.
Charge	*e.s.u.ch.*	$\frac{1}{3}(10)^{-9}$ pr.u.*
Elec. Intensity	*dyne per e.s.u.ch.*	$3(10)^4$ pr.u.*
Elec. Potential	*erg per e.s.u.ch.*	$3(10)^2$ pr.u.*
Capacitance	*centimeter*.	$\frac{1}{9}(10)^{-11}$ pr.u.*

Knowing the relative magnitudes of the units, we can transform formulas from pr.u. to e.s.u., as required. The method of transformation is explained and illustrated in art. 50. However, we may remark here that the formulas so far obtained take the same form in e.s.u. as in pr.u. when they do not contain κ_0, ϵ or D explicitly. Otherwise they differ in form. For example, (18-1) and (21-1) become

$$Q_e = C_e V_e, \qquad U_e = \frac{1}{2}\frac{Q_e^2}{C_e} = \frac{1}{2}Q_e V_e = \frac{1}{2}C_e V_e^2,$$

in e.s.u., but (6-2) transforms to (6-1).

* The factor 3 in the coefficient is more accurately 2.998.

REFERENCES

Corson and Lorrain, *Introduction to Electromagnetic Fields and Waves* (Freeman, 1962). Pp. 59–69, 96–107.

Kip, *Electricity and Magnetism* (McGraw-Hill, 1962). Chap. 4–5.

Chapter III

SOLUTION OF ELECTROSTATIC PROBLEMS

26. Poisson's and Laplace's Equations. We shall develop now the equations which must be satisfied by the potential V in a homogeneous isotropic medium in which are immersed free charges. In most problems of importance the free charges are located on the surfaces of conductors surrounded by a dielectric, and the solution of the problem consists in finding the potential at all points in the dielectric in terms of

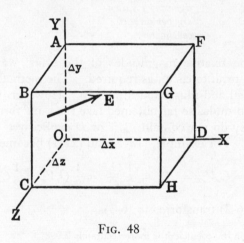

Fig. 48

the assigned potentials of the conducting surfaces. Once the potential is known as a function of the coordinates, the electric intensity is obtained by differentiation (art. 7), and the charge per unit area on the surfaces of the conductors is given in terms of the electric intensity immediately outside by (15-10).

Consider an infinitesimal rectangular parallelepiped (Fig. 48) with its edges parallel to the coordinate axes. If the permittivity of the medium is κ, the flux of displacement inward through the face $OABC$ is

$$\kappa_0 \kappa E_x \Delta y \Delta z,$$

70

and that outward through the face *DFGH* is

$$\kappa_0\kappa\left(E_x + \frac{\partial E_x}{\partial x}\Delta x\right)\Delta y\Delta z.$$

The net flux outward through these two faces perpendicular to the *X* axis is the difference of the two expressions, that is,

$$\kappa_0\kappa\,\frac{\partial E_x}{\partial x}\,\Delta x\Delta y\Delta z.$$

Adding similar expressions for the outward flux through the pairs of faces perpendicular to the *Y* and *Z* axes, we have for the total outward flux

$$\kappa_0\kappa\left(\frac{\partial E_x}{\partial x} + \frac{\partial E_y}{\partial y} + \frac{\partial E_z}{\partial z}\right)\Delta x\Delta y\Delta z.$$

Gauss' law (14-4) requires this to be equal to the free charge contained in the parallelepiped. So if the density of free charge within the medium is ρ,

$$\kappa_0\kappa\left(\frac{\partial E_x}{\partial x} + \frac{\partial E_y}{\partial y} + \frac{\partial E_z}{\partial z}\right)\Delta x\Delta y\Delta z = \rho\Delta x\Delta y\Delta z.$$

The components of electric intensity are given in terms of the potential by (7-7). Using these relations and dividing through by $\kappa_0\kappa\Delta x\Delta y\Delta z$, the equation above becomes

$$\frac{\partial^2 V}{\partial x^2} + \frac{\partial^2 V}{\partial y^2} + \frac{\partial^2 V}{\partial z^2} = -\frac{\rho}{\kappa_0\kappa}. \tag{26-1}$$

This equation is known as *Poisson's equation*. In a region where no free charges are present $\rho = 0$ and (26-1) reduces to *Laplace's equation*,

$$\frac{\partial^2 V}{\partial x^2} + \frac{\partial^2 V}{\partial y^2} + \frac{\partial^2 V}{\partial z^2} = 0. \tag{26-2}$$

If, now, we are given a set of conductors at potentials $V_1, V_2, \cdots V_k$ the determination of the potential in the region between and surrounding the conductors resolves itself into the problem of finding a solution of (26-2) which reduces to V_1 at the surface of the first conductor, V_2 at the surface of the second and so on. Such a solution may be shown to be *unique* and therefore to represent the *only* solution of the problem under consideration. A solution which represents the field outside the conductors, however, does not apply to their interiors, for there is charge on the surface of each conductor and therefore Laplace's equation does not hold across the surface. In fact the potential inside a conductor is always constant, as shown in art. 11.

In (26-2) we have Laplace's equation expressed in rectangular co-ordinates. In many problems other coordinates are more suitable. Therefore we shall deduce this equation again in general orthogonal curvilinear coordinates ξ, η, ζ. The coordinate surfaces consist of the three families $\xi(x, y, z) = $ constant, $\eta(x, y, z) = $ constant, $\zeta(x, y, z) = $ constant, intersecting one another at right angles. Consider a small volume (Fig. 49) bounded by coordinate surfaces. Let E_ξ, E_η, E_ζ be the components of the electric intensity in the directions of increasing ξ, η, ζ respectively, and λ, μ, ν the functions of ξ, η, ζ by which $\Delta\xi$, $\Delta\eta$, $\Delta\zeta$ respectively must be multiplied in order to obtain the distances corresponding to these increments in the coordinates. Then the area of $OABC$ is $\mu\nu\Delta\eta\Delta\zeta$ and the flux through it is

$$\kappa_0 \kappa E_\xi \mu\nu\Delta\eta\Delta\zeta.$$

Similarly the flux through $DFGH$ is

$$\kappa_0\kappa\left\{E_\xi\mu\nu + \frac{\partial}{\partial\xi}(E_\xi\mu\nu)\Delta\xi\right\}\Delta\eta\Delta\zeta.$$

Subtracting, the net outward flux through the two surfaces is seen to be

$$\kappa_0\kappa\frac{\partial}{\partial\xi}(E_\xi\mu\nu)\Delta\xi\Delta\eta\Delta\zeta.$$

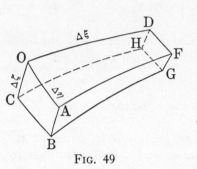

FIG. 49

Adding similar terms for the flux through the remaining two pairs of surfaces, equating the sum to zero and dividing by the common factor $\kappa_0\kappa\Delta\xi\Delta\eta\Delta\zeta$, we get

$$\frac{\partial}{\partial\xi}(\mu\nu E_\xi) + \frac{\partial}{\partial\eta}(\nu\lambda E_\eta) + \frac{\partial}{\partial\zeta}(\lambda\mu E_\zeta) = 0.$$

In accord with (7-6),

$$E_\xi = -\frac{\partial V}{\lambda\partial\xi}, \qquad E_\eta = -\frac{\partial V}{\mu\partial\eta}, \qquad E_\zeta = -\frac{\partial V}{\nu\partial\zeta}.$$

So Laplace's equation takes the form

$$\frac{\partial}{\partial\xi}\left(\frac{\mu\nu}{\lambda}\frac{\partial V}{\partial\xi}\right) + \frac{\partial}{\partial\eta}\left(\frac{\nu\lambda}{\mu}\frac{\partial V}{\partial\eta}\right) + \frac{\partial}{\partial\zeta}\left(\frac{\lambda\mu}{\nu}\frac{\partial V}{\partial\zeta}\right) = 0. \qquad (26\text{-}3)$$

In the case of spherical coordinates ξ, η, ζ become r, θ, ϕ and λ, μ, ν are 1, r, $r\sin\theta$, respectively. Hence Laplace's equation in spherical coordinates is

$$\frac{\partial}{\partial r}\left(r^2\sin\theta\frac{\partial V}{\partial r}\right) + \frac{\partial}{\partial\theta}\left(\sin\theta\frac{\partial V}{\partial\theta}\right) + \frac{\partial}{\partial\phi}\left(\frac{1}{\sin\theta}\frac{\partial V}{\partial\phi}\right) = 0.$$

Dividing by $\sin \theta$ this may be put in the better form,

$$\frac{\partial}{\partial r}\left(r^2 \frac{\partial V}{\partial r}\right) + \frac{1}{\sin \theta} \frac{\partial}{\partial \theta}\left(\sin \theta \frac{\partial V}{\partial \theta}\right) + \frac{1}{\sin^2 \theta} \frac{\partial^2 V}{\partial \phi^2} = 0. \qquad (26\text{-}4)$$

In cylindrical coordinates ξ, η, ζ become r, θ, z and λ, μ, ν assume the values of 1, r, 1. Therefore Laplace's equation becomes

$$\frac{\partial}{\partial r}\left(r \frac{\partial V}{\partial r}\right) + \frac{\partial}{\partial \theta}\left(\frac{1}{r} \frac{\partial V}{\partial \theta}\right) + \frac{\partial}{\partial z}\left(r \frac{\partial V}{\partial z}\right) = 0,$$

or

$$r \frac{\partial}{\partial r}\left(r \frac{\partial V}{\partial r}\right) + \frac{\partial^2 V}{\partial \theta^2} + r^2 \frac{\partial^2 V}{\partial z^2} = 0. \qquad (26\text{-}5)$$

To obtain the charge density σ on the surface of a conductor when we know the potential function V outside the conductor we have, from (15-10) and (7-6),

$$\sigma = \kappa_0 \kappa E = -\kappa_0 \kappa \frac{\partial V}{\partial n}, \qquad (26\text{-}6)$$

where $\frac{\partial V}{\partial n}$ is the space derivative of V along the outward normal n to the surface of the conductor and κ is the permittivity of the surrounding medium.

Problem 26a. Obtain (26–4) directly from (26–2) by transforming the coordinates according to the scheme $x = r \sin \theta \cos \phi$, $y = r \sin \theta \sin \phi$, $z = r \cos \theta$.

Problem 26b. Obtain (26–5) directly from (26–2) by means of the transformations $x = r \cos \theta$, $y = r \sin \theta$.

27. Solutions of Laplace's Equation.

In solving Laplace's equation the two theorems that follow are of importance.

THEOREM I. *If V_1, V_2, $\cdots V_k$ are solutions of Laplace's equation, then*

$$V = A_1 V_1 + A_2 V_2 + \cdots A_k V_k$$

is also a solution, where the A's are arbitrary constants. This theorem is proved at once by substituting the expression above in (26-2).

THEOREM II. *If V is a solution of Laplace's equation, then*

$$\frac{\partial V}{\partial x}, \quad \frac{\partial V}{\partial y}, \quad \frac{\partial V}{\partial z}, \quad \frac{\partial^2 V}{\partial x^2}, \quad \frac{\partial^2 V}{\partial x \partial y}, \quad etc.,$$

and in fact all partial derivatives of V with respect to one or more of the rectangular coordinates x, y, z (but not with respect to spherical or cylindri-

cal coordinates) are solutions. For if we differentiate (26-2) partially with respect to x we have

$$\frac{\partial^2}{\partial x^2}\left(\frac{\partial V}{\partial x}\right) + \frac{\partial^2}{\partial y^2}\left(\frac{\partial V}{\partial x}\right) + \frac{\partial^2}{\partial z^2}\left(\frac{\partial V}{\partial x}\right) = 0.$$

Spherical Coordinates. In many electrostatic problems we are concerned with conducting spheres, and spherical coordinates are indicated for the solution. We shall limit our discussion to those cases in which the potential is a function of the radius vector r and the polar angle θ alone. Then the last term in (26-4) drops out and if we put μ for cos θ Laplace's equation becomes

$$\frac{\partial}{\partial r}\left(r^2 \frac{\partial V}{\partial r}\right) + \frac{\partial}{\partial \mu}\left\{(1-\mu^2)\frac{\partial V}{\partial \mu}\right\} = 0. \tag{27-1}$$

This differential equation has a solution of the form

$$V = r^n P_n,$$

where P_n is a function of μ alone. Substituting in (27-1) we find that P_n must satisfy the differential equation

$$\frac{d}{d\mu}\left\{(1-\mu^2)\frac{dP_n}{d\mu}\right\} + n(n+1)P_n = 0, \tag{27-2}$$

which is known as *Legendre's equation.* Now if we replace n in this equation by $-(n+1)$ the coefficient of the last term becomes

$$\{-(n+1)\}\{-(n+1)+1\} = n(n+1).$$

Therefore, Legendre's equation for $P_{-(n+1)}$ is the same as that for P_n. Consequently, P_n and $P_{-(n+1)}$ are identical. Thus, every P_n satisfying Legendre's equation provides us with *two* solutions of Laplace's equation, namely,

$$r^n P_n \text{ and } \frac{P_n}{r^{n+1}}.$$

Evidently the coefficients of the P's as well as of the V's are arbitrary. Hence, we may introduce any numerical factors. Those included in the P's and V's below are the ones conventionally employed.

Now

$$V_0 = \frac{1}{r}, \qquad P_0 = 1, \tag{27-3}$$

satisfies Laplace's equation, as is seen at once by substitution in (27-1). Let us take the Z axis in the direction of the polar axis of the spherical coordinates, so that $z = r \cos \theta$. We can get a second solution from

(27-3) by differentiating partially with respect to z.   Remembering that
$\frac{\partial r}{\partial z} = \frac{z}{r} = \cos \theta$, we find that

$$V_1 = \frac{z}{r^3} = \frac{\cos \theta}{r^2}, \qquad P_1 = \cos \theta. \qquad (27\text{-}4)$$

Differentiating again with respect to z for a third solution, we get

$$V_2 = \frac{1}{2}\left(\frac{3z^2}{r^5} - \frac{1}{r^3}\right) = \frac{3 \cos^2 \theta - 1}{2r^3},$$

$$P_2 = \tfrac{1}{2}(3 \cos^2 \theta - 1), \qquad (27\text{-}5)$$

and repeating the process for a fourth solution,

$$V_3 = \frac{1}{2}\left(\frac{5z^3}{r^7} - \frac{3z}{r^5}\right) = \frac{5 \cos^3 \theta - 3 \cos \theta}{2r^4},$$

$$P_3 = \tfrac{1}{2}(5 \cos^3 \theta - 3 \cos \theta). \qquad (27\text{-}6)$$

The solutions we have obtained are of the form P_n/r^{n+1}, but since we have found the P_n's we can write down at once solutions of the form $r^n P_n$. Table I contains the solutions which we have deduced and which suffice for the applications which we shall have occasion to make. The functions listed are known as *zonal harmonics*.

Table I

Zonal Harmonics

1,	$\dfrac{1}{r}$,
$r \cos \theta$,	$\dfrac{1}{r^2} \cos \theta$,
$r^2[\tfrac{1}{2}(3 \cos^2 \theta - 1)]$,	$\dfrac{1}{r^3}[\tfrac{1}{2}(3 \cos^2 \theta - 1)]$,
$r^3[\tfrac{1}{2}(5 \cos^3 \theta - 3 \cos \theta)]$.	$\dfrac{1}{r^4}[\tfrac{1}{2}(5 \cos^3 \theta - 3 \cos \theta)]$.

Cylindrical Coordinates. In some problems—such as those having to do with a long straight wire—the potential is not a function of one of the rectangular coordinates, say z, and it is convenient to use polar coordinates in the plane perpendicular to the Z axis. In this case the last term in (26-5) disappears and Laplace's equation reduces to

$$r \frac{\partial}{\partial r}\left(r \frac{\partial V}{\partial r}\right) + \frac{\partial^2 V}{\partial \theta^2} = 0. \qquad (27\text{-}7)$$

Substituting

$$V = r^n C_n,$$

where C_n is a function of θ only, we see that C_n must satisfy the equation

$$\frac{d^2 C_n}{d\theta^2} + n^2 C_n = 0. \tag{27-8}$$

Evidently the differential equation for C_{-n} is the same as that for C_n. Therefore, C_{-n} and C_n are identical, and every C_n satisfying (27-8) leads to two solutions of Laplace's equation, namely,

$$r^n C_n \quad \text{and} \quad \frac{C_n}{r^n}.$$

The simplest solution of (27-7) other than a constant is

$$V_0 = \log r, \tag{27-9}$$

the symbol "log" without subscript indicating the logarithm to the Napierian base $e = 2.718 \cdots$. To get other solutions we note that either $C_n = \cos n\theta$ or $C_n = \sin n\theta$ satisfies (27-8). Hence the *cylindrical harmonics* listed in Table II are solutions of Laplace's equation in cylindrical coordinates.

Table II

Cylindrical Harmonics

1;	$\log r$;
$r \cos \theta, r \sin \theta$;	$\dfrac{\cos \theta}{r}, \dfrac{\sin \theta}{r}$;
$r^2 \cos 2\theta, r^2 \sin 2\theta$;	$\dfrac{\cos 2\theta}{r^2}, \dfrac{\sin 2\theta}{r^2}$;
$r^3 \cos 3\theta, r^3 \sin 3\theta$.	$\dfrac{\cos 3\theta}{r^3}, \dfrac{\sin 3\theta}{r^3}$.

Problem 27. If R is the distance of a point P from the origin O, a the distance of a point Q from O, and r the distance of P from Q,

$$R = \sqrt{r^2 + 2ar \cos \theta + a^2},$$

where θ is the angle between OQ and QP. Expand the reciprocal of R by the binomial theorem both for $r < a$ and for $r > a$. Show that the successive terms in the expansions are zonal harmonics.

28. Sphere in Uniform Field.

We will use zonal harmonics to solve the problem of a sphere placed in a uniform electric field, treating first the case of a conducting sphere immersed in a dielectric and second that of a dielectric sphere in empty space. In each case the problem consists in finding the potential V as a function of r and θ from which the components of electric intensity can be obtained by means of (7-8) and the charge density on the surface of the conducting sphere from (26-6).

Conducting Sphere in Uniform Field. Consider an uncharged conducting sphere of radius a placed in a uniform field E_0. Since potential is a relative quantity, we may take the potential of the sphere as zero. Although the sphere distorts the field in its neighborhood, as shown in Fig. 50, the field at a great distance retains its original uniform character. Therefore, if the origin is taken at the center of the sphere and the Z axis in the direction of E_0, the potential at a great distance

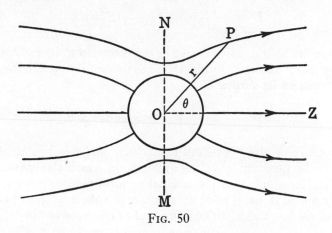

Fig. 50

from the sphere must be $-E_0z = -E_0r \cos \theta$. So we must look for a solution of Laplace's equation which satisfies the two boundary conditions

$$V = -E_0r \cos \theta \quad \text{for} \quad r = \infty,$$
$$V = 0 \qquad\qquad \text{for} \quad r = a.$$

To satisfy the first of these conditions the zonal harmonic $r \cos \theta$ is required and to satisfy the second another harmonic involving only the first power of $\cos \theta$ must be added. Therefore, a glance at Table I shows that the potential at a point P must be of the form

$$V = Ar \cos \theta + \frac{B \cos \theta}{r^2},$$

where the arbitrary constants A and B are to be determined so as to satisfy the boundary conditions. When r is infinite the second term in

V disappears, and the first boundary condition is satisfied if $A = -E_0$. To satisfy the second we put r equal to a and equate the coefficient of $\cos \theta$ to zero, getting $B = E_0 a^3$. Hence the potential outside the sphere is

$$V = -\left(1 - \frac{a^3}{r^3}\right)E_0 r \cos \theta. \tag{28-1}$$

Inside the sphere the potential is everywhere zero.

The components of electric intensity outside the sphere are

$$E_r = -\frac{\partial V}{\partial r} = \left(1 + 2\frac{a^3}{r^3}\right)E_0 \cos \theta \tag{28-2}$$

along the radius vector, and

$$E_\theta = -\frac{\partial V}{r\partial \theta} = -\left(1 - \frac{a^3}{r^3}\right)E_0 \sin \theta \tag{28-3}$$

at right angles to the radius vector in the direction of increasing θ.

As the radius vector is normal to the surface of the sphere the charge per unit area on its surface is

$$\sigma = -\kappa_0 \kappa \left(\frac{\partial V}{\partial r}\right)_{r=a} = 3\kappa_0 \kappa E_0 \cos \theta, \tag{28-4}$$

being positive on the right-hand hemisphere and negative on the left. Here κ is the permittivity of the dielectric in which the sphere is immersed and in which E_0 is the original uniform field.

So far we have considered an uncharged sphere at zero potential. If the sphere has a charge Q, we may add $Q/4\pi\kappa_0\kappa r$ to (28-1), getting

$$V = -\left(1 - \frac{a^3}{r^3}\right)E_0 r \cos \theta + \frac{Q}{4\pi\kappa_0\kappa r}. \tag{28-5}$$

The radial component of the electric intensity is increased by $Q/4\pi\kappa_0\kappa r^2$ and the charge per unit area by $Q/4\pi a^2$.

To return to the case of the uncharged sphere, it is clear from symmetry that the plane MN (Fig. 50) through the center of the sphere at right angles to Z is an equipotential surface at the same potential as the sphere. Therefore, we can replace the portion of this plane outside the sphere by a conducting surface, wiping out the field to the left and leaving that to the right unaltered. We have, then, the case of an infinite conducting plane with a hemispherical boss as illustrated in Fig. 51. The lines of force originate on positive charges on the surface of the plane instead of starting from positive charges at an infinite distance to the left. The potential is still given by (28-1) and the charge per unit area on the hemisphere by (28-4). To find the charge per unit area on the plane portion of the surface write (28-1) in the form

$$V = -\left(1-\frac{a^3}{r^3}\right)E_0 z.$$

As the Z axis is normal to the plane,

$$\sigma = -\kappa_0 \kappa\left(\frac{\partial V}{\partial z}\right)_{z=0} = \left(1-\frac{a^3}{r^3}\right)\kappa_0 \kappa E_0. \qquad (28\text{-}6)$$

Inspection of (28-4) and (28-6) shows that the charge density decreases from $3\kappa_0\kappa E_0$ at the tip of the boss to zero along the line of intersection of the hemisphere and the plane, and then increases to $\kappa_0\kappa E_0$ at a great distance from the boss. This problem illustrates the general rule that the charge density and therefore the adjacent field are greatest where the surface of a conductor is most convex and least where the surface is most concave.

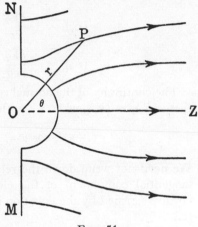

Fig. 51

Dielectric Sphere in Uniform Field. We will now replace the conducting sphere of Fig. 50 by an uncharged dielectric sphere of permittivity κ and suppose the region outside the sphere to be empty space. In this case the surface of the sphere need no longer be an equipotential surface, but instead it is necessary that the normal components of the electric displacement and the tangential components of the electric intensity should be the same on both sides of the surface, as discovered in art. 14.

As in the problem of the conducting sphere we will take

$$V_o = A_o r \cos\theta + \frac{B_o \cos\theta}{r^2}$$

for the potential function outside the sphere. To satisfy the boundary condition at infinity, it is clear that $A_o = -E_0$ as before. The components of the electric intensity are

$$(E_r)_o = -\frac{\partial V_o}{\partial r} = E_0 \cos\theta + \frac{2B_o \cos\theta}{r^3},$$

$$(E_\theta)_o = -\frac{\partial V_o}{r\partial\theta} = -E_0 \sin\theta + \frac{B_o \sin\theta}{r^3}.$$

We have supposed that there is no volume distribution of free charge inside the sphere. Therefore, the potential must be a solution of Laplace's equation. We will try a function of the same form as that used outside:

$$V_i = A_i r \cos \theta + \frac{B_i \cos \theta}{r^2}.$$

Evidently B_i must be zero, for otherwise the potential would become infinite at the origin. At the surface of the sphere V_i must equal V_o. Consequently, if a is the radius of the sphere,

$$A_i a \cos \theta = -E_0 a \cos \theta + \frac{B_o \cos \theta}{a^2}. \tag{28-7}$$

The components of electric intensity inside the sphere are

$$(E_r)_i = -\frac{\partial V_i}{\partial r} = -A_i \cos \theta,$$

$$(E_\theta)_i = -\frac{\partial V_i}{r \partial \theta} = A_i \sin \theta.$$

The continuity of the normal component of the displacement requires that $\kappa(E_r)_i = (E_r)_o$ when $r = a$, that is,

$$-\kappa A_i \cos \theta = E_0 \cos \theta + \frac{2B_o \cos \theta}{a^3}. \tag{28-8}$$

We need not write down the relation expressing the continuity of the tangential component of the electric intensity, for this condition is already satisfied by the equation (28-7) for the continuity of the potential.

Solving (28-7) and (28-8) for A_i and B_o, we find

$$A_i = -\frac{3}{\kappa+2} E_0, \qquad B_o = \frac{\kappa-1}{\kappa+2} a^3 E_0.$$

Consequently, the potential outside the sphere is

$$V_o = -\left(1 - \frac{\kappa-1}{\kappa+2} \frac{a^3}{r^3}\right) E_0 r \cos \theta, \tag{28-9}$$

and inside,

$$V_i = -\frac{3}{\kappa+2} E_0 r \cos \theta = -\frac{3}{\kappa+2} E_0 z. \tag{28-10}$$

Evidently the lines of force inside the sphere are parallel to the Z axis, the electric intensity having the constant value

$$E_i = -\frac{\partial V_i}{\partial z} = \frac{3}{\kappa+2} E_0,$$

and the electric displacement the constant value

$$D_i = \kappa_0 \kappa E_i = \kappa_0 \left(\frac{3\kappa}{\kappa+2}\right) E_0.$$

The number of lines of displacement per unit cross section inside the dielectric is to the number at a great distance in the ratio of 3 to $1+2/\kappa$. As κ is always greater than unity, the lines of displacement are crowded together inside the dielectric as illustrated in Fig. 52. Note that if κ is made infinite (28-9) and (28-10) go over into the corresponding expressions for a conducting sphere. In electrostatic

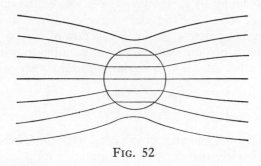

FIG. 52

problems a conductor may be considered as a dielectric of infinite permittivity.

Problem 28a. Find the stress on the surface of the conducting sphere treated in this article, when there is a charge Q on the sphere. Find also the total force on the sphere. Ans. $\dfrac{1}{2\kappa_0\kappa}\left[3\kappa_0\kappa E_0 \cos\theta + \dfrac{Q}{4\pi a^2}\right]^2$, QE_0.

Problem 28b. Find the polarization P in the dielectric sphere of this article, and the polarization charge density σ_P on the surface.

Ans. $P = 3\kappa_0\left(\dfrac{\kappa-1}{\kappa+2}\right)E_0$, $\sigma_P = P\cos\theta$.

Problem 28c. Given a homogeneous dielectric, of permittivity κ and of infinite extent, throughout which there is a uniform field E_0. A spherical cavity of radius a is cut out of the dielectric. Find the potential V_0 in the dielectric and V_i in the cavity, the polarization charge density σ_P on the walls of the cavity and the field E_i inside the cavity.

Ans. $V_o = -\left(1+\dfrac{\kappa-1}{2\kappa+1}\dfrac{a^3}{r^3}\right)E_0 r \cos\theta,$

$$V_i = -\frac{3\kappa}{2\kappa+1}E_0 r \cos\theta,$$

$$\sigma_P = -3\kappa_0\left(\frac{\kappa-1}{2\kappa+1}\right)E_0 \cos\theta,$$

$$E_i = \frac{3\kappa}{2\kappa+1}E_0.$$

Problem 28d. Two point charges q and q' are placed in very small spherical cavities in a rigid, infinite dielectric of permittivity κ, at a distance r apart. The charges do not touch the walls of the cavities. Find the force between them and compare with (16–11). Ans. $\left(\dfrac{3}{2\kappa+1}\right)\dfrac{qq'}{4\pi\kappa_0 r^2}$.

29. Conducting Cylinder in Uniform Field.

Consider an infinitely long uncharged conducting cylinder of circular cross section placed in a uniform electric field E_0 with its axis at right angles to the lines of force. As in the corresponding case of the sphere (art. 28), the cylinder is immersed in a dielectric of permittivity κ. Denote the radius of the cylinder by a, and take the X axis in the direction of the field and the Z axis along the axis of the cylinder. It is clear from symmetry that the potential is not a function of z, and therefore the problem is one in two dimensions for the solution of which polar coordinates are indicated. The boundary conditions are evidently

$$V = -E_0 r \cos \theta \quad \text{for} \quad r = \infty,$$
$$V = 0 \qquad\qquad \text{for} \quad r = a,$$

provided we take the potential of the conductor to be zero. Referring to Table II it is clear that the potential function must be of the form

$$V = Ar \cos \theta + \frac{B \cos \theta}{r},$$

the condition at infinity being satisfied by taking $A = -E_0$, and the condition at the surface of the cylinder being satisfied by making $B = E_0 a^2$. Hence, the potential outside the cylinder is

$$V = -\left(1 - \frac{a^2}{r^2}\right) E_0 r \cos \theta, \tag{29-1}$$

and the components of electric intensity in the directions of increasing r and θ are

$$E_r = -\frac{\partial V}{\partial r} = \left(1 + \frac{a^2}{r^2}\right) E_0 \cos \theta, \tag{29-2}$$

$$E_\theta = -\frac{\partial V}{r \partial \theta} = -\left(1 - \frac{a^2}{r^2}\right) E_0 \sin \theta. \tag{29-3}$$

The charge per unit area of the conducting surface is

$$\sigma = -\kappa_0 \kappa \left(\frac{\partial V}{\partial r}\right)_{r=a} = 2\kappa_0 \kappa E_0 \cos \theta. \tag{29-4}$$

If the cylinder, instead of being uncharged, has a charge per unit length equal to λ, we must add to (29-1) a term involving the cylindrical harmonic $\log r$. A convenient form for the potential in this case is

$$V = -\left(1 - \frac{a^2}{r^2}\right)E_0 r \cos\theta - \frac{\lambda}{2\pi\kappa_0\kappa}\log\frac{r}{a}. \qquad (29\text{-}5)$$

The radial component of the electric intensity is increased by $\lambda/2\pi\kappa_0\kappa r$ and the charge per unit area by $\lambda/2\pi a$.

Problem 29a. Discuss the field of a charged conducting plane of infinite extent having a cylindrical ridge of semicircular cross section, finding the charge per unit area on the surface of the plane. Ans. $\left(1 - \frac{a^2}{r^2}\right)\kappa_0\kappa E_0$.

Problem 29b. A long cylindrical rod of radius a and permittivity κ is placed (in empty space) in a uniform electric field E_0, with its axis at right angles to the lines of force. Find the potential outside and inside the rod.

Ans. $-\left(1 - \frac{\kappa-1}{\kappa+1}\frac{a^2}{r^2}\right)E_0 r \cos\theta$, $\quad -\frac{2}{\kappa+1}E_0 r \cos\theta$.

Problem 29c. A homogeneous dielectric, of permittivity κ and of infinite extent, has a uniform field E_0 throughout its interior. A cylindrical cavity of radius a, with its axis at right angles to the field, is cut out of the dielectric. Find the electric intensity in cavity. Ans. $\frac{2\kappa}{\kappa+1}E_0$.

Problem 29d. Find the stress on the surface of the conducting cylinder discussed in this article, when the cylinder has a charge per unit length equal to λ. Find also the force per unit length on the cylinder.

Ans. $\frac{1}{2\kappa_0\kappa}\left[2\kappa_0\kappa E_0\cos\theta + \frac{\lambda}{2\pi a}\right]^2$, $\quad \lambda E_0$.

30. Electrical Images.

Consider the electric field produced by two point charges. If we replace an equipotential surface surrounding one of the charges by a conducting surface and then transfer the charge to this surface, the field between the other charge and the surface remains unaltered, although that between the first charge and the surface is wiped out. For the potential in the original field satisfies Laplace's equation, and the transfer of the electricity on one of the point charges to a conducting surface coinciding with one of the equipotential surfaces of the field merely replaces the original boundary conditions by equivalent boundary conditions in so far as the portion of the field remaining is concerned. The method of solving electrostatic problems by the use of electrical images consists in its simplest form in placing two point charges in such positions that one of the equipotential surfaces of the field produced coincides with the surface of a conductor which it is desired to place in the field. Then the charge on one side of the conducting surface is transferred to it, the field on the other side remaining unaltered. When this method is feasible, it enables us to determine the field produced by a point charge and a conducting surface from the simple investigation of the field due to two point charges. In such a case the point charge which is transferred to the conducting surface is said to be the *image* of the other point charge. If the latter is surrounded by a dielectric of permittivity κ, the permittivity in the region occupied by the image charge must also be taken to be κ for the purpose of the calculation, even though actually it may be different.

The method may be extended so as to find the field produced by two conductors neither of which constitutes a point charge, such as the field due to two charged conducting spheres. In problems in which the potential is not a function of one of the rectangular coordinates the point charges referred to above are replaced by line charges.

Point and Plane. To find the field due to a point charge q (Fig. 53)

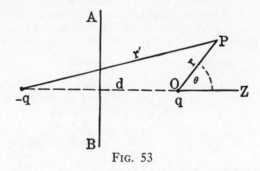

Fig. 53

and a conducting plane AB at a distance $d/2$ from it, we consider the field due to q and a point charge $-q$ placed on the perpendicular dropped from q to the plane as far to the left of the plane as q is to the right. The potential at P due to the two point charges is evidently

$$V = \frac{q}{4\pi\kappa_0\kappa r} - \frac{q}{4\pi\kappa_0\kappa r'}$$

$$= \frac{1}{4\pi\kappa_0\kappa}\left[\frac{q}{r} - \frac{q}{\sqrt{r^2 + 2rd\cos\theta + d^2}}\right], \quad (30\text{-}1)$$

where κ is the permittivity of the medium surrounding the charges.

Evidently the median plane AB is an equipotential surface of zero potential. So if we transfer the charge on the image $-q$ to an earthed conducting plane placed so as to coincide with AB, the field to the right of AB remains unaltered while that to the left is wiped out. The potential function (30-1) still applies to the region to the right of AB and the components of electric intensity are

$$E_r = -\frac{\partial V}{\partial r} = \frac{1}{4\pi\kappa_0\kappa}\left[\frac{q}{r^2} - \frac{q(r+d\cos\theta)}{(r^2+2rd\cos\theta+d^2)^{3/2}}\right], \qquad (30\text{-}2)$$

$$E_\theta = -\frac{\partial V}{r\partial\theta} = \frac{1}{4\pi\kappa_0\kappa}\left[\frac{qd\sin\theta}{(r^2+2rd\cos\theta+d^2)^{3/2}}\right]. \qquad (30\text{-}3)$$

The density of the charge induced on the earthed conducting plane by q is

$$\sigma = -\kappa_0\kappa\left(\frac{\partial V}{\partial z}\right)_{z=-d/2} = \kappa_0\kappa(E_z)_{z=-d/2}$$

$$= \kappa_0\kappa(E_r\cos\theta - E_\theta\sin\theta)_{r=r'} = -\frac{qd}{4\pi r^3}. \qquad (30\text{-}4)$$

As the field in the neighborhood of q is not changed by the substitution of the conducting plane for the image $-q$ it follows from the law of

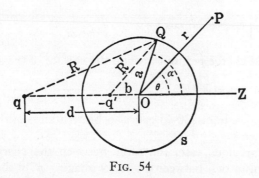

FIG. 54

action and reaction that the total force on the conducting plane due to the attraction of q is the same as that which would be experienced by the image $-q$, that is,

$$\mathscr{F} = -\frac{q^2}{4\pi\kappa_0\kappa d^2}. \qquad (30\text{-}5)$$

Point and Sphere. In this case it is required to find the magnitude and position of the point charge $-q'$ (Fig. 54) such that the spherical surface s of radius a shall be an equipotential in the field produced by the charges q and $-q'$. If the distances of q and $-q'$ from the center

O of the sphere are denoted by d and b, respectively, the potential at a point Q on the surface of the sphere is

$$V = \frac{q}{4\pi\kappa_0\kappa R} - \frac{q'}{4\pi\kappa_0\kappa R'}$$

$$= \frac{1}{4\pi\kappa_0\kappa}\left[\frac{q}{\sqrt{d^2+2da\cos\alpha+a^2}} - \frac{q'}{\sqrt{a^2+2ab\cos\alpha+b^2}}\right],$$

for a medium of permittivity κ.

Choosing $b = a^2/d$, we have

$$V = \frac{1}{4\pi\kappa_0\kappa}\left[\frac{q-\dfrac{d}{a}q'}{\sqrt{d^2+2da\cos\alpha+a^2}}\right].$$

If, in addition, we give q' the magnitude $(a/d)q$, the potential vanishes for all values of α and the sphere is a surface of zero potential. We can now replace the sphere by an earthed conducting surface and transfer the charge $-q'$ to it. This annuls the field inside the sphere leaving the field outside unaltered. Therefore, the potential at any exterior point P due to the point charge q and the earthed conductor is

$$V = \frac{1}{4\pi\kappa_0\kappa}\left[\frac{q}{\sqrt{d^2+2dr\cos\theta+r^2}} - \frac{\dfrac{a}{d}q}{\sqrt{r^2+2r\dfrac{a^2}{d}\cos\theta+\dfrac{a^4}{d^2}}}\right]. \qquad (30\text{-}6)$$

The induced charge per unit area on the surface of the sphere is

$$\sigma = -\kappa_0\kappa\left(\frac{\partial V}{\partial r}\right)_{r=a} = -\frac{q}{4\pi a}\frac{d^2-a^2}{(d^2+2da\cos\theta+a^2)^{3/2}}. \qquad (30\text{-}7)$$

The right-hand side of (30-7) can also be written $-q(d^2-a^2)/4\pi aR^3$, since $\theta \equiv \alpha$ when $r = a$.

As in the previous case, the force between the charge q and the sphere is equal to that between q and its image $-q'$ in the sphere.

In the case we have been considering the potential of the sphere has been made zero. If we wish the sphere to have a potential other than zero, we can add a uniformly distributed charge Q to the surface of the sphere; the effect of such a charge is merely to increase the potential of every point on the surface by $Q/4\pi\kappa_0\kappa a$ and therefore the surface remains equipotential. The potential at an exterior point P will then exceed (30-6) by $Q/4\pi\kappa_0\kappa r$.

Problem 30a. What is the effect of adding a uniformly distributed charge to the conducting plane of Fig. 53?

Problem 30b. Find the potential of an uncharged spherical conductor of radius a whose center is at a distance d from a point charge q.   Ans. $\dfrac{q}{4\pi\kappa_0\kappa d}$.

31. Sphere and Plane. We can use the method of images to find the capacitance of a charged spherical conductor of radius a (Fig. 55) at a distance $d/2$ from an earthed conducting plane AB of infinite extent, a being supposed small compared with d.

In this case we must make use of an infinite series of images. First suppose a charge q_1 placed at the center O of the sphere. This charge gives rise to a field of which the surface of the sphere is an equipotential, but the surface of the plane is not equipotential. Adding the image $-q_1$ of q_1 in the plane, AB becomes equipotential, but the sphere is no longer so. Next add the image q_2 of $-q_1$ in the sphere; this restores the equipotential character of the spherical surface but disturbs that of the plane. Addition of the image $-q_2$ of q_2 in the plane makes the plane an equipotential surface again but disturbs the potential over the surface of the sphere. Each one of the added fields, however, is

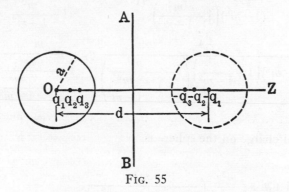

Fig. 55

smaller than the preceding one, so continuation of the process brings us ever nearer to the desired state in which both the plane and the spherical surface are equipotential surfaces. Finally, we transfer the charges inside the sphere to the sphere and the others to the plane. The total charge on the sphere is then the sum of the series $q_1 + q_2 + q_3 + \cdots$ and the charge on the plane is equal but opposite in sign.

The distance of $-q_1$ from the center of the sphere is d, so it follows from the previous article that q_2 is a charge $(a/d)q_1$ at a distance a^2/d from O. Therefore, $-q_2$ is at a distance $d\left(1 - \dfrac{a^2}{d^2}\right)$ from O and q_3 is a charge

$$\frac{\dfrac{a}{d}}{1 - \dfrac{a^2}{d^2}} q_2 = \frac{\dfrac{a^2}{d^2}}{1 - \dfrac{a^2}{d^2}} q_1$$

at a distance

$$\frac{\dfrac{a^2}{d}}{1-\dfrac{a^2}{d^2}}$$

from O. If we put m for the ratio a/d we have the following point charges at the distances specified from the center of the sphere:

Charge	Distance from O
q_1,	0,
mq_1,	ma,
$\dfrac{m^2}{1-m^2}q_1$,	$\dfrac{m}{1-m^2}a$,
$\dfrac{m^3}{(1-m^2)\left(1-\dfrac{m^2}{1-m^2}\right)}q_1$,	$\dfrac{m}{1-\dfrac{m^2}{1-m^2}}a$,
$\dfrac{m^4}{(1-m^2)\left(1-\dfrac{m^2}{1-m^2}\right)\left(1-\dfrac{m^2}{1-\dfrac{m^2}{1-m^2}}\right)}q_1$,	$\dfrac{m}{1-\dfrac{m^2}{1-\dfrac{m^2}{1-m^2}}}a$,

. . . .

The total charge on the sphere is

$$Q = q_1\left\{ 1+m+\frac{m^2}{1-m^2}+\frac{m^3}{(1-m^2)\left(1-\dfrac{m^2}{1-m^2}\right)} \right.$$
$$\left. +\frac{m^4}{(1-m^2)\left(1-\dfrac{m^2}{1-m^2}\right)\left(1-\dfrac{m^2}{1-\dfrac{m^2}{1-m^2}}\right)} + \cdots \right\}$$

$$= q_1\{1+m+m^2+m^3+2m^4+3m^5+\cdots\}. \tag{31-1}$$

Since q_2 is the image of $-q_1$ in the sphere, the potential of the surface of the sphere due to this pair of charges is zero, as shown in the previous article. The same is true of the pairs q_3 and $-q_2$, q_4 and $-q_3$, etc. Consequently the potential of the sphere is

$$V = \frac{q_1}{4\pi\kappa_0\kappa a} \tag{31-2}$$

due to the charge q_1 at its center alone.

Since equal charges of opposite sign are placed symmetrically on the two sides of AB, the potential of the plane is zero. Consequently, the capacitance of a sphere relative to an earthed plane is

$$C = \frac{Q}{V} = 4\pi\kappa_0\kappa a\{1 + m + m^2 + m^3 + 2m^4 + 3m^5 + \cdots\}. \quad (31\text{-}3)$$

Note that the capacitance of the sphere is increased by the proximity of the plane.

The analysis above provides us at once with the solution of the problem of two conducting spheres of the same radius a a distance d apart, the charge on the second sphere being equal but opposite in sign to that on the first. The negatively charged sphere is indicated by a broken circle in Fig. 55. Its potential is

$$V' = -\frac{q_1}{4\pi\kappa_0\kappa a}. \quad (31\text{-}4)$$

The field on the right of AB is the reflection in the plane of the field on the left. Evidently in this case the capacitance is half that specified by (31-3).

Problem 31a. In the case of the conducting sphere and infinite plane let c_{11} be the coefficient of capacitance and c_{12} the coefficient of induction (art. 19). Show that $c_{11} = -c_{12} = C$, where C is given by (31-3).

Problem 31b. A sphere of 10 cm radius is suspended 25 cm above the ground. Calculate the capacitance of the sphere relative to earth. Ans. $1.39(10)^{-5}$ microfarad.

32. Parallel Wires. Consider two infinitely long straight parallel wires of radius a, shown in cross section in Fig. 56. We wish to find the field when one has a charge per unit length equal to λ and the other an equal negative charge distribution. Then we shall compute the capacitance of the one relative to the other.

Begin by considering two parallel filaments intersecting the plane of the figure at O and Q and having charges per unit length λ and $-\lambda$, respectively. Evidently the potential at a

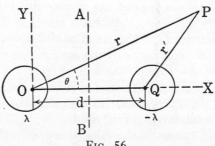

FIG. 56

point P due to them is not a function of the coordinate z at right angles to the plane of the figure. Hence, it must be represented by one of the cylindrical harmonics of Table II, art. 27. From symmetry it is clear that the potential due to each filament is a function only of the distance of P from the filament; therefore, we may take

$$V = -\frac{\lambda}{2\pi\kappa_0\kappa}\log r + \frac{\lambda}{2\pi\kappa_0\kappa}\log r' = \frac{\lambda}{4\pi\kappa_0\kappa}\log\frac{r'^2}{r^2}, \quad (32\text{-}1)$$

for a medium of permittivity κ. This potential function makes the potential zero in the plane AB midway between the two filaments.

The traces of the equipotential surfaces are

$$\frac{r'^2}{r^2} = \frac{r^2 - 2rd\cos\theta + d^2}{r^2} \equiv m^2,$$

or

$$r^2 + 2r\cos\theta\left(\frac{d}{m^2-1}\right) = \frac{d^2}{m^2-1},$$

where m is a positive constant which may assume any value between 0 and ∞.

Transforming to rectangular coordinates $x = r\cos\theta$, $y = r\sin\theta$,

$$\left(x + \frac{d}{m^2-1}\right)^2 + y^2 = \frac{m^2 d^2}{(m^2-1)^2}$$

$$= \frac{d^2}{\left(m - \dfrac{1}{m}\right)^2}.$$

This equation specifies a family of circles, the right-hand member representing the square of the radius. Evidently any two values of m which are reciprocals yield the same value of the radius but different positions of the center. For $m > 1$ the center of the circle is at a distance $d/(m^2-1)$ to the left of the origin O. As this is less than the radius $md/(m^2-1)$, the curve encircles O. On the other hand, for $m < 1$ the center is at a distance to the right of the point Q equal to $d/(1-m^2) - d = m^2 d/(1-m^2)$. As this is less than the radius $md/(1-m^2)$ the curve encircles Q. The set of circles surrounding Q are separated from those surrounding O by the median line obtained by making $m = 1$.

As the equipotential surfaces are cylinders of circular cross section, we may take the two of radius a as the surfaces of the wires, transferring the charge on each filament to the surrounding cylindrical surface and annulling the field inside.

Let m_+ be the value of m greater than unity corresponding to the left-hand wire, and $m_- = 1/m_+$ the value of m less than unity corresponding to the right-hand wire. Then

$$a = \frac{m_+ d}{m_+^2 - 1} = \frac{m_- d}{1 - m_-^2}.$$

Now if b is the distance between the axes of the two wires,

$$b = \frac{d}{m_+{}^2 - 1} + \frac{d}{1 - m_-{}^2}$$

$$= \frac{m_+{}^2 + 1}{m_+{}^2 - 1} d = \frac{1 + m_-{}^2}{1 - m_-{}^2} d.$$

Hence, eliminating d, we find

$$m_+{}^2 - \frac{b}{a} m_+ + 1 = 0, \qquad \text{(greater root)},$$

$$m_-{}^2 - \frac{b}{a} m_- + 1 = 0, \qquad \text{(lesser root)},$$

which give

$$m_+ = \frac{b + \sqrt{b^2 - 4a^2}}{2a},$$

$$m_- = \frac{b - \sqrt{b^2 - 4a^2}}{2a}.$$

Since the potential of the positively charged wire is

$$V_+ = \frac{\lambda}{2\pi\kappa_0\kappa} \log m_+$$

and that of the negatively charged wire is

$$V_- = \frac{\lambda}{2\pi\kappa_0\kappa} \log m_-$$

the difference of potential is

$$V_+ - V_- = \frac{\lambda}{2\pi\kappa_0\kappa} \log \frac{b + \sqrt{b^2 - 4a^2}}{b - \sqrt{b^2 - 4a^2}}, \qquad (32\text{-}2)$$

and the capacitance per unit length,

$$C_l = \frac{\lambda}{V_+ - V_-} = \frac{2\pi\kappa_0\kappa}{\log \dfrac{b + \sqrt{b^2 - 4a^2}}{b - \sqrt{b^2 - 4a^2}}}. \qquad (32\text{-}3)$$

We have noted that the median plane AB is an equipotential surface of zero potential. Therefore, we may transfer the charge on the right-hand filament to a conducting plane placed so as to coincide with AB, wiping out the field to the right of the plane. This device enables us to calculate the capacitance of a wire relative to an earthed conducting plane. If we put $h \equiv b/2$,

$$V_+ = \frac{\lambda}{2\pi\kappa_0\kappa} \log \frac{h+\sqrt{h^2-a^2}}{a},$$

and the capacitance per unit length is

$$C_l = \frac{\lambda}{V_+} = \frac{2\pi\kappa_0\kappa}{\log \dfrac{h+\sqrt{h^2-a^2}}{a}}. \tag{32-4}$$

Problem 32a. Find the force per unit length between the two wires discussed in this article. Ans. $-\dfrac{\lambda^2}{2\pi\kappa_0\kappa d}$.

Problem 32b. In the case to which (32–4) applies, find the potential at any point in terms of r and θ (Fig. 56), assuming that the radius of the wire is very small. Ans. $\dfrac{\lambda}{4\pi\kappa_0\kappa} \log\left(1-4\dfrac{h}{r}\cos\theta+4\dfrac{h^2}{r^2}\right)$.

Problem 32c. What is the capacitance per unit length of a wire of 5 mm diameter (a) relative to a parallel wire at a distance of 13 mm, (b) relative to an earthed plane at the same distance? Assume $\kappa=1$. Ans. (a) $1.73(10)^{-5}$ microfarad/meter, (b) $2.38(10)^{-5}$ microfarad/meter.

Problem 32d. A wire of 3 mm radius is placed with its axis 5 mm from an earthed conducting plane. When the wire is raised to a potential 1000 volts what is its charge per unit length? Ans. $0.506(10)^{-7}$ coulomb/meter.

Problem 32e. Find the capacitance per unit length of two parallel wires of radii a_1 and a_2 respectively, whose axes are a distance b apart.

Ans. $\dfrac{2\pi\kappa_0\kappa}{\log \dfrac{a_1[b^2-(a_1{}^2-a_2{}^2)+\sqrt{b^4-2b^2(a_1{}^2+a_2{}^2)+(a_1{}^2-a_2{}^2)^2}]}{a_2[b^2+(a_1{}^2-a_2{}^2)-\sqrt{b^4-2b^2(a_1{}^2+a_2{}^2)+(a_1{}^2-a_2{}^2)^2}]}}$.

33. Conjugate Functions.

An electrostatic problem in which the potential is not a function of one of the rectangular coordinates, say z, is called a two-dimensional problem. In such a case Laplace's equation (26-2) reduces to

$$\frac{\partial^2 V}{\partial x^2} + \frac{\partial^2 V}{\partial y^2} = 0. \tag{33-1}$$

We have seen how to solve such a problem in the case where V is expressed in polar coordinates r and θ by the use of cylindrical harmonics. Now we shall consider a more general method involving what are known as *conjugate functions*.

Let $\mathbf{z}$ represent the complex quantity

$$\mathbf{z} \equiv x + iy,$$

where $i \equiv \sqrt{-1}$. To distinguish complex from real quantities we shall use **black face** type to designate the former. A more detailed discussion of such quantities is given in art. 112.

Consider any function of z such as $F(z)$, and let $g(x, y)$ and $h(x, y)$ be respectively the real and the imaginary parts of $F(z)$, so that

$$F(z) = F(x+iy) = g(x, y)+ih(x, y).$$

The functions g and h are called *conjugate functions* of x and y.

Now

$$\left. \begin{array}{ll} \dfrac{\partial F}{\partial x} = \dfrac{dF}{d\mathbf{z}}, & \dfrac{\partial^2 F}{\partial x^2} = \dfrac{d^2 F}{d\mathbf{z}^2}; \\[2ex] \dfrac{\partial F}{\partial y} = i\dfrac{dF}{d\mathbf{z}}, & \dfrac{\partial^2 F}{\partial y^2} = -\dfrac{d^2 F}{d\mathbf{z}^2}. \end{array} \right\} \quad (33\text{-}2)$$

Therefore

$$\frac{\partial^2 F}{\partial x^2}+\frac{\partial^2 F}{\partial y^2} = \frac{d^2 F}{d\mathbf{z}^2}-\frac{d^2 F}{d\mathbf{z}^2} = 0. \tag{33-3}$$

So any function of the complex variable $x+iy$ satisfies Laplace's equation (33-1) for two dimensions. Consequently, the real part $g(x, y)$ of $F(z)$ must satisfy Laplace's equation and the same is true for the imaginary part $h(x, y)$. Hence, either the real part of $F(z)$ or the imaginary part may be taken as the potential function in a possible electrostatic field.

From (33-2) we have

$$\frac{\partial F}{\partial y} = i\frac{\partial F}{\partial x},$$

and therefore

$$\frac{\partial g}{\partial y}+i\frac{\partial h}{\partial y} = i\left(\frac{\partial g}{\partial x}+i\frac{\partial h}{\partial x}\right).$$

So, as g and h are real functions,

$$\frac{\partial g}{\partial y} = -\frac{\partial h}{\partial x}, \qquad \frac{\partial h}{\partial y} = \frac{\partial g}{\partial x},$$

and

$$\frac{\dfrac{\partial g}{\partial x}}{\dfrac{\partial g}{\partial y}} = -\frac{\dfrac{\partial h}{\partial y}}{\dfrac{\partial h}{\partial x}}. \tag{33-4}$$

Now consider the two families of curves

$$g(x, y) = \text{constant}, \qquad h(x, y) = \text{constant}.$$

The slope of the tangent to a curve of the first family is

$$\left(\frac{dy}{dx}\right)_g = -\frac{\dfrac{\partial g}{\partial x}}{\dfrac{\partial g}{\partial y}},$$

and that to a curve of the second family is

$$\left(\frac{dy}{dx}\right)_h = -\frac{\dfrac{\partial h}{\partial x}}{\dfrac{\partial h}{\partial y}}.$$

But (33-4) states that the one slope is the negative reciprocal of the other, that is, that the two families of curves intersect orthogonally. So if one family represents the traces of equipotential surfaces on the XY plane, the other represents lines of force.

Problem 33a. Show that the function

$$F(\mathbf{z}) = (x+iy)^n = (re^{i\theta})^n$$

leads to the cylindrical harmonics of art. 27.

Problem 33b. By finding the function conjugate to $\log r' - \log r$, show that the equation of the lines of force between the two wires of art. 32 is

$$\theta' - \theta = \text{constant},$$

where θ' is the angle which r' makes with the X axis.

34. Examples of Conjugate Functions.

We shall consider a few examples of the use of conjugate functions which are of practical interest.

Field Due to Two Conducting Planes Intersecting at Right Angles. The function of the complex variable $\mathbf{z}$ needed for the solution of this problem is

$$F(\mathbf{z}) = A(x+iy)^2 = A(x^2-y^2)+2iAxy, \tag{34-1}$$

where A is an arbitrary constant. We choose for the potential function the imaginary part,

$$V = 2Axy. \tag{34-2}$$

The equipotential surfaces are the equilateral hyperbolic cylinders whose traces are shown by full lines in Fig. 57. The conducting planes, which coincide with the XZ and YZ coordinate planes, are at zero potential. The equations of the lines of force are the hyperbolas,

$$x^2-y^2 = \text{constant}, \tag{34-3}$$

shown by broken lines in the figure.

The components of the electric intensity are

$$E_x = -\frac{\partial V}{\partial x} = -2Ay,$$

$$E_y = -\frac{\partial V}{\partial y} = -2Ax. \hspace{2cm} \Biggr\} \hspace{1cm} (34\text{-}4)$$

If a dielectric of permittivity κ occupies the region which contains the field, the charge per unit area on the XZ plane is

$$\sigma = -\kappa_0\kappa\left(\frac{\partial V}{\partial y}\right)_{y=0} = -2\kappa_0\kappa Ax, \hspace{1cm} (34\text{-}5)$$

with a similar expression for that on the YZ plane. The density of charge, then, is zero along the line of intersection and it varies linearly

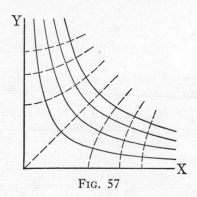

FIG. 57

with the distance from this line. If A is positive, the charge on the conducting planes is negative since the potential increases as x and y are made greater. The lines of force are directed toward the planes and terminate on negative charges on their surfaces.

Field at the Edge of a Conducting Plane. For this case the appropriate function is

$$F(\mathbf{z}) = \{A(x+iy)\}^{1/2} = g(x, y) + ih(x, y). \hspace{1cm} (34\text{-}6)$$

Therefore,

$$Ax = g^2 - h^2, \hspace{1cm} Ay = 2gh,$$

and, choosing $h(x, y)$ for the potential function V, we get, on eliminating $g(x, y)$,

$$A^2y^2 = 4V^2(Ax + V^2). \hspace{1cm} (34\text{-}7)$$

The equipotential surfaces are parabolic cylinders as illustrated in Fig. 58, the positive half of the X axis being the trace of the conducting plane, which is at zero potential.

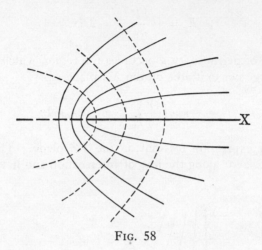

FIG. 58

To get the charge per unit area we differentiate (34-7) partially with respect to y and find

$$\frac{\partial V}{\partial y} = \frac{A^2 y}{4V(Ax + 2V^2)} = \frac{A\sqrt{Ax + V^2}}{2(Ax + 2V^2)}.$$

Then

$$\sigma = -\kappa_0 \kappa \left(\frac{\partial V}{\partial y}\right)_{y=0} = -\frac{\kappa_0 \kappa}{2}\sqrt{\frac{A}{x}}, \qquad (34\text{-}8)$$

since $V = 0$ when $y = 0$. This gives the charge on one side of the plane only, of course. The charge density is infinite at the edge where the convexity of the surface becomes infinitely great.

REFERENCES

Corson and Lorrain, *Introduction to Electromagnetic Fields and Waves* (Freeman, 1962).   Chap. 4, Appendix D.
Peck, *Electricity and Magnetism* (McGraw-Hill, 1953).   Chap. 2.

Chapter IV

MAGNETOSTATICS

35. Attraction and Repulsion. The use of a natural magnet or *lodestone* to indicate direction at sea appears to have been unknown to the ancients, but was certainly familiar to European navigators at the time of the Crusades. As early as the thirteenth century Peregrinus found that, if an iron needle is suspended at different places above the surface of a lodestone and lines drawn so as to have everywhere the direction assumed by the needle, these lines converge at two points on opposite sides of the stone. These points he named *poles*.

Little further progress was made until 1600 when Gilbert noted that there are two kinds of poles, *positive* or *north-seeking poles*, and *negative* or *south-seeking poles*, which are characterized by the fact that like poles repel and unlike poles attract each other. He also explained the action of a freely suspended magnet in assuming a north and south orientation as due to the presence of poles in the earth roughly coincident with the geographical poles. As the north pole of a magnet turns toward the north, it must be attracted by a south magnetic pole in the neighborhood of the north geographical pole and repelled by a north magnetic pole near the south geographical pole. Actually the earth's magnetic field is better represented by supposing it to be due to a comparatively short magnet placed at the center of the earth along a line inclined 17° to the geographical axis.

The early discoveries in magnetism may be summed up in the two qualitative laws:

(I) *Like poles repel, unlike poles attract.*

(II) *The force between two poles decreases as the distance between them is increased.*

These laws are quite analogous to the corresponding laws for electric charges given in art. 1. There are, however, certain fundamental differences between electric charges and magnetic poles. In the first place, every magnet is found to have equal quantities of north and south magnetism. If, for instance, we place a magnet on a cork floating on water, the earth's field, while it may turn the magnet, gives rise to no

97

motion of translation.   This shows that the northward force on the north pole is just balanced by the southward force on the south pole, and therefore that the strength of the two poles is the same.   Moreover, if a needle, magnetized so as to have a north pole at one end and a south pole at the other, is cut in two, we find that we have two complete magnets, each of which has equal north and south poles.   Therefore, it is impossible to isolate north and south poles on different bodies, as can be done in the case of electric charges of opposite sign. This fact suggests that north poles and south poles are merely different aspects of a single mechanism, rather than separate entities.   If we wish to deal experimentally with a north pole alone, the best we can do is to employ a needle so long that the force exerted by the south pole at the remote end is negligible in the neighborhood of the north pole.

A second difference between magnetostatic and electrostatic phenomena lies in the absence of conductors of magnetism.   There is no substance in which magnetic poles move under the influence of magnetic forces with the freedom that electric charges move in a conductor when subject to electric forces.   The poles in a piece of very soft iron—which is the nearest thing to a conductor of magnetism—never move so far under the action of impressed magnetic forces as to annul the field in the interior of the body.

On the other hand there are many similarities between magnetic and electric phenomena.   For instance, an unmagnetized piece of iron, when placed near a pole of a strong magnet, becomes magnetized by induction in the same way that a dielectric becomes polarized when placed in an electric field.

Just as in electrostatics we are concerned only with charges at rest in the observer's inertial system, so in magnetostatics we limit ourselves to a consideration of magnets at rest relative to the observer's reference frame.   It is important to note that the phenomena of electrostatics and of magnetostatics are quite distinct; no force is exerted by an electric charge on a magnetic pole when both are at rest relative to the observer, and vice versa.

36. Molecular Theory of Magnetism.

The fact that two magnets are produced by cutting a magnet in two indicates that if the process could be carried far enough the ultimate particles of a magnetic substance would be found to be themselves tiny magnets.   The molecular theory of magnetism, proposed by Weber and elaborated by Ewing, accounts for many of the characteristics of magnetic substances by attributing magnetic properties to the individual molecules or atoms. In an unmagnetized iron bar the elementary magnets are arranged chaotically, so that in any small volume as many have their axes pointing in one direction as in the opposite.   Therefore, the bar as a whole gives rise to no magnetic forces at outside points.   If, now, the north pole N (Fig. 59) of a strong magnet is brought near one end of the bar, the elementary magnets, represented by arrows with heads at the north ends, experience a torque due to the attraction of N for each south pole and the repulsion on each north pole.   This torque tends to line up the elementary magnets parallel to the axis of the bar.   Each individual magnet, however, was in equilibrium under the magnetic torques exerted by its neighbors in the original chaotic condition.   Therefore, the torque due to N is opposed by these internal torques, and so long as the bar is at a distance from N the elementary magnets are only partially lined up as in (a).   Nevertheless there is a preponderance of south poles at the end s of the bar and of north poles at the end n, while in the interior each north pole is compensated by a neighboring south pole.   Thus the bar has become *magnetized by induction* with a south pole on the end adjacent to N and a north pole on the farther end.

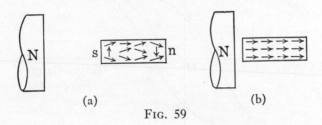

(a)   (b)

FIG. 59

Further approach of N toward the bar increases the torques exerted by the former on the elementary magnets, and they swing more and more into line.   At a certain distance a condition approaching instability is reached, the internal torques becoming very small, and the elementary magnets turning very rapidly as the distance from N is decreased.   If the strength of the pole N is great enough, a point is finally reached where the molecular magnets are all in line, as shown in (b).   In this state the iron bar is said to be *saturated*.   Since the elementary magnets of which it is composed are completely lined up, further increase of the magnetizing force cannot increase the strength of the poles on its ends.

If, now, the pole N is removed, the elementary magnets are no longer subject to torque due to external causes.   They do not, however, resume their original orientations, for now each is acted on by a different set of internal torques from that existing in the original unmagnetized state.   Instead the bar retains a certain fraction of the induced magnetization, which, however, may be partially or completely destroyed by shaking up the molecules, either by tapping the bar with a hammer or by raising its temperature.

Modern experiments show that actually the elementary magnets under discussion are not individual molecules but rather groups of molecules which act in unison. Each group constitutes a *domain*, whose volume may be as great as $(10)^{-6}$ mm^3. Not only do the molecules in a single domain turn together, but the magnetic axes of those in the larger domains, at least, reorient themselves abruptly rather than continuously.

A graph showing how the degree of magnetization of the bar of Fig. 59 varies with the magnetizing force exerted by the pole N is given in Fig. 60. Starting with the bar in the unmagnetized condition represented by the point O, we pass through the state a where the

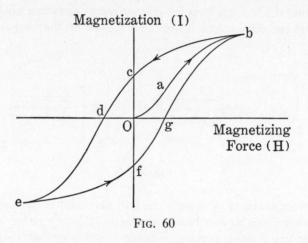

Fig. 60

magnetization increases very rapidly with increase of the magnetizing force to saturation at b. Decreasing the magnetizing force to zero the bar is left with a degree of magnetization represented by the ordinate Oc. This ordinate is a measure of the *retentiveness* of the bar. Reversing the direction of the magnetizing force and increasing its magnitude brings us to the state d in which the bar has completely lost its magnetization, and finally to the condition e of saturation in the opposite sense to that previously existing. The magnetizing force Od necessary to demagnetize completely the bar is often referred to as the *coercive force*. Continuation of the process takes us through the points f and g to b again. The lagging of the magnetization behind the magnetizing force illustrated by the curve is known as *hysteresis* and *bcefb* is called a *hysteresis loop*.

The preceding discussion applies to those substances known as *ferromagnetic*, that is, iron, nickel, cobalt and certain alloys. Another class of magnetic substances, known as *paramagnetic*, exhibits similar magnetic properties to a much smaller degree but does not show the phenomena of saturation and of hysteresis in such fields as are available in the laboratory. It is probable, however, that such substances also would become saturated if subjected to sufficiently large magnetizing forces. Finally, certain substances, when acted on by a magnetizing force, become weakly magnetized in the opposite sense to ferromagnetic or paramagnetic substances. These are said to be *diamagnetic*. Thus a bar of diamagnetic material, placed as in Fig. 59, would acquire a north pole at the end nearer to *N* and a south pole at the opposite end. Although the molecular theory of magnetism accounts satisfactorily for the general features of ferromagnetism and paramagnetism, diamagnetism is due to an entirely different cause. A simple explanation of diamagnetism is given in art. 84, where it is made clear that probably all substances are diamagnetic, the diamagnetism of a paramagnetic medium being masked by the very much more intense paramagnetism. An excellent résumé of the subject of magnetism is given by Bozorth.*

37. Coulomb's Law. Consider two magnetic poles of strengths *m* and *m'* located at points a distance *r* apart. Doubling the pole-strength *m* doubles the force on *m'*, for each half of the doubled pole exerts the same force on *m'* as that exerted by the original pole. Therefore, the force between the two poles is proportional to *m*. Similarly it is proportional to *m'*. Consequently, *the force between two poles is proportional to the product of their pole-strengths*.

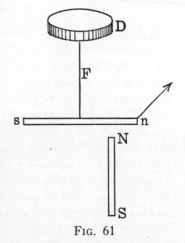

Fig. 61

When the distance between two point poles is changed, it is found that *the force exerted by either on the other is inversely proportional to the square of the distance between them*. This law was stated by Michell in 1750, but it is usually attributed to Coulomb who put it on a firm foundation by his experiments with the torsion balance in 1785. These experiments are the same in principle as those performed by the same investigator in determining how the force between electric charges varies with the distance. A long magnetic needle *ns* (Fig. 61) is suspended at its center of mass by the

* Bozorth, R. M., *Rev. of Mod. Phys.* **19**, 29 (1947).

torsion fibre F of the torsion balance. When the north pole N of a second long magnet is brought up to a predetermined point in front of the north pole n of the suspended magnet, the latter experiences a torque and turns about the fibre as axis. Since the fibre is rigidly attached at both ends, the rotation of ns causes it to twist. Next the drum D is turned far enough in the opposite sense to bring the suspended magnet back to its original orientation. The angle through which the drum has to be turned is a measure of the force between N and n in their final positions. By varying the distance between the two poles the relation stated above is found.

In performing the experiment it is necessary to use long magnets so that the influence of the south poles s, S will be inappreciable. Moreover it is important not to bring the two north poles too close together, as each has a tendency to weaken the other by induction. A more precise method of verifying the law of force, devised later by Gauss, is described in art. 47.

As the force between two point poles varies directly with the product of the pole-strengths and inversely with the square of the distance between them, we may proceed exactly as in the case of the force between point charges (art. 6). Taking the constant of proportionality as unity and using c.g.s. units, here indicated by subscript m, we have

$$\mathscr{F}_m = \frac{m_m m_m{}'}{r_m{}^2}, \tag{37-1}$$

a positive force indicating repulsion and a negative force attraction. As we shall see later, the presence of a magnetic medium in the region between the poles changes the force between them. So equation (37-1) applies exactly only to poles *in vacuo*, although it may be used for poles in air in all but very precise measurements.

Giving all the quantities in (37-1) the magnitude unity, we can see that this equation defines *a unit pole as that pole which repels a like equal pole placed at a distance 1 cm in vacuo with a force 1 dyne.* Putting 1 cm gm sec^{-2} for $\mathscr{F}_m$ and 1 cm for r_m and solving for $m_m = m_m{}'$, we find that this c.g.s. unit of pole-strength is 1 cm$^{3/2}$ gm$^{1/2}$ sec^{-1}. This unit and all other units derived from the fundamental equation (37-1) are known as *electromagnetic units* and are designated by the abbreviation e.m.u. Although the electromagnetic unit of pole-strength has the same physical dimensions as the electrostatic unit of charge, the reader must remember that magnetostatic phenomena are quite independent of those of electrostatics, as pointed out in art. 35.

Electromagnetic units are simply defined and convenient to use. However, they constitute a c.g.s. system, rather than a m.k.s. system which is now more generally preferred.   Hence, let us express the force law for point poles in practical units by writing

$$\mathscr{F} = \frac{mm'}{4\pi\mu_0 r^2}. \tag{37-2}$$

Here μ_0, called the *permeability of free space*, is given by $\mu_0 \equiv 4\pi(10)^{-7}$. Its value, a pure number, makes $1/\sqrt{\kappa_0\mu_0}$ identically equal to c, the velocity of light, and leads to particularly simple numerical coefficients in most of the electromagnetic equations.   Thus, (37-2) defines *a unit pole as that pole which repels a like equal pole placed at a distance 1 meter in vacuo with a force* $[1/16\pi^2](10)^7$ *newtons*.   Evidently the practical unit of pole-strength has the magnitude of $[1/4\pi](10)^8$ electromagnetic units.   Putting $[1/16\pi^2](10)^7$ meter kg sec^{-2} for $\mathscr{F}$ and 1 meter for r and solving for $m=m'$, we find that the practical unit of pole-strength is 1 meter$^{3/2}$ kg$^{1/2}$ sec^{-1}.

38. Magnetic Intensity and Potential.

In order to explore a *magnetic field*—that is, a region in which magnetic forces are acting— we may suppose a unit positive pole of very small dimensions to be carried around the field, all the poles producing the field being kept fixed and of constant strength.   The force experienced by the test pole when at rest relative to the observer at any point in the field is known as the *magnetic intensity* or *magnetic field strength H* at that point. Since the magnetic intensity is a force, it is a vector quantity.   Basically, the unit of magnetic intensity is the *newton per unit pole* or, in terms of the fundamental units, 1 meter$^{-1/2}$ kg$^{1/2}$ sec^{-1}.   However, the coulomb per meter second is dimensionally equivalent, since the coulomb is 1 meter$^{1/2}$ kg$^{1/2}$ (art. 6).   Hence, as a coulomb per second is an *ampere*, by definition, the practical unit of magnetic intensity is commonly called the *ampere per meter*.   The particular advantage of this designation is made evident in Chapter VII, where it is shown that all magnetic fields can be ascribed, ultimately, to moving charge.

The force $\mathscr{F}$ on a pole of strength m placed at a point in a magnetic field where the magnetic intensity is H is given by the equation

$$\mathscr{F} = mH. \tag{38-1}$$

If m is positive $\mathscr{F}$ has the direction of H, otherwise the opposite direction.   The magnetic intensity at a distance r from a point pole of strength m, which is obtained from (37-2) by making m' unity, is

$$H = \frac{m}{4\pi\mu_0 r^2} \tag{38-2}$$

in the direction of the radius vector drawn from m.

The *potential V* at a point in a magnetic field is the work necessary to bring a unit positive pole from outside the field up to the point in question, all the poles producing the field being kept fixed and constant in strength during the process. It is equal to the potential energy of a unit pole placed at the point in question. Its unit is the *joule per unit pole*, that is, the *ampere*, since a joule is a newton meter. Evidently, V is also the work done *by* the field on the unit positive pole as the latter moves *from* the given point to infinity.

To calculate the potential produced at P (Fig. 62) by a point pole m placed at O we shall compute the work done by the field on a unit

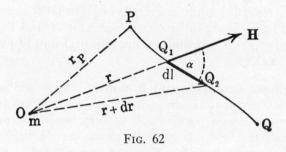

FIG. 62

positive pole as it moves from P to infinity. Let PQ be the path followed. At Q_1 the magnetic intensity is

$$H = \frac{m}{4\pi\mu_0 r^2}$$

in the direction of the radius vector r, and the work done by the field in moving the unit pole the distance dl from Q_1 to Q_2 is

$$\frac{m}{4\pi\mu_0 r^2}\, dl \cos \alpha = \frac{m}{4\pi\mu_0 r^2}\, dr,$$

where α is the angle between H and dl. Integrating from r_P to infinity, the potential at P is found to be

$$V = \frac{m}{4\pi\mu_0} \int_{r_P}^{\infty} \frac{dr}{r^2} = \frac{m}{4\pi\mu_0 r_P}. \tag{38-3}$$

In the case of a number of point poles of strengths m_1, m_2, $\cdots$ at distances r_1, r_2, $\cdots$ from P, the potential is

$$V = \frac{m_1}{4\pi\mu_0 r_1} + \frac{m_2}{4\pi\mu_0 r_2} + \cdots = \frac{1}{4\pi\mu_0} \sum \frac{m}{r}, \tag{38-4}$$

and in the case of a continuous distribution of magnetic pole-strength consisting of ρ units per unit volume inside a volume τ and σ units per unit area on a surface s,

$$V = \frac{1}{4\pi\mu_0} \int_\tau \frac{\rho d\tau}{r} + \frac{1}{4\pi\mu_0} \int_s \frac{\sigma ds}{r}, \tag{38-5}$$

the distance r now being measured from P.

Evidently the potential in a magnetostatic field is a function only of the coordinates of the point P at which it is to be evaluated and is independent of the path along which the unit pole moves.

It follows from the definition of potential that the drop in potential as we pass from one point to another is the work done by the field on a unit positive pole as it moves from the first to the second, all paths

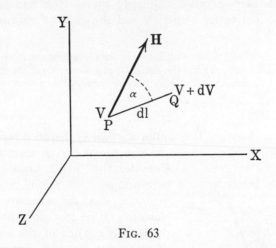

Fig. 63

between the two points being equivalent.   Since the change in potential in going around a closed curve is zero, the net work done vanishes when a unit pole traverses a closed path in a magnetostatic field.

If two points P and Q are very close together, as in Fig. 63, the drop in potential in going from P to Q is

$$V_P - V_Q \equiv -dV = H \cos \alpha \, dl.$$

Hence, the component of H in the direction of the displacement dl is

$$H_l = H \cos \alpha = -\frac{\partial V}{\partial l}. \tag{38-6}$$

Since the left-hand side of this equation is greatest for α equal to zero, the potential decreases most rapidly in the direction of the magnetic intensity.

Making dl in succession equal to dx, dy and dz, we find for the rectangular components of H,

$$H_x = -\frac{\partial V}{\partial x}, \qquad H_y = -\frac{\partial V}{\partial y}, \qquad H_z = -\frac{\partial V}{\partial z}. \qquad (38\text{-}7)$$

Similarly, if V is expressed as a function of the radius vector r, polar angle θ and azimuth ϕ, the components of H in the directions of increasing r, θ and ϕ, respectively, are

$$H_r = -\frac{\partial V}{\partial r}, \qquad H_\theta = -\frac{\partial V}{r\partial \theta}, \qquad H_\phi = -\frac{\partial V}{r \sin \theta \partial \phi}. \qquad (38\text{-}8)$$

It should be noted that we represent magnetic potential and pole-strength density by the symbols already used for electric potential and for charge density, because ordinarily the electric and the magnetic quantities do not appear together and the context indicates which is intended.

Problem 38. Three poles $-m$, $2m$, $-m$ are placed on the Z axis at distances $-l$, 0, l from the origin. Find the potential at a distance r from the origin large compared with l, denoting the angle between the radius vector and the Z axis by θ. Ans. $\frac{ml^2}{4\pi\mu_0 r^3}(1 - 3\cos^2\theta)$.

39. Gauss' Law.

This important law is deduced for a magnetostatic field in precisely the same manner as for an electrostatic field.

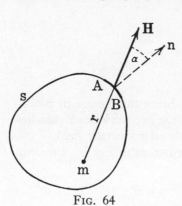

FIG. 64

Consider the closed surface s (Fig. 64) surrounding the point pole m. The magnetic flux dF through the surface element AB of area ds is defined as the product $H \cos \alpha ds$ of the component of H along the outward drawn normal n by the area ds of the element. From (38-2) the flux through AB due to the pole m is

$$dF = H\cos\alpha ds = \frac{mds\cos\alpha}{4\pi\mu_0 r^2}.$$

But the solid angle $d\Omega$ subtended at m by AB is

$$d\Omega = \frac{ds\cos\alpha}{r^2}.$$

Therefore $dF = md\Omega/4\pi\mu_0$ and, integrating over the entire surface, the total outward flux is seen to be

$$F = \frac{m}{\mu_0}. \qquad (39\text{-}1)$$

On the other hand the net flux through the surface due to a pole m outside (Fig. 65) vanishes. To show this, describe a cone of angular aperture $d\Omega$ with m as vertex. Then, if ds_1 and ds_2 are the areas of the surface intercepted at P_1 and P_2,

$$d\Omega = \frac{ds_1 \cos \alpha_1}{r_1{}^2} = \frac{ds_2 \cos \alpha_2}{r_2{}^2}. \tag{39-2}$$

Taking these two elements of surface together, the outward flux is

$$\begin{aligned} dF &= H_1 \cos (\pi - \alpha_1)ds_1 + H_2 \cos \alpha_2 ds_2 \\ &= -H_1 \cos \alpha_1 ds_1 + H_2 \cos \alpha_2 ds_2 \\ &= -\frac{mds_1 \cos \alpha_1}{4\pi\mu_0 r_1{}^2} + \frac{mds_2 \cos \alpha_2}{4\pi\mu_0 r_2{}^2} = 0, \end{aligned}$$

on account of (39-2). As the entire surface can be divided into pairs of elements subtending the same solid angle at m, the net outward flux

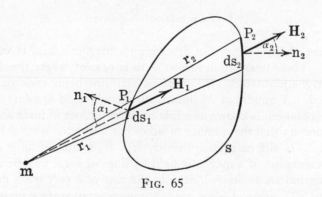

FIG. 65

through it is zero, the inward flux through the nearer side just annulling the outward flux through the more remote side.

If a number of point poles are present, some inside the surface s, and others outside, the normal component of the resultant magnetic intensity equals the sum of the normal components of the magnetic intensities produced by the individual poles. Accordingly, if m_1, m_2, m_3, $\cdots$ are the point poles located *inside* the surface, the entire outward flux through the surface is

$$F = \frac{m_1}{\mu_0} + \frac{m_2}{\mu_0} + \frac{m_3}{\mu_0} + \cdots = \frac{\Sigma m}{\mu_0}, \tag{39-3}$$

since the poles *outside* make no contribution. Furthermore, because every magnet contains equal amounts of positive and negative magnetism, a magnet lying entirely within a surface gives rise to no flux through it. Only when the surface cuts a magnet is the net outward flux of H different from zero.

If magnetic pole-strength is distributed continuously in the volume τ surrounded by the surface s with density ρ units of pole-strength per unit volume,

$$F = \frac{1}{\mu_0} \int_\tau \rho d\tau, \qquad (39\text{-}4)$$

where the integral is taken through the volume τ enclosed by the surface s.

If we write for F the integral of the normal component of the magnetic intensity over the surface s in accord with the definition of magnetic flux, (39-3) and (39-4) take the forms

$$\int_s H \cos \alpha ds = \frac{\sum m}{\mu_0}, \qquad (39\text{-}5)$$

and

$$\int_s H \cos \alpha ds = \frac{1}{\mu_0} \int_\tau \rho d\tau. \qquad (39\text{-}6)$$

The use of *lines of force* in describing a magnetic field is very convenient. These lines are drawn so as to have everywhere the direction of the magnetic intensity, the sense of each line being indicated by an arrowhead. A bundle of M lines of force, where M is a large integer arbitrarily chosen, is known as a *tube of force*. Lines of force are drawn in such density that the number of tubes per unit cross section is everywhere equal to the magnetic intensity H. By taking M large enough, the representation of a magnetic field by lines of force may be made as nearly continuous as desired, even in the case of a very weak field.

If, now, dT_F tubes of force pass through a small surface of area ds at an angle α with the normal to the surface, the cross section of the tubes is $ds \cos \alpha$ and the magnetic intensity is

$$H = \frac{dT_F}{ds \cos \alpha}$$

or

$$dT_F = H \cos \alpha ds.$$

But this is just the magnetic flux through ds. Therefore, *the number of tubes of force passing through a surface is equal to the magnetic flux through that surface.*

Tubes of force are continuous in regions containing no magnetic poles. To prove this, consider a closed surface which is bounded on the sides by lines of force and on the ends by cross sections s_1 and s_2.

Evidently there is no flux through the tubular portion since the magnetic intensity is everywhere parallel to the surface. Hence, the only flux is through the ends s_1 and s_2. But as there are no poles inside the surface under consideration Gauss' law requires that the flux out of one end must equal that in through the other. Therefore, as many tubes of force pass out through one end as enter through the other.

By making m unity in (39-1), we see that the flux through a small surface surrounding a unit positive pole is $1/\mu_0$. Consequently, $1/\mu_0$ tubes of force originate on every unit of positive magnetism. An equal number terminate on every unit of negative magnetism. That is, each tube starts on a positive pole of strength μ_0 and ends on an equal negative pole.

An equipotential surface is one all points of which are at the same potential. Evidently the potential decreases most rapidly in a direction at right angles to an equipotential surface. Therefore, the magnetic intensity is everywhere perpendicular to the equipotential surfaces and lines of force intersect equipotential surfaces orthogonally.

Problem 39. A magnet is bent so as to bring the pole pieces opposite and parallel to one another, the distance between the poles being small compared with the linear dimensions of their surfaces. If σ and $-\sigma$ are the pole-strengths per unit area, show that the magnetic intensity in the space between them is σ/μ_0.

40. Magnetic Dipoles. A magnet consisting of two equal and opposite point poles a short distance apart is known as a *magnetic dipole*. Consider the magnetic dipole consisting of the poles m and $-m$ separated by the distance l (Fig. 66). To find the magnetic potential at a point P at a distance r from the center of the dipole large compared with its length l, we have from (38-4)

$$V = \frac{m}{4\pi\mu_0 r_1} - \frac{m}{4\pi\mu_0 r_2} = \frac{1}{4\pi\mu_0}\left[\frac{m}{r - \frac{l}{2}\cos\theta} - \frac{m}{r + \frac{l}{2}\cos\theta}\right]$$

$$= \frac{1}{4\pi\mu_0}\left[\frac{ml\cos\theta}{r^2 - \frac{l^2}{4}\cos^2\theta}\right] = \frac{ml\cos\theta}{4\pi\mu_0 r^2},$$

as l^2 is negligible compared with r^2. The product ml is called the *magnetic moment* of the magnet and is designated by p. Evidently it is a vector, having the direction of the axis of the dipole. We shall take its positive sense to be that from $-m$ to m. In terms of its magnetic moment the potential due to the dipole considered above is

$$V = \frac{p\cos\theta}{4\pi\mu_0 r^2}. \tag{40-1}$$

No confusion results from the use of p to represent both electric moment and magnetic moment, since these quantities rarely appear together and the context shows which is intended.

The components of the field in the directions of increasing r and θ are obtained with the aid of (38-8):

$$\left.\begin{array}{l} H_r = -\dfrac{\partial V}{\partial r} = \dfrac{p \cos \theta}{2\pi\mu_0 r^3}, \\[4mm] H_\theta = -\dfrac{\partial V}{r\partial \theta} = \dfrac{p \sin \theta}{4\pi\mu_0 r^3}. \end{array}\right\} \qquad (40\text{-}2)$$

The lines of magnetic force have the same configuration as the lines of electric force in the field of an electric dipole, illustrated in Fig. 25.

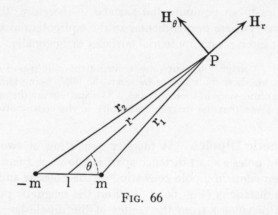

FIG. 66

We have investigated the field produced by a magnetic dipole. Next we shall consider the force and the torque acting on a magnetic dipole placed in an external field H.

To find the force take the X axis (Fig. 67a) parallel to the axis of the dipole. Then the X component of the force on the negative pole is

$$\mathscr{F}_{1x} = -mH_x,$$

whereas the X component of the force on the positive pole is

$$\mathscr{F}_{2x} = m\left(H_x + \frac{\partial H_x}{\partial x} l\right) = mH_x + p\frac{\partial H_x}{\partial x}.$$

The resultant force $\mathscr{F}_x$ in the X direction is the sum of $\mathscr{F}_{1x}$ and $\mathscr{F}_{2x}$. In a similar manner we obtain the Y and Z components. Therefore, we have

$$\mathscr{F}_x = p\frac{\partial H_x}{\partial x}, \qquad \mathscr{F}_y = p\frac{\partial H_y}{\partial x}, \qquad \mathscr{F}_z = p\frac{\partial H_z}{\partial x}. \qquad (40\text{-}3)$$

If the field is uniform, the components of H are constants, and the resultant force vanishes.

The torque exerted on the dipole by the field (Fig. 67b) is due to the couple consisting of the force mH on the positive pole and $-mH$ on the negative pole. As the lever arm of this couple is $l \sin \alpha$, where α is the angle between the axis of the dipole and the field, the torque is

$$\mathscr{L}_\alpha = -mHl \sin \alpha = -pH \sin \alpha, \tag{40-4}$$

the minus sign indicating that the torque is in such a sense as to decrease α. In other words the magnetic axis of the dipole tends to turn parallel to the field.

To find the energy U of the dipole due to its orientation relative to

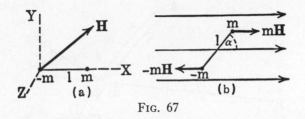

FIG. 67

the lines of force, denote the magnetic potential at $-m$ by V_1 and that at m by V_2. Then,

$$U = -mV_1 + mV_2 = -m(V_1 - V_2).$$

But $V_1 - V_2 = Hl \cos \alpha$. Hence

$$U = -mlH \cos \alpha = -pH \cos \alpha. \tag{40-5}$$

As shown in Chapter VII, the properties of the elementary magnets of which a magnetic substance is constituted are due to the presence of moving electric charges rather than of actual magnetic dipoles. Nevertheless, the external field of an elementary magnet, as well as the magnetic force or torque to which it is subject, is the same as if it were an aggregation of magnetic dipoles. Consequently, we may employ the expressions obtained in this article in discussing the behavior of magnetized media, except when the internal structure and the internal fields of the elementary magnets are involved.

Problem 40a. Two magnets of moments p_1 and p_2 are a distance r apart, the axes of the magnets lying in the line joining them. What is the force between them? Ans. $-\dfrac{3p_1 p_2}{2\pi\mu_0 r^4}$.

Problem 40b. The second magnet of the previous problem is placed with its axis at right angles to the line joining the two. Find the torque exerted by the field of each on the other. Does the result constitute a violation of the law of action and reaction? Why? Ans. $\dfrac{p_1 p_2}{2\pi\mu_0 r^3}$, $\dfrac{p_1 p_2}{4\pi\mu_0 r^3}$; No.

Problem 40c. Deduce (40–4) from 40–5).

41. Magnetic Shells. A *magnetic shell* is a thin sheet magnetized everywhere at right angles to its surface. The *strength* Φ of a shell is the magnetic moment per unit area of its surface. If, therefore, the shell has a pole-strength per unit area equal to σ on its positive side and to $-\sigma$ on its negative side, $\Phi = \sigma l$, where l is the thickness of the shell. The importance of the concept of the magnetic shell lies in the fact that

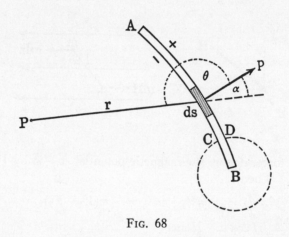

FIG. 68

the magnetic field produced by a current circuit is the same as that due to a shell of strength proportional to the current whose periphery coincides with the circuit. This relationship is demonstrated in art. 70.

Consider an element ds (Fig. 68) of the curved shell AB of surface area s. This element is a small dipole with magnetic moment $p = \Phi ds$. The potential due to it at a point P is

$$dV = \frac{\Phi ds \cos \theta}{4\pi\mu_0 r^2} = -\frac{\Phi ds \cos \alpha}{4\pi\mu_0 r^2}$$

from (40-1). Now the solid angle subtended at P by ds is

$$d\Omega = \frac{ds \cos \alpha}{r^2},$$

this angle being positive since the positive normal to the shell makes the acute angle α with the radius vector.   Therefore,

$$dV = -\frac{\Phi d\Omega}{4\pi\mu_0},$$

and the potential at P due to the entire shell is

$$V = -\frac{1}{4\pi\mu_0}\int \Phi d\Omega.$$

Our chief interest is in shells of constant strength.   In such a case

$$V = -\frac{\Phi\Omega}{4\pi\mu_0}, \tag{41-1}$$

where Ω is the solid angle subtended at P by the entire shell AB.   Now Ω is the same for all shells having the same periphery.   Consequently, (41-1) tells us that all shells of the same strength and the same periphery give rise to the same potential and therefore to the same field everywhere, except, of course, at points between the shells or in the interior of a shell.   The shape of the shell is immaterial, the periphery and the strength being the only determining factors.

Let us calculate the work W done by the field when a unit positive pole moves around the edge of the shell from a point D on the positive surface of the shell to an opposite point C on the negative surface.   If Ω_C is the solid angle subtended at C and Ω_D that at D,

$$W = V_D - V_C = \frac{\Phi(\Omega_C - \Omega_D)}{4\pi\mu_0}.$$

While Ω_C is positive, Ω_D, being the solid angle subtended at a point on the opposite side of the surface, is negative.   But, as the shell is of negligible thickness, the sum of the positive magnitudes of Ω_C and Ω_D is a complete solid angle, that is, 4π.   Hence,

$$W = \frac{\Phi}{\mu_0}. \tag{41-2}$$

So far we have been considering the field produced by a magnetic shell.   Let us next turn our attention to the effect of an external field H on a shell of constant strength.   If now α represents the angle which the positive normal to the shell makes with the lines of force, the energy of an element ds of the shell due to its position in the field is

$$dU = -\Phi ds\, H \cos \alpha$$

from (40-5).   Therefore, the energy of the entire shell is

$$U = -\Phi \int_s H \cos \alpha ds.$$

But $\int_s H \cos \alpha\, ds$ is the magnetic flux F through the shell. Consequently,

$$U = -\Phi F. \tag{41-3}$$

Let the shell suffer a displacement $d\xi$ under the action of the field. If $\mathcal{F}_\xi$ is the component of the force exerted on it in the direction of the displacement,

$$\mathcal{F}_\xi\, d\xi = -dU = \Phi dF, \tag{41-4}$$

since the work done by $\mathcal{F}_\xi$ is at the expense of the energy of the shell. So if the flux through the shell is expressed as a function of the coordinates specifying its position, the force exerted on it by the field in the direction of $d\xi$ is

$$\mathcal{F}_\xi = \Phi \frac{\partial F}{\partial \xi}. \tag{41-5}$$

In like manner the torque $\mathcal{L}_\theta$ corresponding to an angular displacement $d\theta$ is

$$\mathcal{L}_\theta = \Phi \frac{\partial F}{\partial \theta}. \tag{41-6}$$

From these expressions we see that the shell tends to move in such a way as to increase the flux through it, the flux being reckoned as positive when it passes through the shell from the negative to the positive side. The shell is in stable equilibrium in the position in which the flux through it is a maximum. Furthermore, since the flux through the shell is determined solely by its periphery, the energy of the shell and the force or torque acting on it depend only upon its strength and its periphery and not upon its shape.

Problem 41a. A small magnet of moment p with axis parallel to the X axis is located at the origin. A plane circular shell of strength Φ and radius a is placed with its normal parallel to, and with its center on, the X axis a distance x from the origin. Find the force on the shell. Ans. $-\dfrac{3p\Phi a^2 x}{2\mu_0(a^2+x^2)^{5/2}}$.

Problem 41b. A plane shell of area A is placed in a uniform field H with its normal making an angle θ with the lines of force. Find the torque, and the period of vibration for the case where θ is small. Denote the moment of inertia of the shell by $\mathcal{I}$. Ans. $-HA\Phi \sin \theta,\quad 2\pi\sqrt{\dfrac{\mathcal{I}}{HA\Phi}}$.

42. Density of Pole-Strength in a Medium.

We have seen that when a magnetic medium, such as a block of iron, is placed in a magnetic field, the elementary magnets are subject to a torque tending to line them up in the direction of the field. This gives rise to an accumulation of poles in the interior of the medium. As we can detect by ordinary instruments only the *mean* pole-strength averaged over a region containing many elementary magnets, we shall replace the distribution of pole-strength actually present by a smoothed distribution and shall understand by the magnetic intensity H in a medium the smooth field to which this smooth density of pole-strength gives rise. In so doing we ignore the fact, mentioned in art. 40, that the magnetic properties of an elementary magnet are really due to moving charges and that the internal field due to these moving charges differs from that of the aggregation of magnetic dipoles which produces the same external field.   Hence H in a magnetic medium is not the smooth value of the *true* field.   Nevertheless, we shall find that it is of fundamental importance in describing the magnetic behavior of a medium.

We wish to find the pole-strength acquired by a volume element $\Delta\tau$ of dimensions Δx, Δy, Δz (Fig. 69) large enough to contain a great many elementary magnets. As the elementary magnets turn, pole-strength is acquired by $\Delta\tau$ because of the passage of poles through the surfaces bounding this volume.   Let R_x denote the *mean* displacement in the direction of the X axis of the positive poles of the elementary magnets in the neighborhood of the face $ABCD$.   In effect, all the positive poles in a layer $ABCDEFGH$ of

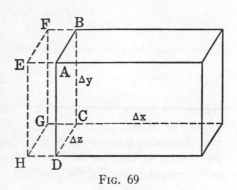

Fig. 69

thickness R_x pass into $\Delta\tau$ through the face $ABCD$ because of the orientation of the elementary magnets.   If, then, m is the strength of each positive pole, and n the number of elementary magnets per unit volume, the positive pole-strength passing into $\Delta\tau$ through the surface under consideration is

$$nmR_x\Delta y\Delta z.$$

Since we may suppose that each elementary magnet rotates about its center, the negative poles suffer displacements equal and opposite to those of the positive poles.   Therefore, an equal negative pole-strength, passes out of $\Delta\tau$ through $ABCD$ from a layer of thickness R_x to the right of this surface, so that the net gain is

$$2nmR_x\Delta y\Delta z.$$

As R_x is measured relative to the unmagnetized state of the medium, $2R_x$ represents the X component of the mean separation of the positive and negative poles of the elementary magnets when the medium is magnetized. Consequently, $2mR_x$ is the X component of the mean magnetic moment and $2nmR_x$ the X component of the resultant magnetic moment per unit volume. The magnetic moment per unit volume is known as the *magnetization* and is designated by I. It is a vector in the direction of the resultant magnetic moment of the elementary magnets involved.

Thus

$$I_x = 2nmR_x, \qquad (42\text{-}1)$$

and the net *increase* of the magnetic pole-strength in $\Delta\tau$ due to the passage of poles through the surface $ABCD$ is

$$I_x \Delta y \Delta z.$$

Similarly the net *decrease* due to the passage of poles through the right-hand face parallel to $ABCD$ is

$$\left(I_x + \frac{\partial I_x}{\partial x}\Delta x\right)\Delta y \Delta z.$$

Subtracting this from the preceding expression, we find

$$-\frac{\partial I_x}{\partial x}\Delta x \Delta y \Delta z$$

for the net pole-strength acquired in so far as the two faces perpendicular to the X axis are concerned. Adding similar expressions for the two remaining pairs of faces and dividing by the volume $\Delta x \Delta y \Delta z$ of the region, we have for the magnetic pole-strength per unit volume due to the magnetization of the medium

$$\rho_I = -\left(\frac{\partial I_x}{\partial x} + \frac{\partial I_y}{\partial y} + \frac{\partial I_z}{\partial z}\right). \qquad (42\text{-}2)$$

This expression is identical in form with (13-1), the magnetization I taking the place of the polarization P of the electrostatic analog.

Since it follows from (42-1) that the pole-strength passing into a region through a surface element is equal to the product of the component of the magnetization along the inward drawn normal and the area of the element, we can express the pole-strength acquired by any volume τ when the medium is magnetized as a surface integral. Let ds be an element of the surface s enclosing τ, and β the angle between I and the outward drawn normal to ds. Then the pole-strength passing into τ through the surface element under consideration is $-I\cos\beta ds$ and the net pole-strength acquired by a volume τ is

$$M_I = -\int_s I\cos\beta ds. \qquad (42\text{-}3)$$

Note that, although M_I is expressed in terms of a surface integral, the pole-strength does not actually reside on the surface.

We can obtain the pole-strength per unit area on the surface of a magnetized body by applying (42-3) to the surface of a short pill-box $ABCD$ (Fig. 70) enclosing an area Δs of the surface. The base AB of the pill-box lies outside the medium where I is zero, and the area of the cylindrical portion of the surface may be made so small that its contribution to the integral is negligible. Therefore, (42-3) reduces to the integral over the base CD lying inside the medium. If, then, σ_I is the pole-strength per unit area on the surface of the body,

$$\sigma_I \Delta s = -I \cos \beta \Delta s = I \cos \gamma \Delta s.$$

Now $I \cos \gamma$ is the component I_n of the magnetization along the outward drawn normal to the surface. Consequently

$$\sigma_I = I_n. \qquad (42\text{-}4)$$

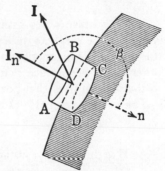

If I is perpendicular to the surface, $\sigma_I = I$. For example, in the case of a uniformly magnetized bar, the pole-strengths per unit area on the ends are I and $-I$. When the magnetization is not uniform, the surface distribution is accompanied by a volume distribution in the interior of the body given by (42-2). To calculate H either outside or inside

Fig. 70

a magnetized body we must add to any externally applied field that due to the body itself. Note that ρ and σ in (38-5) are identical with ρ_I and σ_I given above, since all poles arise from magnetization.

Problem 42a. In actual bar magnets the magnetization is less at the ends than at the center on account of the demagnetizing effect of the poles. Suppose that the magnetization in a bar magnet of length l with its center at the origin and axis parallel to the X axis is $I = k(l^2 - x^2)$. Find the pole-strengths per unit area on the ends and per unit volume in the interior and show that the total pole-strength is zero. Ans. $\pm \frac{3}{4}kl^2$, $2kx$.

Problem 42b. A narrow slit is cut in a magnetic medium so that its normal makes an angle γ with the magnetization I. Show that the magnetic intensity in the slit due to the magnetization is $I \cos \gamma / \mu_0$.

43. Gauss' Law for a Magnetic Medium.

In magnetostatics we have no entities corresponding to free charges in electrostatics. Even the poles on the ends of a permanent steel magnet are due solely to the orientation of the elementary magnets of which the body is composed. Therefore, a magnet, as well as a paramagnetic fluid or solid which may surround it, should properly be treated as a magnetic medium.

Applying Gauss' law (39-5) to a closed surface which may surround or cut through magnets which may themselves be immersed in a paramagnetic medium,

$$\int_s H \cos \alpha \, ds = \frac{\sum m}{\mu_0}.$$

Now the only poles inside the surface s are those due to the magnetization of the media contained within this surface, so the quantity $\sum m$ of this equation is the M_I of (42-3). Hence, after rearranging terms, we have

$$\int_s (\mu_0 H \cos \alpha + I \cos \beta) ds = 0. \qquad (43\text{-}1)$$

If the surface s lies everywhere in the paramagnetic medium surrounding the magnets under consideration, I represents at all points of the surface the magnetization in this paramagnetic medium. If, on the other hand, the surface s cuts a magnet, I represents the magnetization in the magnet over that portion of s lying inside the magnet.

The vector sum $\mu_0\mathbf{H} + \mathbf{I}$ is known as the *magnetic induction* $\mathbf{B}$, that is,

$$\mathbf{B} \equiv \mu_0\mathbf{H} + \mathbf{I}. \qquad (43\text{-}2)$$

As $\mathbf{B}$ is the vector resultant of $\mu_0\mathbf{H}$ and $\mathbf{I}$, the component of B normal to a surface element ds is equal to the sum of the normal components of $\mu_0 H$ and I. So if the angle which B makes with the normal is denoted by γ,

$$B \cos \gamma = \mu_0 H \cos \alpha + I \cos \beta,$$

and Gauss' law becomes

$$\int_s B \cos \gamma \, ds = 0. \qquad (43\text{-}3)$$

If we define the *flux of induction* through a surface ds as the product of the component of B along the outward drawn normal by the area of the surface, Gauss' law (43-3) states that the total outward flux of induction through *any* closed surface is equal to zero. Evidently B has the same physical dimensions as H, and also I, since μ_0 is a pure number by definition (art. 37). Hence the unit of flux of induction is, directly, the *ampere meter*, but it is so frequently used that it is independently named the *weber*. This allows us to distinguish B from H, conveniently, by calling the unit of induction the *weber per meter*[2]. The use of such an alternative designation does not affect the basic physical dimensions of the unit, of course. In terms of the fundamental units the weber is 1 meter$^{3/2}$ kg$^{1/2}$ sec^{-1}.

Lines of induction may be drawn in a magnetic field so as to be everywhere parallel to B and in such density that the number of *tubes of induction*—a tube being a bundle of a specified number of lines—per unit cross section is equal to the magnitude of B. The flux of induction through any surface is equal to the number of tubes of induction passing through the surface, the proof of this statement being identical with that of the corresponding relation between magnetic flux and tubes of force considered in art. 39. If we consider a closed surface which is bounded by lines of induction and terminated by cross sections s_1 and s_2, Gauss' law requires that the flux out of one end must equal that in through the other end. Therefore, as many tubes of induction must pass out of the one end as enter the other. It follows that tubes of induction are everywhere continuous. They form closed curves, never terminating. In particular, tubes of induction are continuous when we pass from one magnetic medium to another or from the interior of a magnet into the space surrounding it.

In the case of isotropic paramagnetic media in such fields as are ordinarily available, the state of saturation is far from being realized and the magnetization I is in the same direction as and proportional to the field H. Hence, we may write

$$I = \mu_0 \chi H, \tag{43-4}$$

the constant χ being known as the *magnetic susceptibility*. Therefore, (43-2) gives

$$B = \mu_0(1+\chi)H = \mu_0\mu H, \tag{43-5}$$

where μ, the *permeability of the medium*, is defined by

$$\mu \equiv 1+\chi. \tag{43-6}$$

As in the case of the permittivity, the value of μ, for a given medium, is the same in all systems of units.

Although μ is constant for paramagnetic substances in available fields, a general relation of the form (43-5) holds only as a rough approximation in the case of ferromagnetic media where, on account of hysteresis, B is not even a one-valued function of H.

We are now ready to compute the field produced by a pole m (Fig. 71) located on the end of a long needle immersed in a paramagnetic medium, such as oxygen. We shall suppose that the pole of opposite sign is too far away to produce any appreciable effect in the neighborhood of m. Describe a sphere of radius r about m as center and apply Gauss' law (43-3) to its surface. Let B be the magnetic induction in the surrounding medium and $B' = \mu_0 H' + I'$ that in the needle NS. We must evaluate the integral involved in Gauss' law in two parts, first writing down the integral over the portion of the spherical surface which lies in the paramagnetic medium and then adding that over the portion of the surface which lies inside the needle. If we denote the cross section of the needle by A, we have

$$(4\pi r^2 - A)B + A(\mu_0 H' + I') = 0.$$

Now the strength of the pole m on the end of the needle is equal, by (42-4), to $-AI'$, since I' is measured as positive in the direction away from N. So

$$4\pi r^2 B - A(B - \mu_0 H') = m.$$

By making the needle thin enough, the term in A can be made negligible. Hence

$$4\pi r^2 B = m. \qquad (43\text{-}7)$$

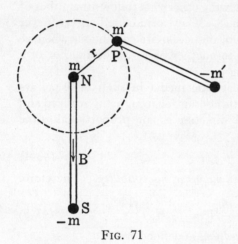

Fig. 71

As the left-hand side of this equation represents the number of tubes of induction passing out through the portion of the surface of the sphere which lies outside the needle, we note that a tube of induction must pass out from each unit positive pole into the medium surrounding it. Since, however, tubes of induction are continuous, the same number of tubes must pass into the unit positive pole under consideration through the interior of the needle.

Replacing B by $\mu_0 \mu H$ in the last equation, where μ is the permeability of the surrounding medium,

$$H = \frac{m}{4\pi\mu_0\mu r^2}. \qquad (43\text{-}8)$$

It follows, then, that the expressions (38-3) and (38-4) for the potential become

$$V = \frac{m}{4\pi\mu_0\mu r_P}, \qquad (43\text{-}9)$$

and

$$V = \frac{1}{4\pi\mu_0\mu} \sum \frac{m}{r}, \qquad (43\text{-}10)$$

when the magnetic poles are immersed in a paramagnetic medium.

Just as in the electrostatic analog treated in art. 16, a paramagnetic medium in a magnetic field is subject to stresses due to the forces acting on the elementary magnets.   In order to apply the formulas of art. 16 to the magnetic case, it is only necessary to replace D by B, E by H, and so on.   Thus the pressure in a paramagnetic medium is

$$p = \frac{\mu_0(\mu-1)}{2} H^2 \tag{43-11}$$

from (16-3).   Similarly, from (16-7) the tension stress on a surface of the medium lying at right angles to the lines of force is

$$\mathscr{F}_s{}'' = \frac{\mu_0}{2}\left(\frac{\mu-1}{\mu}\right)H_o{}^2 \tag{43-12}$$

in terms of the field H_o outside the permeable medium.   The latter should give rise to an increase in length of a solid paramagnetic rod placed parallel to the lines of force, but the permeabilities of paramagnetic media are so nearly unity that this effect has not been detected with certainty.   On the other hand, ferromagnetic materials exhibit a considerable change in length when placed in a magnetic field, a phenomenon known as *magnetostriction*.   The effect is, however, often a shortening instead of a lengthening and is due to mechanical stresses produced by the orientation of the elementary magnets rather than to the magnetic stresses under discussion here.

To return to Fig. 71, suppose that a second magnetic needle is placed with its positive pole m' at P.   For the moment let us consider this pole to be a small sphere with the pole-strength distributed over its surface in such a manner as to annul the field H in its interior.   This sphere constitutes the magnetic analog of an electrical conductor.   Hence, if we follow the line of reasoning employed in the latter part of art. 16, we have for the force between two point poles a distance r apart in a paramagnetic fluid

$$\mathscr{F} = \frac{mm'}{4\pi\mu_0\mu r^2}. \tag{43-13}$$

Problem 43a.   Show that B/μ_0 inside a magnetic medium is the force that would be experienced by a unit positive pole placed in a narrow slit cut so that its faces are perpendicular to I, and that H is the force at the center of a needle-like cavity cut with its axis parallel to I.

Problem 43b.   A long bar magnet is uniformly magnetized with magnetization I.   Find B and H (1) just outside the positive pole, (2) just inside the positive pole, (3) at the center of the magnet.

Ans. (1) $\dfrac{I}{2}$, $\dfrac{I}{2\mu_0}$; (2) $\dfrac{I}{2}$, $-\dfrac{I}{2\mu_0}$; (3) I, 0.

Problem 43c.   Near the middle of the magnet of the previous problem is B the same at a point outside the bar as inside?   Ans. No. (0 and I).

44. Uniformly Magnetized Sphere. The field produced by a uniformly magnetized sphere can be obtained easily by elementary methods. Consider concentric spheres of equal radius a one of which has a uniform volume density ρ' of positive pole-strength and the other an equal volume density of negative pole-strength. If the first is displaced a small distance l (Fig. 72) relative to the second, every element of positive pole-strength is displaced a distance l from the negative pole-strength with which it originally coincided, forming therewith a magnetic dipole. By this displacement we have arrived at a uniformly magnetized sphere of magnetization $I = \rho' l$.

Now the field at outside points due to a spherical distribution of pole-strength is the same as if the entire pole-strength were concentrated at the center of the sphere. The proof of this statement follows from Gauss' law in exactly the same manner as in the case of the electrostatic

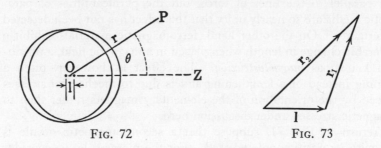

FIG. 72   FIG. 73

analog treated in art. 9. Consequently, the magnetic field at an outside point P is that produced by a dipole of moment

$$p = \tfrac{4}{3}\pi a^3 \rho' l = \tfrac{4}{3}\pi a^3 I \qquad (44\text{-}1)$$

located at the origin. The potential outside the sphere is given by (40-1) and the radial and transverse components of the magnetic intensity by (40-2).

To find the field inside the sphere we must remember that the magnetic intensity at a point distant r from the center of a sphere which has a uniform distribution of pole-strength is that produced by the pole-strength inside a sphere of this radius. Following the same method as was employed for the electrostatic case in art. 9, we have from (9-2)

$$H = \frac{M'}{4\pi\mu_0 a^3}\, r,$$

if we replace Q by the spherical pole $M' = \tfrac{4}{3}\pi a^3 \rho'$. As H is directed along the radius vector, the vector fields $\mathbf{H}_1$ and $\mathbf{H}_2$ due to the positive and negative spheres of Fig. 72 are proportional to the vector distances $\mathbf{r}_1$ and $\mathbf{r}_2$ (Fig. 73) from their respective centers, the first being directed along $\mathbf{r}_1$ and the second, since the pole is negative, in the direction opposite to $\mathbf{r}_2$. But the vector sum of $\mathbf{r}_1$ and $-\mathbf{r}_2$ is $-\mathbf{l}$, the separation of the two spheres. Therefore, the resultant field is in the Z direction and is given by

$$H_i = -\frac{M'}{4\pi\mu_0 a^3} l = -\frac{\rho' l}{3\mu_0} = -\frac{1}{3\mu_0} I. \qquad (44\text{-}2)$$

Evidently it is constant throughout the magnetized sphere.

Since the field inside the sphere is in the direction opposite to I, it tends to weaken the magnetization. It is known as a *demagnetizing field*. The presence of the demagnetizing field means that the magnetization is always less than the retentiveness of the magnetic material involved.

The magnetic induction inside the sphere is

$$B_i = \mu_0 H_i + I = \tfrac{2}{3}I, \qquad (44\text{-}3)$$

in the Z direction.

So far we have been considering a permanent magnet in the form of a uniformly magnetized sphere, such as a spherical steel magnet. Let us now consider a paramagnetic sphere of permeability μ placed in a uniform external field H_0 parallel to the Z axis. As the field H_0 is uniform, the dipoles in the interior of the sphere will be in equilibrium if the sphere becomes uniformly magnetized by induction so as to produce a field of its own of precisely the same character as that of the permanent spherical magnet just considered. The total field is the resultant of H_0 and the field of the magnetized sphere. The components of the latter at points outside the sphere are given by (40-2). Therefore, the components of the resultant field outside the sphere are

$$(H_r)_o = H_0 \cos\theta + \frac{2a^3 I}{3\mu_0 r^3}\cos\theta \qquad (44\text{-}4)$$

in the direction of the radius vector, and

$$(H_\theta)_o = -H_0 \sin\theta + \frac{a^3 I}{3\mu_0 r^3}\sin\theta \qquad (44\text{-}5)$$

at right angles thereto in the direction of increasing θ.

Inside the sphere the field is in the Z direction and equal to the sum of H_0 and the internal field (44-2). It is

$$H_i = H_0 - \frac{1}{3\mu_0} I. \qquad (44\text{-}6)$$

If we apply Gauss' law in the manner of art. 14, we find that when we pass from one magnetic medium to another the components of B normal to the surface of separation and the components of H parallel to the surface are the same in the two media. The proof is identical with that given for the electrostatic analog, B taking the place of D and H that of E.

Therefore, we have from (44-4) and (44-6)

$$\left(H_0 + \frac{2}{3\mu_0} I\right) \cos \theta = \mu \left(H_0 - \frac{1}{3\mu_0} I\right) \cos \theta$$

for the normal components of B, or

$$I = 3\mu_0 \left(\frac{\mu - 1}{\mu + 2}\right) H_0. \tag{44-7}$$

Equating the tangential components of H gives no new information since an identity is obtained.

Equation (44-7), then, specifies the magnetization produced in the paramagnetic sphere by the impressed field H_0. The reader should compare this result with that obtained in problem *28b* for a dielectric sphere placed in a uniform electric field.

Substituting (44-7) in (44-6), the resultant field in the interior of the sphere is seen to be

$$H_i = \left(1 - \frac{\mu - 1}{\mu + 2}\right) H_0 = \frac{3}{\mu + 2} H_0. \tag{44-8}$$

This is less than H_0 if μ is greater than unity, because the induced poles on the surface of the sphere give rise to the demagnetizing field

$$H_i' = -\frac{\mu - 1}{\mu + 2} H_0 = -\frac{1}{3\mu_0} I. \tag{44-9}$$

The ratio of the magnitude of the demagnetizing field to that of the magnetization is sometimes called the *demagnetizing factor*. Our analysis shows that its value for a sphere is $1/3\mu_0$.

The magnetic induction inside the sphere is

$$B_i = \mu_0 \mu H_i = \mu_0 \left(\frac{3\mu}{\mu + 2}\right) H_0, \tag{44-10}$$

which is more or less than $\mu_0 H_0$ according as μ is greater or less than unity. Therefore, lines of induction are crowded together in a paramagnetic sphere as illustrated in Fig. 52. In a diamagnetic sphere, on the contrary, $\mu < 1$ and the lines of induction are spread apart.

Problem 44a. As a rough approximation, the earth may be considered to be a uniformly magnetized sphere. If the horizontal field strength at the equator is 40 amperes per meter, what is the magnetization? Ans. $1.51(10)^{-4}$ weber/meter^2.

Problem 44b. A long paramagnetic cylinder of circular cross section is placed in a uniform magnetic field H_0 with its axis at right angles to the lines of force. By the method of this article show that the magnetic induction in the cylinder is

$$\mu_0\left(\frac{2\mu}{\mu+1}\right) H_0,$$

and that the demagnetizing factor is $1/2\mu_0$.

Problem 44c. Solve the problem of the paramagnetic sphere, treated in this article, by the use of zonal harmonics.

45. Magnetic Shielding.

A sensitive magnetic instrument can be shielded very effectively from outside fields by placing it inside a cylindrical shell made of soft iron of high permeability. We shall investigate the field in the interior of a cylindrical shell of constant permeability placed in a uniform magnetic field at right angles to the axis of the cylinder.

As the same inverse square law of attraction and repulsion holds for magnetic poles as for electric charges, the magnetic potential in a region containing no magnetic poles must satisfy Laplace's equation (26-2) for the same reason that this equation is satisfied by the electric potential in a region containing no

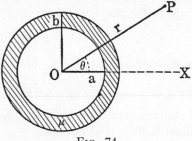

Fig. 74

electric charges. Consider, now, an infinitely long cylindrical shell (Fig. 74) of inner radius a and outer radius b placed in a uniform magnetic field H_0 parallel to the X axis. Following the same line of reasoning as in the case of a homogeneous isotropic dielectric (art. 15), we conclude that there can be no volume distribution of poles inside a magnetic medium in which I is proportional to H. Consequently, we need three solutions of Laplace's equation: a solution V_1 to represent the potential outside the shell, a second solution V_2 to represent the potential in the material of the shell, and a third V_3 to represent the potential in the cavity. Evidently cylindrical harmonics are indicated, the potential being a function of r and θ alone.

The boundary conditions which must be satisfied are the following:

(*a*) For r very large V_1 must become $-H_0 x = -H_0 r \cos \theta$, provided the potential is taken to be zero on the axis of the cylinder.

(*b*) At each surface of the shell the radial component of the magnetic induction and the transverse component of the magnetic intensity must be continuous as we pass from the outside to the inside of the shell.

The latter of these two conditions is satisfied if the potential itself is continuous.

As the potential at infinity must be $-H_0 r \cos \theta$, it is clear that we are limited to harmonics involving only the first power of $\cos \theta$. Referring to Table II, page 76, we see that there are only two cylindrical harmonics satisfying this condition and that the three potentials must be of the form

$$
\left.
\begin{aligned}
V_1 &= -H_0 r \cos \theta + \frac{B_1 \cos \theta}{r}, \\[2mm]
V_2 &= A_2 r \cos \theta + \frac{B_2 \cos \theta}{r}, \\[2mm]
V_3 &= A_3 r \cos \theta,
\end{aligned}
\right\}
\qquad (45\text{-}1)
$$

where we have omitted the term in $1/r$ from V_3 since its presence would make the potential infinite at the origin.

In order that $V_1 = V_2$ for $r = b$, it is necessary that

$$
-H_0 b^2 + B_1 = A_2 b^2 + B_2, \qquad (45\text{-}2)
$$

and, in order that $V_2 = V_3$ for $r = a$,

$$
A_2 a^2 + B_2 = A_3 a^2. \qquad (45\text{-}3)
$$

Continuity of the radial component of the magnetic induction at the outer surface requires that

$$
H_0 b^2 + B_1 = \mu(-A_2 b^2 + B_2), \qquad (45\text{-}4)
$$

and at the inner surface that

$$
\mu(-A_2 a^2 + B_2) = -A_3 a^2. \qquad (45\text{-}5)
$$

In equations (45-2) to (45-5) we have four relations from which we can eliminate B_1, A_2, B_2 so as to find A_3 in terms of H_0. Putting the value of A_3 so found into the expression (45-1) for V_3,

$$
V_3 = -\frac{4\mu}{(\mu+1)^2 - \dfrac{a^2}{b^2}(\mu-1)^2} H_0 r \cos \theta.
$$

The ratio of the field H_0 existing before the introduction of the shell to the uniform field

$$
H_3 = -\frac{\partial V_3}{\partial x} = \frac{4\mu}{(\mu+1)^2 - \dfrac{a^2}{b^2}(\mu-1)^2} H_0
$$

in the cavity is called the *shielding ratio*. It is

$$g = \frac{H_0}{H_3} = \frac{1}{4\mu}\left\{(\mu+1)^2 - \frac{a^2}{b^2}(\mu-1)^2\right\}$$

$$= 1 + \frac{1}{4}\frac{(\mu-1)^2}{\mu}\left(1 - \frac{a^2}{b^2}\right). \tag{45-6}$$

If the permeability of the shell is large compared with unity, as in the case of soft iron where it may be several hundred, the shielding ratio is given very closely by

$$g = \frac{1}{4}\mu\left(1 - \frac{a^2}{b^2}\right)$$

$$= \frac{\mu}{4\pi b^2}[\pi(b^2 - a^2)]. \tag{45-7}$$

Since $\pi(b^2 - a^2)$ is the cross section of the cylindrical shell, the shielding ratio for a given amount of soft iron is greater the smaller the outside radius b.

The effectiveness of magnetic shielding is somewhat increased by using several coaxial cylindrical shells with air gaps between. Wills has analyzed the case of three such shells and finds that for a given amount of iron the most effective arrangement is that in which the radii of the successive surfaces form a geometrical progression.

Problem 45a. A cylindrical shell made of iron of permeability 300 has radii 4 cm and 5 cm. What is the shielding ratio? Ans. 27.

Problem 45b. Find the radial and transverse components of the magnetization inside the cylindrical shell of this article for μ large. Sketch roughly the lines of induction.

$$\text{Ans. } 2\mu_0 H_0 \left[\frac{1 - \dfrac{a^2}{r^2}}{1 - \dfrac{a^2}{b^2}}\right]\cos\theta, \quad -2\mu_0 H_0 \left[\frac{1 + \dfrac{a^2}{r^2}}{1 - \dfrac{a^2}{b^2}}\right]\sin\theta.$$

46. Energy in the Magnetic Field. Since any system of magnets may be built up of magnetic dipoles (art. 40), a certain amount of work being performed in the process, it is evident that such a system has a potential energy associated with it. That is, during the establishment of the given configuration an amount of energy is stored which may be obtained again on scattering the magnetic elements to infinity. As in the case of charged conductors (art. 21), it is the final state of the system that determines the potential energy. We may build up the system in any manner convenient for calculation. For simplicity let us consider the case of k long thin fixed magnets (Fig. 75) immersed in a medium of permeability μ, the pole-strengths being m_1, $-m_1$, m_2, $-m_2$, $\cdots m_k$, $-m_k$. These poles are built up by bringing small increments from infinity in such a way that at any instant all poles are in magnitude the same fraction of final values. That is, during the building process the pole-strengths are αm_1, $-\alpha m_1$, αm_2, $-\alpha m_2$, and so on, where α varies from 0 to 1. Furthermore, under the above conditions the potential at every point varies in the same way as the pole-strengths. Thus, if V is the final value of the potential at any one of the poles m, the potential is αV when the pole-strength is αm. This follows at once from (43-9). A single step in the magnetizing process consists of increasing every pole αm by an amount $md\alpha$, since by so doing all poles are kept the same fraction $(\alpha + d\alpha)$ of their final value. By definition the potential at a pole is the work done against the magnetic forces in bringing a unit positive pole from infinity. Hence, the work done in the step described above is given by

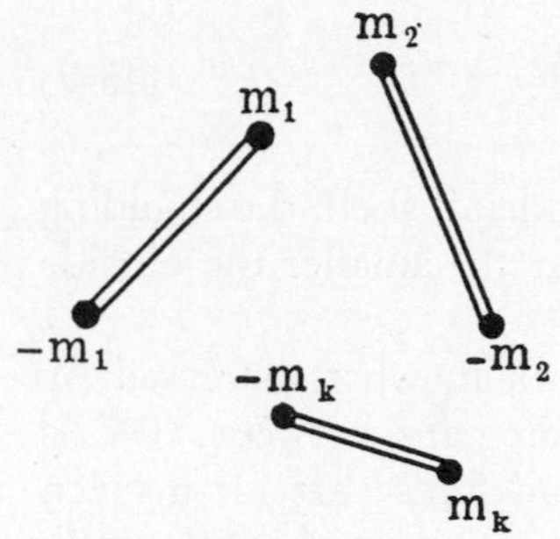

$$dU = \sum mV\alpha d\alpha = \alpha d\alpha \sum mV,$$

the summation being taken over all poles, positive and negative, with appropriate sign. Thus the potential energy of the final configuration is

$$U = \left\{ \int_0^1 \alpha d\alpha \right\} \sum mV = \tfrac{1}{2}\sum mV. \tag{46-1}$$

FIG. 75

The location of the energy is to some extent indeterminate, as is also the case with electrostatic energy (art. 21). However, when there is a permeable medium present some of the energy at least is distributed through it, on account of the induced magnetization. It is convenient, therefore, to consider all the energy as distributed through the medium, even when the latter consists only of free space. This may be done by observing that the tubes of induction, which are continuous, pass through the given point poles to the number of one per unit pole, as shown in art. 43. Consider the portion of a tube of induction running from a unit pole on the positive end of some magnet through the permeable medium to a unit pole on some negative end. Evidently the energy which is associated with it is

$$\tfrac{1}{2}V_a - \tfrac{1}{2}V_b = \tfrac{1}{2}(V_a - V_b) = \tfrac{1}{2}\int_a^b H dl, \tag{46-2}$$

where V_a and V_b are the potentials at the beginning and end of the section of tube considered. This energy we may distribute along the tube as we choose. The simplest way is at the rate of $H/2$ joules per meter at every point along the given portion of tube. Since there are B tubes per meter^2 of cross section (art. 43), energy is distributed through the field in the amount $BH/2$ joules per meter^3. Replacing B by $\mu_0\mu H$ we have for a paramagnetic medium

$$U = \frac{\mu_0}{2} \int_\tau \mu H^2 d\tau, \tag{46-3}$$

where the volume integral may be taken through all space, since the excluded volume occupied by the long thin magnets is negligible.

The distribution of energy specified in (46-3) is an arbitrary one, since we may add to the integrand any function whose integral through space is zero without changing the total energy. It is, however, a reasonable distribution, as it is everywhere positive. Using (43-2), we have

$$\frac{1}{2} BH = \frac{\mu_0}{2} H^2 + \frac{1}{2} IH, \tag{46-4}$$

the term involving I representing the energy per unit volume assignable to the permeable medium.

If some part of the magnetic system, say one of the fixed magnets, is allowed to move a distance $d\xi$ the force is, as in (41-4),

$$\mathscr{F}_\xi = -\frac{\partial U}{\partial \xi}. \tag{46-5}$$

Similarly the torque corresponding to an angular displacement $d\theta$ is

$$\mathscr{L}_\theta = -\frac{\partial U}{\partial \theta}. \tag{46-6}$$

Problem 46. A fixed magnet of large cross section and uniform magnetization I_0 is bent around until its pole faces are parallel. These pole faces are planes perpendicular to the direction of magnetization. Between the faces is a plate of soft iron of thickness t and permeability μ. It is withdrawn until only a length x remains between the poles. Find the force per meter of width tending to draw the plate back to its original position. Ans. $\dfrac{I_0^2 t}{2\mu_0}\left(\dfrac{\mu-1}{\mu}\right)$.

47. Magnetic Instruments and Measurements.

One of the most useful magnetic instruments is the *magnetometer* (Fig. 76). It appears in a variety of special forms but consists essentially of a small magnet suspended by a long torsionless fibre in a non-magnetic case attached to the base of which are two horizontal arms with sliding cradles. In these may be placed small auxiliary magnets which deflect the suspended magnet from its normal equilibrium position in the magnetic meridian of the earth's field. The suspended system usually carries a small mirror, so that the deflection may be observed by means of an external telescope and scale, or some such device.

Fig. 76

To measure the horizontal component H_t of the earth's field, we first determine the magnetic meridian and set the arms in a direction perpendicular to it. A small magnet M of unknown moment p (Fig. 77) is placed in one of the cradles with its axis perpendicular to the meridian and its center a distance d from the center of the suspended magnet M' whose moment is p'. The movable system is deflected through an angle α. Let H be the field of M at the center of M'. As M' is very short the variation of the field over the region occupied by M' may be neglected.   Then α is determined by the equation

$$p'H \cos \alpha - p'H_t \sin \alpha = 0, \qquad (47\text{-}1)$$

obtained by equating the resultant torque on M' to zero.   If M is so small that it may be regarded as a magnetic dipole at distance d, then, by (40-2),

$$H = \frac{p}{2\pi\mu_0 d^3},$$

and (47-1) reduces to

$$\frac{p}{H_t} = 2\pi\mu_0 d^3 \tan \alpha. \qquad (47\text{-}2)$$

In order to eliminate the unknown p, we must find another relation between p and H_t.   This is conveniently done by suspending M in

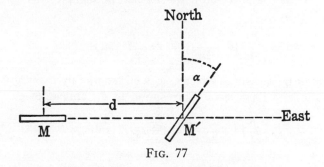

Fig. 77

the earth's field and allowing it to oscillate in a horizontal plane about a vertical axis passing through its center of mass.   A torsionless fibre is used, and the oscillations are so small that the motion is effectively simple harmonic.   The equation of motion is then

$$\mathscr{I} \frac{d^2\theta}{dt^2} = -pH_t\theta,$$

where $\mathscr{I}$ is the moment of inertia about the given axis, and θ is the angular deflection.   The period is given by

$$P_0 = 2\pi \sqrt{\frac{\mathscr{I}}{pH_t}}. \qquad (47\text{-}3)$$

Eliminating p between this equation and (47-2) gives

$$H_t = \frac{2\pi}{P_0} \sqrt{\frac{\mathscr{I}}{2\pi\mu_0 d^3 \tan \alpha}}. \qquad (47\text{-}4)$$

Evidently we may eliminate H_t and obtain

$$p = \frac{2\pi}{P_0}\sqrt{2\pi\mu_0\mathscr{I}d^3\tan\alpha}. \tag{47-5}$$

Unfortunately in practice the value of θ is usually too small for accurate measurement if d is made so large that the length of M is negligible.   In fact, the ratio of these quantities is rarely as great as ten. Hence we require a more exact expression for H.   Referring to art. 40, we see that if we do not neglect $l^2/4$ in comparison with d^2

$$H = \frac{pd}{2\pi\mu_0\left(d^2-\dfrac{l^2}{4}\right)^2} = \frac{p}{2\pi\mu_0 d^3}\left(1+\frac{l^2}{2d^2}+\cdots\right),$$

where l is the distance between the poles of M, a quantity in general slightly less than the geometrical length of the magnet.   Usually sufficient accuracy is obtained if we neglect the higher order terms and replace (47-2) by

$$\frac{p}{H_t}\left(1+\frac{l^2}{2d^2}\right) = 2\pi\mu_0 d^3\tan\alpha. \tag{47-6}$$

As l cannot be measured exactly, it is eliminated by making two sets of observations.   Thus let α_1 correspond to d_1, and α_2 to d_2.   Then

$$\frac{p}{H_t}\left(1+\frac{l^2}{2d_1{}^2}\right) = 2\pi\mu_0 d_1{}^3\tan\alpha_1,$$

$$\frac{p}{H_t}\left(1+\frac{l^2}{2d_2{}^2}\right) = 2\pi\mu_0 d_2{}^3\tan\alpha_2,$$

and, on eliminating l^2,

$$\frac{p}{H_t} = 2\pi\mu_0\left[\frac{d_1{}^5\tan\alpha_1-d_2{}^5\tan\alpha_2}{d_1{}^2-d_2{}^2}\right]. \tag{47-7}$$

This last equation is used with (47-3) to obtain H_t and p.

In order to avoid errors due to lack of magnetic and mechanical symmetry, the auxiliary magnet is turned end for end and then transferred from the west arm to the east arm and the process repeated.   The mean of the four observations gives the value of α to be used.   Also, care must be taken that the magnetometer fibre is really torsionless, or that the effect of any existing torsion is removed by turning the upper end of the fibre through the same angle as the lower for each deflection. In the *Kew* method of making the observations this result is obtained automatically by rotating the entire instrument.

Similarly, in the oscillation observations various refinements and corrections are necessary. For example, the period can be determined accurately only by observing the time for a large number of vibrations. Because of the mechanical damping, the initial amplitude must then be too large strictly to satisfy the condition for simple harmonic motion. If $\bar{P}_0$ is the average period determined for 100 vibrations, say, and θ_1, θ_2 are the amplitudes in radians at the beginning and the end of the interval over which $\bar{P}_0$ is determined, then approximately

$$P_0 = \bar{P}_0\left(1 - \frac{\theta_1\theta_2}{16}\right), \tag{47-8}$$

provided the difference between θ_1 and θ_2 is small compared with either of these quantities. Corrections for temperature effects, residual torsion in the fibre, and variation of p due to H_t are of somewhat less importance. For a description of these the reader is referred to some more elaborate discussion of magnetometer measurements. (See, for example, Glazebrook: *Dictionary of Applied Physics*, Vol. II, pp. 532 ff.)

It is interesting to note that Gauss used the magnetometer to demonstrate the validity of the inverse square law (art. 37). Considering the arrangement shown in Fig. 77, we obtain

$$\frac{p}{H_t} = 2\pi\mu_0 d^3 \tan\alpha,$$

as has been shown. Suppose now M is turned end for end and then moved parallel to itself in the horizontal plane until its center lies in the meridian at a distance d again from the center of M'. The field produced by M becomes $p/4\pi\mu_0 d^3$ and the deflection α' is given by

$$\frac{p}{H_t} = 4\pi\mu_0 d^3 \tan\alpha'. \tag{47-9}$$

Thus,

$$\frac{\tan\alpha}{\tan\alpha'} = 2. \tag{47-10}$$

On the other hand, it may be shown that if the force between magnetic poles varies as $1/r^n$ we must have

$$\frac{\tan\alpha}{\tan\alpha'} = n. \tag{47-11}$$

As the ratio of the tangents is found experimentally to be 2, the inverse square law is confirmed.

Another instrument of use in the measurement of terrestrial magnetism is the *dip-circle* (Fig. 78). It consists of a light magnetic needle arranged to rotate about a horizontal axis through its center, and a circular scale over which the ends of the needle move. The axis of rotation being set perpendicular to the magnetic meridian, the needle assumes a position tangent to the lines of force of the earth's field. The angle which the needle makes with the horizontal, that is, the *angle*

FIG. 78

of dip, is determined from the position of the ends of the needle on the scale. As in the case of the magnetometer, various precautions are necessary to avoid errors due to lack of mechanical and magnetic symmetry in the instrument. A detailed discussion of the use of the dip-circle is given by Glazebrook in the article to which reference has been made.

REFERENCE

Shire, *Classical Electricity and Magnetism* (Cambridge Univ. Press, 1960). Chap. 5.

Chapter V

STEADY CURRENTS

48. Current and Electromotive Force. A free charge placed in an electric field experiences a force and moves under the influence of this force in accordance with the usual laws of mechanics. Let us place a conductor in the field. As the conductor contains a great number of free charges and as the field, initially at least, penetrates into its interior, a flow of electricity takes place. If the conductor is isolated, the charge soon distributes itself in such a way as to make the field within the conductor everywhere zero, and motion of charge then ceases. This static state is considered in earlier chapters, and we are not concerned with it here. If, on the other hand, the conductor is connected to reservoirs which supply or absorb charge as required to maintain the original electric field, charge passes continuously through the conductor. As there can be no continual accumulation of charge at any point along the conductor, the amount of charge passing per second is the same for every cross section which cuts all the lines of flow. Moreover, although each free charge is continuously accelerated by the field, it progresses through the conductor at a constant speed on the average because of the mechanical retardation it experiences from frequent collisions with the atoms of which the conductor is composed. The total charge passing any cross section per second is the *electric current* in the conductor. We will denote it by i. Suppose the conductor is a wire of cross section A. Let dq be the charge passing through this cross section in time dt. Then if there are n free charges per unit volume, each with charge e and average speed of progression v, $dq = Anevdt$. Consequently,

$$i \equiv \frac{dq}{dt} = Anev. \tag{48-1}$$

The current per unit area of cross section, called the *current density*, is given by

$$j \equiv \frac{i}{A} = nev. \tag{48-2}$$

135

The positive direction of the current is that of the electric field, the direction in which positive charges tend to move. As the free charges in a metal are electrons, with $e = -1.60(10)^{-19}$ coulomb, the actual direction of flow in a metallic conductor is opposite to the conventional direction of the current.

Evidently the magnitude of the current between two points depends on the nature of the conductor and on the forces which urge the free charges through it. The effect of such forces is most easily calculated in terms of the *work performed per unit positive charge*. This quantity is called the *electromotive force*, often abbreviated e.m.f., and is denoted by $\mathscr{E}$. Thus, suppose a unit positive charge moves along some path from P to Q (Fig. 79) in a field of force. If E is the magnitude of the force per unit positive charge, and α is the angle which the force makes with an element dl of the path, we see that

$$\mathscr{E} \equiv \int_P^Q E \cos \alpha dl, \qquad (48\text{-}3)$$

for this is the work done by the field on the unit charge.

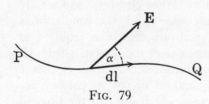

FIG. 79

The total force per unit charge may be due to any one or to any combination of several types of force. If E represents an electrostatic field E_q, with which we are already familiar, the integral of (48-3) is identical with the potential drop from P to Q as defined in art. 7 and is consequently independent of the path. With other types of force, which we shall study later, there is in general no definite potential difference between the two points, that is, the integral is not independent of the path. Therefore, to include all cases, we must define the e.m.f. from P to Q along a given path as the work done on the unit charge when it moves from P to Q *by that path*.

We are usually interested in the electromotive force around a complete circuit. Let α_q be the angle which an electrostatic field E_q makes with dl. Since the integral of $E_q \cos \alpha_q dl$ along any path is the potential difference $V_P - V_Q$ of the end points, its value is zero when these points are brought together to form a circuit. In this case, then,

$$\mathscr{E} \equiv \oint E_q \cos \alpha_q dl = 0, \qquad (48\text{-}4)$$

where the symbol $\oint$ indicates integration around a closed path. It is, therefore, clear that *no static distribution of charge can produce an e.m.f.*

around a circuit, a fact important in circuit theory. In general, however, the electromotive force

$$\mathscr{E} \equiv \oint E \cos \alpha \, dl \qquad (48\text{-}5)$$

around a circuit does not vanish but depends on the path followed.

Since current represents charge per second, there is a unit of current corresponding to each of the previously defined units of charge (art. 6). The practical unit of current, which of course has the magnitude of $3(10)^9$ electrostatic units,* is the *coulomb per second*, or *ampere*. In terms of the fundamental units it is 1 meter$^{1/2}$ kg$^{1/2}$ sec^{-1}.

As explained in Chapter VII, a current gives rise to a magnetic field. Because of this field, a coil of wire carrying a current exerts a torque on a magnet and vice versa. If one is fixed and the other suspended so that it may rotate, we have a means of detecting and measuring current. Current indicators of this type are called *galvanometers*. A complete description of such instruments is deferred until a study of electromagnetism is made. Some important applications of the galvanometer are given, however, in connection with various electrical measurements described in this chapter.

49. Metallic Conduction and Ohm's Law. Let us now examine the mechanism of conduction in solids, that is, in metals, as all good conductors are metals. We picture the interior of a solid conductor as a three-dimensional lattice of atoms with free electrons moving about between the atoms and colliding frequently with them. As the effective radius of an atom is of the order of $(10)^{-10}$ meter, while that of an electron is of the order of $(10)^{-15}$ meter, we may neglect the collisions between electrons in comparison with the collisions between electrons and atoms. The atoms vibrate about their equilibrium positions, and the electrons move, with a mean energy determined by the absolute temperature. In fact, the atoms have the usual thermal agitation of any solid, while the electrons collectively behave like a gas at the temperature of the conductor, or approximately so, at least.

As long as no external field is applied to the conductor, the average field in the interior is zero, since there is as much positive charge as negative in any small volume. Therefore, there is on the whole no motion of free charges through the conductor. If now we apply a field of intensity E, each charge experiences an acceleration of magnitude eE/m, where m is the mass of the charge. This superposes on the random thermal motions of the charges a general drift, which constitutes the current. The drift velocity is small compared with the thermal velocities, so that the two motions may be treated as independent.

* More accurately $2.998(10)^9$ e.s.u.

The *mean free time* t_f between successive collisions of a free charge with some atom is thus determined by the structure of the conductor and the temperature, but not by E.

We may now calculate the mean drift velocity and hence the current. Between collisions the drift velocity is increased on the average by the amount $(eE/m)t_f$. The effect of each collision, however, is to restore the random thermal distribution of velocities, that is, to reduce the drift velocity to zero. Therefore, the mean drift velocity v is given by

$$v = \frac{0 + \left(\frac{eE}{m}\right)t_f}{2} = \frac{1}{2}\left(\frac{eE}{m}\right)t_f,$$

and, from (48-2),

$$j = \left(\frac{ne^2t_f}{2m}\right) E. \tag{49-1}$$

Defining the *electrical conductivity* γ as the current density produced by a field of unit strength, we have

$$\gamma = \frac{j}{E} = \frac{ne^2t_f}{2m}. \tag{49-2}$$

Under all ordinary conditions the conductivity is a characteristic of the conducting substance independent of j or E. It does, however, vary with the temperature. According to the kinetic theory of gases t_f is inversely proportional to the square root of the absolute temperature. Experimentally it is found, however, that γ is more nearly proportional to the inverse first power of the absolute temperature.

The most satisfactory check on the general validity of the electron theory of conduction is obtained by considering thermal conduction as well as electrical. The mean energy of both the electrons and the atoms in a body depends on the temperature, so that when a temperature gradient exists there is also an energy gradient. Energy is transferred from a region of higher temperature to one of lower by diffusion of the electrons. We may ascribe heat conduction almost entirely to this cause, since in dielectrics, where there are no free charges, there is very small conduction of heat. By an analysis similar to that used for electrical conductivity it may be shown* that the thermal conductivity γ_t is given by

$$\gamma_t = \left(\frac{3nk^2t_f}{2m}\right) T, \tag{49-3}$$

where k is a universal constant having the value $1.38 (10)^{-23}$ joule per degree, and T is the absolute temperature.

* Page, L., *Introduction to Theoretical Physics*, 3rd Ed., D. Van Nostrand Co. Inc., 1952, p. 469.

Taking the ratio of (49-3) to (49-2) we find

$$\frac{\gamma_t}{\gamma} = 3\left(\frac{k}{e}\right)^2 T, \qquad (49\text{-}4)$$

a relation known as the *law of Wiedemann and Franz*. It is found to be in good agreement with experiment, at least in the case of the best conductors, such as gold, silver and copper.

Returning now to (49-2), the *resistivity* ρ is defined as the reciprocal of the conductivity, so that, using (48-2),

$$E = \rho j = \frac{\rho}{A} i. \qquad (49\text{-}5)$$

Let us apply the last equation to a wire of length l, the composition and cross section being uniform throughout its length. Since E is then constant and directed along the wire, El is the electromotive force and we may write

$$\mathscr{E} = \frac{\rho l}{A} i. \qquad (49\text{-}6)$$

The quantity $\rho l/A$, called the *resistance* of the conductor, depends only on the absolute temperature under ordinary conditions, being in fact approximately proportional to it. If we denote $\rho l/A$ by R, we have

$$\mathscr{E} = Ri, \qquad (49\text{-}7)$$

which is *Ohm's law*. This important law may be stated in general terms as follows: *The ratio of the electromotive force between two points on a conductor to the current flowing between these points is a constant, at any given temperature, known as the resistance.*

The unit of resistance is named the *ohm*. Since resistance is measured basically in volts per ampere, the ohm is 1 meter sec^{-1} when expressed in terms of the fundamental units. In practice, it is convenient to measure very large resistances in *megohms*, a megohm being $(10)^6$ ohms.

The passage of current through a conductor evidently is attended by an evolution of heat, since the moving charges lose their energy to the atoms at each collision. The heat generated per second in a conductor is easily calculated. Using the notation of art. 48, the force on the moving charge contained in a length dl is $(Anedl)E$. Therefore, the work done on the charge in the length dl of the conductor in a time dt is

$$(Anedl)Evdt = (Edl)idt$$

by (48-1). The work for the entire conductor is

$$(\textstyle\int Edl)idt = \mathscr{E}idt,$$

so that the work done per second, called the *power*, is $\mathcal{E}i$. This energy all appears in heat, as there is no storage of energy in the interior of the conductor. Denoting power by $\mathcal{P}$, and using (49-7),

$$\mathcal{P} = \mathcal{E}i = Ri^2. \qquad (49\text{-}8)$$

The unit of power is known as the *watt*. Evidently a watt is a joule per second.

A table of resistivities is appended for reference. The metals are arranged in order of increasing resistivity, the values being given in ohm meters for a temperature of $0°$ C. Note that the resistivity is equal in magnitude to the resistance of a unit cube of the given material. The total resistance of a conductor of any length and cross section is calculated by means of the relation $R = \rho l / A$. The resistivity at a temperature not greatly different from $0°$ C is given by the formula $\rho = \rho_0(1 + \alpha t)$ where ρ_0 is the resistivity at $0°$ C, t is the centigrade temperature, and α is the *temperature coefficient*.

Substance	ρ_0 (ohm meter)	α (1/deg)
Metals :		
Silver	$1.47(10)^{-8}$	$41(10)^{-4}$
Copper (annealed) .	$1.60(10)^{-8}$	$39(10)^{-4}$
Gold	$2.28(10)^{-8}$	$34(10)^{-4}$
Aluminum . . .	$2.63(10)^{-8}$	$39(10)^{-4}$
Tungsten . . .	$5.06(10)^{-8}$	$45(10)^{-4}$
Iron	$9.90(10)^{-8}$	$50(10)^{-4}$
Tin	$10.6(10)^{-8}$	$42(10)^{-4}$
Platinum . . .	$11.0(10)^{-8}$	$38(10)^{-4}$
Lead	$20.3(10)^{-8}$	$43(10)^{-4}$
Mercury . . .	$94.1(10)^{-8}$	$9(10)^{-4}$
Alloys :		
Brass	$6.50(10)^{-8}$	$20(10)^{-4}$
Manganin . . .	$42.0(10)^{-8}$	$0(10)^{-4}$
Nichrome . . .	$99.0(10)^{-8}$	$4(10)^{-4}$

50. Conversion of Units. We know the magnitudes of the basic electrostatic units in terms of the magnitudes of the corresponding practical units (art. 25). Similarly, the electromagnetic unit of

Force	is the *dyne.*	In magnitude it is $(10)^{-5}$ newton.
Energy	*erg.*	$(10)^{-7}$ joule.
Pole-Strength	*e.m.u. pole-strength.*	$4\pi(10)^{-8}$ pr.u.
Mag. Intensity	*dyne per e.m.u. pole.*	$\dfrac{1}{4\pi}(10)^3$ pr.u.
Mag. Potential	*erg per e.m.u. pole.*	$\dfrac{1}{4\pi}(10)$ pr.u.
Strength of Shell	*e.m.u. pole per cm.*	$4\pi(10)^{-6}$ pr.u.

Transformations of formulas are now simply effected when it is remembered that the magnitude of any quantity in a formula represents the measure of a definite physical entity in terms of a given unit. Thus, suppose we observe a certain current. Let it be denoted in m.k.s. practical units by i and in c.g.s. electrostatic units by i_e. Inasmuch as the ampere has the magnitude of $3(10)^9$ electrostatic units (art. 48), the measure of the current in pr.u. is $\frac{1}{3}(10)^{-9}$ times the measure of the current in e.s.u. Hence the complete conversion equation is

$$ i = \frac{1}{3}(10)^{-9} \frac{\text{ampere}}{\text{e.s.u. current}} i_e, $$

the dimension ratio being required to make the equation dimensionally homogeneous. This and several other common conversion relations are listed in the adjoining table, subscripts e and m indicating e.s.u. and e.m.u., respectively, as usual. The distance and force relations are the same for e.s.u. as for e.m.u., so these are listed with double subscripts, the appropriate one to be chosen in any given case. The dimension ratios are omitted in the table for the sake of compactness, their existence being understood.

Quantity	Conversion Equation *
Length . . .	$l = (10)^{-2}l_{em}$
Force . . .	$\mathscr{F} = (10)^{-5}\mathscr{F}_{em}$
Charge . . .	$Q = \frac{1}{3}(10)^{-9}Q_e$
Electric intensity .	$E = 3(10)^4 E_e$
Electric displacement .	$D = \frac{1}{12\pi}(10)^{-5}D_e$
Pole-strength .	$m = 4\pi(10)^{-8}m_m$
Magnetic intensity .	$H = \frac{1}{4\pi}(10)^3 H_m$
Magnetic induction .	$B = (10)^{-4}B_m$
E.m.f. or Elec. Pot. .	$\mathscr{E} = 3(10)^2 \mathscr{E}_e$
Current . . .	$i = \frac{1}{3}(10)^{-9}i_e$
Resistance . . .	$R = 9(10)^{11}R_e$
Capacitance . .	$C = \frac{1}{9}(10)^{-11}C_e$

Actually the dimension ratios can be omitted in the transformation of a formula, as well as in the table, since in a complete transformation they merely cancel out or, at most, provide the dimensions for a simple dimensional constant which can be recognized without difficulty and represented by its proper dimensional symbol.

* The factor 3 in any coefficient is more accurately 2.998.

To illustrate the use of the conversion equations, let us transform (18-1), $Q = CV$, to e.s.u. Making the indicated substitutions, we have

$$\tfrac{1}{3}(10)^{-9}Q_e = \tfrac{1}{9}(10)^{-11}C_e[3(10)^2 V_e], \qquad Q_e = C_e V_e.$$

Hence this relation has exactly the same form in both systems of units. The same is true of Ohm's law and a few other relations, but in general the constant factors are different. For example, transformation of (18-5) to e.s.u. gives

$$\frac{1}{9}(10)^{-11}C_e = \frac{1}{9}(10)^{-9}\kappa\left[\frac{(10)^{-2}a_e b_e}{b_e - a_e}\right], \qquad C_e = \frac{\kappa a_e b_e}{b_e - a_e}.$$

Note that the dimensions of κ_0 must be omitted when the dimension ratios are omitted. Finally, the conversion equations can be used equally well in reverse. Thus, if we transform (6-1) to pr.u., we have

$$(10)^5\mathscr{F} = \frac{[3(10)^9 q][3(10)^9 q']}{(10)^4 r^2}, \qquad \mathscr{F} = 9(10)^9\frac{qq'}{r^2}.$$

Recognizing the dimensional constant $9(10)^9$, we represent it by $1/4\pi\kappa_0$, as explained above, and so obtain (6-2) correctly.

There is a comprehensive discussion of units in Chapter XII and a general conversion table at the beginning of the book.

Problem 50a. Include the dimension ratios explicitly in the transformations of (18-1) and (18-5) and show that they cancel out.

Problem 50b. Find the conversion equations for the polarization P and the magnetization I. Hence show that $D_e = E_e + 4\pi P_e = \kappa E_e$ and $B_m = H_m + 4\pi I_m = \mu H_m$. Ans. $P = \tfrac{1}{3}(10)^{-5}P_e$, $I = 4\pi(10)^{-4}I_m$.

51. The Voltaic Cell.

In order to maintain a steady flow of current a constant electromotive force is necessary. This is readily obtained by chemical means, for if two dissimilar conductors are dipped in a conducting liquid which reacts with them there is in general a potential difference between them, which is maintained even when current flows steadily from one to the other through some external resistance. Such a device is called a *voltaic cell*. The two conductors are the *poles*, the positively charged one being the *positive pole*, and the other the *negative pole*.

Let us consider for example copper oxide and zinc dipped in an aqueous solution of potassium hydroxide (Fig. 80). This is an *Edison cell*. Within the cell chemical forces exist which tend to transfer charge from one pole to the other. These forces are capable of doing a definite amount of work $\mathscr{E}$ per unit charge. They build up a positive charge on one pole, the CuO, and a negative charge on the other, the Zn, giving rise to electrostatic forces which, in the interior of the cell, act in opposition to the chemical forces. Let E be the force per unit charge in the cell due to chemical causes, and E_q the force per unit charge due to static distribution of charge. Then the total electromotive force around a circuit consisting of any path from the positive pole to the negative outside the cell and any path from the negative to the positive inside—regardless of whether current is flowing or not—is

$$\int_o E_q \cos \alpha_q dl + \int_i (E_q \cos \alpha_q + E \cos \alpha) dl$$
$$= \oint E_q \cos \alpha_q dl + \int_i E \cos \alpha dl. \quad (51\text{-}1)$$

Here α_q is the angle between E_q and dl and α that between E and dl. The subscripts o and i indicate integration along the outside path and the inside path respectively, and $\oint E_q \cos \alpha_q dl$ is the line integral of the electrostatic force around the complete circuit. By (48-4) this line

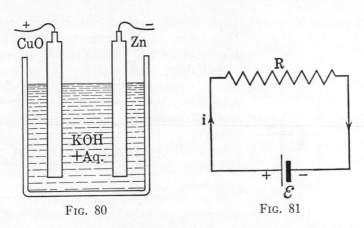

FIG. 80   FIG. 81

integral is zero, and, as the last integral in (51-1) is $\mathscr{E}$, we see that *the total e.m.f. around the circuit equals the chemical e.m.f. of the cell.* Any e.m.f., such as this chemical e.m.f., which is the primary agent in the production of a current, is called an *applied e.m.f.*

First suppose that the poles are not connected externally. Then no current flows, and the condition of equilibrium in the cell requires that $E_q \cos \alpha_q + E \cos \alpha = 0$ everywhere inside. Hence using (51-1),

$$\int_o E_q \cos \alpha_q dl = \mathscr{E}. \quad (51\text{-}2)$$

The integral represents the potential difference of the poles. Therefore, *the open circuit potential difference equals the chemical e.m.f. of the cell.*

Next let us connect the poles by a conductor of resistance R. A current i flows, the circuit being shown schematically in Fig. 81. We know that the total work done on a unit charge as it passes around the circuit is $\mathscr{E}$. While this work is *generated* chemically in the cell, it can be *performed* only in overcoming resistance. Referring to the integrals in (51-1), Ohm's law requires that

$$\int_o E_q \cos \alpha_q dl = Ri$$

when a current is flowing. Also we may write

$$\int_i (E_q \cos \alpha_q + E \cos \alpha)dl \equiv ri,$$

where r is called the *internal resistance* of the cell. Thus (51-1) becomes

$$\mathscr{E} = (R+r)i, \quad i = \frac{\mathscr{E}}{R+r}. \tag{51-3}$$

The quantity r is not strictly an ohmic resistance, being dependent to some extent on the current and on the past history of the cell. In the type of cell described above, it is usually negligibly small, but in some cells, particularly *dry cells* in which the liquid is replaced by a paste, the internal resistance may be appreciable. Observe that the potential difference of the poles, which is given by $Ri = \mathscr{E} - ri$, is now less than its open circuit value by an amount ri.

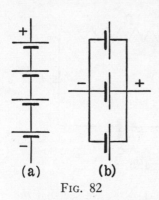

(a) (b)

Fig. 82

It is interesting to note that, although the charge on the poles does not contribute to the e.m.f. of the circuit, it provides the mechanism by which work generated internally is performed externally. In fact, if the cell has no internal resistance, the chemical forces are just balanced by the internal electrostatic forces, so that all the work is done outside the cell. If r is not entirely negligible, there is, of course, a small amount of work per unit charge done inside the cell.

Referring to (51-3), it is evident that we may state Ohm's law for a complete circuit in which a steady or *direct* current is flowing in the form: *The current equals the applied e.m.f. divided by the total resistance of the circuit.*

The e.m.f. of all commonly used cells lies between one and two volts. When a higher e.m.f. is desired, it can be obtained by connecting several cells in *series*, that is, by connecting the positive pole of one to the negative pole of the next (Fig. 82a). As the work done on a unit charge as it moves around a circuit passing through all the cells is the sum of the $\mathscr{E}$'s, the resultant e.m.f. is the sum of the separate e.m.f.'s. Obviously a *parallel* connection (Fig. 82b) of identical cells does not change the e.m.f., but it does decrease the effective internal resistance. Any combination of cells is called a *battery*.

Problem 51a. Show that if n identical cells of e.m.f. $\mathscr{E}$ and resistance r are connected in series they will produce a current through an external resistance R equal to $n\mathscr{E}/(R+nr)$, whereas if they are connected in parallel the current is $n\mathscr{E}/(nR+r)$.

Problem 51b. Using the results of the preceding problem find the relation between R and r when (a) the series connection produces a greater current than the parallel, (b) the parallel produces greater than the series, (c) both produce the same. Ans. (a) $R>r$, (b) $R<r$, (c) $R=r$.

52. Combinations of Resistances and Kirchhoff's Laws.

In the construction of circuits it is often necessary to connect several resistances together in *series* (Fig. 83a), or in *parallel* (Fig. 83b), or in more complicated *networks*.

In the series case the total e.m.f. $\mathscr{E}$ through the combination is clearly the sum of the e.m.f.'s through the individual resistance

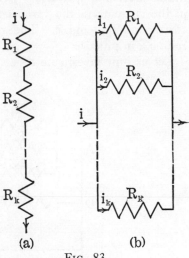

(a)   (b)

FIG. 83

elements. Hence if a total current i is flowing, we have

$$\mathscr{E} = R_1 i + R_2 i + \cdots R_k i = \left[\sum_1^k R_j \right] i. \qquad (52\text{-}1)$$

Now the equivalent or total resistance R of the series combination is given by $\mathscr{E} = Ri$. Comparing this with (52-1), we see that

$$R = \sum_1^k R_j. \qquad (52\text{-}2)$$

In the parallel case the e.m.f. is the same for all the resistance elements, whereas the currents, $i_1, i_2, \cdots i_k$ are, in general, different. Applying Ohm's law to each resistance,

$$\mathscr{E} = R_1 i_1 = R_2 i_2 = \cdots R_k i_k, \qquad (52\text{-}3)$$

and also

$$\mathscr{E} = Ri, \qquad (52\text{-}4)$$

where R and i denote total resistance and total current as before. As $i = i_1 + i_2 + \cdots i_k$, we have with the aid of (52-3) and (52-4),

$$\frac{\mathscr{E}}{R} = \frac{\mathscr{E}}{R_1} + \frac{\mathscr{E}}{R_2} + \cdots \frac{\mathscr{E}}{R_k} = \mathscr{E}\sum_1^k \frac{1}{R_j},$$

or

$$\frac{1}{R} = \sum_1^k \frac{1}{R_j}. \tag{52-5}$$

In either of the cases considered above, the calculation of R is but a means to an end, of course.   In most circuit problems we are interested in the currents in the various resistance elements, together with the corresponding e.m.f.'s.   The resistance elements are usually called *resistors*, in practice.

Let us now investigate resistance networks in general.   Although it

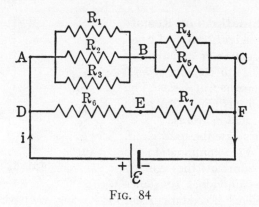

Fig. 84

sometimes happens that a network may be analyzed into series and parallel groups, more often—in fact whenever a junction in the circuit is connected to more than two other junctions—no such simple treatment is possible.   The first case is illustrated in Fig. 84.   The resistance from A to B and that from B to C are obtained by use of (52-5).   These are combined by (52-2) to obtain the resistance of the path ABC.   Similarly the resistance of DEF is calculated and combined with that of ABC by (52-5) to obtain the total resistance of the circuit.   An example of the second and more complex case is shown in Fig. 85.   To analyze this circuit we must evidently return to fundamentals, where two facts at once present themselves.   First, since there can be no continual accumulation of charge at any point, the sum of the currents flowing to a junction must equal the sum of the currents flowing from it.   Second, if a unit positive charge moves around any closed path in the network, the total electrical work done on the charge as it passes through the resistance elements must equal the total applied e.m.f. in the given path, just as in the case of the simple circuit discussed and analyzed in art. 51. Having assigned positive directions, as indicated in the figure, we may put the above statements in a more analytical form, known as *Kirchhoff's laws*.

LAW I.   *The algebraic sum of all the currents meeting at a junction is zero.*

LAW II.   *The algebraic sum of the Ri terms around any closed path equals the algebraic sum of the applied e.m.f.'s in the given path.*

Let us now find the six unknown branch currents of Fig. 85, in terms of the R's and $\mathscr{E}$'s, as an illustration of the application of Kirchhoff's laws to a circuit problem.   We require six independent equations,

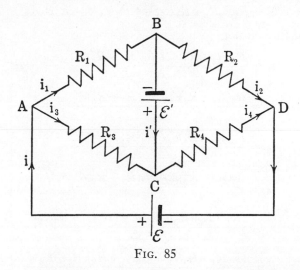

FIG. 85

that is, six equations no one of which can be derived from a combination of the others.   From the first law we may write the *junction equations*

$$i \; -i_1-i_3 = 0, \qquad (1)$$
$$i_1-i_2-i' \; = 0, \qquad (2) \qquad (52\text{-}6)$$
$$i_3+i' \; -i_4 = 0, \qquad (3)$$

and from the second law the *loop equations*

$$R_1 i_1 + R_2 i_2 - R_4 i_4 - R_3 i_3 = 0, \qquad (4)$$
$$R_1 i_1 - R_3 i_3 = \mathscr{E}', \qquad (5) \qquad (52\text{-}7)$$
$$R_3 i_3 + R_4 i_4 = \mathscr{E}. \qquad (6)$$

There are several other equations directly obtainable, but they are not independent of the six chosen. For example, the junction equation $i_2 + i_4 - i = 0$, applying to the point D, may be obtained by adding the first three equations above, and the loop equation $R_1 i_1 + R_2 i_2 = \mathscr{E}$ by adding the fourth equation to the sixth. Actually, with any number N_J of junctions, there are always $N_J - 1$ independent junction equations, since, if charge does not accumulate at $N_J - 1$ junctions, the rate at which charge leaves the remaining junction must equal the rate at which it arrives. Hence there can be only $N_B - (N_J - 1) = N_B - N_J + 1$ independent loop equations, where N_B is the number of branches. Evidently the group of equations to be solved is to some extent arbitrary.

The algebraic solution of the equations (52-6) and (52-7), which is most easily effected by means of determinants, is left to the reader. If we set

$$\Delta \equiv R_1 R_2 R_3 + R_2 R_3 R_4 + R_3 R_4 R_1 + R_4 R_1 R_2,$$

we find for the solution

$$\left.
\begin{aligned}
i_1 &= \frac{R_3(R_2 + R_4)\mathscr{E} + R_2(R_3 + R_4)\mathscr{E}'}{\Delta}, \\[4pt]
i_2 &= \frac{R_4(R_1 + R_3)\mathscr{E} - R_1(R_3 + R_4)\mathscr{E}'}{\Delta}, \\[4pt]
i_3 &= \frac{R_1(R_2 + R_4)\mathscr{E} - R_4(R_1 + R_2)\mathscr{E}'}{\Delta}, \\[4pt]
i_4 &= \frac{R_2(R_1 + R_3)\mathscr{E} + R_3(R_1 + R_2)\mathscr{E}'}{\Delta}, \\[4pt]
i &= \frac{(R_1 + R_3)(R_2 + R_4)\mathscr{E} + (R_2 R_3 - R_4 R_1)\mathscr{E}'}{\Delta}, \\[4pt]
i' &= \frac{(R_2 R_3 - R_4 R_1)\mathscr{E} + (R_1 + R_2)(R_3 + R_4)\mathscr{E}'}{\Delta}.
\end{aligned}
\right\} \tag{52-8}$$

Observe that under certain conditions some of the currents may be negative. A negative current is, of course, one which flows in a direction opposite to that arbitrarily chosen as positive.

There are several points of interest in connection with (52-8). In the first place each e.m.f. makes its contribution to the various currents independently of the other e.m.f. This is a general property of networks and, often, a useful one; a complicated network containing a number of e.m.f.'s may be solved for each separately, and the complete solution obtained by addition. Again, we see that, when $\mathscr{E}' = 0$, i' has the same form as i when $\mathscr{E} = 0$. This illustrates another important general property of networks: namely, if an e.m.f. $\mathscr{E}$ in the jth branch of a network produces a current i in the kth branch, then an e.m.f. $\mathscr{E}$ in the kth branch will produce the same current i in the jth branch. The foregoing statement is sometimes called the *reciprocity theorem*. Finally, note that if $R_2R_3 = R_4R_1$, $\mathscr{E}$ makes no contribution to i', and $\mathscr{E}'$ makes none to i. Any two branches of a network with this mutual property are said to be *conjugate*.

Problem 52a. Resistances 3, 5 and 7 ohms, respectively are connected in parallel, the entire group being placed in series with a resistance 1 ohm. What is the total resistance? Ans. 2.48 ohm.

Problem 52b. The combination of resistances described in the preceding problem is connected to a battery of two identical cells in series. Each cell has an e.m.f. 1.5 volts and an internal resistance 0.1 ohm. Find the total current which passes through the battery, and also the partial currents in the 3, 5 and 7 ohm resistances. Ans. 1.12 amp; 0.55, 0.33, 0.24 amp.

Problem 52c. Eight equal resistances R are arranged to form a square with diagonals connected at the midpoint. Find the total resistance between adjacent corners of the square; between opposite corners. Ans. $\frac{8}{15}R$, $\frac{2}{3}R$.

Problem 52d. Twelve equal resistances R are arranged to form a hexagon with diagonals connected at the midpoint. Find the total resistance between adjacent vertices; between opposite vertices. Ans. $\frac{11}{20}R$, $\frac{4}{5}R$.

Problem 52e. Let n identical cells of e.m.f. $\mathscr{E}$ and internal resistance r be connected in p rows each of which contains s cells in series. The p rows are connected in parallel with an external resistance R. Find the current through R and show that it is greatest when the cells are so grouped that the total resistance of the cells is as nearly equal as possible to R. Ans. $\frac{n\mathscr{E}}{pR+sr}$.

Problem 52f. Two batteries of electromotive forces 6 and 10 volts and resistances 0.5 and 1 ohm, respectively, are connected in parallel with a resistance 12 ohms. Find the current through each branch of the circuit and the potential difference between the two junctions. Ans. -2.27 amp, 2.86 amp, 0.59 amp; 7.14 volt.

Problem 52g. Show that if a resistance R' is placed in series with $\mathscr{E}'$ (Fig. 85) the current through it is given by

$$i' = \frac{i_0'}{1 + \frac{R'}{\Delta}(R_1 + R_2)(R_3 + R_4)},$$

where i_0' is the current through $\mathscr{E}'$ when $R' = 0$ and Δ has the same significance as in (52-8).

53. The Wheatstone Bridge.

In laboratory practice rapid and accurate measurement of resistance is essential. Numerous methods have been devised, almost all of which depend upon a special type of resistance network known as a *Wheatstone bridge* (Fig. 86). This differs from the network of Fig. 85 only in that $\mathscr{E}'$ is replaced by a galvanometer or other current indicator G, of resistance R_g. There is now a potential drop from B to C equal to $R_g i_g$, where $i_g \equiv i'$, instead of an applied e.m.f. Hence i_g may be obtained from the last equation of (52-8) by substituting $-R_g i'$ for $\mathscr{E}'$, and solving for i' ($\equiv i_g$). This gives

$$i_g = \frac{(R_2 R_3 - R_4 R_1)\mathscr{E}}{\Delta + R_g(R_1 + R_2)(R_3 + R_4)}, \tag{53-1}$$

and we see that $i_g = 0$ when $R_2 R_3 = R_4 R_1$. As a matter of fact the condition for $i_g = 0$ may be found without solving the network equations. For when $i_g = 0$ there is no difference of potential between B and C,

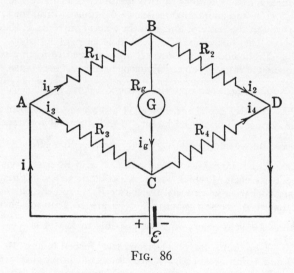

Fig. 86

which requires that the potential drop from A to B equals that from A to C. That is,

$$R_1 i_1 = R_3 i_3. \tag{53-2}$$

Similarly we must have

$$R_2 i_2 = R_4 i_4. \tag{53-3}$$

Since with $i_g = 0$ we have $i_1 = i_2$ and $i_3 = i_4$, we may divide (53-2) by (53-3) and obtain

$$\frac{R_1}{R_2} = \frac{R_3}{R_4}, \tag{53-4}$$

which is the same relation as found from (53-1).

Now let us suppose that one of the resistances, say R_1, is unknown, and that R_2, R_3, R_4 are known, at least one of them being variable. The variable resistance is adjusted until G indicates that $i_g = 0$. Then the relation (53-4) is established between the resistances, and R_1 becomes known in terms of R_2, R_3 and R_4. The adjustment of the bridge to the condition of no current in the galvanometer arm is called *balancing* and is the essential feature of resistance measurements by the bridge method. Calibration of G is not required, since it is used only as a null indicator.

Although the existence of the balance depends upon only (53-4), the *accuracy* with which the balance can be established experimentally depends on the magnitudes of the individual resistances, as well as on the applied e.m.f. and on S_g the galvanometer deflection per unit current. In order to discover the best arrangement of the bridge, let us suppose, for example, balance is obtained by adjustment of R_2. Then, since the precision of adjustment is greater, the larger the galvanometer deflection for a given fractional change of R_2 at the point of balance, the *bridge sensitivity* is given by

$$S \equiv S_g R_2 \frac{\partial i_g}{\partial R_2}, \quad R_2 = \frac{R_4 R_1}{R_3}. \tag{53-5}$$

Using (53-1), we find

$$S = S_g R_2 \left\{ \frac{R_3}{\Delta + R_g(R_1 + R_2)(R_3 + R_4)} \right.$$

$$\left. + (R_2 R_3 - R_4 R_1) \frac{\partial}{\partial R_2} \left[\frac{1}{\Delta + R_g(R_1 + R_2)(R_3 + R_4)} \right] \right\} \mathscr{E}$$

$$= \frac{S_g R_2 R_3 \mathscr{E}}{\Delta + R_g(R_1 + R_2)(R_3 + R_4)}$$

$$= \frac{S_g R_4 R_1 \mathscr{E}}{\Delta + R_g(R_1 + R_2)(R_3 + R_4)}. \tag{53-6}$$

Evidently S has exactly the same form if adjustment is made by means of R_3 or R_4, and therefore for a given set of resistances the bridge is equally sensitive to a variation of any arm. If all the known resistances are variable, as is often the case, adjustment to balance should be made by means of that resistance which can be varied by the smallest fraction of itself.

We first investigate the condition for a maximum value of S, with a given battery and galvanometer. That is, $\mathscr{E}$ and R_g are constant, but R_2, R_3 and R_4 may be varied, subject to the relation $R_2 R_3 = R_4 R_1$. In addition to this mathematical restriction there are certain physical limitations which must be observed, for each resistance element has a definite *current capacity* or maximum safe current, the magnitude of which depends on the construction of the element. Therefore, with the given e.m.f. there is a minimum permissible value for $R_1 + R_2$, and also for $R_3 + R_4$. The minimum value may be different in the two cases, of course. In fact, the current capacity of a given type of resistance element or of a variable resistance is usually greater for low resistance than for high. We may avoid any restriction on R_2 by supposing that $\mathscr{E}$ is small enough so that the current through R_1 can never be excessive regardless of the value of R_2. We cannot, however, escape the condition

$$R_3 + R_4 = R + \delta, \qquad \delta \geqslant 0, \tag{53-7}$$

where R is the minimum safe value of $R_3 + R_4$. Since (53-6) reduces to the simple form

$$S = \frac{S_g \mathscr{E}}{(R_1 + R_2 + R_3 + R_4) + R_g\left(\dfrac{R_1}{R_2} + 2 + \dfrac{R_2}{R_1}\right)}, \tag{53-8}$$

the desired maximum corresponds to a minimum of the denominator

$$D = (R_1 + R_2 + R_3 + R_4) + R_g\left(\frac{R_1}{R_2} + 2 + \frac{R_2}{R_1}\right), \tag{53-9}$$

subject to the conditions

$$\left.\begin{aligned} R_2 R_3 &= R_4 R_1, \\ R_3 + R_4 &= R + \delta, \qquad \delta \geqslant 0. \end{aligned}\right\} \tag{53-10}$$

Minimum D evidently requires $\delta = 0$, and in addition $\dfrac{\partial D}{\partial R_2} = 0$. That is,

$$\frac{\partial}{\partial R_2}\left\{(R_1 + R_2 + R) + R_g\left(\frac{R_1}{R_2} + 2 + \frac{R_2}{R_1}\right)\right\} = 0,$$

which leads to

$$1 - R_g\frac{R_1}{R_2{}^2} + R_g\frac{1}{R_1} = 0,$$

or

$$R_2 = R_1\sqrt{\frac{R_g}{R_1 + R_g}}. \tag{53-11}$$

From (53-10) and (53-11) with $\delta = 0$ we find

$$\left.\begin{aligned} R_3 &= \frac{R}{1 + \sqrt{\dfrac{R_g}{R_1 + R_g}}}, \\ R_4 &= \frac{R\sqrt{\dfrac{R_g}{R_1 + R_g}}}{1 + \sqrt{\dfrac{R_g}{R_1 + R_g}}}. \end{aligned}\right\} \tag{53-12}$$

Inspection of these results shows that if R_g is large compared with R_1, the best arrangement of the bridge is $R_1 = R_2$ and $R_3 = R_4 = R/2$.

Now let us consider the effect of varying R_g. When there is a choice between several galvanometers with different values of R_g, differences in S_g also must be taken into account, maximum S for each galvanometer being calculated with the aid of (53-8). If, however, a galvanometer is designed especially for a given bridge, R_g being adjusted to any desired value by proper choice of wire size in the winding, we have, approximately at least, $S_g = h\sqrt{R_g}$, where h is a constant. That this is so may be seen by considering two galvanometer coils of the same dimensions, one coil having half as many turns of twice as large wire as the other. The deflections per unit current will be in the ratio of one to two, while the resistances will be in the ratio of one to four. Substituting $S_g = h\sqrt{R_g}$ in (53-8) and setting $\dfrac{\partial S}{\partial R_g}$ equal to zero to find the maximum, gives

$$R_g = R_2 R_3 \frac{R_1 + R_2 + R_3 + R_4}{(R_1 + R_2)(R_3 + R_4)} = \frac{(R_1 + R_3)(R_2 + R_4)}{R_1 + R_2 + R_3 + R_4},$$

since $R_2 R_3 = R_4 R_1$. Hence

$$\frac{1}{R_g} = \frac{1}{R_1 + R_3} + \frac{1}{R_2 + R_4}. \tag{53-13}$$

Thus *the resistance of the galvanometer should equal the parallel resistance of the bridge*. This is a perfectly general result, quite independent of other conditions or restrictions.

It only remains to solve (53-11) to (53-13) inclusive for R_2, R_3, R_4 and R_g in terms of R_1 and R. In practice we usually find that R is small compared with R_1. Then approximately $R_g = R_2 R_3 / R = R_4 R_1 / R$ and the solution is

$$\left. \begin{array}{ll} R_2 = \tfrac{1}{2} R_1, & R_g = \tfrac{1}{3} R_1, \\ R_3 = \tfrac{2}{3} R, & R_4 = \tfrac{1}{3} R. \end{array} \right\} \tag{53-14}$$

This optimum arrangement of the bridge can rarely be attained in the laboratory because of limitations of one sort or another in equipment. However, the equations (53-14) may serve as a guide, at least, to the best arrangement under the existing experimental limitations. Evidently for a given set of resistances the galvanometer should be connected between the junction of the two larger resistances and the junction of the two smaller resistances. Also the galvanometer resistance should correspond to the resistance to be measured. That is, while the standard galvanometer resistance of about 100 ohms is quite satisfactory for ordinary measurements, a bridge designed to measure a few ohms should be supplied with a low resistance galvano-meter, and a bridge for high resistance measurements should have a high resistance galvanometer. The application of these principles is made clear in the following articles.

Problem 53. Deduce (53-1) by direct application of Kirchhoff's laws.

54. Resistance Boxes and Resistance Standards. A variable resistance is usually enclosed in a box, with some external device for

(a)

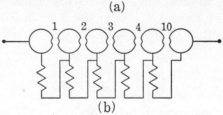

(b)

Fig. 87

adjusting its magnitude, the entire assembly being called a *resistance box*. The most common types are the *plug box* (Fig. 87) and the *dial box* (Fig. 88). The plug box consists of a number of resistance elements of different magnitudes connected in series. Each junction between elements is connected to a metal block; so that if a metal plug is inserted between adjacent blocks the corresponding resistance is short-circuited, that is, removed from the circuit (Fig. 87b). The total resistance of the box is thus the sum of the resistances whose plugs have been removed.   The resistance elements are spools of some resistance wire with a small temperature coefficient, such as manganin wire (see Table, p. 140).   The lower resistance elements are usually wound

(a)

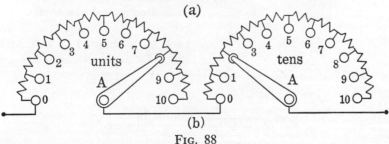

(b)

FIG. 88

with larger wire than the higher resistances, so that their current capacity is greater, as mentioned previously.

The dial box also consists of a number of resistance elements in series, the junctions in this case being connected to a set of metal buttons over which a contact arm *A* moves.   This *dial switch* allows any number of the elements to be included in the circuit. Usually the elements are arranged in groups of ten of equal magnitude, successive groups however differing in magnitude by a factor of ten (Fig. 88b). With this scheme the position of the switch arms indicates the total resistance directly, a convenience not offered by the plug box. The latter has some advantages, however, as it is less bulky than the other and less subject to errors arising from contact resistance, the plugs being more positive in action than the sliding contact arm.

For the most accurate resistance determinations fixed standards are used. In the Bureau of Standards type (Fig. 89) the resistance coil is sealed into an oil filled container. A thermometer well in the center allows the temperature to be determined. The terminals are heavy lugs of such shape that they may be dipped in mercury cups to avoid contact resistance.

FIG. 89

A special form of known resistance called a *shunt* is of great utility in reducing the effective sensitivity of a current indicator in order to increase its range or to prevent excessive deflections. By the *effective sensitivity* we mean the deflection per unit current to be measured. A small resistance connected in parallel with the instrument achieves the desired result by shunting or by-passing all but a small fraction of the total current. Suppose an instrument of resistance R_g is shunted by a resistance αR_g. If the total current through the combination is i and that through the instrument only is i_g, we have

$$R_g i_g = \frac{1}{\dfrac{1}{R_g} + \dfrac{1}{\alpha R_g}} i = R_g \left(\frac{\alpha}{1+\alpha} \right) i,$$

or

$$i_g = \left(\frac{\alpha}{1+\alpha} \right) i. \tag{54-1}$$

If, for instance, $\alpha = 1/9$, the current through the instrument is 1/10 of the total and the effective sensitivity is reduced to a tenth of its full value. Similarly if $\alpha = 1/99$ the sensitivity factor is a hundredth. A calibrated or direct-reading current meter is usually equipped with a set of shunts to allow it to be used for different ranges of measurement.

In the adjustment of a bridge it is desirable to start with the galvanometer in a relatively insensitive condition and to increase its sensitivity as the condition of balance is approached. A convenient adjustable shunt in the form of a dial box is shown in Fig. 90. The terminals marked G are connected to the galvanometer, those marked B to the bridge. If the total resistance of the shunt is R_s and the resistance between the zero button and any other is βR_s, the galvanometer current for the 1-position of the contact arm is

$$i_g = \frac{R_s}{R_g + R_s} i,$$

and for the β-position it is

$$i_g' = \frac{\beta R_s}{[R_g + (1-\beta)R_s] + \beta R_s} i = \frac{\beta R_s}{R_g + R_s} i,$$

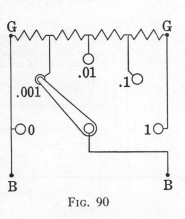

Fig. 90

where i is the total current in either case, and R_g is the galvanometer resistance. The effective sensitivity for the second position relative to that for the first is $i_g'/i_g = \beta$. The factor β is usually taken as a tenth, a hundredth, and so on for successive positions, as shown in the figure. Since the relative sensitivity is independent of R_g this type of shunt is described as *universal*. In practice R_s should be large compared with R_g so that the effective sensitivity in the 1-position is practically the full sensitivity of the unshunted galvanometer.

55. Resistance Bridge Measurements. The most important applications of the bridge principle to resistance measurements are described below.

The Post Office Box. This is a plug box with the resistance elements arranged as indicated in Fig. 91. Two keys (K) and four binding posts (P) are mounted on the box. Internal connections are shown by broken lines and external connections by full lines. The resistance to be measured is R_1. Comparing Fig. 91 with Fig. 86 we see that the circuit is a simple Wheatstone bridge. The keys are included to prevent continuous flow of current with the attendant heating. This is a necessary precaution in all bridge measurements, for steady heating even at a low rate will in time raise the temperature of the coils enough to change their resistances appreciably. In making an observation the battery key is closed *first* to permit a steady flow of currents to be established, then the galvanometer key is tapped. If there is a deflection, the battery key is released and a readjustment of the bridge is made. This process is repeated until the galvanometer shows no deflection when its key is opened and closed.

Returning to Fig. 91, the bridge arms indicated by R_3 and R_4 are known as the *ratio arms*, since they may be set in certain definite ratios, 100 : 1, 10 : 1, and so on down to 1 : 100. The remaining resistances R_2 constitute the adjustable arm. For any given R_1 there are usually several possible arrangements of the bridge. The primary considera-

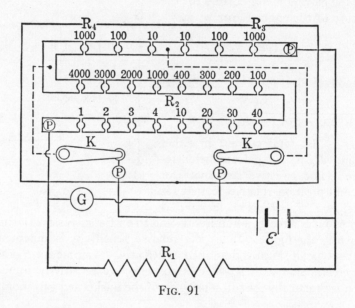

FIG. 91

tion is to set the ratio arms so that R_2 is as large as possible, for the smaller the fraction of itself by which it can be varied the greater the accuracy of the balance. Any further choice in arrangement should be made in accordance with the principles for best sensitivity as set forth in art. 53. The position of the galvanometer and the battery may be interchanged if necessary. For example, if R_1 is of the order of a thousand ohms we take $R_3 = 10$, $R_4 = 100$, or $R_3 = 100$, $R_4 = 1000$. In this case it makes little difference which pair of values we choose except that the latter pair allows the use of a larger battery. The galvanometer is as shown in the figure.

On the other hand if the resistance to be measured is of the order of ten ohms we set the ratio arms at 10 and 1000, and interchange the galvanometer and battery, so that the former is connected from the junction of the larger resistances to the junction of the smaller.

The Slide Wire Bridge.   This is a more accurate device than the post office box.   The resistances R_3 and R_4 are replaced by a single straight resistance wire.   The junction with the galvanometer arm is made through a sliding contact, which also serves as a tap key.   Assuming that the resistance w per unit length of the wire is constant,

$$\frac{R_3}{R_4} = \frac{wl_1}{wl_2} = \frac{l_1}{l_2},$$

where l_1 and l_2 are the lengths into which the slider divides the wire. Therefore

$$R_1 = R_2 \frac{l_1}{l_2}, \tag{55-1}$$

and we require only one known resistance to determine R_1, the lengths l_1 and l_2 being obtained by direct measurement after the bridge is

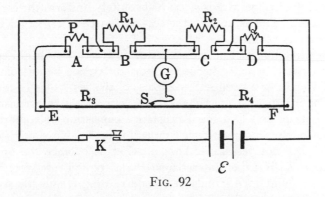

FIG. 92

balanced.   The construction of the slide wire unit is shown schematically in Fig. 92, together with the external connections.   The wire EF is connected to a heavy copper strip with four gaps.   Into two of them, B and C, the unknown and the standard resistance are connected. The other gaps, A and D, may be short-circuited with metal straps, or may contain two auxiliary resistances P and Q whose purpose is explained below.   The wire actually lies on a scale by means of which the ratio l_1/l_2 is determined.   In making an observation the battery key K is closed first, then the key incorporated in the slider S.

The slide wire bridge may be balanced very accurately, so it is worth while to eliminate any possible errors associated with the wire itself. In the first place the ends of the wire may not coincide with the ends of the scale, or there may be a small resistance where the wire is connected to the copper strip. Let us suppose that the extra resistance at the zero end of the scale is equal to that of a section of the wire α units long. Similarly let β be the equivalent end correction at the other end of the scale. Then, short-circuiting P and Q and using known resistances for R_1 and R_2,

$$\frac{R_1}{R_2} = \frac{l_1 + \alpha}{l_2 + \beta}, \tag{55-2}$$

when the bridge is balanced. Next, interchanging R_1 and R_2 and re-balancing,

$$\frac{R_2}{R_1} = \frac{l_1' + \alpha}{l_2' + \beta}. \tag{55-3}$$

From (55-2) and (55-3) α and β may be obtained by solution, since all other quantities are known. The ratio R_1/R_2 should be large, $10:1$ or $20:1$, in order to include as much of the wire as possible and thereby determine the end corrections in terms of the mean resistance per unit length; for the bridge wire is seldom absolutely uniform throughout its entire length. This is, in fact, the second source of error, to eliminate which we must calibrate the wire.

The best method of calibration is due to Carey-Foster. Let P and Q be two nearly equal resistances, their difference being some small fraction, a tenth or a twentieth, perhaps, of the resistance of the whole wire. For instance we may make P the effectively zero resistance of the metal strap, and Q a small resistance consisting of a short length of resistance wire soldered to two connecting lugs. Now R_1/R_2 must be adjustable, but not necessarily known. Let us balance the bridge for any value of R_1/R_2; then interchange P and Q and rebalance. If the first balance point corresponds to a scale reading l_1 and the second to l_1', it is evident that the resistance of the portion of the wire in the interval $l_1 - l_1'$ equals $Q - P$, since there has been an exchange of equal amounts of resistance between the R_3 arm and the R_4 arm of the bridge. By manipulating R_1 and R_2 we may cause the interval $l_1 - l_1'$ to fall anywhere along the wire, thus dividing it into a number of sections of equal resistance. The lengths of the sections differ slightly due to lack of uniformity of the wire. By adding the lengths and dividing by the number of sections, the mean length of a section is found. If now we subtract the length of each section from the mean length and divide by the length of the section, we obtain the correction per unit length which we must apply over the section to obtain the corresponding length of an ideal uniform wire whose resistance per unit length is w. This enables us to construct a calibration curve, plotting total correction against scale reading.   By starting with a correction α for zero on the scale, the end correction is included with the other, and the total length λ_1 of the ideal uniform wire equivalent to R_3 is obtained by adding to l_1 the corresponding correction as shown on the graph.   If l is the scale length, the total equivalent length of $R_3 + R_4$ is given by

$$\lambda = l + \alpha + \beta,$$

and the equivalent length λ_2 for R_4 is then $\lambda - \lambda_1$.   Therefore, for an accurate determination of an unknown resistance, (55-1) is replaced by $R_1 = R_2(\lambda_1/\lambda_2)$.

When the bridge is used to make a direct measurement of resistance as described above, it is often called a *meter bridge*, because the slide wire is usually a meter long.   Obviously, however, the bridge may be used to measure the difference between two nearly equal resistances by inverting the process used for the calibration of the wire.   When thus used, the bridge is called a *Carey-Foster bridge*.   An important application is the determination of the temperature coefficient of resistance (art. 49).   The method consists of measuring the difference between two approximately equal resistances, the temperature of one being kept constant and that of the other varied.   From a series of observations the change of resistance per degree is obtained, and thence the temperature coefficient.   As the resistances must not be removed from the temperature baths or other thermostats in which they are placed, the transfer from one arm of the bridge to the other is accomplished by a mercury-cup switching device of negligible resistance.

The Callendar and Griffiths Bridge.   This is a variety of slide wire bridge specially adapted to resistance thermometry, that is, the determination of temperature by measurement of the resistance of a coil at the given temperature.   Pure platinum wire is used for the coil, which is enclosed in a long tube of porcelain or refractory metal capable of withstanding temperatures as high as 1200° C.   By means of flexible leads the resistance element T is connected into one arm of the bridge (Fig. 93).   A pair of identical dummy or compensating leads is connected into the opposite arm to eliminate temperature and contact effects associated with the leads.   In the same arm is a set of resistances arranged in the manner of a plug box.   The resistances, R_1 and R_2, of the other arms are equal.   The slide wire and all other resistances, except T, are assembled as a unit in one case, the only external connections being galvanometer, battery and flexible leads.

It is customary in using this particular bridge to measure positions on the wire with reference to its electrical center C, a point that may be found by balancing the bridge with both sets of leads short-circuited and all adjustable resistance removed from R_3.   If in making a measurement of T the balance point is a distance l (taken positive to the right) from C,

$$T + r + \tfrac{1}{2}W - wl = S + r + \tfrac{1}{2}W + wl,$$

where S is the amount of adjustable resistance included in R_3, r is the resistance of either set of leads, W is the total resistance of the wire, and w is its resistance per unit length. The above equation reduces to

$$T = S + w(2l). \qquad (55\text{-}4)$$

As usually constructed the smallest resistance element in S has a

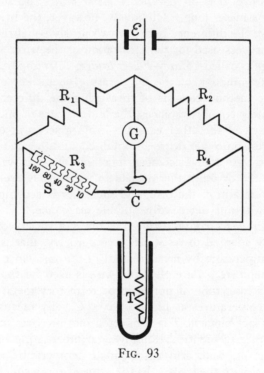

Fig. 93

resistance exactly equal to 20 cm of the wire. It is, therefore, equivalent to a 10-cm displacement of the slider and is so marked. Similarly, the second coil has a resistance equal to 40 cm of the wire and is equivalent to a 20-cm displacement. If l' is the total equivalent displacement corresponding to S, (55-4) becomes simply $T = 2w(l + l')$. When not otherwise known, the value of w may be found by some such method as that of Carey-Foster.

The actual calculation of the temperature may be performed in two ways.   Callendar has shown that the resistance of a platinum coil at $t°$ C is accurately represented by

$$T = T_0(1 + \alpha_1 t + \alpha_2 t^2),\qquad(55\text{-}5)$$

where T_0 is the resistance at $0°$ C, and α_1 and α_2 are constants.   These may be determined by measuring T at two known temperatures.   The formula then gives implicitly at least the temperature corresponding to any measured value of the resistance.   A simpler method is to define a *platinum temperature t_p* by

$$T = T_0(1 + \alpha_p t_p),$$

or more explicitly,

$$t_p = 100\,\frac{T - T_0}{T_{100} - T_0},\qquad(55\text{-}6)$$

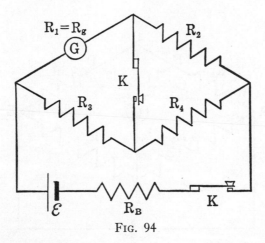

FIG. 94

the two scales being made to agree at $0°$ and $100°$.   To obtain the true temperature t, an empirical formula is used, namely,

$$t - t_p = \delta\left\{\left(\frac{t}{100}\right)^2 - \left(\frac{t}{100}\right)\right\}.$$

It is usually convenient to plot the curve represented by this equation and find the correction for t_p graphically.   The quantity δ depends on the degree of purity of the platinum; for extremely pure samples it is very close to 1.5.

Galvanometer Resistance.   An ingenious application of the Wheatstone network is Kelvin's method of measuring galvanometer resistance (Fig. 94).   The galvanometer is placed in one of the resistance arms, R_1 say, and serves as its own balance indicator.   In the regular galvanometer arm there is only a short-circuiting key.   As opening or closing this key does not affect the bridge in any way when the latter is balanced, R_2, R_3 and R_4 are adjusted until the galvanometer deflection is the same with the key open as it is with it closed. Under this condition

$$\frac{R_g}{R_2} = \frac{R_3}{R_4}.$$

With a sensitive instrument a large resistance R_B must be placed in series with the battery to prevent excessive deflections.

The Kelvin Double Bridge. Although the Wheatstone bridge has a wide range of utility, it is not well adapted to the measurement of very small resistances, that is, resistances of the order of one hundredth of

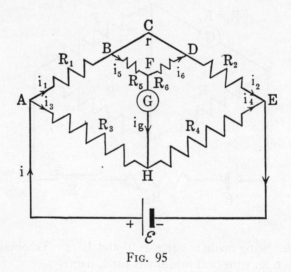

Fig. 95

an ohm or less. This is due in part to the fact that with the equipment usually available it is impossible to make a sensitive arrangement, but more particularly to the difficulty of avoiding contact and junction resistances of the same order of magnitude as the resistance to be measured. The *double bridge* (Fig. 95) devised by Kelvin does not suffer from either of these defects. Here R_1 is the unknown resistance and R_2 a continuously variable resistance such as a slide wire. The connection between these, which has some small unknown resistance r, is shunted by a pair of resistances R_5 and R_6. It is this shunting of the junction resistance that distinguishes the double bridge from the simple Wheatstone bridge.

To find the conditions for balance, we observe that, when there is no current through the galvanometer, F and H are at the same potential. Therefore,

$$R_1 i_1 + R_5 i_5 = R_3 i_3, \qquad R_6 i_6 + R_2 i_2 = R_4 i_4, \qquad (55\text{-}7)$$

and

$$i_1 = i_2, \qquad i_3 = i_4, \qquad i_5 = i_6, \qquad (55\text{-}8)$$

where i_1 is the current through R_1, and so on. Also, considering the parallel paths BCD and BFD,

$$i_5 = \frac{r}{r + R_5 + R_6}\, i_1, \qquad i_6 = \frac{r}{r + R_5 + R_6}\, i_2. \qquad (55\text{-}9)$$

Combining (55-7) and (55-9) gives

$$\left(R_1 + \frac{rR_5}{r + R_5 + R_6}\right) i_1 = R_3 i_3,$$

$$\left(R_2 + \frac{rR_6}{r + R_5 + R_6}\right) i_2 = R_4 i_4.$$

Dividing one by the other leads with the aid of (55-8) to

$$\frac{R_1(r + R_5 + R_6) + rR_5}{R_2(r + R_5 + R_6) + rR_6} = \frac{R_3}{R_4},$$

or

$$(R_1 R_4 - R_2 R_3)(r + R_5 + R_6) + (R_4 R_5 - R_3 R_6)r = 0,$$

which is satisfied if

$$\frac{R_1}{R_2} = \frac{R_3}{R_4} = \frac{R_5}{R_6}. \qquad (55\text{-}10)$$

This set of conditions represents the only balance independent of the junction resistance r, an essential point.

The double bridge appears in several standard forms. A convenient one is shown schematically in Fig. 96. In order to avoid the double adjustment of ratios indicated by (55-10), the resistances R_3, R_4, R_5 and R_6 each consist of a set of coils with plugs, so arranged that the ratio $R_3/R_4 = R_5/R_6$ may be set at definite values 100 : 1, 10 : 1 and so on down to 1 : 100, as desired. The unknown resistance R_1, shown as a rod, is clamped in pairs of jaws, J_1 and J_2. The adjustable resistance R_2 consists of the portion of the slide wire included between two sliding contacts, S_1 and S_2. The end portions of the wire do not enter into the balance as they come into the junction resistance r and into the battery arm respectively.

Calibration of the wire is accomplished by dividing it into a number of sections of equal resistance, with the aid of a known resistance in place of R_1, in the manner described for the Carey-Foster bridge. A curve is plotted showing resistance per unit length, or total resistance from one end, along the wire, whereby the resistance in any interval S_1S_2 is readily determined. In making measurements of the unknown resistance, R_2 is taken as the mean of several observations in which S_1S_2 is allowed to fall on different parts of the wire. Then R_1 is obtained on multiplying by the appropriate ratio factor.

An analysis of sensitivity similar to that carried out for the Wheat-

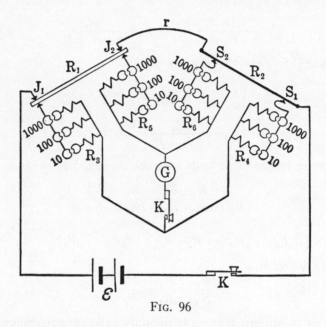

FIG. 96

stone bridge shows that for best sensitivity a low resistance galvanometer should be used.

56. The Potentiometer. Equally important as the measurement of resistance is the measurement of electromotive force, or potential difference. For when $\mathscr{E}$ and R are known, the current i is determined, and the electrical condition of a circuit is therefore completely specified. For accurate measurements it is essential that no current whatever be taken by the measuring apparatus, otherwise the e.m.f. measured may differ appreciably from the true value, which exists in the absence of the measuring equipment. This stringent requirement is met by a resistance network device called a *potentiometer*, whose main features are indicated in Fig. 97. A battery $\mathscr{E}_B$ causes a current i to flow through a resistance R_P. The magnitude of the current may be varied by means of an auxiliary adjustable resistance R_B in series with R_P. Across

a certain portion r_1 of R_P is bridged a source of e.m.f. $\mathscr{E}_1$ and a galvanometer in series.   By Kirchhoff's second law $r_1(i+i_g)+R_g i_g=\mathscr{E}_1$, R_g
being the galvanometer resistance.   Let us suppose that r_1 is chosen so
that $i_g=0$.   Then evidently $r_1 i=\mathscr{E}_1$.   Balancing the potentiometer
consists therefore in adjusting r_1 until the galvanometer shows no
deflection.   Note that this cannot be done unless $\mathscr{E}_1$ is connected with
the proper polarity.   If, now, $\mathscr{E}_1$ is replaced by another e.m.f. $\mathscr{E}_2$ and
a new balance obtained with r_2, *i being unchanged*, we see that

$$\frac{\mathscr{E}_1}{\mathscr{E}_2} = \frac{r_1}{r_2}, \tag{56-1}$$

that is, the potentiometer compares e.m.f.'s in terms of resistances.

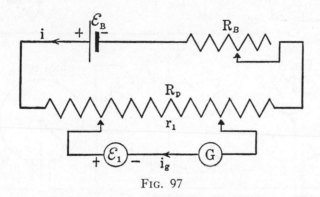

FIG. 97

Supposing that $\mathscr{E}_1$ is due to a *standard cell* $\mathscr{E}_S$, and that $\mathscr{E}_2$ refers to any
unknown e.m.f. $\mathscr{E}$, (56-1) becomes

$$\mathscr{E} = \mathscr{E}_S \frac{r}{r_S}. \tag{56-2}$$

The construction of standard cells of known e.m.f. is described in
Chapter VI.   The Weston standard cell, with an e.m.f. of 1.0186 volts
at 20° C, is the most common.

If the current through R_P is always kept the same, we may mark the
elements of which R_P is composed to read directly in volts.   Consequently, in several standard types of potentiometer the standard cell is
applied to a fixed portion of R_P only, and the balance effected by adjustment of R_B.   This establishes a definite current in R_P and a definite
potential drop across each resistance element, so that when the unknown
$\mathscr{E}$ is balanced by varying r the desired magnitude is indicated directly.

The *Leeds and Northrup potentiometer* employs the above principle.
The wiring diagram of this instrument is given in Fig. 98, the binding

posts for external connections being indicated by P. The resistances in Dial 1, Dial 2, and the slide wire represent R_P. A double-pole double-throw switch is used to change from the standardizing position to the measuring. Thus when the switch is up in the figure, $\mathscr{E}_S$ and G are across ten coils in Dial 2 and a certain number in Dial 1, depending on the value of $\mathscr{E}_S$. The balance is obtained by varying R_B. The switch is now thrown down, placing $\mathscr{E}$ and G across part of Dial 2 and part of the slide wire, and balance is obtained by adjusting both of these. The slide wire is actually a long wire wound on a drum with a revolving

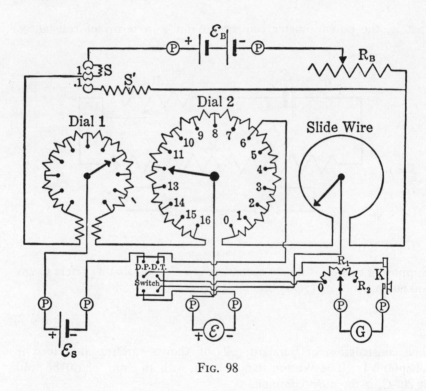

FIG. 98

contact and scale. The resistances S and S' are so arranged that with a plug in the normal position, marked 1, the current through R_P is 0.02 amp and the figures on Dial 2 indicate tenths of a volt. Under these conditions the slide wire may be read directly to 0.00005 volt. When the plug is in the 0.1 position, the current through R_P is reduced to 0.002 amp, and consequently the voltage indications are reduced to a tenth of their normal value. The high resistances R_1 and R_2 in series with G serve to protect the latter from excessive deflections and $\mathscr{E}_S$ from excessive current drain while adjustments for balance are being made.

A potentiometer which is not direct-reading is somewhat more flexible than the direct-reading type and is therefore sometimes used. The *Wolff potentiometer* (Fig. 99) is a good example. Dial 1 has nine 1000-ohm resistances and Dial 2 nine 100-ohm resistances. The blocks A and B represent two identical plug box arrangements totaling 100 ohms each, with only *one* set of plugs. Plugs are moved only from one to the corresponding position in the other; so that the total included resistance of A plus B is always 100 ohms. The resistance of the entire potentiometer is always 10,000 ohms, and consequently the current is

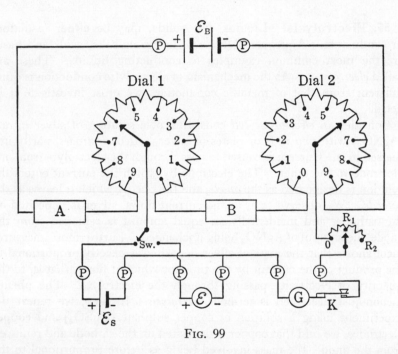

FIG. 99

constant. Balancing consists of adjusting the dials and transferring plugs between A and B until G shows no deflection. The total bridged resistance, r_S or r as the case may be, is the sum of that shown on the dials and in B. Then $\mathscr{E}$ is calculated by (56-2).

As suggested at the beginning of the article, one of the most important uses of the potentiometer is the determination of current and the calibration of current indicators, the method being simply to introduce a known resistance into the given current circuit and to measure the e.m.f. across it. There are also several other useful applications of the potentiometer which are described at appropriate places in later chapters.

Chapter VI

CHEMICAL AND THERMAL EFFECTS

57. Electrolysis. Liquids, like solids, may be either insulators or conductors. Aqueous solutions of inorganic salts, acids and bases are the most common examples of conducting liquids. These are called *electrolytes*. As the mechanism of electrolytic conduction is quite different from that of metallic conduction, we must investigate it in detail.

Consider an *electrolytic cell* consisting of a solution of silver nitrate ($AgNO_3$) with two rods or plates of silver, called *electrodes*, partly immersed in it. Current is caused to pass through the electrolyte from one electrode to the other. The electrode by which the current enters the solution is designated as the *anode*, and the one by which it leaves as the *cathode*. We observe that, as the current flows, silver is deposited on the cathode, and incidentally an equal amount is removed from the anode, the amount of $AgNO_3$ being unchanged. Furthermore, measurement shows that the mass of silver deposited is exactly proportional to the product of the current by the time for which it flows, that is, to the quantity of electricity passing through the electrolyte. The phenomenon just described is termed *electrolysis*. If, now, we repeat the experiment using a solution of copper sulphate ($CuSO_4$) and copper electrodes, we find that copper is deposited on the cathode and removed from the anode, the mass involved being as before proportional to the quantity of electricity which passes. However, the constants of proportionality, namely, the masses deposited per unit charge, are not the same in the two cases. They are, in fact, in the same ratio as the chemical equivalents of silver and copper. The *chemical equivalent* of a substance is the atomic weight, or in the case of a compound substance the group weight, divided by the valence.

Faraday, who was the first to make a systematic study of electrolysis, discovered that the simple relations described above represent general laws. Thus, we may write:

(I) *The mass of a substance liberated at an electrode is proportional to the charge passing.*

170

(II) *The mass of a substance liberated at an electrode by a unit charge is proportional to the chemical equivalent of that substance.*

These laws may be expressed analytically in simple form. Let $\mathcal{M}$ be the mass of substance liberated, i the current, and t the time of flow. Then for the first law,

$$\mathcal{M} = Zit, \tag{57-1}$$

where Z is a constant called the *electrochemical equivalent* of the given substance. Since we are using m.k.s. practical units, Z is expressed in kilograms per coulomb. For the second law let w be the atomic, or group, weight of the substance involved, and v its valence. Then

$$Z = \frac{w}{v}\left(\frac{1}{F}\right). \tag{57-2}$$

Evidently the quantity $1/F$ is the mass per coulomb for a substance of unit atomic weight and valence. As the atomic weight of hydrogen is 1.008 and its valence is unity, F, called *Faraday's constant*, is the number of coulombs required to liberate 1.008 kilograms of hydrogen. Its numerical value is $9.649(10)^7$. Thus a charge $9.649(10)^7$ coulombs liberates at an electrode a mass in kilograms of any substance numerically equal to its chemical equivalent. This amount of a substance is called a *kilogram-equivalent*, so $F = 9.649(10)^7$ coulomb kg-equiv^{-1}. When $v = 1$ a kilogram-equivalent is the same as a kilogram-mol.

An explanation of the underlying principles of electrolysis has been given by Arrhenius and elaborated by later investigators. According to their theory of *electrolytic dissociation*, a certain fraction δ of the molecules of the dissolved material is separated into two or more parts, each of which bears a charge. These charged carriers are called *ions*. Under the influence of an applied e.m.f. they move to the electrodes, the positively charged *cations* to the cathode and the negatively charged *anions* to the anode. At the electrodes the ions give up their charges and the substances of which they are composed are liberated. The continuous arrival of positive charge at one electrode and negative charge at the other is equivalent to a transfer of charge from one to the other, and constitutes the current passing through the electrolyte. Material liberated may actually appear on an electrode, or it may be involved in some secondary chemical reaction. For example, the ions in the silver nitrate solution are Ag^+ and NO_3^-. The Ag^+ is deposited as metallic silver on the cathode, thereby increasing the latter's mass. The NO_3^- is liberated at the anode, but it cannot exist alone in the neutral state; so, in effect, it combines with the silver of which the anode is composed. The silver nitrate thus formed remains in the solution and the net result is loss of silver by the anode. Simultaneously the concentration of silver nitrate increases in the vicinity of the anode and diminishes in the vicinity of the cathode. With currents of ordinary magnitude the change is slow, since even in a dilute solution the amount of ionic charge present is relatively great. Eventually the rate of change of concentration is balanced by diffusion and a steady state is reached. The working of Faraday's laws of electrolysis is often confused by secondary reactions of the sort just described, particularly in cases where the material of the electrodes is different from that of the ions. Thus, if current passes through a solution of sulphuric acid (H_2SO_4) in water, the electrodes being of platinum, hydrogen is liberated at the cathode and appears directly in small bubbles, but oxygen is released at the anode. This is an interesting case because the water is continually decomposed, the concentration of the solution becoming therefore steadily greater. We shall return to this case later.

The question now arises as to the magnitude of the charge carried by the individual ions. We know that a kilogram-equivalent of any substance carries $9.649(10)^7$ coloumbs. Moreover the number of atoms or molecules in a kilogram-equivalent depends only on the valence. For a monovalent substance the number is $6.023(10)^{26}$, the number of atoms in 1.008 kilograms of hydrogen. For a bivalent substance the number is one half of this, and so on. These facts indicate that every monovalent ion carries the same basic charge, positive or negative as the case may be. A bivalent ion carries two of these charges, a trivalent ion three. We suspect at once, of course, that the magnitude of this basic charge is equal to that of the electron and the proton, $1.60(10)^{-19}$ coloumb. Dividing $9.649(10)^7$ by $6.023(10)^{26}$, we do obtain this exact value; which we may regard as a confirmation not only of the theory of electrolysis but also to some extent of the entire electron theory of matter.

Problem 57a. Given that the valence of silver is one and that the valence of copper is two, calculate the chemical equivalents of these metals and also of the *acid radicals* NO_3 and SO_4. Ans. 107.9, 31.8; 62.0, 48.0.

Problem 57b. Calculate the electrochemical equivalents of Ag and Cu. Ans. $1.118(10)^{-6}$ kg/coulomb, $0.329(10)^{-6}$ kg/coulomb.

Problem 57c. Determine for how long 1 amp must flow through a dilute solution of sulphuric acid to liberate 1 gm of oxygen. How much hydrogen is produced at the same time? Ans. 3 hr 21 min, 0.126 gm.

58. Conductivity of Electrolytes. The electrical conductivity γ of an electrolyte is equal to the sum of the partial conductivities due to the various types of ion present. Evidently each partial conductivity depends on the amount of ionic charge per unit volume and on the ionic *mobility*, that is, the transport velocity of the ions per unit applied electric field. For simplicity, consider an electrolyte in which there are equal numbers of positive and negative ions, of mobilities u_+ and u_-, respectively.   Then

$$\gamma = F\delta\nu(u_+ + u_-),\tag{58-1}$$

where F and δ have the same significance as in the preceding article and ν is the concentration, expressed in kilogram-equivalents of solute per unit volume of solution.   In electrolysis it is customary to use the *equivalent conductivity* λ given by

$$\lambda \equiv \frac{\gamma}{\nu} = F\delta(u_+ + u_-),\tag{58-2}$$

since this quantity does not contain the concentration explicitly. Actually λ increases to a limiting value λ_0 as ν converges to zero.   When the solute is a salt or a "strong" acid or base, the dissociation is essentially complete ($\delta = 1$), but the mobilities change with concentration because of change in the electrostatic forces between the ions.   This change is relatively small, so that the *conductivity ratio* λ/λ_0 does not differ greatly from unity.   On the other hand, when the solute is a "weak" acid or base, the mobilities are practically constant, but δ increases rapidly from a small value as ν approaches zero and there is a corresponding rapid increase in λ/λ_0.   Since $\delta = 1$ for $\nu = 0$, it is evident that $\delta = \lambda/\lambda_0$ for any finite concentration.   This allows the degree of dissociation to be determined experimentally.

The measurement of the conductivity of an electrolyte is quite simple if the passage of current does not cause any change in the surface of the electrodes, since, with the small currents employed, any change in composition of the electrolyte is so slow that its homogeneity is not appreciably disturbed in the period of time required for the measurement.   In such a case any ordinary direct-current method may be used. Usually, however, the measurement of conductivity is complicated by a phenomenon known as *polarization*.   Consider, for example, platinum electrodes in a solution of sulphuric acid in water.   As we have seen (art. 57), hydrogen is liberated at the cathode and oxygen at the anode.   A layer of gas collects on each electrode, so that in effect the electrodes are converted from platinum to hydrogen and to oxygen respectively.   But dissimilar electrodes in a solution with which they can react constitute a voltaic cell (art. 51), so there is an internal polarization voltage $\mathscr{E}_p$ which opposes the external or applied e.m.f.   Unless the external e.m.f. is greater than $\mathscr{E}_p$, current cannot be made to pass through the cell.   Unfortunately the magnitude of the polarization voltage depends somewhat on the current, but its limiting value for small currents is 1.67 volts.   This actually exceeds the calculated e.m.f. of an "ideal" hydrogen-oxygen cell by 0.44 volt, the *over-voltage* being attributed to concealed secondary reactions which occur at the anode as the oxygen is liberated. (See, for example, MacDougall, *Physical Chemistry*, 3rd Ed., Chapter XIX.)

When polarization is present, measurement of conductivity can be made by a method due to Kohlrausch. The electrodes are contained in two flasks which are connected by a straight glass tube (Fig. 100). The area of the electrodes is made large in order to increase the time necessary for $\mathscr{E}_p$ to build up. The entire unit is inserted in one arm of a slide wire bridge, whose applied e.m.f. is not steady but alternating; that is, it reverses direction periodically. Hence, the current through the electrolytic cell reverses direction and, if the frequency of reversal is great enough (500 to 1000 alternations per second), polarization is unable to develop to any appreciable extent. The measured resistance is then the true resistance of the electrolytic cell. Of course, a special alternating-current instrument of some sort must be used in balancing the bridge, instead of an ordinary direct-current galvanometer. In

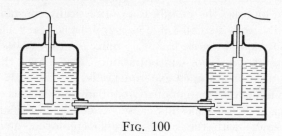

Fig. 100

order to eliminate the unknown resistance of the electrodes and the electrolyte in the flasks, measurement is first made with a long tube between the flasks, then with a short tube of the same cross section. The difference between the two resistance values obtained is the resistance of a column of liquid of length equal to the difference of the tubes. Knowing the cross section of the tubes, we may calculate the conductivity of the electrolyte at once.

Electrolytic conductivity like metallic conductivity is independent of e.m.f. and current, that is, electrolytes obey Ohm's law. The dependence on temperature, however, is different in the two cases; metallic conductivity decreases slowly as the temperature rises, whereas electrolytic conductivity increases quite rapidly, as much as 2 or 3 percent per degree centigrade at room temperature.

In order to apply Ohm's law to a cell which is subject to polarization, we must write

$$i = \frac{\mathscr{E} - \mathscr{E}_p}{r_0}$$

where $\mathscr{E}$ is the applied e.m.f. and r_0 is the true ohmic resistance.   If, now, we define the *apparent resistance* r by the equation $i = \mathscr{E}/r$, we see that

$$r = r_0 + \frac{\mathscr{E}_p}{i}.$$ (58-3)

As $\mathscr{E}_p$ depends in a complex manner not only on the current but also on the length of time it has flowed and on the previous condition of the electrodes, r is in general variable and to some extent indeterminate. This result evidently applies to a voltaic cell, itself causing the flow of current, as well as to a simple electrolytic cell with an external applied e.m.f., which explains the statement made about r in art. 51.

59. The Voltameter.   Electrolytic cells are frequently used for the absolute measurement of current.   It is only necessary to determine the mass $\mathscr{M}$ of substance liberated at an electrode in a time t. Then by the first law of electrolysis the current is

$$i = \frac{\mathscr{M}}{Zt},$$ (59-1)

where Z is the electrochemical equivalent of the substance liberated. We usually choose a cell in which a metal is deposited directly on the cathode without any secondary chemical reaction.   A cell used for current measurements is called a *voltameter*.

For ordinary laboratory use a copper voltameter is convenient and sufficiently accurate.   The electrolyte is a solution of copper sulphate made by dissolving copper sulphate crystals in about four times their weight of water.   The electrodes are copper plates, usually arranged as shown in Fig. 101 in order to utilize both sides of the cathode.   It is necessary to determine the increase in mass of the cathode rather than the decrease in mass of the anode, as the latter may contain impurities which dissolve out during electrolysis.

The cathode, having been cleaned and weighed, is placed in the cell and current is allowed to pass for a known time.   In order to obtain a hard smooth deposit, the current density at the cathode should not exceed 0.02 ampere per centimeter^2.   The cathode is now removed, washed in distilled water and weighed again.   As the electrochemical equivalent of copper is $0.329(10)^{-6}$ kilograms per coulomb we have all the necessary data for the calculation of i by (59-1).

For the most accurate absolute determination of current a silver voltameter is invariably used.   The electrolyte is a solution of silver nitrate, about 15 or 20 parts by weight of silver nitrate to 100 parts of water.   The anode is, of course, silver.   The cathode, however, is usually a platinum cup which serves as a container for the electrolyte

(Fig. 102). In order to prevent impurities from reaching the cathode a small porcelain cup P—porous to the electrolyte—surrounds the anode. The voltameter shown schematically in Fig. 102 is the Richards' type. There are several other types which differ considerably in details.

To obtain the highest accuracy, a few parts in 100,000, great care in the preparation and assembly of the apparatus is essential.* Because of the high accuracy obtainable under proper conditions, the silver voltameter is used to establish the standard current at the Bureau of Standards and at other standardizing laboratories. That is, the ampere

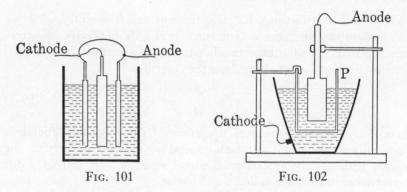

Cathode   Anode   Anode
                                            P
                                Cathode

FIG. 101   FIG. 102

is specified in terms of the amount of silver deposited in it per second. This quantity, the electrochemical equivalent of silver, is $1.118(10)^{-6}$ kilograms per coulomb.

60. Theory of the Voltaic Cell. The physical characteristics of voltaic cells have been described in art. 51. Since these cells are simply electrolytic cells in which the electrodes react with the electrolyte in such a way as to produce an internal e.m.f., their electrochemical behavior is governed by Faraday's laws of electrolysis. It remains, however, to investigate the mechanism by which the internal e.m.f. is produced. An explanation of this mechanism has been given by Nernst.

In order to understand Nernst's theory it is necessary first to familiarize ourselves with the phenomenon of *osmosis*. Suppose we have a U-tube (Fig. 103) with water in one arm and an aqueous solution of some sort in the other. The liquids are separated by a semipermeable membrane or plug M which permits free passage of water but not of the dissolved substance in the solution. It is found that the height of

* A detailed discussion of the technique of voltameter measurements is given by Glazebrook, *Dictionary of Applied Physics*, Vol. II, pp. 247 ff.

the liquid is not the same in the two arms of the tube, being greater for the solution than for the pure water. The pressure p_s just to the right of M is therefore greater than the pressure p_w to the left. Now p_s is made up of two partial pressures, due to the water and to the dissolved substance respectively. Moreover, as water passes through M freely, its partial pressure on the right of M must be equal to the total pressure p_w on the left; so that $p_s = p_w + p$, where p is due to the dissolved substance. The quantity p, which is thus the difference of pressure across M, is called the *osmotic pressure*. A few measurements of p under different conditions suffice to show that in a sufficiently dilute solution at least it is proportional to the absolute temperature and to the number of dissolved molecules or ions per unit volume of solution. In other words, the dissolved particles behave as if they constituted an ideal gas, quite independent of the solvent. With this fact we may return to Nernst's theory.

When a metal electrode is dipped into an electrolyte, there is a tendency for positively charged metallic ions to go into solution. According to Nernst, we can measure this tendency in terms of a pressure p_i called the *electrolytic solution pressure*. If some of the metallic ions are present in the solution before the electrode is introduced, we are able to distinguish three cases.

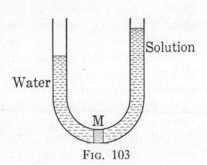

FIG. 103

Thus if p_i is greater than p, the osmotic pressure of the ions in the solution, ions must pass into solution from the electrode, leaving the latter negatively charged. If p_i is equal to p nothing occurs, whereas, if it is less, ions are deposited on the electrode, charging it positively. If the electrolyte does not contain ions of the same substance as the electrode, p is zero, of course. In any event, equilibrium occurs when the electric forces between the electrode and the ions are just sufficient to balance the difference between p_i and p. For example, a silver electrode dipped in a solution of silver nitrate becomes positive relative to the solution, for the electrolytic solution pressure of silver is very small. The difference of potential between an electrode and a solution can be measured by suitable means and serves to confirm Nernst's theory.

We are now in a position to understand the difference between a simple electrolytic cell, without resultant e.m.f., and a voltaic cell, which has an e.m.f. If two identical electrodes are placed in an electrolyte, each in general differs in potential from the electrolyte, but by the same amount, so there is no difference of potential between the electrodes.   On the other hand, electrodes of different materials differ in potential from the solution by different amounts, and therefore differ in potential from each other, this potential difference being the e.m.f. of the cell.   Basically, therefore, the electrolytic cell is a special case of the voltaic cell rather than the other way, as we have heretofore considered it.

Incidentally, it appears from the solution pressure theory that we can produce an e.m.f. without chemical reactions.   The potential difference between an electrode and an electrolyte containing the same substance depends on the osmotic pressure of the metallic ion, which in turn depends on the concentration.   If, then, a cell with identical electrodes is arranged so that the concentration of the solution differs as we pass from one electrode to the other, an e.m.f. is produced and we have a *concentration cell*.   The e.m.f of a concentration cell is usually quite small.   Thus a silver nitrate cell with silver electrodes has an e.m.f of about 0.05 volt at ordinary temperatures if the concentration at one electrode is ten times as great as it is at the other.

There are several ways in which cells may be classified.   For theoretical purposes it is usually best to classify them as *reversible* and *irreversible*.   A reversible cell is one which may be restored to its original condition after discharge by passing a reverse current through it, the energy required for charging being exactly equal to that obtained from the cell during discharge.   An irreversible cell does not have this property, either because energy is dissipated or because there are secondary chemical actions which cannot be reversed.   For practical purposes it is convenient to classify cells as *primary* and *secondary*.   A primary cell is used for discharge only.   It is usually, but not necessarily, irreversible.   A secondary cell, often called a *storage cell*, is alternately charged and discharged and is necessarily reversible, therefore.   Various cells will be described under this classification in following articles.

There is an important theorem relative to reversible cells, originally deduced by Gibbs and by Helmholtz independently.   Let us suppose that a given reversible cell at an absolute temperature T generates Q units of electricity.   If H is the *heat of formation* of the chemical compounds which appear in the cell during the process, that is, the energy released during the formation of the compounds, and H' is the external heat absorbed, the electromotive force $\mathscr{E}$ is determined by the equation,

$$Q\mathscr{E} = H + H'. \tag{60-1}$$

This follows immediately from the law of conservation of energy.

Let us now apply a cyclic process to the cell in order to establish a relation between heat absorbed and work performed. Thus suppose the cell first generates Q units of charge at temperature T absorbing external heat H'. This is represented graphically by ab in Fig. 104. Now insulate the cell thermally and pass a reverse current through it. If heat was absorbed before, it must now be evolved. It cannot escape because of the thermal insulation, so the temperature of the cell rises. We limit this step in the cycle, represented by bc, to infinitesimal changes. Thus the temperature rises to $T+dT$ and the e.m.f. changes to $\mathscr{E}+d\mathscr{E}$. The insulation is now removed and the reverse current continued until we reach the point d, $H'+dH'$ units of heat being given up at the temperature $T+dT$. The point d is chosen in such a way that, if we replace the thermal insulation and allow the cell to generate charge, the cell is restored exactly to its original condition when the temperature reaches the value T. Since we have a complete cycle, the

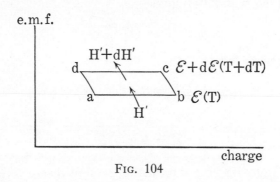

FIG. 104

energy dH' given up by the cell in the form of heat must be equal to the energy received electrically. To calculate this electrical energy, we observe that the total charge produced by the cell during the cycle equals the total charge absorbed by it and therefore, as bc and da are infinitesimals, ab equals cd. Thus the electrical energy received is $Q(\mathscr{E}+d\mathscr{E})-Q\mathscr{E}=Qd\mathscr{E}$ and we have

$$dH' = Qd\mathscr{E}. \qquad (60\text{-}2)$$

The cycle is reversible since we are dealing with a reversible cell, so we may give the cell dH' units of heat and receive $Qd\mathscr{E}$ units of electrical work if we choose.

This reversibility leads us to a very interesting fact. Suppose we have two reversible cells working in cycles with the same temperature limits. We may arrange the cells so that, in effect, one cell runs the other backwards, that is, the external work $Q_1 d\mathscr{E}_1$ supplied by one is equal to the amount $Q_2 d\mathscr{E}_2$ absorbed by the other. Thus $dH_1' = dH_2'$. Also $H_1' = H_2'$; otherwise we can run the combination of cells in a direction such that heat is removed from bodies at a temperature T and is delivered to other bodies at a temperature $T + dT$ without expenditure of energy, a procedure contrary to the second law of thermodynamics. Hence $dH_1'/H_1' = dH_2'/H_2'$, and as we are dealing with *any* two reversible cells it is evident that the ratio dH'/H' is the same for *all* reversible cells, for all reversible mechanisms of any sort, in fact, working between the temperatures T and $T + dT$. As dH'/H' is independent of material properties, it offers an ideal means of establishing an absolute temperature scale, and, as it happens, the *thermodynamic* or *Kelvin scale* to which we are accustomed is obtained by making T proportional to H'. That is,

$$\frac{dT}{T} = \frac{dH'}{H'}. \tag{60-3}$$

Combining this with (60-2) gives

$$H' = QT \frac{d\mathscr{E}}{dT}, \tag{60-4}$$

and finally, using (60-1),

$$Q\mathscr{E} = H + QT \frac{d\mathscr{E}}{dT},$$

or

$$\mathscr{E} = h + T \frac{d\mathscr{E}}{dT}, \tag{60-5}$$

where $h \equiv H/Q$ is the heat of formation per unit charge.

The *Gibbs-Helmholtz* equation (60-5) shows us that the electrical energy developed by a cell at constant temperature is equal in amount to the energy supplied by the internal chemical processes only if $\frac{d\mathscr{E}}{dT} = 0$. Otherwise, the cell absorbs heat as it generates charge, or evolves it, depending on whether $\frac{d\mathscr{E}}{dT}$ is positive or negative.

61. Primary Cells. Several different types of primary cell have been devised to meet various practical requirements. The most important feature in any of them is the depolarizing mechanism, for the primary chemical process almost always involves polarization effects which must be neutralized by secondary reactions of some sort. A cell that polarizes appreciably is of little practical value.

The Daniell Cell. In its simplest form this cell has a zinc electrode in a solution of sulphuric acid and a copper electrode in a solution of copper sulphate, the two liquids being separated by a porous cup (Fig. 105). The zinc is amalgamated to eliminate the effect of impurities which cause a local electrolytic action that wears away the electrode. When the cell is in action, SO_4^{--} ions combine with zinc at the electrode to form $ZnSO_4$ while the H^+ ions move out through the walls of the cup. On reaching the copper sulphate they displace copper ions and form H_2SO_4 with the remaining SO_4^{--}, the copper being deposited on the copper electrode. The copper sulphate solution is thus the depolarizer, for it prevents hydrogen, the most common source of polarization, from appearing at the electrode.

Use of the porous cup may be avoided by placing the zinc electrode above the copper, and relying on the different densities of the solutions to keep them from mixing. A Daniell cell so arranged is often called a *gravity cell*. In any form of Daniell cell, mixture will take place by diffusion if the cell is allowed to stand idle. This cell is therefore adapted only to a service where there is a continuous flow of current. The internal resistance of the cell is rather large, of the order of an ohm.

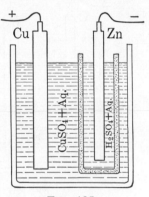

Fig. 105

Ideally, at least, the Daniell cell is reversible, so we may calculate its e.m.f. by means of the Gibbs-Helmholtz equation. As $\dfrac{d\mathscr{E}}{dT}$ is very close to zero (60-5) reduces to $\mathscr{E} = h$. The resultant action in the cell is the formation of zinc sulphate and the decomposition of copper sulphate, so h is the heat of formation of $ZnSO_4$ minus that of $CuSO_4$. The first of these heats in joules per coulomb is 0.82 and the second -0.27, so that $\mathscr{E} = 1.09$ volt. This is the observed value, subject to slight variation with different concentrations.

The Leclanché Cell. In its basic form this cell has zinc and carbon electrodes in a solution of ammonium chloride (NH_4Cl). The carbon electrode is in a porous cup packed with manganese peroxide (MnO_2) which is the depolarizer (Fig. 106). When current flows, Cl^- ions move to the zinc electrode where they form zinc chloride. The NH_4^+ ions move to the carbon where they separate into ammonia (NH_3) and hydrogen. The latter reacts with the MnO_2, forming Mn_2O_3 and water. As the depolarizing action is rather slow, the cell becomes somewhat polarized if used continually, but recovers on being allowed to stand idle for a time. It is, therefore, particularly suited to intermittent service. Its e.m.f. is 1.5 volts.

The common *dry cell* is a special form of Leclanchè cell.   In this case both the depolarizer and the electrolyte are made into a paste. The cell is contained in a zinc can which serves as one electrode, the whole being sealed to prevent the paste from drying out.   The internal resistance of a new dry cell is one-tenth of an ohm or less, so fairly large currents may be drawn momentarily before polarization develops.

The Weston Standard Cell.   When carefully prepared and cared for, this cell provides a highly accurate standard of electromotive force. The somewhat complicated construction of the cell is indicated in Fig. 107.   The cell is contained in a closed glass tube of H-form.   Platinum wires sealed into the glass make contact with the electrodes, which are mercury and cadmium amalgam respectively.   Above the mercury is a paste composed of mixed cadmium sulphate and mercurous sulphate,

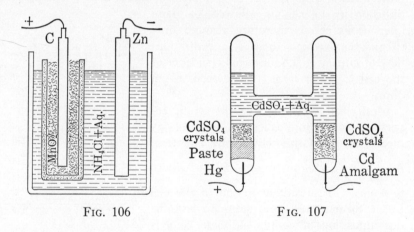

FIG. 106   FIG. 107

which is the depolarizer.   The electrolyte is a solution of cadmium sulphate, crystals being included to insure saturation.   The e.m.f. at 20° C is 1.0186 volts with a negative temperature coefficient of 4 parts in 100,000.

Extensive research has been devoted to the preparation of the Weston cell.*   In use, care should be taken to maintain the entire cell at a uniform temperature, and to protect it from agitation.   Measurements are always made by a potentiometer method (art. 56) to avoid appreciable flow of current.

62. Secondary Cells.   There are two types of secondary cell of practical value.

The Lead Cell.   Of the two types this is distinctly the more important.

* A full discussion of the Weston cell may be found in Glazebrook, *Dictionary of Applied Physics*, Vol. II, pp. 260 ff.

It was devised by Planté in 1859 and has been highly developed commercially since that time. When the cell is fully charged, the electrodes are lead oxide (PbO_2) and lead in a spongy form, respectively. The electrolyte is a solution of sulphuric acid with a specific gravity of 1.20 to 1.28. Usually, in order to obtain a large capacity, each electrode consists of a number of *plates* connected together (Fig. 108). Insulating *separators* prevent plates of opposite polarity from coming into contact.

As the cell discharges, SO_4^{--} ions move to the negative (lead) plate with which they combine to form $PbSO_4$. The action at the positive plate is more complex. The H^+ ions reduce the PbO_2 to PbO, forming water in the process. Then the PbO combines with the sulphuric acid forming $PbSO_4$ again, and more water. As lead sulphate appears on both plates according to the foregoing explanation of the chemical reactions, this explanation is called the *double sulphate theory*. Some objections have been raised against it since the intermediate reaction at the positive plate cannot actually be observed. However, the theory is in agreement with the known facts.* The reactions in charging are, of course, the exact reverse of those described above.

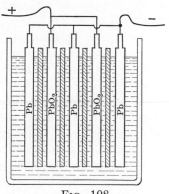

FIG. 108

Since acid is removed from the electrolyte during discharge, the specific gravity of the solution falls. This provides a convenient indication of the state of charge, as the specific gravity is easily measured with a *hydrometer*. When this quantity has fallen to about 1.15 the cell should be considered fully discharged, for at lower values the lead sulphate tends to change from the normal form in which it is deposited to an insoluble form which is not decomposed on charging. This not only destroys part of the active material but, by covering the plates, causes a serious increase in the internal resistance of the cell. A cell which has suffered in this way is said to be *sulphated*. Prolonged idleness also causes sulphation unless the cell is fully charged.

The e.m.f. at full charge is 2.05 volts or slightly more. The value when discharged is about 1.80 volts. The internal resistance is 0.01 ohm or less if the cell is not sulphated, and there is no appreciable polarization, so very large currents may be obtained. The capacity of

* An alternative theory is given in MacDougall, *Physical Chemistry*, 3rd Ed., pp. 641 ff.

a cell is usually expressed in terms of the quantity of electricity it can generate, the unit being the *ampere-hour*. That is, a 100 ampere-hour cell will provide 10 amperes for 10 hours, or 5 amperes for 20 hours, and so on. The ordinary cell varies in capacity from 50 to 200 ampere-hours. For such a cell a current which charges or discharges it in 8 or 9 hours is considered to have a good working value. As has been pointed out, a cell should not be discharged beyond a certain point, but it may be overcharged without any particular harm except the decomposition of water in the electrolyte. This loss may be repaired by adding the proper amount of *distilled* water.

The construction of the plates is a matter of some interest. Originally Planté *formed* the plates electrolytically by placing pure lead in dilute sulphuric acid and passing current first in one direction and then in the other. This process is slow and expensive, so that other methods have been devised. The simplest method consists of casting skeleton plates, or *grids*, of lead and filling these with a paste which is easily converted by electrolysis to the desired form. For the positive plates the paste may be made of Pb_3O_4 and for the negative plates of PbO. Pasted negatives are quite satisfactory and are widely used. Pasted positives, although frequently used, are somewhat less desirable as they have a tendency to crack or buckle.

For both commercial and laboratory use several cells—usually three —are connected in series and assembled in one case, the resulting unit being called a *storage battery*, or an *accumulator*.

The Iron-Nickel Cell. This cell has electrodes of iron and of nickel oxide. The electrolyte is a solution of potassium hydroxide. It is not described in detail as it is not extensively used. It has however certain valuable characteristics. For a given energy content it is lighter than a lead cell. Moreover it is capable of withstanding considerable abuse both electrically and mechanically. When charged, the cell has an e.m.f. of about 1.4 volts.

Problem 62. The temperature coefficient of the lead storage cell is 0.0004 volt per degree centigrade. How much heat at 20° C does the cell absorb per ampere-hour of discharge? Ans. 422 joule.

63. Thermo-Electricity. It is possible to produce an e.m.f. by thermal means without resort to chemical reactions. Seebeck in 1821 discovered that a current flows in a circuit composed of two metallic conductors of different materials if the temperatures of the two junctions are different. There is therefore an e.m.f. in such a circuit, dependent on thermal conditions, called a *thermal electromotive force*. The combination of conductors in which this e.m.f. is generated is known as a *thermocouple*. The energy expended as the current flows is supplied by the absorption of heat from external sources, assuming the temperature at every point in the circuit is maintained unchanged, for there is no other possible means of supply. The first experimental observation of this phenomenon was made by Peltier, who discovered that, when current flows across a junction between two metallic conductors at constant temperature, heat is absorbed or evolved, depending on the direction of the current. The quantity of the *Peltier heat* is proportional to the quantity of charge which crosses the junction. It depends also on the temperature of the junction and the materials of the two conductors. Thus when current flows in a thermocouple circuit because of a temperature difference of the junctions, heat is absorbed at the high temperature junction and evolved, in a smaller amount, at the low temperature junction. The difference between the two quantities is converted into electrical energy by the thermocouple. The Peltier heat is perfectly reversible. If a reverse current is forced through the thermocouple by means of an external e.m.f., heat is absorbed at the low temperature junction and evolved at the high. Care must be taken to distinguish between the reversible Peltier heat and the irreversible *Joule heat* due to resistance. We need not include the latter in the thermodynamical discussion, as we can make it negligibly small by using small currents and conductors of large cross section. This follows from the fact that the Joule heat is generated at a rate equal to Ri^2, R being the resistance of the circuit and i the current, while the Peltier heat is developed at a rate proportional to i alone.

The existence of the Peltier heat at the junction of two conductors indicates the presence there of an e.m.f. Suppose a charge Q passes across the junction in the positive direction, that is, the direction in which the e.m.f. tends to produce current flow. If Π is the e.m.f., the electrical work generated is $Q\Pi$, and this must be equal to the heat H_p absorbed. Thus Π equals the Peltier heat per unit charge. We can understand the production of the e.m.f. at the junction, in a general way at least, from our knowledge of the structure of conductors (art. 49). In the interior of a metal there are free electrons which, taken collectively, behave like a gas. When two metals are placed in contact, the electron gas in each diffuses into the other, but the densities differ in general, so the rates of diffusion are different, and the metals become oppositely charged. As the charges are built up, an opposing electric field develops and equilibrium is soon established. The differential diffusion thus creates an e.m.f., which is measured internally from the negative metal to the positive, as that is the direction in which it tends to produce current in a closed circuit.

The discussion of the junction e.m.f. contains a valuable suggestion. If the temperature is different at two points in a conductor, the density of the electron gas must differ.   We may therefore expect an e.m.f. in a conductor whenever there is a temperature gradient.   This effect, which is easily found experimentally, was first predicted by Thomson (Lord Kelvin) and is called the *Thomson effect*.   As the electron density is greater at lower temperatures, the Thomson e.m.f. should be from cold to hot.   In some metals, however, it is in the other direction, an anomaly for which no simple explanation has been given.   When current flows, there is a reversible absorption or evolution of heat just as in the case of the junction e.m.f.   The Thomson e.m.f. between two points on a conductor which differ in temperature by dT may be expressed in the form of σdT, where σ, called the *specific heat of electricity*, is some function of the temperature.

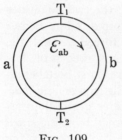

FIG. 109

We are now able to express the e.m.f. of a thermocouple analytically and to deduce some important theorems.   Denoting the conductors of which the thermocouple is composed by a and b, the total e.m.f. is $\mathscr{E}_{ab}$, measured around the circuit in such a direction that a positive current flows from a to b at the warm junction.   If the upper junction in Fig. 109 is the warm one, the positive direction of e.m.f. and current is indicated by the arrow.   Let the temperature of the warm junction be T_1 and that of the cool junction be T_2.   Then

$$\mathscr{E}_{ab} = \left[\Pi_{ab}\right]_{T_1} - \int_{T_2}^{T_1} \sigma_b dT - \left[\Pi_{ab}\right]_{T_2} + \int_{T_2}^{T_1} \sigma_a dT$$

$$= \left|\Pi_{ab}\right|_{T_2}^{T_1} + \int_{T_2}^{T_1} (\sigma_a - \sigma_b)dT. \tag{63-1}$$

The first important property of $\mathscr{E}_{ab}$ is apparent if we choose some temperature T intermediate between T_1 and T_2 and calculate the e.m.f.'s $\mathscr{E}_{ab}'$ and $\mathscr{E}_{ab}''$ for the temperature intervals $T_1 - T$ and $T - T_2$, respectively.   We have

$$\mathscr{E}_{ab}' = \left|\Pi_{ab}\right|_{T}^{T_1} + \int_{T}^{T_1} (\sigma_a - \sigma_b)dT,$$

$$\mathscr{E}_{ab}'' = \left|\Pi_{ab}\right|_{T_2}^{T} + \int_{T_2}^{T} (\sigma_a - \sigma_b)dT.$$

Adding these,

$$\mathscr{E}_{ab}' + \mathscr{E}_{ab}'' = \left|\Pi_{ab}\right|_{T_2}^{T_1} + \int_{T_2}^{T_1} (\sigma_a - \sigma_b)dT = \mathscr{E}_{ab}. \tag{63-2}$$

We may evidently divide $T_1 - T_2$ into any number of intervals with the same result. Hence, *the e.m.f. of a thermocouple for any temperature interval $T_1 - T_2$ is the sum of the e.m.f.'s corresponding to any smaller intervals into which $T_1 - T_2$ may be subdivided.*

Next let us introduce a third metal, c, and compare the thermo-couples ac, bc and ab. For the temperature interval $T_1 - T_2$

$$\mathscr{E}_{ac} = \left| \Pi_{ac} \right|_{T_2}^{T_1} + \int_{T_2}^{T_1} (\sigma_a - \sigma_c) dT,$$

$$\mathscr{E}_{bc} = \left| \Pi_{bc} \right|_{T_2}^{T_1} + \int_{T_2}^{T_1} (\sigma_b - \sigma_c) dT,$$

and by subtraction,

$$\mathscr{E}_{ac} - \mathscr{E}_{bc} = - \left| \Pi_{bc} + \Pi_{ca} \right|_{T_2}^{T_1} + \int_{T_2}^{T_1} (\sigma_a - \sigma_b) dT, \qquad (63\text{-}3)$$

as $\Pi_{ac} = -\Pi_{ca}$.

Now consider a closed circuit abc composed of the three metals, all parts of which are kept at the same temperature. There can be no resultant e.m.f. in this circuit; otherwise current would flow and heat energy would be converted directly into electrical or mechanical work without any temperature difference available, which is contrary to the laws of thermodynamics. As there are no temperature gradients, the Thomson e.m.f.'s are all zero and we must have

$$\Pi_{ab} + \Pi_{bc} + \Pi_{ca} = 0. \qquad (63\text{-}4)$$

Combining this with (63-3) gives

$$\mathscr{E}_{ac} - \mathscr{E}_{bc} = \left| \Pi_{ab} \right|_{T_2}^{T_1} + \int_{T_2}^{T_1} (\sigma_a - \sigma_b) dT = \mathscr{E}_{ab}. \qquad (63\text{-}5)$$

Consequently, *if we know the thermal e.m.f. for each of two metals in combination with a third, we may obtain the e.m.f. for the combination of the two metals by subtraction.* This allows us to measure and tabulate the e.m.f. for each metal against some one chosen as a standard. The e.m.f. for any pair of metals is then given by the difference of the corresponding tabular values. Evidently the same thing is true of the rate of change of e.m.f. with temperature, a fact which we shall find useful later. Lead is usually chosen for the reference metal because its Thomson coefficient is found to be zero.

Lastly, let us include a third metal c in the thermocouple circuit ab

(Fig. 110), keeping the junctions bc and ca at the same temperature T_2, however. The e.m.f. is

$$\mathcal{E}_{abc} = \left[\Pi_{ab}\right]_{T_1} - \int_{T_2}^{T_1} \sigma_b dT + \left[\Pi_{bc}\right]_{T_2} + \int_{T_2}^{T_2} \sigma_c dT + \left[\Pi_{ca}\right]_{T_2} + \int_{T_2}^{T_1} \sigma_a dT$$

$$= \left[\Pi_{ab}\right]_{T_1} + \left[\Pi_{bc} + \Pi_{ca}\right]_{T_2} + \int_{T_2}^{T_1} (\sigma_a - \sigma_b) dT.$$

Using (63-4), we obtain

$$\mathcal{E}_{abc} = \left| \Pi_{ab} \right|_{T_2}^{T_1} + \int_{T_2}^{T_1} (\sigma_a - \sigma_b) dT = \mathcal{E}_{ab}. \tag{63-6}$$

This result evidently may be extended to include any number of added metals. Thus, *any number of intermediate metals may be included in a thermocouple circuit without affecting its e.m.f., provided each such conductor has the same temperature at both ends.* This is a most useful property of thermocouple circuits from a practical standpoint; for it permits the introduction of instruments, copper connecting wires and other accessories, which must be included in the circuit for measurement purposes, without any disturbing effect.

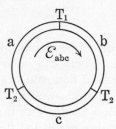

FIG. 110

It remains to determine the form of $\mathcal{E}_{ab}$ as a function of the temperature. Suppose the thermocouple works between the absolute temperatures T and $T + dT$. As the Peltier and Thomson heats are both reversible, we have a device whose thermodynamical properties are identical with those of the reversible voltaic cell. Therefore the fraction of the heat passing through the thermocouple which is converted into electrical energy must be equal to dT/T, just as in relation (60-3). This means

$$\frac{d\Pi_{ab} - \sigma_b dT + \sigma_a dT}{\Pi_{ab}} = \frac{dT}{T},$$

or

$$\frac{d\Pi_{ab}}{dT} - \frac{\Pi_{ab}}{T} + \sigma_a - \sigma_b = 0,$$

which may be expressed in the convenient form

$$\frac{d}{dT}\left(\frac{\Pi_{ab}}{T}\right) + \frac{\sigma_a - \sigma_b}{T} = 0. \tag{63-7}$$

This equation establishes a general relation between the Peltier and

Thomson coefficients.   Now experiment shows that σ is very nearly proportional to T for most substances.   Let us set

$$\left.\begin{array}{ll} \sigma_a = k_a T, & \sigma_b = k_b T, \\ \sigma_a - \sigma_b = k_{ab} T, & \end{array}\right\} \quad (63\text{-}8)$$

where $k_{ab} \equiv k_a - k_b$.   This enables us to integrate (63-7) obtaining

$$\Pi_{ab} = k_{ab} T (T_{ab} - T). \qquad (63\text{-}9)$$

The quantity T_{ab}, which is equal to the constant of integration divided by k_{ab}, is called the *neutral temperature*.

Finally, using (63-1), (63-8) and (63-9), we have for the total e.m.f.

$$\begin{aligned} \mathscr{E}_{ab} &= \left| k_{ab} T (T_{ab} - T) \right|_{T_2}^{T_1} + \int_{T_2}^{T_1} k_{ab} T \, dT \\ &= k_{ab} T_{ab} (T_1 - T_2) - k_{ab} (T_1{}^2 - T_2{}^2) + \tfrac{1}{2} k_{ab} (T_1{}^2 - T_2{}^2) \\ &= k_{ab} (T_1 - T_2) [T_{ab} - \tfrac{1}{2} (T_1 + T_2)]. \end{aligned}$$

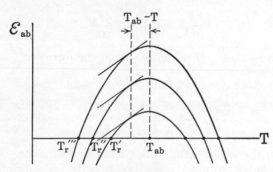

FIG. 111

Since in practice we always keep one junction at a fixed temperature, we may set $T_2 = T_r$, a constant reference temperature, and $T_1 = T$, a variable quantity.   Then

$$\mathscr{E}_{ab} = k_{ab} (T - T_r) [T_{ab} - \tfrac{1}{2} (T + T_r)]. \qquad (63\text{-}10)$$

It appears that $\mathscr{E}_{ab}$ is a parabolic function of the temperature (Fig. 111), being zero when $T = T_r$, of course, and again when $T = 2T_{ab} - T_r$, that is, when the *average* temperature of the junctions $\tfrac{1}{2}(T + T_r)$ equals T_{ab}.   Curves are shown in the figure for various values of T_r.   Evidently $\mathscr{E}_{ab}$ has a maximum for any value of T_r, when $T = T_{ab}$.

As (63-10) depends on (63-8), it is sometimes not sufficiently accurate when the temperature varies over a wide range.   In such a case the thermocouple must be calibrated.   On the other hand, when only small temperature differences are involved, as is often the case, (63-10) serves very well. We are then interested in the rate of change of $\mathscr{E}_{ab}$. This quantity, called the *thermo-electric power*, is given by

$$\frac{d\mathscr{E}_{ab}}{dT} = k_{ab}(T_{ab} - T). \tag{63-11}$$

Since T_r does not appear, the fixed temperature is of no consequence. This is indicated graphically in Fig. 111 by the parallel tangents, whose slope is the thermo-electric power. In order that $\frac{d\mathscr{E}_{ab}}{dT}$ shall be large, it is necessary that T be kept well away from T_{ab}. Equation (63-11), being linear, offers a more convenient means of recording data on thermocouples, either graphically or in tabular form, than (63-10). The thermo-electric power for each metal in combination with lead is determined experimentally. Then the value for any pair of metals is obtained by subtraction, as explained in connection with equation (63-5) above. Thus, for example,

$$\frac{d\mathscr{E}_{ab}}{dT} = \frac{d\mathscr{E}_{al}}{dT} - \frac{d\mathscr{E}_{bl}}{dT}, \tag{63-12}$$

where l indicates lead. If we write this in the form

$$k_{ab}(T_{ab} - T) = k_{al}(T_{al} - T) - k_{bl}(T_{bl} - T)$$

and note that $k_{ab} = k_{al} - k_{bl}$, we see that

$$k_{ab}T_{ab} = k_{al}T_{al} - k_{bl}T_{bl}, \tag{63-13}$$

indicating that the various constants are not independent. For tabulation it is convenient to use the centigrade scale. Denoting centigrade temperature by t, $T = t + 273°$ and (63-11) may be written

$$\frac{d\mathscr{E}_{ml}}{dt} = k_{ml}(t_{ml} - t) \equiv \alpha + \beta t, \tag{63-14}$$

where m indicates any metal. Thermal e.m.f.'s are usually very small, of the order of a few microvolts. Values of α and β for some metals and a few alloys are given in the adjoining table, which is based on the very complete work of Bridgman.* The values of the constants vary considerably with the condition of the substances, and must be regarded as approximate only. To find the basic constants in terms of α and β, we have $k_{ml} = -\beta$ and $T_{ml} = t_{ml} + 273° = (-\alpha/\beta) + 273°$. Note that we have taken the e.m.f. to be positive when it causes current to flow from m to l at the *warm* junction. Practice varies in this regard.

* Bridgman, P. W., *Amer. Acad. of Arts and Sci.* **53**, 269 (1918).

The thermal electromotive force for any metal in combination with lead expressed in terms of α and β is obtained by integrating (63-14). This gives

$$\mathscr{E}_{ml} = \alpha(t - t_r) + \tfrac{1}{2}\beta(t^2 - t_r{}^2), \qquad (63\text{-}15)$$

where t_r is the fixed reference temperature of one junction.

Substance	α (volt/deg)	β (volt/deg^2)
Bismuth . .	$74.42(10)^{-6}$	$-0.0320(10)^{-6}$
Cadmium . .	$-12.002(10)^{-6}$	$-0.3238(10)^{-6}$
Cobalt . .	$17.32(10)^{-6}$	$0.0780(10)^{-6}$
Copper . .	$-2.777(10)^{-6}$	$-0.00966(10)^{-6}$
Iron . . .	$-16.18(10)^{-6}$	$0.0178(10)^{-6}$
Magnesium .	$0.095(10)^{-6}$	$-0.00008(10)^{-6}$
Nickel . .	$17.61(10)^{-6}$	$0.0356(10)^{-6}$
Platinum . .	$3.092(10)^{-6}$	$0.02668(10)^{-6}$
Silver . .	$-2.566(10)^{-6}$	$-0.00864(10)^{-6}$
Tin . . .	$-0.230(10)^{-6}$	$0.00134(10)^{-6}$
Tungsten . .	$-1.594(10)^{-6}$	$-0.03410(10)^{-6}$
Zinc . . .	$-3.047(10)^{-6}$	$0.00990(10)^{-6}$
Constantan .	$34.76(10)^{-6}$	$0.0794(10)^{-6}$
Manganin . .	$-1.366(10)^{-6}$	$-0.000828(10)^{-6}$

Problem 63a. Show that

$$\Pi_{ab} = T\frac{d\mathscr{E}_{ab}}{dT},$$

$$\sigma_a - \sigma_b = -T\frac{d^2\mathscr{E}_{ab}}{dT^2},$$

are general relations applying to all thermocouples. Verify these relations for the special case in which $\mathscr{E}_{ab}$ has the form given by (63-10).

Problem 63b. Referring to the table of thermo-electric powers, calculate Π_{ab} and $\sigma_a - \sigma_b$ for a bismuth-cadmium thermocouple at $0°$ C. Ans. 0.0236 joule/coulomb, $-79.7(10)^{-6}$ volt/degree.

Problem 63c. Express the thermal e.m.f. of a copper-constantan couple in terms of centigrade temperatures, the cool junction being at $0°$ C. Ans. $\mathscr{E}_{ab} = -37.54(10)^{-6}t - 0.0445(10)^{-6}t^2$ (in volts).

64. Thermocouple Measurements and Instruments.

Thermocouples are of great value for the measurement of temperatures and temperature intervals of any magnitude up to $1600°$ C. The type of thermocouple is determined by the use for which it is intended. Up to $300°$ C, copper and constantan—a copper-nickel alloy—are satisfactory. Iron and constantan will serve up to $800°$ C. For the higher temperatures platinum and some platinum alloy must be used. Temperature measurements in commercial practice usually consist in obtaining the thermal e.m.f., either directly by means of a potentiometer or from the deflection of a high-resistance galvanometer, and referring the result to a calibration curve.   In the laboratory it is often necessary to determine small changes in temperature accurately.   In this case a potentiometer is always used to measure the e.m.f.'s to avoid a possible error due to Peltier heat developed at the junctions of the thermocouple. One junction is kept at any convenient fixed temperature while the other varies.   The change in e.m.f. divided by the thermo-electric power gives the corresponding temperature change.

Thermocouples are used, indirectly, to measure several physical quantities in addition to temperature.   For example, if radiant energy in the form of heat or light falls on one junction, it produces a rise of temperature and consequently an e.m.f., which may be used to measure the intensity of the radiation.   Great sensitivity may be obtained if a number of thermocouples are connected in series (Fig. 112), alternate

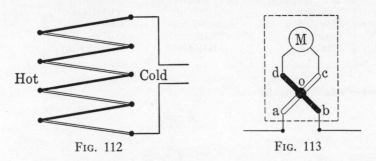

FIG. 112   FIG. 113

junctions being exposed to the heating influence so that the e.m.f.'s add. A device of this sort is called a *thermopile*.

In alternating-current electrical measurements thermocouples play an important role, especially for high frequencies where the coil type of measuring instrument is not effective.   A *thermocouple meter* consists of a sensitive direct-current meter element, a thermocouple and a small resistance unit, all included in a single case.   The external current to be measured is passed through the resistance or *heater* unit.   This is so arranged that the heat generated warms one junction of the thermocouple.   The resulting thermal e.m.f. produces a direct current through the meter element.   In most direct-current indicators the deflection is proportional to the current, which in this case is proportional to the thermal e.m.f.   This latter quantity, in turn, is proportional to the average rate at which heat is generated, that is, to the mean value of the square of the alternating current.   Thus the scale of a thermocouple meter is not uniform but is more extended at the upper end than at the lower.   A convenient arrangement for a thermocouple meter is shown in Fig. 113.   The meter element is designated by M.   The thermocouple and heater are formed jointly by crossing two dissimilar conductors, ac and bd, such as iron and constantan for example, and welding or soldering them at the point of contact o.   The external current flows along aob, which serves as the heater.   The thermocouple proper is cod.

65. Contact Potential Difference.   Although we have studied various phenomena dependent on the existence of free electrons in the interior of a conductor, we have as yet made no mention of the restraining forces which must exist at the surface of the conductor to oppose the escape of these electrons.   There are several effects which depend on these surface forces.

In the first place, experiment shows that a definite amount of work ϕ must be done against electrical forces in carrying an electron from the interior of a conductor out through the surface.   This quantity, called

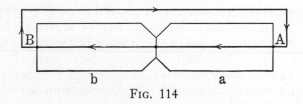

FIG. 114

the *work function*, depends primarily on the substance of which the conductor is composed.   It varies slightly with the temperature.

Now suppose that we place two conductors a and b (Fig. 114) in contact.   If we carry a unit positive charge around a closed path such as that indicated in the figure, the total *electrical* work performed is zero since the forces are of an electrostatic nature (art. 48).   Let V_{AB} be the potential drop, if any, from a point A just outside the surface of conductor a to a point B just outside the surface of conductor b. The work equation is

$$\frac{\phi_a}{e} - \Pi_{ab} - \frac{\phi_b}{e} - V_{AB} = 0,$$

or

$$V_{AB} = \frac{\phi_a - \phi_b}{e} - \Pi_{ab},$$

where the Peltier coefficient Π_{ab} appears with the negative sign since the electric field to which it refers is in the direction opposite to the Peltier e.m.f., and where e is the charge of the electron (a negative quantity). The quantity V_{AB} is the *contact potential difference* of the conductors. Its existence is readily confirmed by experiment, although accurate measurement is very difficult. Its magnitude is of the order of a few tenths of a volt, so Π_{ab} is entirely negligible and we may write

$$V_{AB} = \frac{\phi_a - \phi_b}{e}. \tag{65-1}$$

Actually, it can be shown that (65-1) becomes an exact relation if ϕ_a and ϕ_b represent the regular independent work functions, rather than those for a and b in contact as assumed above.

66. Thermionic Emission. The work function ϕ, described in the preceding article, is the controlling factor in an effect of great practical importance called *thermionic emission*. When a conductor is heated, electrons are emitted, the number increasing with great rapidity as the temperature rises. This phenomenon is utilized by many devices which involve electron currents, such as X-ray tubes, radio vacuum tubes, alternating-current rectifiers, and electron relays. The mechanism of the emission is easily understood when we consider the properties of the electron gas in the interior of the conductor. The free electrons move about with a random distribution of velocities, their mean kinetic energy, however, being always proportional to the absolute temperature. Whenever an electron with kinetic energy greater than ϕ happens to move toward the surface from a point just inside, it is able to escape, losing an amount ϕ of kinetic energy in the process. The higher the temperature, the greater is the number of electrons with the necessary energy for escape, so the emission increases as the temperature rises.

From the kinetic theory of gases, and from thermodynamics, it is possible to calculate the rate at which electrons are emitted as a function of the temperature. This calculation was first made by Richardson, who showed that if ϕ is a constant the emission current per unit area must have the form

$$j = A'T^{1/2}e^{-b'/T}, \tag{66-1}$$

where T is the absolute temperature and A', b' are constants for any substance, b' being proportional to ϕ. If variation of ϕ with temperature is taken into account the emission current equation is

$$j = AT^2e^{-b/T}. \tag{66-2}$$

It is difficult to distinguish between the two equations experimentally with the range of temperatures available in the laboratory. However, (66-2) is superior theoretically and is therefore to be preferred.

Electron emission usually takes place in a vacuum, the emitting body being in the form of a *filament F* (Fig. 115) heated by a current from an external battery $\mathscr{E}_F$. Included in the vacuum space is another conductor P, usually called the *plate*. When this is maintained at a positive potential V relative to F by a plate battery $\mathscr{E}_P$, the emitted electrons are drawn away from the filament as they appear and a steady emission current exists. Evidently if the plate is at a negative potential, no current can pass. In order to obtain the full emission current predicted by (66-2), it is necessary that V be great enough to remove the electrons from the vicinity of F very rapidly, otherwise a *space charge*

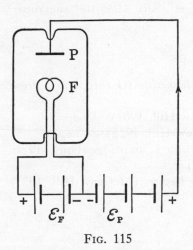

FIG. 115

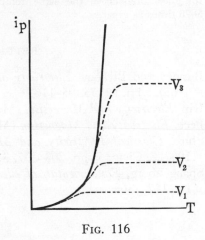

FIG. 116

(art. 81) accumulates between P and F and limits the current to the plate. This effect is shown in Fig. 116 where the full line curve, representing (66-2), gives the current i_p to the plate when V is very large. The broken curves show the currents actually obtained for smaller values of V. Evidently the higher the temperature, the greater must be the value of V to obtain the full emission current.

The magnitude of the emission from any substance is greatly affected by the condition of the surface. For example, the presence of a minute amount of thorium on the surface of tungsten increases the emission many thousand times. Use is made of this fact in constructing filaments. Platinum filaments coated with various barium and strontium salts also have very high emission. Values of A and b for a few substances are given in the table.

Substance	$A \left(\dfrac{\text{amp}}{\text{meter}^2 \text{ deg}^2} \right)$	b (deg abs)
Molybdenum . .	$55(10)^4$	48,700
Tantalum . .	$55(10)^4$	48,600
Thorium . . .	$70(10)^4$	39,200
Tungsten. . .	$60(10)^4$	38,900
Thoriated Tungsten .	$3(10)^4$	30,500

Problem 66a. For pure tungsten filaments the normal working temperature is about 2400° K (absolute). Calculate the emission current at this temperature. Ans. $1.14(10)^3$ amp/meter².

Problem 66b. The normal temperature for thoriated tungsten filaments is about 1900° K. Calculate the emission current. Compare it with the current for pure tungsten at the same temperature. Ans. $11.56(10)^3$ amp/meter², 5070 times as great.

REFERENCES

Bleaney and Bleaney, *Electricity and Magnetism* (Oxford Univ. Press, 1965). Pp. 61–75, 95–116.

Kip, *Electricity and Magnetism* (McGraw-Hill, 1962). Chap. 7.

Peck, *Electricity and Magnetism* (McGraw-Hill, 1953). Chap. 6.

Shire, *Classical Electricity and Magnetism* (Cambridge Univ. Press, 1960). Chap. 7, pp. 203–207, 314–317.

Spangenberg, *Fundamentals of Electron Devices* (McGraw-Hill, 1957). Pp. 137–156.

Chapter VII

MAGNETIC FIELD OF A CURRENT

67. Scalar and Vector Products. So far our use of vectors has been confined to the addition and subtraction of directed quantities. In the study of the magnetic fields due to currents and of induced electromotive forces certain products of vectors play such an important part that the treatment of the subject becomes very clumsy if we limit ourselves to the scalar methods employed for the most part in the preceding chapters.

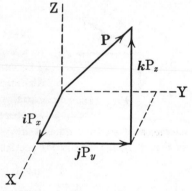

FIG. 117

In order to represent a vector in terms of its rectangular components we employ unit vectors i, j, k directed along the X, Y, Z axes respectively. If, then, the magnitudes of the rectangular components of a vector $\mathbf{P}$ are designated by P_x, P_y, P_z we have

$$\mathbf{P} = iP_x + jP_y + kP_z, \quad (67\text{-}1)$$

as is evident at once from Fig. 117.

Writing a second vector $\mathbf{Q}$ in the same form,

$$\mathbf{Q} = iQ_x + jQ_y + kQ_z, \tag{67-2}$$

and the sum of the two vectors is given by

$$\mathbf{P} + \mathbf{Q} = i(P_x + Q_x) + j(P_y + Q_y) + k(P_z + Q_z), \tag{67-3}$$

since each component of the sum is equal to the sum of the corresponding components of the two vectors.

Two products of vectors are important in physics, the scalar product and the vector product.

Scalar Product. The scalar product of two vectors $\mathbf{P}$ and $\mathbf{Q}$ is defined as the product of the magnitude of $\mathbf{P}$ by that of $\mathbf{Q}$ by the cosine of the angle between them. It is a scalar quantity and is

197

designated by **P·Q**, the dot representing the cosine of the angle between the positive directions of the two vectors. It is equal to the component of either vector in the direction of the other multiplied by the magnitude of the other.

Many examples of the scalar product occur in physics. If a body on which a force $\mathscr{F}$ is acting suffers a displacement $d\mathbf{l}$ in a direction making an angle α with the force, the work done is

$$dW = \mathscr{F} \cos \alpha dl = \mathscr{F} \cdot d\mathbf{l}. \qquad (67\text{-}4)$$

A plane surface may be represented as a vector directed along its positive normal and having a magnitude equal to its area. Therefore the electric flux through an element of surface $d\mathbf{s}$ (the element ds may always be considered plane even if the surface of which it forms a part is curved) is

$$dF = \mathbf{E} \cdot d\mathbf{s},$$

and Gauss' law (8-5) may be written

$$\int_s \mathbf{E} \cdot d\mathbf{s} = \frac{1}{\kappa_0} \int_\tau \rho d\tau. \qquad (67\text{-}5)$$

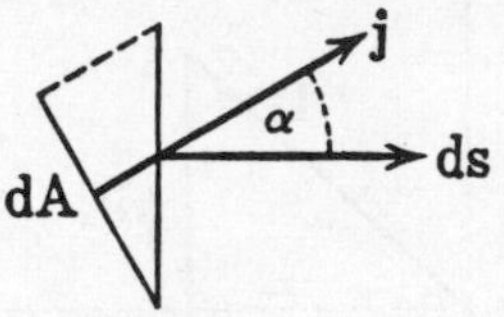

Fig. 118

Next consider a current, whether it be due to a flow of electricity or of a material fluid. The current density $\mathbf{j}$ is a vector having the direction of the current and a magnitude equal to the current per unit cross section. In terms of $\mathbf{j}$ the current di through an element of surface $d\mathbf{s}$ is $\mathbf{j} \cdot d\mathbf{s}$. For the current through ds (Fig. 118) is that through the cross section $dA = ds \cos \alpha$. Consequently,

$$di = jdA = j \cos \alpha ds = \mathbf{j} \cdot d\mathbf{s}.$$

Hence the total current through any surface s is given by the integral

$$i = \int_s \mathbf{j} \cdot d\mathbf{s}. \qquad (67\text{-}6)$$

Vector Product. This product is of great importance in electromagnetism. The vector product of two vectors **P** and **Q** is a vector normal to their plane in the sense of advance of a right-handed screw rotated from the first to the second of the two vectors through the smaller angle between them. Its magnitude is equal to the product of the magnitudes of the two vectors by the sine of the angle between their positive directions, that is, equal to the magnitude of either vector by the normal component of the other. This product is designated by the symbol **P** × **Q**, the cross between the two vectors representing the sine of the angle between them.

If, then, the two vectors $\mathbf{P}$ and $\mathbf{Q}$ are oriented as in Fig. 119, the vector $\mathbf{P} \times \mathbf{Q}$ is directed toward the reader and has the magnitude $PQ \sin \alpha$.   On the other hand, $\mathbf{Q} \times \mathbf{P}$ is a vector of the same magnitude oppositely directed.   Hence

$$\mathbf{Q} \times \mathbf{P} = -\mathbf{P} \times \mathbf{Q}. \tag{67-7}$$

Whenever, then, we interchange two vectors appearing in a vector product, we must change the sign of the product.

Since the area of the parallelogram $OABC$ is $PQ \sin \alpha$, the vector product $\mathbf{P} \times \mathbf{Q}$ has a magnitude equal to the area of the parallelogram of which the vectors $\mathbf{P}$ and $\mathbf{Q}$ are the sides.   Moreover, as the vector product of $\mathbf{P}$ and $\mathbf{Q}$ is directed along the normal to the parallelogram, the vector representing the surface is $\mathbf{P} \times \mathbf{Q}$ or $\mathbf{Q} \times \mathbf{P}$ according as the one or the other face of the parallelogram is chosen as positive.

The torque $\mathscr{L}$ exerted by a force $\mathscr{F}$ about a point O provides a simple example of the vector product.   For if $\mathbf{r}$ is the position vector of the point of application of the force relative to O,

$$\mathscr{L} = \mathbf{r} \times \mathscr{F}, \tag{67-8}$$

the vector product having the magnitude of the moment of the force and the direction of the axis about which it tends to produce rotation.

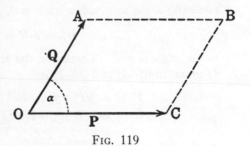

Fig. 119

We shall find it very convenient to use the compact notation which we have developed here. In so far as the major portion of the text is concerned no more vector analysis will be used than that which has been presented up to this point. All that the reader needs to remember is that $\mathbf{P} \cdot \mathbf{Q}$ represents the scalar $PQ \cos \alpha$, where α is the angle between the vectors $\mathbf{P}$ and $\mathbf{Q}$, and that $\mathbf{P} \times \mathbf{Q}$ represents a vector perpendicular to the plane of $\mathbf{P}$ and $\mathbf{Q}$ in the sense of advance of a right-handed screw rotated from $\mathbf{P}$ to $\mathbf{Q}$ having a magnitude equal to $PQ \sin \alpha$.   To solve a few of the problems and to develop part of the theory given in Chapter XVI, however, it is necessary to express the scalar and vector products in terms of the components of the vectors involved.   Therefore, we shall now investigate the expansion of the two products.

Expansion of the Scalar Product.   First we must note that the distributive law of multiplication holds for the scalar product.   This law states that

$$(\mathbf{P} + \mathbf{Q}) \cdot \mathbf{R} = \mathbf{P} \cdot \mathbf{R} + \mathbf{Q} \cdot \mathbf{R}, \tag{67-9}$$

which is evidently true since it amounts to nothing more than the statement that the component of $P + Q$ in the direction of R is equal to the sum of the component of P in the direction of R and the component of Q in the direction of R.

Having shown that the distributive law is valid for the scalar product of the sum of two vectors by a third, it follows at once that it holds for the sum of any number of vectors. For example,

$$(P + Q + R) \cdot S = \{(P + Q) + R\} \cdot S = (P + Q) \cdot S + R \cdot S$$
$$= P \cdot S + Q \cdot S + R \cdot S,$$

and similarly,

$$(P + Q + R) \cdot (S + T + U) = P \cdot S + P \cdot T + P \cdot U$$
$$+ Q \cdot S + Q \cdot T + Q \cdot U + R \cdot S + R \cdot T + R \cdot U.$$

The scalar products of the unit vectors, i, j, k are

$$i \cdot i = j \cdot j = k \cdot k = 1,$$

since the angle involved in each is 0, and

$$i \cdot j = j \cdot k = k \cdot i = 0,$$

as the angle is $\pi/2$. Therefore, the scalar product of the vectors P and Q given in (67-1) and (67-2) is

$$P \cdot Q = (iP_x + jP_y + kP_z) \cdot (iQ_x + jQ_y + kQ_z)$$
$$= i \cdot i P_x Q_x + i \cdot j P_x Q_y + i \cdot k P_x Q_z + \text{etc.}$$
$$= P_x Q_x + P_y Q_y + P_z Q_z. \tag{67-10}$$

Thus the work done by a force

$$\mathscr{F} = i\mathscr{F}_x + j\mathscr{F}_y + k\mathscr{F}_z$$

when the body on which it is acting undergoes a displacement

$$d1 = idx + jdy + kdz$$

is

$$\mathscr{F} \cdot d1 = \mathscr{F}_x dx + \mathscr{F}_y dy + \mathscr{F}_z dz,$$

each term on the right representing the work done by one component of the force.

Expansion of the Vector Product. The distributive law holds also for the vector product, that is,

$$(P + Q) \times R = P \times R + Q \times R. \tag{67-11}$$

To prove this, consider the vectors P, Q, $P + Q$, R as illustrated in Fig. 120a. Project the triangle formed by the vectors P, Q, $P + Q$ on a plane perpendicular to R. The sides of the projected triangle

represent the components of the three vectors $\mathbf{P}$, $\mathbf{Q}$, $\mathbf{P}+\mathbf{Q}$ normal to
$\mathbf{R}$. If, therefore, the projected triangle is rotated in its plane through
a right angle and the length of each side increased in the ratio $R:1$,
the sides of the resulting triangle (Fig. 120b) will represent in magni-
tude and direction the vectors $\mathbf{P}\times\mathbf{R}$, $\mathbf{Q}\times\mathbf{R}$, $(\mathbf{P}+\mathbf{Q})\times\mathbf{R}$. These
three vectors, then, form a closed triangle, showing that the third is
the sum of the first and second.

In developing the expansion of the vector product it is important that
the axes employed should be right-handed, that is, that the Z axis
should have the direction of advance of a right-handed screw rotated

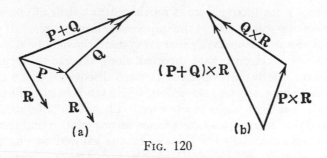

FIG. 120

from X to Y through the right angle between them. If this condition
is satisfied, the vector products of the unit vectors i, j, k are

$$i \times i = j \times j = k \times k = 0,$$

$$i \times j = k, \qquad j \times k = i, \qquad k \times i = j.$$

Consequently,

$$\begin{aligned}
\mathbf{P} \times \mathbf{Q} &= (iP_x + jP_y + kP_z) \times (iQ_x + jQ_y + kQ_z) \\
&= i \times iP_xQ_x + i \times jP_xQ_y + i \times kP_xQ_z + \text{etc.} \\
&= i(P_yQ_z - P_zQ_y) + j(P_zQ_x - P_xQ_z) + k(P_xQ_y - P_yQ_x).
\end{aligned} \qquad (67\text{-}12)$$

This expansion can be written very compactly in determinant notation
as

$$\mathbf{P} \times \mathbf{Q} = \begin{vmatrix} i & j & k \\ P_x & P_y & P_z \\ Q_x & Q_y & Q_z \end{vmatrix}. \qquad (67\text{-}13)$$

As an example, suppose we wish to write down the components of
the torque given by (67-8). Since

$$\mathbf{r} = ix + jy + kz,$$

the components of $\mathscr{L}$ are

$$\mathscr{L}_x = y\mathscr{F}_z - z\mathscr{F}_y,$$
$$\mathscr{L}_y = z\mathscr{F}_x - x\mathscr{F}_z,$$
$$\mathscr{L}_z = x\mathscr{F}_y - y\mathscr{F}_x.$$

Problem 67a. A rigid body has an angular velocity $\boldsymbol{\omega}$ about an axis through the origin. Show that the linear velocity of a point whose position vector is $\mathbf{r}$ is $\mathbf{v} = \boldsymbol{\omega} \times \mathbf{r}$.

Problem 67b. Show that the scalar $(\mathbf{P} \times \mathbf{Q}) \cdot \mathbf{R}$ represents the volume of the parallelepiped of which $\mathbf{P}$, $\mathbf{Q}$, $\mathbf{R}$ are the edges. Show, therefore, that $(\mathbf{P} \times \mathbf{Q}) \cdot \mathbf{R} = \mathbf{P} \cdot (\mathbf{Q} \times \mathbf{R})$, that is, the dot and the cross are interchangeable.

68. Ampère's Law.

As we already know from art. 48 an electric current along a conducting wire is attributed to a drift of electrons in the direction opposite to that of the impressed electric force. If a point charge is at rest in the oberver's inertial system, the only field to which it gives rise is an electric field directed along the radius vector. In 1820, however, the Danish physicist Oersted discovered that a current exerts a torque on a magnet held near it, which tends to turn the magnet until its axis is at right angles to the wire. Then, soon afterward, Ampère showed that currents also exert forces on one another and succeeded in formulating analytically the force or torque exerted by one current circuit on another. Although Oersted's and Ampère's experiments were confined to conduction currents in wires, Rowland showed in 1876 that the convection current due to a moving electrified body produces the same effect on a magnet as a conduction current.

We conclude, then, that a charge moving relative to the observer's inertial system produces a magnetic field as well as an electric field. The magnitude of the magnetic field is proportional to the velocity of the charge relative to the observer, provided the velocity is small compared with the velocity of light, as it usually is. Using c.g.s. electromagnetic units, we find that the magnetic intensity at a distance $\mathbf{r}_m$ from a charge q_m moving with a velocity $\mathbf{v}_m$ is given by

$$\mathbf{H}_m = \frac{q_m \mathbf{v}_m \times \mathbf{r}_m}{r_m^3}. \tag{68-1}$$

Since the *electromagnetic unit charge*, in terms of which q_m is measured, has not been established previously, it is in effect defined by (68-1), just as the electrostatic unit charge is defined by (6-1). Its relation to the other unit charges must, of course, be determined by experiment, as explained in art. 74. Actually, the electromagnetic unit charge has the magnitude of $3(10)^{10}$ electrostatic units, that is, of 10 coulombs. In terms of the fundamental units the electromagnetic unit charge is $1 \text{ cm}^{1/2} \text{ gm}^{1/2}$.

To express the law represented by (68-1) in m.k.s. practical units, it is only necessary to transform this equation according to the method described in art. 50. Referring to the conversion table in that article and noting from above that the conversion equation for charge is $q = 10q_m$, we make the indicated substitutions and obtain at once

$$\mathbf{H} = \frac{q\mathbf{v} \times \mathbf{r}}{4\pi r^3}. \tag{68-2}$$

The magnetic field specified by (68-2) is perpendicular to the plane of $\mathbf{v}$ and $\mathbf{r}$ in the direction of advance of a right-handed screw rotated from the first to the second of these vectors. At the point P (Fig. 121), therefore, $\mathbf{H}$ is directed toward the reader. Its magnitude is given by

$$H = \frac{qv \sin \theta}{4\pi r^2},$$

where θ is the angle between $\mathbf{v}$ and $\mathbf{r}$.

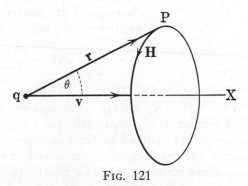

Fig. 121

If we take instead of P other points on the circumference of a circle passing through P and lying in a plane perpendicular to $\mathbf{v}$ with its center on the X axis, we note that the magnitude of $\mathbf{H}$ remains unaltered. Its direction, however, changes so as to be everywhere tangent to the circle. The magnetic lines of force, therefore, are circles in planes perpendicular to the velocity with their centers on a line through the charge in the direction of the velocity. Moreover, the sense in which these lines of force are described is that of the rotation of a right-handed screw advancing in the direction of the velocity. Finally, if we consider different points on the surface of a sphere with center at q, we note that H vanishes at the poles $\theta = 0$ and $\theta = \pi$ and is a maximum along the equator $\theta = \pi/2$.

Consider, now, a small tube of a conducting medium (Fig. 122) of cross section A carrying a current $\mathbf{i}$. We shall confine ourselves to the case where the moving charges responsible for the current are of one sign only. If n is the number of free charges per unit volume, e the charge of each, and $\mathbf{v}$ their mean drift velocity,

$$\mathbf{i} = An e \mathbf{v}. \tag{68-3}$$

When the conducting medium is a metallic wire, in which the moving charges are electrons, $\mathbf{i}$ has the direction opposite to $\mathbf{v}$ since e is negative. The total moving charge in a length dl of the tube is

$$q = An e \, dl. \tag{68-4}$$

Substituting this in (68-2), the field at P due to a length dl of a current is found to be

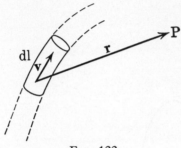

FIG. 122

$$d\mathbf{H} = \frac{(An e \mathbf{v}) \times \mathbf{r}}{4\pi r^3} \, dl = \frac{\mathbf{i} \times \mathbf{r}}{4\pi r^3} \, dl, \tag{68-5}$$

by virtue of (68-3). As $d\mathbf{l}$ may be considered to be a vector in the direction of the current this may be written equally well

$$d\mathbf{H} = i\frac{d\mathbf{l} \times \mathbf{r}}{4\pi r^3}. \tag{68-6}$$

This is Ampère's law for the magnetic field due to a *current element $id\mathbf{l}$*. Although we have formulated it for a conduction current, it is equally valid for a convection current produced by the motion of charged particles in empty space. In the case of a conduction current in a wire, the electric field due to the moving electrons is annulled by the opposite electric field produced by the stationary atomic nuclei, so that the only electric field inside the wire is the impressed field along its length which is responsible for the current.

Conversely, the force on a current element due to an external magnetic field $\mathbf{H}$ is found to be given by

$$d\mathscr{F} = \mu_0 i d\mathbf{l} \times \mathbf{H}, \tag{68-7}$$

or by its equivalent expression

$$d\mathscr{F} = \mu_0 \mathbf{i} \times \mathbf{H} dl. \tag{68-8}$$

Neither (68-6) nor (68-7) in their presently accepted forms were given explicitly by Ampère, but they are in accord with his measurements of the forces between complete current circuits as well as with the observations of Oersted, Biot and Savart, and others. Actually, Ampère's original formulas gave correct results only when applied to complete circuits. His investigations and conclusions have been carefully examined and discussed by Tricker.* It should be noted that the mechanical law of action and reaction cannot be applied to electromagnetic forces in all cases.† Although it holds for the forces between two complete circuits and consequently (art. 75) for those between a single circuit and a magnetic pole, it does not hold for the forces between a separate current element and a pole. Hence (68-6) cannot properly be used with this law to derive (68-7).

Now, dividing (68-8) by dl, the force per unit length of the circuit is

$$\mathscr{F}_l = \mu_0 \mathbf{i} \times \mathbf{H}. \tag{68-9}$$

Again, if we replace $\mathbf{i}$ by $\mathbf{j}A$ in (68-8),

$$d\mathscr{F} = \mu_0 \mathbf{j} \times \mathbf{H} A dl,$$

and the force per unit volume of the current is

$$\mathscr{F}_\tau = \mu_0 \mathbf{j} \times \mathbf{H}. \tag{68-10}$$

To find the force on a moving charge due to a magnetic field through which it may be passing, replace $\mathbf{i}$ in (68-8) by the right-hand member of (68-3) and then use (68-4). This gives

$$\mathscr{F} = q\mu_0 \mathbf{v} \times \mathbf{H}. \tag{68-11}$$

We must consider next what modifications, if any, are required in the formulas of this article when the circuits under consideration are surrounded by a magnetic medium. First, consider Ampère's law for the field produced by a current element. As the lines of force in the neighborhood of the current are closed curves surrounding the circuit, the magnetization in the medium has no component normal to the surface of the cavity in which the circuit lies. Therefore, the field due to the current is not altered by the induction of magnetic poles on the surface of the medium adjacent to the circuit, and equations (68-5) and (68-6) are valid whether the current is surrounded by a magnetic medium or not. The same statement applies to the expression (68-2) for the magnetic intensity produced by a moving charge.

When we come to consider the force (68-8) on a current element due to an external magnetic field, we must distinguish several cases. A

---

* Tricker, R. A. R., *Early Electrodynamics*, Pergamon Press, Inc., 1965.
† Page and Adams, *Am. Jour. Physics* **13**, 141 (1945).

case often encountered in practice is that of a non-magnetic wire CD (Fig. 123) carrying a current **i** which is free to move in a slot in a solid magnetized medium, such as iron. If we understand by **H** the magnetic intensity in the slot, (68-8) remains unaltered. But it is often more convenient to express the force in terms of the field in the iron. At first, take the case where **B**, the magnetic induction in the iron, lies in the plane of the wire and the normal n to the face of the slot. Since the force on the current is determined solely by the component H_n of the field in the slot at right angles to the circuit, the force on a length dl of the current is $d\mathscr{F} = \mu_0 i H_n dl$ directed away from the reader. But, as the normal component of the magnetic induction is continuous across the sides of the slot, $\mu_0 H_n = B \sin \alpha$, where α is the angle between **i** and **B**, and we may write

$$d\mathscr{F} = iB \sin \alpha dl,$$

or, in vector notation,

$$d\mathscr{F} = \mathbf{i} \times \mathbf{B} dl. \qquad (68\text{-}12)$$

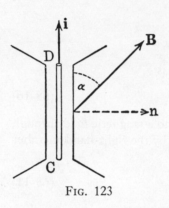

Fig. 123

If, now, the field has a component at right angles to the plane of the figure, this component of the magnetic intensity, being tangent to the face of the slot, has the same value in the iron as in the slot. So far as the force due to it is concerned, we must employ (68-8), not (68-12). But the force on the current due to the component of the field under consideration is along the normal n. Hence, if we are concerned only with the component of the force parallel to the face of the slot, formula (68-12) will always yield the correct result, **B** representing the total magnetic induction in the iron.

Next we have the case of a current in a non-magnetic wire which is immersed in a paramagnetic fluid. The detailed treatment of this case is beyond the scope of this book. It may be shown, however, that formula (68-12) holds, **B** representing the magnetic induction in the medium before the wire is placed in it.

Finally we have the case of a current passing through a magnetic medium, such as occurs when a current flows through a magnet. This case is examined in art. 75, where it is shown that (68-12) is the correct expression for the force on a length dl of the current.

Problem 68a. A current element idl is located at the origin, the current having the direction of the Z axis. What are the components of H at a point $P(x, y, z)$? Ans. $-\dfrac{iydl}{4\pi r^3}$, $\dfrac{ixdl}{4\pi r^3}$, 0.

Problem 68b. A current of density j lies in a magnetic field H parallel to the X axis. If the direction cosines of the current are l, m, n, find the components of the force on it per unit volume. Ans. 0, $\mu_0 njH$, $-\mu_0 mjH$.

Problem 68c. A current element $i_2 d\mathbf{l}_2$ is at a distance $\mathbf{r}$ from a current element $i_1 d\mathbf{l}_1$. Find the force exerted by each current element on the other. Discuss the result from the point of view of the law of action and reaction, when the two current elements are (a) parallel, (b) not parallel.

$$\text{Ans.} \frac{\mu_0 i_2 i_1}{4\pi r^3} d\mathbf{l}_2 \times (d\mathbf{l}_1 \times \mathbf{r}), \qquad -\frac{\mu_0 i_1 i_2}{4\pi r^3} d\mathbf{l}_1 \times (d\mathbf{l}_2 \times \mathbf{r}).$$

69. Magnetic Fields of Simple Circuits. The magnetic field at the center O (Fig. 124) of a circular circuit of radius a consisting of a single turn of wire is easily found. The magnetic intensity due to the

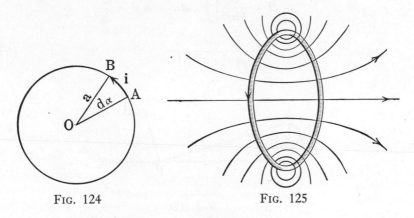

Fig. 124   Fig. 125

current element AB of length dl evidently is perpendicular to the plane of the circle toward the reader. From (68-5) its magnitude is

$$dH = \frac{i}{4\pi a^2} dl,$$

since the angle between AB and AO is $\pi/2$. Now $dl = a\,d\alpha$, and consequently the total field at O is

$$H = \frac{i}{4\pi a}\int_0^{2\pi} d\alpha = \frac{i}{2a} \tag{69-1}$$

directed out from the plane of the figure. The lines of force in the field of a circular current are illustrated in Fig. 125. If the circuit consists of n turns of wire lying close together, each turn gives rise to a field of this magnitude and we have

$$H = \frac{ni}{2a}. \tag{69-2}$$

Next we shall find the field due to a circular circuit of one turn at a point P (Fig. 126) on the axis of the circle at a distance x from the center O. First consider the field $d\mathbf{H}$ due to the current element AB. It is directed at right angles to i and the radius vector AP, and as the angle between these is $\pi/2$ its magnitude is

$$dH = \frac{iad\alpha}{4\pi r^2}.$$

Two diametrically opposite current elements give rise to fields whose components normal to OX annul each other. Therefore the resultant field is along the X axis and equal to

$$H = \frac{ia}{4\pi r^2}\left[\int_0^{2\pi} d\alpha\right]\cos\gamma = \frac{ia^2}{2r^3}$$

$$= \frac{ia^2}{2(a^2+x^2)^{3/2}}. \tag{69-3}$$

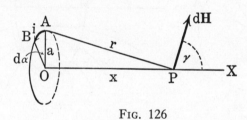

Fig. 126

Note that H is in the direction of advance of a right-handed screw rotated in the same sense as the current.

We are ready now to compute the magnetic intensity on the axis of a straight solenoid or coil of circular cross section such as is shown in longitudinal section in Fig. 127. If n_l is the number of turns per unit length, the number of turns in a length dx is $n_l dx$, and the field at O due to an element dx of a solenoid of radius a is

$$dH = \frac{ia^2 n_l dx}{2(a^2+x^2)^{3/2}}$$

from (69-3). The magnetic intensity is directed along the axis OX of the solenoid in the sense of advance of a right-handed screw rotated in the same sense as the current.

Now

$$x = a\cot\beta, \qquad dx = -a\csc^2\beta d\beta,$$

and hence

$$H = -\frac{n_l i}{2}\int_{\beta_1}^{\beta_2} \sin \beta d\beta$$

$$= \frac{n_l i}{2}(\cos \beta_2 - \cos \beta_1).$$ (69-4)

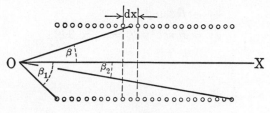

FIG. 127

Near the center of a solenoid of length very great compared with its radius, $\cos \beta_1 = -1$, $\cos \beta_2 = 1$ and

$$H = n_l i.$$ (69-5)

At the end of the solenoid $\cos \beta_1 = 0$, $\cos \beta_2 = 1$ and

$$H = \frac{n_l i}{2}.$$ (69-6)

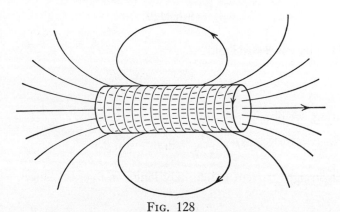

FIG. 128

Therefore, half the lines of force passing through the central section of a long solenoid pass out through the sides before reaching the end. The distribution of the lines of force is shown in Fig. 128.

Next we shall calculate the field H at a point O (Fig. 129) due to a straight current AB parallel to the Y axis. As $\sin \theta = \cos \beta$, the magnetic intensity at O due to the current element idy is

$$dH = \frac{idy \cos \beta}{4\pi r^2}$$

directed toward the reader. If R is the perpendicular distance OC of the current from O and the angle β is as shown in the figure,

$$y = R \tan \beta,$$
$$dy = R \sec^2 \beta d\beta = r \sec \beta d\beta.$$

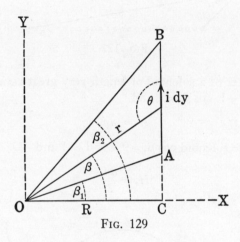

FIG. 129

Therefore, $dy \cos \beta = rd\beta$ and

$$dH = \frac{id\beta}{4\pi r} = \frac{i \cos \beta d\beta}{4\pi R}.$$

Integrating, we obtain

$$H = \frac{i}{4\pi R} (\sin \beta_2 - \sin \beta_1). \tag{69-7}$$

If the straight current is infinitely long, $\sin \beta_1 = -1$, $\sin \beta_2 = 1$ and

$$H = \frac{i}{2\pi R}, \tag{69-8}$$

an expression known as *the law of Biot and Savart*. Evidently the lines of force are circles in planes perpendicular to the current with centers on the latter. They are depicted in Fig. 130, the current being directed toward the reader. The sense in which they are described is that of rotation of a right-handed screw which advances in the direction of the current.   We can use (69-7) to compute the field at any point due to a circuit in the shape of a polygon, whether plane or not.

Finally we shall evaluate the field due to a small plane circuit of any shape (Fig. 131) at a point P whose distance from the circuit is large compared with the linear dimensions of the latter.   Take an origin at some point O inside the circuit and orient the axes so that the Z axis is along the positive normal to the plane of the circuit and OP lies in the XZ plane.   If $\mathbf{R} \equiv R (\mathbf{i} \sin \Theta + \mathbf{k} \cos \Theta)$ is the distance of P from O and $\boldsymbol{\rho} \equiv \mathbf{i}x + \mathbf{j}y$ is the position vector of the current element QS relative to O, the vector distance QP is

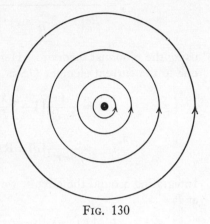

$$\mathbf{r} = \mathbf{R} - \boldsymbol{\rho}.$$

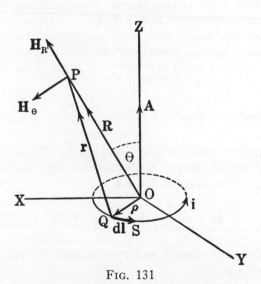

FIG. 131

The square of the distance QP is

$$r^2 = (\mathbf{R} - \boldsymbol{\rho}) \cdot (\mathbf{R} - \boldsymbol{\rho}) = R^2 - 2\mathbf{R} \cdot \boldsymbol{\rho} + \rho^2,$$

where $\rho^2 = x^2 + y^2$.   Now $\mathbf{R} \cdot \boldsymbol{\rho} = Rx \sin \Theta$, so that

$$r^2 = R^2 - 2Rx \sin \Theta + \rho^2.$$

As x and y are small compared with R we can neglect terms involving the squares of these coordinates throughout our analysis and write

$$\frac{1}{r^3} = \frac{1}{R^3\left(1-2\dfrac{x}{R}\sin\Theta\right)^{3/2}} = \frac{1}{R^3}\left(1+3\frac{x}{R}\sin\Theta\right),$$

using the binomial theorem. Hence, Ampère's law (68-6) for the field due to the current element QS is

$$d\mathbf{H} = \frac{i}{4\pi R^3}\left(1+3\frac{x}{R}\sin\Theta\right)(d\mathbf{l}\times\mathbf{R}-d\mathbf{l}\times\boldsymbol{\rho})$$

$$= \frac{i}{4\pi R^3}\left(d\mathbf{l}\times\mathbf{R}-d\mathbf{l}\times\boldsymbol{\rho}+3\frac{x}{R}\sin\Theta d\mathbf{l}\times\mathbf{R}\right).$$

Integrating around the circuit, we have for the total magnetic intensity at P

$$\mathbf{H} = \frac{i}{4\pi R^3}\left[\left(\oint d\mathbf{l}\right)\times\mathbf{R}-\oint(d\mathbf{l}\times\boldsymbol{\rho})+3\frac{\sin\Theta}{R}\left(\oint x d\mathbf{l}\right)\times\mathbf{R}\right].$$

Now $\oint d\mathbf{l}=0$ as the circuit is a closed curve. The vector representative of the triangle OQS is $\frac{1}{2}\boldsymbol{\rho}\times d\mathbf{l}$ since the area of this triangle is half that of the parallelogram of which $\boldsymbol{\rho}$ and $d\mathbf{l}$ are the sides. Therefore, $\oint\boldsymbol{\rho}\times d\mathbf{l}$ is twice the vector area $\mathbf{A}$ of the circuit, this vector being directed perpendicular to the circuit along the Z axis. Finally, as $d\mathbf{l}=\boldsymbol{i}dx+\boldsymbol{j}dy$, where $\boldsymbol{i}$ and $\boldsymbol{j}$ are unit vectors along the X and Y axes respectively,

$$\oint x d\mathbf{l} = \boldsymbol{i}\oint x dx+\boldsymbol{j}\oint x dy = \boldsymbol{i}\left.\frac{x^2}{2}\right|_x^x+\boldsymbol{j}A = \boldsymbol{j}A;$$

for the first integral vanishes since the upper and lower limits are the same and the second integral is the familiar expression for the area under a curve. Therefore, as $\mathbf{A}=\boldsymbol{k}A$,

$$\mathbf{H} = \frac{iA}{4\pi R^3}\left(2\boldsymbol{k}+3\frac{\sin\Theta}{R}\boldsymbol{j}\times\mathbf{R}\right).$$

Taking components along R and at right angles thereto in the direction of increasing Θ,

$$\left. \begin{aligned} H_R &= \frac{iA}{2\pi R^3}\cos\Theta, \\[2mm] H_\Theta &= \frac{iA}{4\pi R^3}\sin\Theta. \end{aligned} \right\} \quad (69\text{-}9)$$

Comparing these expressions with (40-2), we see that the field at a distance from a current circuit large compared with its linear dimensions is identical with that produced by a small magnet of moment equal to μ_0 times the product of the current by the area of the circuit, the magnetic axis of the equivalent magnet being normal to the plane of the circuit in the direction of advance of a right-handed screw rotated in the sense in which the current is flowing. For this reason the quantity $\mu_0 iA$ is known as the *magnetic moment* of the circuit.

As a small current circuit produces the same field as a small magnet of moment $\mu_0 iA$ we can use the law of action and reaction to prove that it must experience the same force or torque as the magnet when placed in an external magnetostatic field.

Problem 69a.   A circuit carrying a current i is in the form of a square of side l.   Find the magnetic intensity at its center.   Ans. $\dfrac{2\sqrt{2}i}{\pi l}$.

Problem 69b.   A circuit has the form of a regular polygon of n sides inscribed in a circle of radius a.   Find the field at the center and show that the result goes over into (69-1) as n is indefintely increased.   Ans. $\dfrac{i}{2a}\left(\dfrac{n}{\pi}\tan\dfrac{\pi}{n}\right)$

Problem 69c.   Find the field due to the circuit of problem *69a* at a point on the axis of the square at a distance d from its center.

$$\text{Ans. } \frac{il^2}{2\pi\left(d^2+\dfrac{l^2}{4}\right)\sqrt{d^2+\dfrac{l^2}{2}}}.$$

Problem 69d.   Two long parallel wires a distance $2d$ apart carry equal but oppositely directed currents.   Find the field at a point in the plane of the wires distant R from a line half-way between the two.   Ans. $\dfrac{id}{\pi(R^2-d^2)}$.

Problem 69e.   The length of a solenoid is ten times its radius.   What is the percentage error in using (69-5) to calculate the field at the center? Ans. 2%.

Problem 69f.   The windings of an actual solenoid are in the form of a helix rather than a succession of circles such as was assumed in the previous article. Show, however, that (69-4) for the axial field is valid also for helical windings.

Problem 69g.   A solenoid 2 cm in diameter and 20 cm long has 100 turns and carries a current 1 ampere.   Calculate and plot the axial field in terms of distance from the center of the solenoid.

Problem 69h.   A solenoid of n_l turns per unit length carrying a current i is wound in a number of layers extending from a distance a from the axis to a distance b.   Find the axial field at a point in the interior distant l_1 and l_2 from the two ends.

$$\text{Ans. } \frac{n_l i}{2(b-a)}\left\{l_1\log\frac{\sqrt{l_1{}^2+b^2}+b}{\sqrt{l_1{}^2+a^2}+a}+l_2\log\frac{\sqrt{l_2{}^2+b^2}+b}{\sqrt{l_2{}^2+a^2}+a}\right\}.$$

Problem 69i.   A circular coil of n turns is wound in a rectangular channel of width $2d$ and depth $2h$, these dimensions being small compared with a, the mean radius of the coil.   Find the field at the center of the coil.

$$\text{Ans. } \frac{ni}{2a}\left\{1+\frac{2h^2-3d^2}{6a^2}+\cdots\right\}.$$

Problem 69j.   A unit positive pole is carried along the axis of a circular current i from infinity on the negative side of the circuit to infinity on the positive side.   Show that the work done by the field is equal to i.

70. Magnetic Shell Equivalent to Current Circuit.   We shall show now that the magnetic field produced by a current circuit is identical with that produced by a magnetic shell whose strength is equal to μ_0 times the current and whose periphery coincides with the circuit.   This statement is limited, however, to the region outside the equivalent shell, for at points inside the shell the field of the latter differs both in magnitude and direction from that of the circuit.

We start by considering a magnetic shell of constant strength Φ in the shape of the plane figure $ABCD$ (Fig. 132) of infinitesimal width extending from AB an infinite distance to the left.   The sides CB and DA make the angle $d\alpha$ at P and the front face of the shell is positive. Let us calculate the magnetic intensity at P due to the shell.   The magnetic moment of the section of the shell included between the arcs

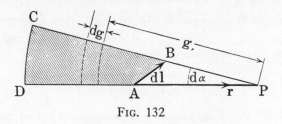

FIG. 132

of radii g and $g+dg$ described about P is $\Phi g\,d\alpha\,dg$ directed outward toward the reader, and from (40-2) the field at P due to this element of the shell is

$$d^2H = \frac{\Phi g\,d\alpha\,dg}{4\pi\mu_0 g^3} = \frac{\Phi\,d\alpha\,dg}{4\pi\mu_0 g^2}$$

directed inward.   Integrating with respect to g from r to infinity the field at P due to the entire shell is found to be

$$dH = \frac{\Phi\,d\alpha}{4\pi\mu_0}\int_r^\infty \frac{dg}{g^2} = \frac{\Phi\,d\alpha}{4\pi\mu_0 r} = \frac{\Phi r^2\,d\alpha}{4\pi\mu_0 r^3}.$$

Now $r^2 d\alpha$ is twice the area of the triangle ABP.   But if $\mathbf{r}$ is the vector distance AP and $d\mathbf{l}$ the vector AB then $d\mathbf{l} \times \mathbf{r}$ is a vector directed inward having a magnitude equal to the area of the parallelogram of which AP and AB are the sides, that is, equal to twice the area of the triangle ABP.   Therefore, the magnetic intensity at the point P is given in magnitude and direction by the vector expression

$$d\mathbf{H} = \Phi\,\frac{d\mathbf{l} \times \mathbf{r}}{4\pi\mu_0 r^3}. \tag{70-1}$$

Comparing with Ampère's law (68-6) we see that this expression is identical with that for the field due to a current element $id\mathbf{l}$ along AB provided that Φ the strength of the shell is equal to $\mu_0 i$. Hence we conclude that the field at any point P due to a current element is equal to that of a long narrow magnetic shell of constant strength equal to μ_0 times the current, extending from the current element to infinity between two straight lines drawn from P through the extremities of the current element.

Now consider the circuit $ABCD$ (Fig. 133). To find the magnetic intensity at P due to the current i we may replace the circuit by a conical magnetic shell of strength equal to $\mu_0 i$, having the point P as vertex and extending from the curve $ABCD$ to infinity. As here described the shell is open at infinity. We may, however, close the farther end by means of a shell of the same strength in the form of a

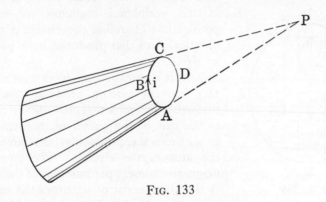

FIG. 133

spherical cap without affecting the field at P. For the magnetic intensity at P due to an element of such a cap which subtends a solid angle $d\Omega$ at P is

$$dH = \frac{\Phi r^2 d\Omega}{2\pi\mu_0 r^3} = \frac{\Phi d\Omega}{2\pi\mu_0 r}$$

in the radial direction by (40-2). As r approaches infinity dH approaches zero, and the field of an infinitely distant spherical cap vanishes.

We see then that the field at P due to the current is identical with that of a magnetic shell of constant strength equal to $\mu_0 i$, which is closed everywhere except over the curve $ABCD$. But it is proved in art. 41 that all shells of the same strength and the same periphery produce the same field at all outside points. Consequently we may replace the shell under consideration by any other shell of the same strength whose periphery coincides with the circuit.　Such an *equivalent shell* produces at all outside points a field identical with that of the current circuit. The positive face of the shell is related to the sense in which the current is flowing by the usual convention, that is, a right-handed screw, rotated in the sense of the current, advances from the negative toward the positive face of the equivalent shell.

The same conclusion may be reached by the following somewhat different line of reasoning.　Let *ABCD* (Fig. 134) be the circuit under consideration.　Divide this circuit into a number of elementary circuits such as *abcd* by means of the network shown in the figure and suppose that the same current i is flowing in each of these in the sense *ABCD*.　Any one of the interior branches of the network, such as *ab*, is a part of two adjacent circuits and carries two equal and opposite currents the magnetic fields of which annul each other.　Only those currents flowing in the peripheral branches are uncompensated.　Therefore the resultant field is identical with that produced by a current i in *ABCD*.

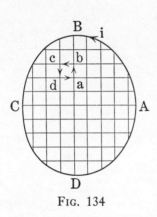

FIG. 134

Now it is shown in art. 69 that an elementary current circuit produces the same magnetic field as a magnetic dipole parallel to the axis of the circuit of moment equal to μ_0 times the product of the current by the area of the circuit.　The equivalent magnetic moment per unit area of the circuit is therefore equal to μ_0 times the current. Consequently the field produced by the network at exterior points is identical with that of a shell of strength $\mu_0 i$ having the same periphery as the network, its positive face being uppermost.

As an illustration of the method which has just been developed for finding the field produced by a current circuit by substituting an equivalent magnetic shell, let us deduce H near the center of a long solenoid of n_l turns per unit length.　Each turn of wire may be replaced by a plane shell of strength $\mu_0 i$.　By making the thickness of each shell equal to $1/n_l$ the solenoid is replaced by a uniformly magnetized bar of the same outside dimensions having magnetization $I = \mu_0 n_l i$.　At all outside points the field due to this equivalent magnet is identical with that of the solenoid.　The equivalence, however, applies only to points outside the magnet.　Therefore, in order to calculate the field inside the solenoid, we must leave a narrow transverse slit between the magnetic shells corresponding to the turns of wire on either side of the point P at which we wish to obtain the field strength.   The poles on the ends of the bar being too far away to produce an appreciable effect at P, the field is due entirely to the magnetic poles on the surfaces of the slit.   Consequently, if we make use of the result of problem $42b$,

$$H = \frac{1}{\mu_0} I - n_l i,$$

in accord with (69-5).   This method of treatment reveals one fact, however, which was not evident from the solution of art. 69, namely, that the field is uniform through the entire cross section of the solenoid provided the region under consideration is far away from the ends. Now the force on a unit positive pole placed inside a transverse slit in a magnetic medium is not H, but B/μ_0, as is shown in the problem $43a$. Therefore H inside the solenoid has the same value as B/μ_0 inside the equivalent magnet.

As pointed out in art. 68, the magnetic intensity due to a current is unaltered when it is immersed in a permeable medium.   The same is true of an infinitely thin magnetic shell; for, as the thickness of the shell approaches zero, the surface density of pole-strength on the shell increases without limit, while that induced on the adjacent surface of the medium remains finite and becomes negligible.   We conclude, therefore, that the equivalent shell has a strength equal to μ_0 times the current even in a magnetic medium.

Problem 70a.   Equal currents are flowing in opposite senses in two circuits not lying in the same plane.   Show that the resultant magnetic field due to the two currents is the same as that due to a single tubular magnetic shell extending from the one circuit to the other.

Problem 70b.   A sphere of radius a carrying a uniform surface charge density σ rotates about a diameter with a constant angular velocity ω.   Show that the magnetic field outside the sphere is the same as that of a stationary uniformly magnetized sphere of the same radius with magnetization $I = \mu_0 \sigma a \omega$.

Problem 70c.   Making use of (44-3), show that the magnetic field inside the charged rotating sphere of $70b$ is a uniform field parallel to the axis of intensity $(2/3)\sigma a \omega$.

71. Circuital Form of Ampère's Law.   The results of the last article enable us to express Ampère's law in another form, which is often more useful than (68-5) or (68-6).   Suppose the current circuit whose field we wish to investigate to be replaced by a very thin magnetic shell whose periphery coincides with the circuit and whose strength Φ is equal to μ_0 times the current i.   It is shown in art. 41 that the work done by the field of a shell of constant strength when a unit positive pole moves from a point on the positive side around the edge of the shell to an opposite point on the negative side is Φ/μ_0.

Such a path encircles the current in the equivalent circuit in the sense of rotation of a right-handed screw which is advancing in the direction in which the current is flowing. Therefore the work done by the magnetic field produced by a current when a unit positive pole follows a path of any shape encircling the current in the sense of rotation of a right-handed screw advancing in the direction of the current is

$$W = i. \tag{71-1}$$

In deducing this expression we have neglected the portion of the path of the pole lying inside the equivalent magnetic shell. In the field of a shell the work done on a pole in passing through the shell is equal and opposite to that done along the part of the path lying outside the shell, so that the net work done around a closed path is zero. The field in the interior of the equivalent shell, however, is not the same as that due to the circuit. In the case of the latter the field is continuous all the way around. So, as the equivalent shell is extremely thin, the work done on a pole as it passes from a point on one side around to an opposite point on the other does not differ appreciably from the work done on it in completely encircling the current circuit.

If α is the angle between the magnetic intensity **H** produced by a current circuit and an element $d\mathbf{l}$ of a closed curve surrounding the current, the work done by the field when a unit positive pole describes a closed path around the current is

$$\mathscr{H} \equiv \oint H \cos \alpha\, dl = \oint \mathbf{H} \cdot d\mathbf{l}. \tag{71-2}$$

This integral is the *magnetomotive force*, abbreviated m.m.f., around the closed curve. It is analogous to the *electromotive force* (48-5), namely,

$$\mathscr{E} \equiv \oint E \cos \alpha\, dl = \oint \mathbf{E} \cdot d\mathbf{l}.$$

The unit of magnetomotive force is, properly, the *ampere*, since magnetomotive force has the same physical dimensions as magnetic potential (art. 38). However, the unit is often called the *ampere-turn*, in order to distinguish $\mathscr{H}$ from i.

Comparison of (71-1) and (71-2) enables us to put Ampère's law in the *circuital form*

$$\oint \mathbf{H} \cdot d\mathbf{l} = i. \tag{71-3}$$

The closed path around which the integral is taken may be *any* closed curve arbitrarily chosen, i being the current passing through the curve in the direction of advance of a right-handed screw rotated in the sense

in which the closed path is described.   If the closed curve surrounds
no current, the right-hand side of (71-3) is zero; if it encircles n wires
each of which carries a current i the right-hand member becomes ni.
Since the field produced by a current circuit is unaltered when the
circuit is immersed in a magnetic medium, (71-3) holds no matter
whether the circuit is located in empty space or is surrounded by a
magnetic fluid or solid.

The circuital form of Ampère's law is especially useful in calculating
the magnetic intensity when symmetry shows that it has the same
magnitude at all points on a closed line of force which we choose for the
path involved in (71-3).   Consider, for instance, a straight wire AB
(Fig. 135) of radius a along which a current i is flowing.   We will provide a return circuit in the form of a
cylindrical shell of radius b coaxial with the
wire, the two being connected at their
extremities by conducting disks in planes
perpendicular to the wire.   It is clear from
symmetry that the lines of force are circles
in planes perpendicular to the wire with
their centers on its axis. Applying Ampère's
law (71-3) to the circular line of force PQ
of radius R lying between the wire and the
cylindrical shell,

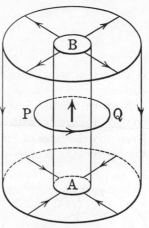

$$2\pi RH = i \qquad (71\text{-}4)$$

or

$$H = \frac{i}{2\pi R}, \qquad (71\text{-}5)$$

Fig. 135

in agreement with the formula (69-8) for
an infinitely long straight current.

If, however, R is less than a the path PQ lies inside the wire and
encircles only a part of the current.   If the current is steady and therefore distributed uniformly through the cross section of the wire, the
current surrounded is iR^2/a^2 and (71-4) becomes

$$2\pi RH = \frac{iR^2}{a^2},$$

leading to

$$H = \frac{i}{2\pi a^2}R \qquad (71\text{-}6)$$

at a point inside the wire.

On the other hand, if R is greater than b the path PQ encircles the
return circuit as well as the current in the wire.   Therefore, the net

current passing through the closed curve along which we are integrating is zero and H vanishes. Similarly there is no field beyond the closed ends. Consequently the field is confined entirely to the enclosed region inside the outer cylinder.

Plotting H against the distance R from the axis of the wire we obtain the graph shown in Fig. 136. By making b large enough we approach

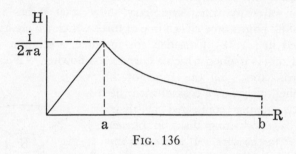

FIG. 136

as closely as we choose to the ideal case of an infinitely long straight current.

Next we shall investigate the ring or toroidal solenoid (Fig. 137) wound uniformly with n turns, each of which carries a current i. Evidently the lines of force are circles in planes parallel to the plane of the figure with centers on the axis through O. If H is the magnetic intensity along the path l lying inside the solenoid which encircles all n turns of wire, we have

$$Hl = ni$$

from (71-3). Therefore,

$$H = \left(\frac{n}{l}\right)i \qquad (71\text{-}7)$$

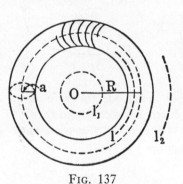

FIG. 137

inside the coil. If the radius a of the solenoid is small compared with the radius R of its circular axis, all paths such as l lying in its interior have nearly the same length and the field is nearly uniform. In this case (71-7) goes over into the formula (69-5) for the field at a point on the axis of a straight solenoid far from its ends.

A path such as l_1 lying outside the solenoid surrounds no current and therefore H vanishes. On the other hand, a path such as l_2 encircles as many currents directed outward from the figure as inward and therefore H is zero here too.   Consequently the field is confined entirely to the inside of the coil.   Evidently these conclusions, as well as formula (71-7), apply no matter whether the cross section of the ring is circular or not.

The straight solenoid previously discussed may be considered to be the limiting case of a ring solenoid when R becomes infinitely great, at least in so far as the field far from the ends is concerned.   However, we can show very simply that the field inside a straight solenoid near the middle must be uniform throughout its cross section by applying (71-3) to the path *ABCD* (Fig. 138).   As the lines of force are parallel to the axis inside the solenoid and the field outside is negligibly small, the magnetomotive force reduces to the integral along *AB*.   If the length of this line is l and n_l is the number of turns per unit length,

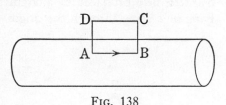

Fɪɢ. 138

$$Hl = n_l li,$$

or

$$H = n_l i,$$

anywhere inside the solenoid far from the ends.

Problem 71a.   A current flowing along a surface is known as a *current sheet*. Two parallel plane current sheets of infinite extent, oppositely directed, have currents per unit width equal to k.   Find the magnitude of the magnetic field (a) between the sheets, (b) outside.   Ans. (a) k, (b) 0.

Problem 71b.   Show that, if the lines of force of a magnetic field are straight and parallel in a region containing no current or magnetic poles, the magnetic intensity must remain constant in magnitude as we move in a direction at right angles to the field.

Problem 71c.   Show that the field inside a ring solenoid is the same as that due to a straight current ni flowing along the axis of symmetry of the ring, n being the number of turns on the ring and i the current per turn.

Problem 71d.   Show that a many-valued potential of the form

$$V = -\frac{i}{4\pi}(\Omega + 4\pi\nu)$$

exists in the case of the field of a current circuit, when Ω is the solid angle subtended by the circuit and ν is an integer which changes by unity every time the circuit is linked.

72. Field of a Circular Current.

By the use of Ampère's law for the magnetic intensity due to a current element we have been able to calculate the field strength on the axis of a circular current (69-3) directly.   Usually, however, the field produced by a current circuit can be computed more readily if the circuit is replaced by its equivalent shell and the magnetic potential is found. As noted in art. 45, the magnetic potential in a magnetostatic field must satisfy Laplace's equation. Therefore, the magnetic potential must be expressible as a solution or as the sum of a number of solutions of Laplace's equation so chosen as to satisfy the assigned boundary conditions. Once the potential is known, the components of the magnetic intensity are obtained by means of (38-7) or (38-8).

We shall apply this method of solution to the calculation of the magnetic field produced by a circular current AB (Fig. 139) of radius a lying in a plane through the origin O at right angles to the Z axis.

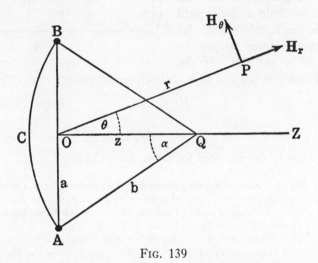

FIG. 139

Suppose that the current i enters the plane of the figure at A and emerges at B. Then the magnetic potential V at any point Q on the Z axis may be calculated by replacing the circuit by a magnetic shell ACB of strength $\mu_0 i$ in the shape of a spherical cap with Q as center, the concave face of the shell being positive.

If the angle which any radius vector drawn from Q to a point on the cap makes with the line QO is denoted by ϕ, where ϕ varies from zero to α, the area of the cap is

$$S = \int_0^\alpha 2\pi b^2 \sin \phi d\phi = 2\pi b^2 (1 - \cos \alpha),$$

and the solid angle subtended at Q by the cap is

$$\Omega = -\frac{S}{b^2} = -2\pi(1 - \cos \alpha) = -2\pi\left\{1 - \frac{z}{\sqrt{a^2 + z^2}}\right\}.$$

Therefore, the potential at Q is

$$V = -\frac{i\Omega}{4\pi} = \frac{i}{2}\left\{1 - \frac{z}{\sqrt{a^2+z^2}}\right\} \qquad (72\text{-}1)$$

from (41-1), since the point Q here is on the positive side of the shell. The field strength (69-3) at any point on the Z axis is obtained at once from (72-1) by taking the negative of the derivative with respect to z.

We wish to obtain the field at a point P off the Z axis. It is evident from symmetry that the potential at such a point can be a function of the coordinates r and θ only. Therefore, it must consist of a series of zonal harmonics so chosen as to reduce to (72-1) at points on the Z axis. The form of the potential function depends on whether the distance r of the point P is less than or greater than the radius a of the current. Let us consider the case where r is less than a. Then we can expand the radical in (72-1) in powers of z/a by the binomial theorem, getting

$$V = \frac{i}{2}\left\{1 - \frac{z}{a} + \frac{1}{2}\frac{z^3}{a^3} + \cdots\right\}. \qquad (72\text{-}2)$$

This equation expresses the boundary condition which must be satisfied by the potential function. Remembering that r becomes z and $\cos\theta$ unity along the axis, we see by consulting Table I, art. 27, that the desired series for the potential is

$$V = \frac{i}{2}\left\{1 - \frac{r}{a}\cos\theta + \frac{1}{4}\frac{r^3}{a^3}(5\cos^3\theta - 3\cos\theta) + \cdots\right\}. \qquad (72\text{-}3)$$

Differentiating, we find for the components of magnetic intensity at P in the directions of increasing r and θ respectively,

$$\left.\begin{aligned}
H_r &= -\frac{\partial V}{\partial r} = \frac{i}{2a}\left\{\cos\theta - \frac{3}{4}\frac{r^2}{a^2}(5\cos^3\theta - 3\cos\theta) + \cdots\right\}, \\
H_\theta &= -\frac{\partial V}{r\partial\theta} = \frac{i}{2a}\left\{-\sin\theta + \frac{3}{4}\frac{r^2}{a^2}(5\cos^2\theta - 1)\sin\theta + \cdots\right\}.
\end{aligned}\right\} \qquad (72\text{-}4)$$

These expressions are useful in finding the field at a distance from the center of the circular current small compared with its radius. If, for instance, r is not greater than one quarter of a, the first two terms in the series specify the field with an error less than one percent.

The solution for the case where r is greater than a is found by a procedure similar to that employed above.

Often it is desirable to obtain a field more uniform than that given by a circular current without having recourse to a long solenoid. This may be effected by the use of two parallel circular currents of the same radius a placed a distance $2b$ apart as illustrated in Fig. 140. By a suitable separation of the circuits the field at a point O half-way between the two may be made more uniform than the field at any point due to either circuit alone. To find the optimum value of $2b$, we have from (69-3) for the field at a point P a distance x from O

$$H = \frac{ia^2}{2}\left\{\frac{1}{[a^2+(b+x)^2]^{3/2}} + \frac{1}{[a^2+(b-x)^2]^{3/2}}\right\}. \qquad (72\text{-}5)$$

Expanding by means of the binomial theorem in powers of x,

$$H = \frac{ia^2}{(a^2+b^2)^{3/2}}\left\{1 + \frac{3(4b^2-a^2)}{2(a^2+b^2)^2}\,x^2 + \cdots\right\}. \qquad (72\text{-}6)$$

If $2b=a$, the coefficient of x^2 vanishes and the field is very uniform for some distance to either side of the mid-point O. Therefore, the coils should be placed a distance apart equal to their radius. The magnetic intensity at O is then

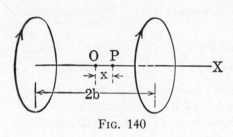

FIG. 140

$$H = \frac{8i}{(5)^{3/2}a} = \frac{0.72i}{a}. \qquad (72\text{-}7)$$

Problem 72a. Find the field off the axis of a circular current at a distance r from the center of the circle greater than the radius a.

$$\text{Ans. } H_r = \frac{i}{2a}\left\{\frac{a^3}{r^3}\cos\theta - \frac{3}{4}\frac{a^5}{r^5}(5\cos^3\theta - 3\cos\theta) + \cdots\right\},$$

$$H_\theta = \frac{i}{2a}\left\{\frac{1}{2}\frac{a^3}{r^3}\sin\theta - \frac{9}{16}\frac{a^5}{r^5}(5\cos^2\theta - 1)\sin\theta + \cdots\right\}.$$

Problem 72b. Show from the result of the previous problem that the field at a distance from a small circular current large compared with the radius of the circuit is the same as that due to a magnetic dipole of moment equal to μ_0 times the product of the current by the area of the circuit, in accord with (69-9).

Problem 72c. Using the result of problem 71b, show that the uniformity of the field in the vicinity of O (Fig. 140) holds off the axis as well as on the axis.

73. Galvanometers. An instrument devised to measure the strength of a current, whose operation depends on the interaction between the current and a magnet, is known as a *galvanometer*. In some galvanometers the circuit is fixed and the magnet, in the form of a compass needle, suffers a deflection when the current passes through the circuit; in others the magnet, shaped so as to bring the poles close together with their faces parallel, is fixed, and the circuit, placed between the poles of the magnet, is deflected by the magnetic field of the latter. In either case the moving part must be subject to a control torque of restitution. Galvanometers may be described as *absolute* or *sensitive*. The current passing through an instrument of the first type may be calculated in terms of its constants and the observed deflection. Instruments of the second type are designed to secure great sensitivity and generally are not absolute, but must be calibrated by comparison with an absolute galvanometer.

Tangent Galvanometer. This instrument consists of a vertical circular coil of n turns of radius a (Fig. 141) at the center of which is suspended a compass needle free to turn in a horizontal plane about its center of mass. The length l of the needle must be small compared with a. The coil is oriented so that its plane is parallel to the earth's

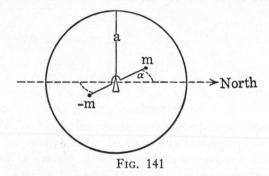

FIG. 141

field, which supplies the control torque. When a current i passes through the coil, the field at its center is

$$H = \frac{ni}{2a}$$

along the axis of the coil, from (69-2). If H_t is the horizontal component of the earth's field, the compass needle assumes the direction of the resultant of the two perpendicular fields H and H_t. Consequently, if α is its deflection from the plane of the coil,

$$\tan \alpha = \frac{H}{H_t} = \frac{ni}{2aH_t},$$

or

$$i = \frac{2aH_t}{n} \tan \alpha = K_i \tan \alpha, \tag{73-1}$$

where $K_i \equiv 2aH_t/n$ is known as the *galvanometer constant*. We are able to determine H_t in absolute units as shown in art. 47. Therefore, i may be measured in absolute units by means of this instrument.

If the needle is not so short that the distance l between its poles is negligible compared with the radius a of the coil, the field at the poles differs slightly from the field at the center of the coil and we must make use of (72-4). The torque due to the current in the direction of decreasing θ is

$$-mlH_\theta = \frac{npi}{2a} \sin \theta \left\{1 - \frac{3}{16} \frac{l^2}{a^2} (5 \cos^2 \theta - 1)\right\}$$

$$= \frac{npi}{2a} \cos \alpha \left\{1 - \frac{3}{16} \frac{l^2}{a^2} (5 \sin^2 \alpha - 1)\right\}, \qquad (73\text{-}2)$$

since the deflection α of the needle from the plane of the coil is the complement of the angle θ of Fig. 139. The opposite torque due to the earth's field is $pH_t \sin \alpha$. Equating the two torques and solving for the current,

$$i = \frac{2aH_t}{n} \tan \alpha \left\{1 + \frac{3}{16} \frac{l^2}{a^2} (5 \sin^2 \alpha - 1)\right\}. \qquad (73\text{-}3)$$

Since the poles of the needle are not always located at its ends, it is difficult to determine the value of l needed for the correction term. The latter, however, may be made negligibly small by using the instrument so that the deflection is near arc $\sin (1/\sqrt{5}) = 26°.6$.

Helmholtz has improved this type of galvanometer by locating the needle half-way between two parallel coils placed a distance apart equal to their common radius. As was shown in the last article the field is very uniform in the neighborhood of this point. Therefore, no correction term is needed, the current being given by

$$i = \frac{(5)^{3/2} aH_t}{8n} \tan \alpha \qquad (73\text{-}4)$$

from (72-7), where n is the number of turns in each coil.

The current sensitivity of the tangent galvanometer is

$$\frac{d\alpha}{di} = \frac{n}{2aH_t} \cos^2 \alpha = \frac{1}{K_i} \cos^2 \alpha \qquad (73\text{-}5)$$

from (73-1). To make this great, a large number of turns, small radius and small control field H_t are needed, and the deflections should be small. Increasing the sensitivity by increasing n and decreasing a increases the magnitude of the necessary corrections. On the other hand, if the control field is made small, the disturbing effect of stray fields, such as those due to neighboring power circuits, is magnified.

A modification of the tangent galvanometer which secures increased sensitivity by decreasing the magnitude of the control torque consists of two fixed coils A and B (Fig. 142) in the same vertical plane wound so that the current traverses them in opposite senses. The needles (ns) at the centers of the coils are rigidly connected and free to rotate as a pair about a vertical axis. As they are of equal moments and oppositely oriented the earth's field exerts no torque on the movable part. Instead the control torque is supplied by the torsion fibre F. By using a fine fibre the torque of restitution can be made very small, thereby making the sensitivity very great. As the current traverses the two coils in opposite senses, the torque exerted by it on each needle is in the same sense. Therefore, the torque on the suspension due to the current is as great as in a single coil having a number of turns equal to the sum of those of the two coils. A mirror M is rigidly attached to the suspended system so that the deflection may be read with a telescope and scale in a manner to be described later. The whole apparatus is placed inside a cylindrical shell, or several coaxial shells, of soft iron so as to shield it from outside magnetic fields as explained in art. 45. The type of instrument under discussion is known as an *astatic galvanometer*. As usually constructed it is not absolute.

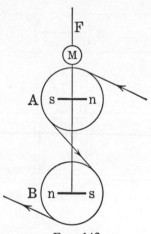

If the needles are short compared with the radius a of each coil, the torque on the suspended system due to the current is

$$\frac{npi}{2a} \cos \alpha$$

FIG. 142

for a deflection α, where p is the magnetic moment of either of the needles and n the sum of the number of turns in the two coils. Equating this to the torque of restitution $k\alpha$ of the twisted fibre,

$$i = \frac{2ak}{np \cos \alpha} \alpha. \tag{73-6}$$

If the deflection is small $\cos \alpha$ remains sensibly unity, and

$$i = \frac{2ak}{np} \alpha = K_i \alpha, \tag{73-7}$$

where $K_i \equiv 2ak/np$ is the galvanometer constant for this type of instrument.

D'Arsonval Galvanometer. The moving needle type of galvanometer is easily disturbed by stray fields unless carefully shielded. This difficulty is obviated in the moving coil instrument depicted in plan in the upper part of Fig. 143 and in vertical section in the lower part of the figure. The flat rectangular coil *BCDE* of *n* turns surrounding a fixed cylinder of soft iron, is suspended by the torsion fibre *F* between the poles *N*, *S* of a strong magnet so as to lie in a plane parallel to the lines of force when no current is flowing. The current *i* enters the coil through the upper suspension and leaves below.

If *l* is the length $DE = BC$, the force on *DE* due to the field *H* of the magnet is $\mu_0 iHl$ in the backward direction from (68-9). An equal forward force is experienced by *BC*. If *h* is the width $EB = CD$, the torque due to this couple is $\mu_0 iHlh$. This is the total torque on one turn, as the currents in the horizontal arms are subject to no turning moment. Multiplying by the number of turns the torque on the entire coil is seen to be $\mu_0 niHA$, where *A* is the area *lh* of the rectangle.

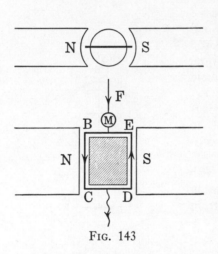

FIG. 143

The soft iron core which the coil surrounds concentrates the lines of induction in its interior, so that for small deflections of the coil the deflecting field is effectively radial and the torque remains proportional to the current alone. For larger deflections, however, the vertical arms of the coil come into a portion of the field which is more nearly transverse and the lever arm of the couple is therefore approximately $h \cos \alpha$, where α is the deflection, instead of *h*. Consequently, the torque becomes $\mu_0 niHA \cos \alpha$.

The torque of restitution exerted by the torsion fibre is proportional to the deflection and may be written $k\alpha$, where *k* is a constant. Equating this to the torque on the coil, we have for small deflections

$$i = \frac{k}{\mu_0 nHA} \alpha = K_i \alpha, \qquad (73\text{-}8)$$

where $K_i \equiv k/\mu_0 nHA$ is the galvanometer constant, and for large deflections,

$$i = \frac{k}{\mu_0 nHA \cos \alpha} \alpha. \qquad (73\text{-}9)$$

In Fig. 144 the current is plotted against the deflection, the lower broken line corresponding to (73-8) and the upper one to (73-9). The actual curve observed, shown by the full line, lies between these, following the straight line very closely near the origin.

The current sensitivity of the d'Arsonval galvanometer for small deflections is

$$\frac{d\alpha}{di} = \frac{\mu_0 n H A}{k} = \frac{1}{K_i}. \qquad (73\text{-}10)$$

To obtain high sensitivity the coil should have many turns of fine wire, the field H should be large, and the stiffness of the suspension small. For this reason the coil is suspended by a fine wire, usually of phosphor-bronze. The sensitivity may be made great enough to measure currents of $(10)^{-11}$ ampere. As the field of the fixed magnet is large, stray

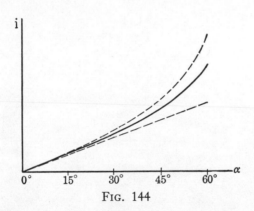

Fig. 144

fields produce relatively unimportant disturbances. The instrument, as generally constructed, is not absolute and must be calibrated by comparison with an absolute galvanometer.

Sensitive galvanometers of this type are usually provided with a mirror M (Fig. 143), which turns with the coil. A telescope T and scale S (Fig. 145) are placed in front of the mirror. A deflection α of the mirror brings on the cross-hair of the telescope a point P on the scale at an angular distance 2α from O. To make the scale reading proportional to the angle of deflection, the scale is often bent into an arc of a circle rather than left straight as shown in the figure. The scale reading is then proportional to the current, or very nearly so, which is desirable in practice.

The ammeters and the voltmeters used for direct-current measurements are merely d'Arsonval galvanometers, of low resistance and of high resistance, respectively, provided with a pointer instead of a mirror and a fine spiral spring instead of a torsion fibre. Such an instrument with the case removed is shown in Fig. 146.

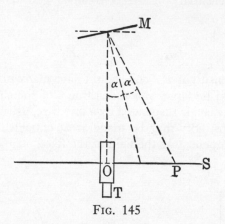

FIG. 145

FIG. 146

Problem 73a. Show that if the coil of the tangent galvanometer is rotated about a vertical axis through an angle α' so as to lie in the same vertical plane as the needle when its deflection is read,

$$i = \frac{2aH_t}{n} \sin \alpha'.$$

Compare the sensitivity of this *sine galvanometer* with that of the tangent instrument found from (73-1).

Problem 73b. The coil of a tangent galvanometer is 1 meter in diameter and consists of a single conductor. Compute the deflection produced by a current 1 ampere, if the horizontal component of the earth's field is 16 amperes per meter. Ans. 0.06 radian.

74. Determination of the Electromagnetic Unit Charge. As remarked in art. 68, the relation between the electromagnetic unit charge and the other unit charges must be found by experiment. Treating this relation as unknown, it is convenient to write the conversion equation in the form $Kq = 10q_m$, where K is a constant to be determined.

The tangent galvanometer described in the preceding article provides a simple, although not the most accurate, method of measuring K. In the derivation of (73-1) we assume K to have a known value (unity) and so determine i in terms of α, since H_t is given by (47-4). If, however, we retain K throughout the analysis, (73-1) is replaced by

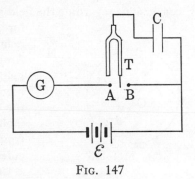

FIG. 147

$$Ki = \frac{2aH_t}{n} \tan \alpha. \qquad (74\text{-}1)$$

Hence, to find K, it is only necessary to make an independent measurement of i when observing α. This can be done by means of the circuit of Fig. 147, which contains the tangent galvanometer G, a known electromotive force $\mathscr{E}$ and a known capacitance C. The prong T of the tuning fork inserted in the circuit makes contact alternately with A and with B, charging the capacitor through the galvanometer when in contact with A, and discharging it directly when in contact with B. If ν is the number of vibrations per second of the tuning fork, the current measured by the galvanometer is

$$i = \nu C \mathscr{E}. \qquad (74\text{-}2)$$

75. Ampère's Theory of Magnetism. We know that a small current circuit produces a magnetic field which is indistinguishable, at distances large compared with the dimensions of the circuit, from that of a magnetic dipole. In fact, in art. 70 it is shown that the field outside a magnetic shell of constant strength Φ is identical with that of a current i flowing around a circuit which coincides with the periphery of the shell, provided $\Phi = \mu_0 i$. These considerations led Ampère to suggest that the magnetic moments exhibited by the molecules of paramagnetic and ferromagnetic substances are due not to the presence of magnetic dipoles but to the existence of intra-molecular currents. As the magnetic properties of such Ampèrian circuits are permanent, the currents involved must be supposed to flow without resistance. Ampère's theory, which is universally accepted today, makes unnecessary the supposition of the existence of a magnetic entity, all magnetic phenomena being attributed to moving electric charges. Our present knowledge of the structure of atoms leads us to believe that the Ampèrian circuits existing in the molecules of magnetic media consist of rings of electrons revolving about the nuclei of the atoms, or possibly of electrons spinning, like the earth, about a diameter as axis.

While it is a matter of indifference in describing the field outside a magnet whether we attribute magnetic properties to actual dipoles or to intra-molecular currents, the two points of view lead to different conclusions regarding the field in the interior of the substance. Therefore, we must investigate the field inside a magnetic medium from the point of view of Ampère's theory. As it is only the smooth field (art. 42) which we can detect experimentally, our problem is to discover how the smooth field inside a medium whose molecules contain Ampèrian circuits differs from that inside a medium whose molecules contain equivalent magnetic shells.

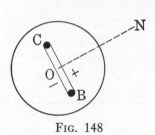

FIG. 148

Consider a single atom (Fig. 148) containing a plane Ampèrian circuit shown in cross section by BC, the current i entering the plane of the figure at B and emerging at C. If we replace the current by an equivalent magnetic shell whose periphery coincides with the circuit, the field is altered only in the interior of the shell. Let the thickness of the shell be l. Then, since the strength of the shell is $\mu_0 i$, the pole-strength per unit area of its surface (art. 41) is $\sigma = \mu_0 i / l$.

As the shell is the magnetic analog of a parallel plate capacitor, it gives rise to a field in its interior equal to σ/μ_0 in the direction opposite to that of the normal ON. So, if A is the area of the shell and τ_0 the volume of the atom, the contribution of the field inside the shell to the mean field averaged over the volume of the atom is

$$H_0 = \frac{1}{\tau_0}\left(\frac{\sigma}{\mu_0}\right)(Al) = \frac{iA}{\tau_0}$$

in the direction opposite to ON. As $\mu_0 iA$ is the magnetic moment p of the shell and $1/\tau_0$ is equivalent to n the number of atoms per unit volume, this field becomes $-n\mathbf{p}/\mu_0$ in vector form, the minus sign indicating that it has the direction opposite to $\mathbf{p}$.

So far we have averaged over a single atom only. If now we average over a volume τ containing a large number of atoms, the field under consideration is $\mathbf{H}_0 = -n\bar{\mathbf{p}}/\mu_0$, the bar indicating the mean value of the quantity over which it appears. But $n\bar{\mathbf{p}}$ is just the magnetic moment per unit volume, that is, the magnetization $\mathbf{I}$ of the medium. So the contribution to the magnetic intensity due to the fields in the interiors of the magnetic shells by which we have replaced the Ampèrian circuits actually existing inside the atoms is

$$\mathbf{H}_0 = -\frac{1}{\mu_0}\mathbf{I}. \tag{75-1}$$

We wish to compare (75-1) with the contribution to the total field provided by the portion of the field of the Ampèrian circuits which occupies the space previously filled by the equivalent shells. As the field due to a circuit is continuous all the way around we can, however, make the latter contribution vanishingly small by taking l small enough. Therefore, we conclude that the magnetic intensity inside a medium composed of Ampèrian circuits exceeds that inside an exactly similar medium composed of equivalent magnetic shells by $\mathbf{I}/\mu_0$. If $\mathbf{H}_i$ is the magnetic intensity in the first and $\mathbf{H}_s$ that in the second,

$$\mathbf{H}_i = \mathbf{H}_s + \frac{1}{\mu_0}\mathbf{I}. \tag{75-2}$$

Now, as $\mathbf{H}_s$ is the quantity which we have denoted by $\mathbf{H}$ in the discussion of magnetic media in Chapter IV, $\mathbf{H}_s + \mathbf{I}/\mu_0$ is the magnetic induction $\mathbf{B}$ divided by μ_0. Therefore we conclude that on Ampère's theory of magnetism the true magnetic intensity inside a magnetic medium is given by $\mathbf{B}/\mu_0$, while the quantity $\mathbf{H}$ is not the magnetic intensity actually existing at all, but the fictitious field which would exist if each Ampèrian circuit were replaced by an equivalent magnetic shell. Outside a magnetic medium $\mathbf{B}/\mu_0$ and $\mathbf{H}$ are the same and either represents the true magnetic intensity.

The conclusions reached in this article enable us to generalize the force equations (68-8), (68-9), (68-10) and (68-11). Thus, if we replace $\mathbf{H}$ by $\mathbf{B}/\mu_0$ in these equations, the resulting expressions apply whether a magnetic medium is present or not, since $\mathbf{B}/\mu_0$ gives the true magnetic intensity in either case. The general expression for the force on a current element is then (68-12), as stated in art. 68, rather than (68-8). Similarly, (68-9) becomes

$$\mathscr{F}_l = \mathbf{i} \times \mathbf{B} \tag{75-3}$$

and (68-10) becomes

$$\mathscr{F}_\tau = \mathbf{j} \times \mathbf{B}. \tag{75-4}$$

Chapter VIII

MOTION OF IONS IN ELECTRIC AND MAGNETIC FIELDS

76. Equation of Motion. We shall use the term *ion* in this chapter to designate any free charged particle. It may be an atom, molecule or aggregation of atoms or molecules which has acquired a positive charge through the loss of one or more electrons or a negative charge through the attachment of extra electrons, or it may be a free electron, such as a β-ray emitted by a radioactive atom, or a free proton. Unless otherwise stated, we shall limit our discussion to ions which have velocities relative to the observer small compared with the velocity of light, and shall suppose that the ions under consideration are so far apart and moving through a region where the gas pressure is so low that we can neglect both the collisions of ions with other ions or with neutral molecules and the forces exerted by the ions on one another.

The electrical force on an ion of charge e moving through an electric field where the electric intensity is $\mathbf{E}$ is $e\mathbf{E}$. The magnetic force on a moving charge is given by (68-11). For an ion of charge e this force is $e\mu_0\mathbf{v} \times \mathbf{H}$, where $\mathbf{v}$ represents the velocity of the ion relative to the observer. Adding the electric and magnetic forces together, the total force on an ion of charge e moving with velocity $\mathbf{v}$ is

$$\mathscr{F} = e(\mathbf{E} + \mu_0\mathbf{v} \times \mathbf{H}). \tag{76-1}$$

The force due to the magnetic field exists only when the ion is moving relative to the observer. It is directed at right angles to both $\mathbf{v}$ and $\mathbf{H}$ in the direction of advance of a right-handed screw rotated from the first to the second of these vectors. Being at right angles to $\mathbf{v}$, the force due to the magnetic field does no work on the moving ion. Since the force due to the magnetic field is proportional to the sine of the angle between $\mathbf{v}$ and $\mathbf{H}$, it is maximum when the motion is at right angles to the magnetic lines of force and zero when the motion is along the lines of force. If the ion should be moving in a magnetic medium, as in the case of a current passing through a magnet, $\mathbf{H}$ must be replaced by $\mathbf{B}/\mu_0$ as noted in art. 75, giving for the force on the ion,

$$\mathscr{F} = e(\mathbf{E} + \mathbf{v} \times \mathbf{B}). \tag{76-2}$$

Thus, when we can treat each ion as an isolated particle not subject to collisions with neighboring ions or neutral particles, the equation of motion of an ion of mass m moving through an electric field $\mathbf{E}$ and a magnetic field $\mathbf{H}$ is

$$\mathbf{f} = \frac{e}{m}\left(\mathbf{E} + \mu_0 \mathbf{v} \times \mathbf{H}\right), \qquad (76\text{-}3)$$

the vector $\mathbf{f}$ representing the acceleration of the ion.

77. Uniform Fields. We shall consider three cases, using (76-3): (a) a uniform electric field alone, (b) a uniform magnetic field alone, (c) combined uniform electric and magnetic fields.

Uniform Electric Field. The equation of motion of an ion in a uniform electric field $\mathbf{E}$ is

$$\mathbf{f} = \frac{e}{m}\,\mathbf{E}. \qquad (77\text{-}1)$$

The ion has a constant acceleration in the direction of the lines of force. If it starts from rest, it gains a velocity ft in a time t and traverses a distance of $\frac{1}{2}ft^2$. If it is projected with an initial velocity which is not parallel to the lines of force, it describes a parabola of the same type as that of a projectile moving without resistance through the earth's gravitational field.

Uniform Magnetic Field. The equation of motion of an ion moving through a uniform magnetic field $\mathbf{H}$ in the absence of an electric field is

$$\mathbf{f} = \frac{e}{m}\,\mu_0 \mathbf{v} \times \mathbf{H}. \qquad (77\text{-}2)$$

Since the acceleration is always perpendicular to the velocity, v remains constant throughout the motion of the ion. Moreover, as the acceleration is perpendicular to $\mathbf{H}$, the component of the velocity along the lines of force does not change with the time. Therefore, it is only the motion at right angles to the field which requires consideration, and we can limit our discussion for the moment to the special case where $\mathbf{v}$ is perpendicular to $\mathbf{H}$. Then the magnitude of $\mathbf{v} \times \mathbf{H}$ is vH, so that f is constant and the ion describes a circle (Fig. 149). If r is the radius of this circle, the normal acceleration has the value v^2/r. Since it is desirable to treat v and H as positive, the sign of r depends upon that of e. Examination of the figure shows that if e is positive the rotation is in such a sense as to cause a right-handed screw to advance in the direction opposite to $\mathbf{H}$. According to the usual convention this is a negative rotation.   Hence, we write the equation of motion in the scalar form

$$\frac{v^2}{r} = -\frac{e}{m}\mu_0 vH,$$

positive r corresponding to positive rotation and vice versa.

The radius of the circular path is then

$$r = -\frac{v}{\dfrac{e}{m}\mu_0 H},\qquad (77\text{-}3)$$

proportional to the linear velocity of the ion, while the magnitude of the angular velocity with which the circular path is described is

$$\omega = \frac{v}{r} = -\frac{e}{m}\mu_0 H,$$

independent of the linear velocity.   Considered as a vector, the angular velocity is directed along the axis of rotation in the sense of advance of a right-handed screw.   Since ω is opposite to $\mathbf{H}$ when e is positive, the last equation assumes the vector form

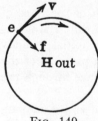

FIG. 149

$$\omega = -\frac{e}{m}\mu_0\mathbf{H}.\qquad (77\text{-}4)$$

When the initial velocity of the ion is not perpendicular to the lines of force, equation (77-3) holds if we replace v by the normal component of the velocity.   In addition to motion about the lines of force with angular velocity ω specified by (77-4) in a circle of radius r given by (77-3), the ion has a uniform translation parallel to the lines of force with a speed equal to the component of the initial velocity parallel to the field.   Therefore, the path is a helix with its axis in the direction of $\mathbf{H}$.

By allowing a stream of ions to pass through a uniform magnetic field the velocities of the individual particles can be calculated by (77-3) from the observed deflections.   This method is used in obtaining the *magnetic spectrum* of β-rays (electrons) from radio-active sources.   The rays, proceeding from the source S (Fig. 150), pass through the slit L into a magnetic field at right angles to the plane of the paper, and, after completing a semicircle, impinge on the photographic plate PQ.   On account of the finite angular width of the beam, different electrons describe different circular paths, but all those of the same velocity cross at approximately the same point after completing a half revolution.   This focussing action results in a single line at P corresponding to a group of electrons of a definite initial velocity, another group of greater velocity coming to a focus at Q and so on.

Combined Electric and Magnetic Fields. We come now to the motion of an ion in a region where it is acted on by both a uniform electric field and a uniform magnetic field. As no force is exerted by the magnetic field in the direction of the lines of force, the motion parallel to **H** is uniformly accelerated motion produced by the component of **E** parallel to the magnetic lines of force. The only part of the motion which requires examination, then, is that in the plane perpendicular to the magnetic intensity. Consequently, we may confine our attention to the special case where the two fields are perpendicular and the initial velocity is at right angles to **H**.

Let us orient the right-handed axes XYZ fixed in the observer's inertial system so that Y is parallel to **E** and Z to **H**. Consider, now,

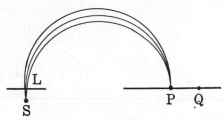

FIG. 150

a second set of parallel axes $X'Y'Z'$ which are moving relative to the observer's system in the X direction with a constant velocity

$$u = \frac{1}{\mu_0} \left(\frac{E}{H} \right),$$

that is, in vector notation,

$$\mathbf{u} = \frac{\mathbf{E} \times \mathbf{H}}{\mu_0 H^2}. \qquad (77\text{-}5)$$

Denoting by **v** the velocity of the ion relative to XYZ and by $\mathbf{v}'$ its velocity relative to the moving axes $X'Y'Z'$, we have

$$\mathbf{v} = \mathbf{u} + \mathbf{v}'. \qquad (77\text{-}6)$$

The equation of motion of the ion relative to the observer is

$$\mathbf{f} = \frac{e}{m} \left(\mathbf{E} + \mu_0 \mathbf{v} \times \mathbf{H} \right). \qquad (77\text{-}7)$$

From (77-6) we have for the acceleration

$$\mathbf{f} = \frac{d\mathbf{v}}{dt} = \frac{d\mathbf{v}'}{dt} = \mathbf{f}'. \qquad (77\text{-}8)$$

Substituting (77-6) and (77-8) in (77-7), we find for the equation of motion relative to the moving axes

$$\mathbf{f}' = \frac{e}{m}\left[\mathbf{E} + \mu_0(\mathbf{u}\times\mathbf{H} + \mathbf{v}'\times\mathbf{H})\right]. \tag{77-9}$$

But

$$\mu_0\mathbf{u}\times\mathbf{H} = \frac{(\mathbf{E}\times\mathbf{H})\times\mathbf{H}}{H^2} = -\frac{\mathbf{E}H^2}{H^2} = -\mathbf{E},$$

as is clear from Fig. 151. Therefore, (77-9) becomes

$$\mathbf{f}' = \frac{e}{m}\mu_0\mathbf{v}'\times\mathbf{H}. \tag{77-10}$$

By passing to a set of axes moving relative to the observer with the velocity $\mathbf{u}$ at right angles to the two fields we have eliminated $\mathbf{E}$. An observer moving with these axes would detect no electric field. He would assert that the ion under consideration was moving under the influence of a magnetic field alone. This is in accord with the statement made in art. 6 that the description of an electromagnetic field depends as much upon the state of motion of the observer as upon the distribution of charges, poles and currents.

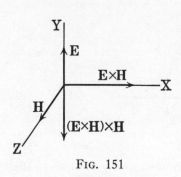

Fig. 151

Since equation (77-10) for the motion of the ion is identical in form with equation (77-2) for the case of zero electric field, we know at once that the ion under consideration describes a circle of radius

$$r' = -\frac{v'}{\dfrac{e}{m}\mu_0 H} \tag{77-11}$$

in the $X'Y'$ plane with angular velocity

$$\boldsymbol{\omega} = -\frac{e}{m}\mu_0\mathbf{H} \tag{77-12}$$

relative to the moving axes $X'Y'Z'$, the quantity v' remaining constant during the motion. Relative to the axes XYZ fixed in the observer's inertial system the center of this circle moves in the X direction with a uniform velocity of translation u. Therefore, the path of the ion is a cycloid described by a point at a distance r' from the center of a circle rolling on a line parallel to the X axis. As the velocity of the center of the rolling circle is u, its radius is

$$a = \frac{u}{\omega} = -\frac{E}{\frac{e}{m}\mu_0{}^2H^2}, \qquad (77\text{-}13)$$

independent of the velocity of the ion. The ratio of r' to a is

$$\frac{r'}{a} = \frac{v'}{u}. \qquad (77\text{-}14)$$

According as v' is greater than, equal to, or less than u, the generating point lies outside, on the circumference of, or inside the rolling circle, and the cycloid is curtate, common, or prolate. Typical paths are shown in Fig. 152 for the case of a positive ion, $\mathbf{H}$ being directed toward the reader. The rolling circle is indicated by a broken line, (a) representing a curtate, (b) a common, and (c) a prolate cycloid. The drift $\mathbf{u}$

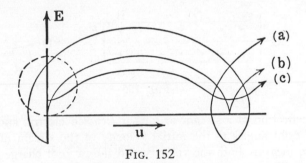

Fig. 152

resembles the precession of a rotating top in that it is at right angles to the impressed fields $\mathbf{E}$ and $\mathbf{H}$.

Since $\mathbf{u}$ depends only on $\mathbf{E}$ and $\mathbf{H}$, it is in the same sense for a negative ion as for a positive ion and is independent of the magnitude of charge or mass. The paths for negative ions are obtained by rotating those in Fig. 152 through the angle π about the horizontal axis.

If the initial velocity $\mathbf{v}_0$ of an ion relative to the observer's inertial system has the components v_{0x} and v_{0y},

$$v'^2 = (v_{0x} - u)^2 + v_{0y}{}^2. \qquad (77\text{-}15)$$

We can classify all possible paths in terms of the initial velocity as follows:

(1) $v' = 0$. This case requires $v_{0x} = u$ and $v_{0y} = 0$. The path is a straight line at right angles to $\mathbf{E}$ and $\mathbf{H}$, the force due to the electric field being exactly balanced by the opposite force due to the magnetic field.

(2) $v' \neq 0$.   We have three subcases, namely;

(a) $v_0 = 0$.   Then $v' = u$ and the path is a common cycloid, the ion starting at the cusp.

(b) $0 < v_0 \leqslant 2u$.   It is necessary to calculate the value of v'/u from (77-15) in order to determine the type of cycloid described.

(c) $v_0 > 2u$.   Then $v' > u$ and the path is a curtate cycloid.

In the preceding discussion we have supposed the electric and magnetic fields to be at right angles and the initial velocity to lie in the plane perpendicular to the magnetic field.   If these conditions are not satisfied, we must replace E in our formulas by the component of the electric intensity at right angles to H and the various velocities involved by the component velocities in the plane perpendicular to H.   Then, in addition to the motion depicted in Fig. 152, the ion has a uniform acceleration at right angles to the plane of the figure due to the component of the electric intensity parallel to the magnetic field.

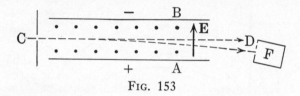

FIG. 153

The deflection of a stream of ions in crossed electric and magnetic fields at right angles to the initial velocity of the stream may be employed to measure both the velocity and the ratio of charge to mass of the ions.   The electric field may be produced by the parallel plate capacitor AB (Fig. 153) between the plates of which the stream of ions CD passes, the magnetic field (indicated by dots) at right angles to the plane of the figure being produced by a solenoid.

First the potential difference of the capacitor is adjusted until the stream suffers no deflection.   Under these conditions the upward force due to the electric field is just balanced by the downward force due to the magnetic field, and the velocity v of the ions is equal to the drift velocity u, that is,

$$v = u = \frac{1}{\mu_0}\left(\frac{E}{H}\right).$$

If, now, the electric field is suppressed, the ions describe the circular arc CF of radius

$$r = -\frac{v}{\dfrac{e}{m}\,\mu_0 H}.$$

The radius r is obtained at once from the observed deflection, and as v is known, e/m can be calculated by means of the formula

$$\frac{e}{m} = -\frac{1}{r}\left(\frac{v}{\mu_0 H}\right),$$ (77-16)

obtained from the preceding equation.

The deflection may be observed by placing at F a metal cylinder with a narrow opening, known as a *Faraday cylinder*, which is connected to an electrometer. The strength of the magnetic field is varied until the electrometer shows a maximum rate of deflection, indicating that all the ions in the stream are entering the chamber. Another method of measuring the deflection is by means of a photographic plate placed at D at right angles to the stream.

By employing this method J. J. Thomson was able to determine, in

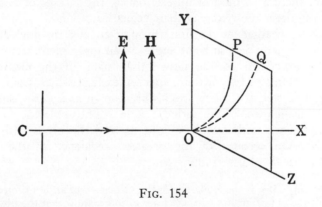

FIG. 154

1897, the ratio e/m of electrons coming from the cathode of an evacuated tube through which a discharge is passing. The most recent value of the ratio of charge to mass of the electron is

$$\frac{e}{m} = -1.7588(10)^{11} \text{ coulomb/kg.}$$ (77-17)

In Thomson's experiments the velocity of the electrons was of the order of one-tenth the velocity of light.

Sometimes, as in the *positive ray spectrograph*, it is convenient to have the electric and magnetic fields parallel. Suppose both fields have the direction of the Y axis (Fig. 154), the ions entering the field at C along the X axis. Assuming both deflections to be small, the deflection due to the electric field at the end of the time t is

$$y = \frac{1}{2}\left(\frac{eE}{m}\right)t^2,$$

and that due to the acceleration (77-2) caused by the magnetic field is

$$z = \frac{1}{2}\left(\frac{e\mu_0 vH}{m}\right)t^2 = \left(\frac{e}{2m}\right)\mu_0 Hlt,$$

where $l = vt$ is the length of the path through the fields. Eliminating t, we get the parabola

$$y = \left[\frac{E}{\left(\frac{e}{2m}\right)\mu_0^2 H^2 l^2}\right]z^2.$$

All ions having the same value of e/m strike a photographic plate lying in the YZ plane somewhere along the arc OP of this parabola, whatever their velocities may be. Ions with a greater value of e/m give rise to another parabolic arc, such as OQ. If the particles under consideration are singly ionized, the charge e is the same for all. We have here, then, a method of differentiating the masses of ions which does not require a knowledge of their velocities.

By passing charged atoms first through an electric field and then through a magnetic field at right angles in an instrument known as the *mass spectrograph*, Aston has shown that many of the elements are mixtures of atoms of two or more species, each of which has a characteristic atomic weight. Such species are known as *isotopes*, since they occupy the same place in the periodic table. Thus chlorine consists of two isotopes, one with atomic weight 35 and the other with atomic weight 37. On account of the greater prevalence of the former, chemical methods of determining the atomic weight give 35.46.

Problem 77a. If α is the angle which the velocity $\mathbf{v}$ of an ion projected in a uniform magnetic field makes with the lines of force, show that the pitch of the helix described is $-2\pi\left(\dfrac{v\cos\alpha}{\dfrac{e}{m}\mu_0 H}\right)$.

Problem 77b. Under the influence of ultra-violet light electrons are emitted normally with negligible velocities from one plate of a parallel plate capacitor placed in a magnetic field H parallel to the plates. Find the relation between the potential drop V across the capacitor, the separation d of the plates, and the field H so that the electrons may just get across. Ans. $V = -\left(\dfrac{e}{2m}\right)\mu_0^2 H^2 d^2$.

Problem 77c. Referring to the case of an ion moving in crossed electric and magnetic fields, described in this article, find the integrated equations of motion. Express the results in terms of u and ω, assuming that the ion passes through the fixed (XYZ) origin at time $t = 0$.

$$\text{Ans. } x = \frac{1}{\omega}\left\{(v_{0x} - u)\sin\omega t - v_{0y}(1 - \cos\omega t)\right\} + ut,$$

$$y = \frac{1}{\omega}\left\{v_{0y}\sin\omega t + (v_{0x} - u)(1 - \cos\omega t)\right\}.$$

78. Charge and Mass of the Electron. In the last article we have seen how the ratio of the charge to the mass of the electron may be measured by means of the deflection of a stream of cathode rays in crossed electric and magnetic fields. We shall now describe the method used by Millikan* for measuring the charge alone. From this measurement and that of the ratio of charge to mass we can calculate the mass of the electron, as well as certain other important physical constants.

Let oil drops of radii between $(10)^{-4}$ and $(10)^{-3}$ mm be sprayed into the space between the horizontal plates (Fig. 155) of a parallel plate capacitor. If the air between the plates is ionized by a flash of X-rays or by other means, occasionally one or more ions attach themselves to an oil drop, the motion of which can be observed through a microscope provided with cross-hairs. By charging the capacitor to a potential V the oil drop is subjected to an upward electrical force $-eE$, where e is the charge on the drop and $E = V/d$ is the electric intensity.

For simplicity we shall suppose that only a single electron is attached to the drop. Then e is the charge of the electron. It is a simple matter to differentiate experimentally the cases where two or three electrons have become fastened to the drop from the case where only a single electron is involved.

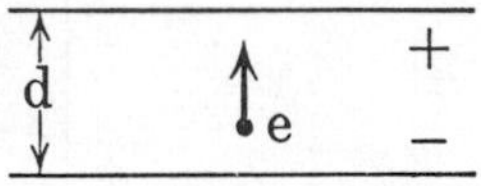

Fig. 155

The forces acting on the drop are the downward force of gravity, the upward force due to the buoyancy of the air, and the upward force due to the electric field. Let a be the radius of the drop, which must assume a spherical form on account of surface tension, σ the density of the oil of which it is composed, and ρ the density of the air. Then the three forces just enumerated are $\frac{4}{3}\pi a^3 \sigma g$, $\frac{4}{3}\pi a^3 \rho g$, and $-eE$ respectively. So, if the potential is adjusted until the drop is in equilibrium,

$$\tfrac{4}{3}\pi a^3(\sigma - \rho)g = -eE. \tag{78-1}$$

Although σ, ρ and E are easily measured, we cannot calculate e until we determine the radius a of the drop. To do this we remove the electric field and observe v, the rate at which the drop falls. A deduction from hydrodynamics, known as *Stokes' law*, shows that v is related to a and the viscosity η of the air through which the drop is falling by the equation

$$a = \sqrt{\frac{9}{2}\left(\frac{\eta}{\sigma - \rho}\right)\frac{v}{g}}. \tag{78-2}$$

* Millikan, R. A., *The Electron*, University of Chicago Press, 1917.

Eliminating a from (78-1) by means of this relation and denoting the value of e so obtained by e_1,

$$e_1 = -\frac{4\pi}{3}\left(\frac{9\eta}{2}\right)^{3/2}\left\{\frac{1}{(\sigma-\rho)g}\right\}^{1/2}\frac{v^{3/2}}{E}. \tag{78-3}$$

If the charge of the electron is computed from this formula, it is found that the value obtained depends upon the density of the air and the radius of the drop. The trouble is that the drops are so close to molecular dimensions that the hydrodynamical assumption underlying Stokes' law that the fluid through which the drop is falling has a continuous structure is no longer altogether valid. Consequently, (78-3) can be expected to hold accurately only when ρ and a are relatively large, that is, when the quantity $1/\rho a$ is small. This means that e_1 approaches e as $1/\rho a$ approaches zero. In practice $1/\rho a$ is always proportional to $1/\not p a$, where $\not p$ is the pressure, since the temperature is kept

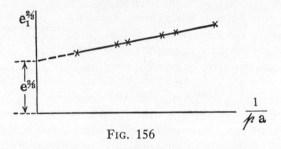

FIG. 156

constant to avoid variation of η. The limiting value of e_1 can now be determined graphically. Following Millikan, we plot $e_1^{2/3}$ against $1/\not p a$ and obtain a straight line whose intercept equals $e^{2/3}$, as shown in Fig. 156. This gives e.

The charge of the electron is found to be

$$e = -1.60210(10)^{-19} \text{ coulomb.} \tag{78-4}$$

Combining this with (77-17), we see that the mass of the electron is

$$m = 9.109(10)^{-31} \text{ kg.} \tag{78-5}$$

The deflection method of the previous article shows that the ratio of charge to mass is but $1/1836.1$ as big for a hydrogen nucleus or proton as for an electron. Therefore, the mass of the proton is

$$m = 1.673(10)^{-27} \text{ kg.} \tag{78-6}$$

As noted in art. 57, Faraday's constant F, representing the charge carried in electrolysis by one kilogram-equivalent, is $9.649(10)^7$ coulombs.

Therefore, *Avogadro's number*, the number of atoms per kilogram-atom or of molecules per kilogram-molecule, is

$$A = \frac{9.649(10)^7}{1.60210(10)^{-19}} = 6.023(10)^{26} \text{ molecule/kg-mol.} \quad (78\text{-}7)$$

Since one kilogram-molecule of an ideal gas is found to occupy 22.414 meter³ at 0° C and one atmosphere pressure, *Loschmidt's number*, the number of molecules per meter³ under standard conditions, is

$$L = \frac{6.023(10)^{26}}{22.414} = 2.687(10)^{25} \text{ molecule/meter}^3. \quad (78.8)$$

The equation of state of an ideal gas composed of N molecules is

$$pV = kNT,$$

where *Boltzmann's constant* k is one that appears in many important physical relations. As (78-8) gives us

$$\frac{N}{V} = 2.687(10)^{25} \text{ molecule/meter}^3$$

for the standard temperature $T = 273.15°$ K and standard pressure $p = 1.0133(10)^5$ newton/meter², we can calculate k, getting

$$k = \frac{1.0133(10)^5}{2.687(10)^{25} \times 273.15} = 1.381(10)^{-23} \text{ joule/deg molecule.}$$

If M represents the number of kilogram-molecules of an ideal gas in a volume V, it follows from Avogadro's law that the gas constant R in the equation $pV = MRT$ is a universal constant. Its value is

$$R = kA = 8.31(10)^3 \text{ joule/deg kg-mol.}$$

79. The Cyclotron. An important application of the motion of ions in combined fields is the *cyclotron*, first constructed by E. O. Lawrence in 1931. This device generates a beam of high-speed ions whose energies are great enough to produce atomic transmutations and disintegrations when they collide with atomic nuclei. A metal pill-box (Fig. 157) is cut into two semicircular parts, D_1 and D_2, called *dees*. These are placed within an evacuated container C between the poles N, S of a magnet. The latter is composed of a large soft iron core wound with a heavy copper conductor so that a strong magnetizing current may be used. The magnetic intensity H between the poles is then very large and uniform over the region occupied by the dees. Simultaneously an electric field which alternates direction with a high frequency v_o is established in the gap between D_1 and D_2 by means of an electric oscillator. Consider positive ions introduced at a point P near the center of the gap when the electric field is from D_1 to D_2. They are accelerated toward D_2 and enter the interior of the pill-box with a velocity v. Here they are shielded from the electric field but not from the magnetic field. Hence they describe the circular path shown in the figure with an angular velocity of magnitude $(e/m)\mu_0 H$ independent of v, as demonstrated in art. 77. Suppose now, that the frequency of the electric field is made equal to the frequency of revolution of the ions, that is, $\nu_o = (e/2\pi m)\mu_0 H$. Then by the time the ions have passed out of D_2 into the gap, the electric field has reversed and the ions are again

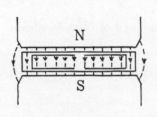

accelerated. This process continues, the ions receiving an impulse twice in each complete revolution. The maximum velocity attainable is limited by the radius R of the dees. For, in accord with (77-3), the ions spiral outwards as their velocity increases, the maximum velocity attainable being

$$v_R = \frac{e}{m}\mu_0 HR. \qquad (79\text{-}1)$$

When this has been reached, the ions are deflected out through a window W by means of the high-potential deflecting electrode E.

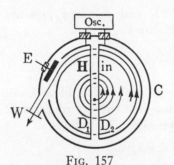

Fig. 157

The ions most commonly used in a cyclotron are the deuterons from heavy hydrogen. As each is a combination of a proton and a neutron, $e = 1.60(10)^{-19}$ coulomb and $m = 3.34(10)^{-27}$ kg. Using $H = 1.25(10)^6$ amp/meter and $R = 0.75$ meter as typical values for a cyclotron of medium size, we find $\nu_o = 12.0(10)^6$ cycle/sec and $v_R = 56.4(10)^6$ meter/sec. The most important characteristic of the emergent ion beam is the energy $\frac{1}{2}mv_R^2$ of the ions. In practice it is customary to express beam energies in units of a *million electron volts*, abbreviated Mev. An *electron volt* is the amount of energy acquired by an electron as it passes through a potential difference of one volt, that is, $1.60(10)^{-19}$ joule. The beam energy for the case under consideration is found to be 33.2 Mev. In order to make the spacing between successive paths inside the dees large enough to produce a satisfactory beam, it is necessary to use a large electric field. If the potential difference between the dees when the ions cross the gap is 50,000 volts, an appropriate value for the cyclotron under discussion, the ions make 332 revolutions before emerging.

Heretofore, we have treated the mass m of a particle as a constant independent of its velocity v. Actually, as predicted by the relativity theory of Einstein, the mass increases with increasing velocity in accord with the formula

$$m = \frac{m_0}{\sqrt{1 - \dfrac{v^2}{c^2}}}, \tag{79-2}$$

where the constant m_0 represents the *rest mass*, that is, the mass for velocities so small that v^2/c^2 is negligible compared with unity. Consequently, the angular velocity (77-12) of an ion in a uniform magnetic field is no longer independent of the linear velocity at velocities comparable with c the velocity of light.

Newton's second law of motion retains the form

$$\mathscr{F} = \frac{d}{dt}(m\mathbf{V}) \tag{79-3}$$

at all velocities. So, if we designate components parallel and transverse to the path by the subscripts l and t, respectively, we have

$$\left.\begin{aligned}
\mathscr{F}_l &= \frac{m_0}{\left(1 - \dfrac{v^2}{c^2}\right)^{3/2}} f_l = \frac{d}{dt}(mv), \\[2em]
\mathscr{F}_t &= \frac{m_0}{\sqrt{1 - \dfrac{v^2}{c^2}}} f_t = m f_t.
\end{aligned}\right\} \tag{79-4}$$

The kinetic energy acquired when the velocity increases from 0 to v is

$$\int \mathscr{F}_l v\, dt = m_0 \int_0^v \frac{v\, dv}{\left(1 - \dfrac{v^2}{c^2}\right)^{3/2}} = m_0 c^2 \left\{ \frac{1}{\sqrt{1 - \dfrac{v^2}{c^2}}} - 1 \right\}, \tag{79-5}$$

since $f_l = \dfrac{dv}{dt}$. For $v^2 \ll c^2$ this reduces to the Newtonian expression $\frac{1}{2} m_0 v^2$, as it should. Since we measure only differences of energy, it is permissible to regard

$$U = \frac{m_0 c^2}{\sqrt{1 - \dfrac{v^2}{c^2}}} = mc^2 \tag{79-6}$$

as the total kinetic energy and $m_0 c^2$ as the kinetic energy for zero velocity relative to the observer's inertial system. In the table we give, for the electron, proton and deuteron, the ratio of the mass to the rest mass and the ratio of the velocity to that of light, for various values of $U - m_0 c^2$.

$U - m_0 c^2$ (Mev)	Electron		Proton		Deuteron	
	m/m_0	v/c	m/m_0	v/c	m/m_0	v/c
1	2.95	0.941	1.001	0.05	1.000	0.03
10	20.5	0.999	1.011	0.15	1.005	0.10
20	40.0	1.000	1.021	0.20	1.011	0.15
30	59.5	1.000	1.032	0.25	1.016	0.18
50	98.5	1.000	1.053	0.31	1.027	0.23
100	196	1.000	1.106	0.43	1.053	0.31

It is seen that the mass of an electron with an energy of 1 Mev is already three times its rest mass, and its velocity is 94 percent of the velocity of light. Consequently, an ordinary cyclotron cannot be used to obtain electron beams of high energy. On the contrary, the mass of a proton or deuteron does not differ appreciably from unity until an energy of from 30 to 50 Mev has been reached.

Substituting (79-6) in (77-12), we have for the angular velocity

$$\omega = -\frac{ec^2}{U} \mu_0 \mathbf{H}. \tag{79-7}$$

Hence the angular velocity of an ion which is being accelerated in a cyclotron decreases in magnitude as the energy increases. This destroys the necessary phase relation between the times at which the ion crosses the gap and the accelerating electric field. If the frequency of the oscillator remains unchanged, the ion acquires a greater and greater lag with respect to the field, until it may cross the gap during the part of the cycle in which the electric field is decelerating. This results in a decrease in energy and a consequent increase in angular velocity, and soon the ion is again crossing the gap during the part of the cycle in which the electric field is accelerating. Evidently the energy of the ion oscillates about a value U_o determined by the ratio of the frequency v_o of the oscillator to the magnetic field H in accord with the equation (+ for positive ions, − for electrons)

$$U_o = \pm \frac{ec^2}{2\pi v_o} \mu_0 H \tag{79-8}$$

and after a few revolutions the ion will settle down in an orbit of this energy, in such a phase as to cross the gap between the dees when the electric field is zero. If, now, either the frequency of the oscillator is slightly decreased or the magnetic field is slightly increased, the ion will pass to an equilibrium orbit of slightly greater energy.

The Synchro-Cyclotron. This device makes use of the first of the two methods cited above for increasing the energy of an ion beyond the value at which the variation of mass with velocity becomes appreciable. The frequency of the oscillator is decreased very slowly, of course, as compared with the rate of revolution of the ion inside the dees. The synchro-cyclotron is generally used for high energy protons and deuterons.

The Synchrotron. The synchrotron increases the energy of an ion by slowly increasing the magnetic field, keeping the frequency of the oscillator constant. When used for electrons, for which it is particularly suited, the ions are given an initial energy high enough so that they enter the device with a velocity nearly equal to that of light. Consequently, there is very little increase in the size of the orbit as further increments of energy are added. Therefore, the solid magnet of the ordinary cyclotron may be replaced by a magnet in the form of a hollow cylinder, saving weight and expense.

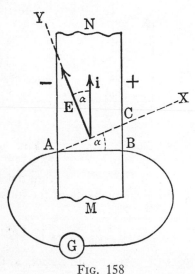

Fig. 158

80. The Hall Effect. If the terminals of a galvanometer *G* (Fig. 158) are attached to two opposite points *A* and *B* of a thin metal strip *MN* carrying a current *i*, the galvanometer will remain undeflected, showing that the equipotential line *AB* is perpendicular to the current. If, however, the strip is placed in a magnetic field *H* at right angles to its plane, a deflection is observed which does not vanish until the lead at *B* is displaced to a point *C* beyond *B*. The equipotential lines, therefore, are rotated from the direction of *AB* to that of *AC* by the magnetic field. This effect was discovered by E. H. Hall in 1879.

Since the free paths of the electrons responsible for metallic conduction are relatively short, these electrons describe only small portions of the cycloidal arcs depicted in Fig. 152 when subject to crossed electric and magnetic fields. Suppose that **E** is directed along the *Y* axis and **H** along the *Z* axis as in art. 77. The component velocities of an ion due to the circular motion about the lines of magnetic force relative to the moving axes $X'Y'Z'$ are

$$v_x' = -v' \sin (\omega t + \theta_0'),$$
$$v_y' = v' \cos (\omega t + \theta_0'),$$

from (77-12), where θ_0' (Fig. 159) is the angle which $\mathbf{v}'$ makes with the Y' axis when $t = 0$. Therefore, the components of velocity relative to the axes XYZ fixed in the observer's inertial system are

$$\left.\begin{array}{l} v_x = u + v_x' = u - v' \cos \theta_0' \sin \omega t - v' \sin \theta_0' \cos \omega t, \\ v_y = v_y' = v' \cos \theta_0' \cos \omega t - v' \sin \theta_0' \sin \omega t. \end{array}\right\} \quad (80\text{-}1)$$

If $\mathbf{v}_0$ is the initial velocity of the ion, it follows from (77-6) that

$$-v' \sin \theta_0' = v_{0x} - u, \qquad v' \cos \theta_0' = v_{0y}.$$

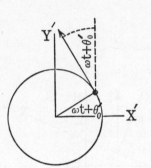

FIG. 159

Substituting these in (80-1) and putting

$$\sin \omega t = \omega t,$$
$$\cos \omega t = 1 - \tfrac{1}{2}\omega^2 t^2,$$

since t is small, we get

$$v_x = v_{0x}(1 - \tfrac{1}{2}\omega^2 t^2) - v_{0y}\omega t + \tfrac{1}{2}u\omega^2 t^2,$$
$$v_y = v_{0y}(1 - \tfrac{1}{2}\omega^2 t^2) + v_{0x}\omega t - u\omega t.$$

First we find the mean velocity of an ion between successive collisions. If t_f is the time taken to describe a mean free path, the X and Y components of the mean velocity are, respectively,

$$\frac{1}{t_f} \int_0^{t_f} v_x\, dt, \qquad \frac{1}{t_f} \int_0^{t_f} v_y\, dt.$$

Next we average with respect to the initial velocities. As the electrons may be assumed to start out indiscriminately in all directions after collision with the fixed atoms in the conductor, the average values of v_{0x} and v_{0y} are zero. Therefore, the average components of velocity are

$$\bar{v}_x = \tfrac{1}{6}u\omega^2 t_f^2,$$
$$\bar{v}_y = -\tfrac{1}{2}u\omega t_f.$$

Consequently, if n is the number of free electrons per unit volume, the current densities in the X and Y directions are

$$\left.\begin{array}{l} j_x = ne\bar{v}_x = \tfrac{1}{6}neu\omega^2 t_f^2, \\ j_y = ne\bar{v}_y = -\tfrac{1}{2}neu\omega t_f. \end{array}\right\} \quad (80\text{-}2)$$

The resultant current, therefore, makes an angle α with the electric field given by

$$\tan \alpha = \frac{j_x}{j_y} = \frac{1}{3}\left(\frac{e}{m} \mu_0 H\right) t_f, \tag{80-3}$$

since $\omega = -(e/m)\mu_0 H$. Hence, the resultant electric intensity, represented by $\mathbf{E}$ in Fig. 158, is not parallel to the axis of the strip. The transverse component of the electric field is due to the deflection of the electrons, which produces charges on the edges of the strip.

If E_t is the transverse component of the electric intensity,

$$E_t = \frac{j_x}{j}E = \frac{j_x}{j_x{}^2+j_y{}^2} jE.$$

Since $j_x \ll j_y$, this reduces to

$$E_t = \frac{2}{3neu} jE = \frac{2}{3ne} j\mu_0 H. \tag{80-4}$$

This equation is usually written

$$E_t = \pi_H j\mu_0 H, \tag{80-5}$$

the constant π_H being known as the *Hall coefficient*. According to the simple electron theory outlined above, this coefficient has the value

$$\pi_H = \frac{2}{3ne}, \tag{80-6}$$

and, as the charge on the electron is negative, the Hall coefficient should always be negative. This means that the angle α should be laid off in the opposite sense to that illustrated in Fig. 158. Experiment shows, however, that the Hall coefficient is positive in nearly as many cases as it is negative. Although a more rigorous development of the theory of the Hall effect leads to a slightly different numerical coefficient than that of (80-6), the sign remains unchanged. Actually, as far as classical electron theory is concerned, no satisfactory explanation of the positive Hall coefficient has been proposed.

In terms of the Hall coefficient the deflection of the equipotential lines is given by

$$\sin \alpha = \frac{E_t}{E} = \pi_H\left(\frac{j}{E}\right)\mu_0 H = \frac{\pi_H}{\rho} \mu_0 H, \tag{80-7}$$

where ρ is the electrical resistivity of the strip.

Values of the Hall coefficient for some common metals at 18° C are given in the table. The reader will find a detailed account of this effect and other related effects in L. L. Campbell's *Galvanomagnetic and Thermomagnetic Effects*.

Metal	$\pi_H \left(\dfrac{\text{meter}^3}{\text{coulomb}} \right)$
Ag	$-8.9(10)^{-11}$
Au	$-7.2(10)^{-11}$
Cu	$-5.3(10)^{-11}$
Al	$-3.9(10)^{-11}$
Pb	$0.9(10)^{-11}$
Cd	$5.9(10)^{-11}$
Zn	$10.0(10)^{-11}$

Problem 80. The resistivity of a gold strip is $2.43(10)^{-8}$ ohm meter. Find the deflection of the equipotential lines when a current is passing through the strip and a normal magnetic field $(10)^6$ amperes per meter is applied. Ans. $-3.72(10)^{-3}$ radian.

81. Space Charge. So far in our treatment of the motion of ions in external electric and magnetic fields we have neglected the forces exerted by the ions on one another. This procedure is justifiable if ions of both signs are present in equal numbers so that attractions and repulsions balance, or, in the case of ions of one sign, if the ions are few enough and far enough apart so that the forces they exert on one another are negligibly small. In some cases, however, such as that of the hot filament vacuum tube (art. 66), we have a dense current of ions of one sign without the presence of compensating ions of the opposite sign. Then, in addition to the external field, we must take into account the electric field due to the ions themselves. In the usual case, considered here, the external field is entirely electric.

Let ρ be the charge per unit volume of the ions and V the electric potential in the region through which they are passing. Then Poisson's equation (26-1) must be satisfied. As $\kappa = 1$ in the empty space under consideration,

$$\frac{\partial^2 V}{\partial x^2} + \frac{\partial^2 V}{\partial y^2} + \frac{\partial^2 V}{\partial z^2} = -\frac{\rho}{\kappa_0}. \tag{81-1}$$

Next we have from the definition of the current density j,

$$j = \rho v, \tag{81-2}$$

where v is the velocity of the ions, and finally the law of conservation of energy requires that

$$\tfrac{1}{2}mv^2 + eV = \text{cons.} \tag{81-3}$$

If we eliminate ρ and v from these equations, we are left with a relation between the current density j and the potential for the case of a current consisting of ions of one sign only.

We shall discuss two typical cases; first a current of ions passing from one of two parallel plates to the other, and second a current passing from the inner of two coaxial cylinders to the outer. In both cases we shall assume that the ions have negligible velocity at the initial electrode and that they accumulate there in very great numbers so as to produce a finite current in accord with (81-2).

Parallel Plates. Let us take the potential at the plate A (Fig. 160) to be zero and denote the potential at the plate B by V_d. Take the X axis at right angles to the plates with the origin at plate A. As the potential is a function of x only, (81-1) becomes

$$\frac{d^2V}{dx^2} = -\frac{\rho}{\kappa_0}. \qquad (81\text{-}4)$$

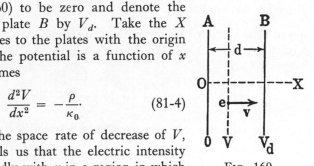

FIG. 160

Since E equals the space rate of decrease of V, this equation tells us that the electric intensity must change rapidly with x in a region in which the charge density ρ is large.

As $V=0$ when $v=0$, the constant in (81-3) is zero, and we have

$$v = \sqrt{-\left(\frac{2e}{m}\right)V}. \qquad (81\text{-}5)$$

If we eliminate ρ and v from (81-2), (81-4) and (81-5),

$$\frac{d^2V}{dx^2} = -\frac{j}{\kappa_0\sqrt{-\left(\frac{2e}{m}\right)V}}. \qquad (81\text{-}6)$$

Multiplying by

$$2\frac{dV}{dx}dx = 2dV$$

and integrating, we obtain

$$\left(\frac{dV}{dx}\right)^2 - \left(\frac{dV}{dx}\right)^2_{x=0} = \frac{4j}{\kappa_0}\left(\frac{m}{2e}\right)\sqrt{-\left(\frac{2e}{m}\right)V}.$$

Note that j always has the same sign as e. Furthermore $-(2e/m)V$ is always positive, since if e is positive V must be negative to produce a current, whereas if e is negative, as in the case of electrons, V must be positive.

The large number of ions in the neighborhood of the plate A neutralizes the field E_0 at the plate, so that

$$E_0 = -\left(\frac{dV}{dx}\right)_{x=0} = 0.$$

We have then

$$\frac{dV}{dx} = -\left(\frac{m}{2e}\right)\sqrt{\frac{4j}{\kappa_0}\left(\frac{2e}{m}\right)}\left[-\left(\frac{2e}{m}\right)V\right]^{1/4},$$

where we have taken the negative sign before the radical since $\frac{dV}{dx}$ is opposite in sign to e. Integrating again and solving for the current density,

$$j = \frac{4\kappa_0}{9}\left(\frac{m}{2e}\right)\frac{\left[-\left(\frac{2e}{m}\right)V\right]^{3/2}}{x^2}.$$

If we make x equal to the distance d between the plates, V becomes V_d. Hence

$$j = \frac{4\kappa_0}{9}\left(\frac{m}{2e}\right)\frac{\left[-\left(\frac{2e}{m}\right)V_d\right]^{3/2}}{d^2}. \tag{81-7}$$

Generally the ions giving rise to space charge are thermionic electrons (art. 66) and consequently e is negative and V_d is positive. In this case we can write (81-7) in the form

$$j = -\frac{4\kappa_0}{9}\sqrt{-\left(\frac{2e}{m}\right)}\frac{V_d^{3/2}}{d^2}. \tag{81-8}$$

If we substitute the values of κ_0 and e/m, omitting dimensions for simplicity, we obtain

$$j = -2.33(10)^{-6}\frac{V_d^{3/2}}{d^2}. \tag{81-9}$$

Evidently the current flows from plate B to plate A when the space charge is negative, as indicated by the negative sign.

The right-hand side of equation (81-8) represents the maximum current density that can be obtained for a given V_d and d. Until this maximum is reached, the current increases with increasing rate of production of ions at A. After the maximum current has been obtained, however, no further increase in the rate of production of ions has any effect on the current so long as V_d remains unchanged, the current being limited by the *space charge* due to the ions between the two plates. The maximum current does not obey Ohm's law, since it is proportional to the three-halves power of the potential difference rather than to the first power.

Coaxial Cylinders. This is the case of a heated *filament* emitting ions which move radially through an evacuated space to a cylindrical receiving electrode called the *plate.* Let a be the radius of the filament and b that of the plate. It is convenient to use cylindrical coordinates, since then V is a function of the radius vector r alone and Poisson's equation reduces to the simple form

$$\frac{1}{r}\frac{d}{dr}\left(r\frac{dV}{dr}\right) = -\frac{\rho}{\kappa_0}. \tag{81-10}$$

This relation follows from (26-3), if the latter is converted to Poisson's equation by changing the zero on the right to $-(\rho/\kappa_0\kappa)\lambda\mu\nu$.

Using j_l to represent the current per unit length of the cylinders, we have

$$j_l = 2\pi r\rho v. \tag{81-11}$$

Also, taking the potential of the filament to be zero, we have, as before,

$$v = \sqrt{-\left(\frac{2e}{m}\right)V}.$$

Eliminating ρ and v from these three equations, we obtain

$$\frac{d}{dr}\left(r\frac{dV}{dr}\right) = -\frac{j_l}{2\pi\kappa_0\sqrt{-\left(\frac{2e}{m}\right)V}}. \tag{81-12}$$

The integration of (81-12) is difficult and leads, finally, to the relation

$$j_l = \frac{8\pi\kappa_0}{9}\left(\frac{m}{2e}\right)\frac{\left[-\left(\frac{2e}{m}\right)V\right]^{3/2}}{r\psi^3},$$

where the quantity ψ satisfies the equation

$$\psi\left[\frac{d^2}{ds^2}(\psi^2)+2\frac{d}{ds}(\psi^2)+\psi^2\right] = 1, \qquad s \equiv \frac{2}{3}\log\frac{r}{a}.$$

The form of the solution of this non-linear differential equation depends upon the magnitude of s. For the specified boundary conditions we find*

$$\psi = (\tfrac{3}{2}s)^{2/3}[1-0.400s+0.098s^2-0.015s^3+0.002s^4-\cdots], \qquad s < 1;$$

$$\psi = 1-e^{-s}[0.652\cos\gamma]-e^{-2s}[0.116\cos 2\gamma+0.055\sin 2\gamma]$$
$$-e^{-3s}[0.035\cos 3\gamma+0.029\sin 3\gamma+0.008\cos\gamma$$
$$+0.032\sin\gamma]-\cdots, \qquad s > 1;$$

where $\gamma \equiv 0.707s+0.399$ radian.

* Page and Adams, *Phys. Rev.* **76**, 381 (1949).

To express the maximum current per unit length in terms of the plate potential V_b we set $r=b$, and designate the corresponding value of ψ by ψ_b. Then

$$j_l = \frac{8\pi\kappa_0}{9}\left(\frac{m}{2e}\right)\frac{\left[-\left(\frac{2e}{m}\right)V_b\right]^{3/2}}{b\psi_b{}^3}. \tag{81-13}$$

Similarly, as j_l corresponds to an area $2\pi b$ of the plate, the current per unit area is

$$j = \frac{4\kappa_0}{9}\left(\frac{m}{2e}\right)\frac{\left[-\left(\frac{2e}{m}\right)V_b\right]^{3/2}}{b^2\psi_b{}^3}.$$

The variation of $\psi_b{}^3$ with b/a is shown in Fig. 161.   Note that if b/a is

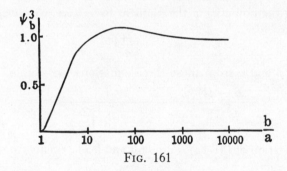

FIG. 161

greater than 10, as is usually the case in practice, $\psi_b{}^3$ does not differ appreciably from unity.

If a and b are both large, the difference between them being small,

$$\psi_b{}^3 = \left[\log\frac{b}{a}\right]^2 = \left[-\log\left(1-\frac{b-a}{b}\right)\right]^2 = \left[\frac{b-a}{b}\right]^2,$$

to a sufficiently close approximation, and therefore

$$j = \frac{4\kappa_0}{9}\left(\frac{m}{2e}\right)\frac{\left[-\left(\frac{2e}{m}\right)V_b\right]^{3/2}}{(b-a)^2}$$

in agreement with (81-7).

Actually the ions are electrons here, so (81-13) can be put in the form

$$j_l = -\frac{8\pi\kappa_0}{9}\sqrt{-\left(\frac{2e}{m}\right)}\frac{V_b{}^{3/2}}{b\psi_b{}^3}. \tag{81-14}$$

If we substitute numerical values, as in the case of (81-8), we have

$$j_l = -14.66(10)^{-6} \frac{V_b^{3/2}}{b\psi_b^3}. \tag{81-15}$$

Problem 81. If $a = 1$ mm, $b = 10$ mm, what is the maximum current that can be obtained from the filament of a cylindrical vacuum tube under a potential 12 volts? Ans. 0.062 amp/meter.

82. The Discharge Tube.

The study of the passage of electric currents through gases at low pressure reveals many of the properties of gaseous ions. The gas is usually contained in a glass tube, called a *discharge tube*, which is provided with metal electrodes through which the current enters and leaves.

In a gas at atmospheric pressure a few ions are normally present. The number may be greatly augmented by *ionizing* the gas through the agency of X-rays or rays from a radio-active substance, which ejects electrons from neutral molecules, forming pairs of oppositely charged ions. While many of the ejected electrons remain free at very low pressures, they generally become attached to neutral molecules at higher pressures, forming negative ions of molecular dimensions. The ions of opposite sign attract one another and tend to recombine into neutral molecules. If no impressed field is present a state of equilibrium is speedily reached, in which recombination goes on at the same rate as the production of new ions by the ionizing agent.

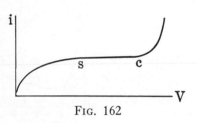

FIG. 162

Consider a gas at a pressure of a few millimeters of mercury in a discharge tube, the gas being subject to a constant ionizing agent. If a potential drop V exists between the electrodes, positive ions are driven by the field toward the cathode and negative ions toward the anode, and those which do not recombine on the way ultimately reach the electrodes, giving rise to a current i through the tube. As the field is increased, the ions are swept more rapidly towards the electrodes and therefore have less opportunity to recombine before reaching them. Consequently, the current increases until the field becomes so great that all the ions produced reach the electrodes, when a condition of *saturation*, represented by s on the current curve of Fig. 162, is attained. Further increase of V gives rise to no additional current until the point c is reached, when a very rapid growth of current takes place. This increase is due to the fact that the field has become so great that an ion acquires sufficient energy between successive collisions to eject an electron from the next neutral molecule which it strikes.   This process, known as *ionization by collision*, gives rise to a greatly increased number of ions in the gas, and consequently the current grows very rapidly, the discharge assuming the nature of a *spark*.

When a gas is not subject to an applied ionizing agent, the only current at low potentials is that due to the few ions normally present. Not until the field has been increased sufficiently to produce ionization by collision is there an appreciable current.   The field necessary to produce a discharge, however, varies greatly with the pressure, as indicated in Fig. 163 for air.   At pressures of several millimeters of mercury the discharge is easily produced, but as the pressure is decreased below a millimeter or thereabout the potential required increases very rapidly.

Let us now examine the nature of the discharge in more detail.   The spark observed at atmospheric pressure, which requires a potential of

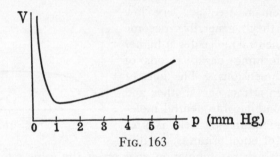

Fig. 163

some hundreds or thousands of volts, becomes broadened out as the pressure is reduced, until, at pressures of a few millimeters of mercury, a steady discharge is obtained of a quite different character from that at atmospheric pressure.   The luminosity, which is observed on the surface of the cathode at higher pressures, stretches out into the tube, separating into the *negative glow n* (Fig. 164) and the *cathode glow c*, the two being separated by a dark region C known as the *Crookes dark space*.   Similarly the glow on the anode extends out into the tube, becoming striated under suitable conditions.   This region of luminosity, p, is known as the *positive column* and is separated from the negative glow by the *Faraday dark space F*.   If the length of the tube is increased, the pressure of the gas remaining constant, the positive column extends so as to fill the additional space, the other regions remaining unchanged in dimensions.   As the current through the tube is increased, the cathode glow extends further over the surface of the cathode, the potential difference between the electrodes remaining nearly constant until the entire surface of the cathode is covered. Investigation of the field in the tube by means of exploring electrodes indicates that most of the drop in potential takes place near the surface of the cathode, the electric intensity varying from point to point somewhat as shown in Fig. 165.

The current is initiated by the collision of ions already present with neutral molecules, the negative ions produced by collision at low pressures being largely free electrons and the positive ions charged

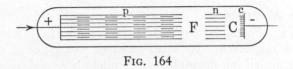

FIG. 164

molecules. The negative ions, on account of their smaller mass, have a much greater mobility than the positive ions. Consider first the positive ions. Moving toward the cathode, they acquire greater kinetic energy between successive collisions close to the cathode than elsewhere in the tube, as the field is most intense there. Consequently, most of the ionization produced by impact of the positive ions takes place at the surface of the cathode. The negative ions formed there are swept away more quickly than the positive ions on account of their

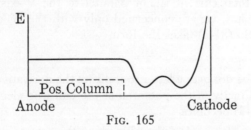

FIG. 165

greater mobility. This action results in the formation of a positive space charge in the region close to the cathode, which explains the rapid fall in potential and large electric field.

The negative ions formed near the cathode acquire sufficient kinetic energy in passing through the Crookes dark space to ionize by collision in the negative glow, thus producing the luminosity found there. The striations existing in the positive column are probably separated by distances just sufficient for the ions to acquire an energy that will enable them to excite if not to ionize the neutral molecules with which they collide.   In this way the periodic luminosity in the positive column is explained.

At very low pressures many of the electrons liberated from the cathode by impact of positive ions travel the whole length of the tube without colliding with gaseous molecules.   These streams of electrons are the *cathode rays* (art. 77) which J. J. Thomson deflected by perpendicular electric and magnetic fields in his determination of the ratio of charge to mass.   When these electrons strike the walls of the tube, or a metallic *anticathode* placed in their path, their sudden stoppage gives rise to the electromagnetic waves known as *X-rays*.

83. The Magnetron.   A thermionic vacuum tube (art. 81) provided with a uniform magnetic field at right angles to its electric field is known as a *magnetron*.   We shall consider two types of magnetron: first, one in which the electrodes are parallel plates and, second, one in which the electrodes are coaxial cylinders.   In both cases we shall assume that the ions have negligibly small initial velocities at the electrode from which they are emitted and that they are present at its surface in sufficiently great numbers to neutralize the electric field.

Parallel Plates.   We shall take the X axis perpendicular to the plates as in Fig. 160 and the Z axis parallel to the magnetic field H.   Then equation (81-1) becomes, as before,

$$\frac{d^2V}{dx^2} = -\frac{\rho}{\kappa_0}. \tag{83-1}$$

Although the total current is not parallel to the x axis at all points between the plates, we are concerned only with the X component of the current.   So (81-2) takes the form

$$j = \rho\dot{x}, \tag{83-2}$$

where we use the dot over a letter to indicate the derivative with respect to the time.   Finally, if the potential at the emitting electrode is taken to be zero, (81-3) becomes

$$\tfrac{1}{2}m(\dot{x}^2 + \dot{y}^2) + eV = 0. \tag{83-3}$$

In addition we have for the deflecting acceleration due to the magnetic field

$$\ddot{y} = -\frac{e}{m}\mu_0\dot{x}H$$

from (77-2).   This gives on integration

$$\dot{y} = -\frac{e}{m}\mu_0 xH, \tag{83-4}$$

since the initial velocity is negligible.

Eliminating $\dot{y}$ between (83-3) and (83-4), we get

$$\dot{x}^2 = -\left(\frac{2e}{m}\right)V - \left(\frac{e}{m}\mu_0 H\right)^2 x^2. \tag{83-5}$$

Since the quantity $-(2e/m)V$ is always positive, as noted in art. 81, the greatest distance x_0 which the ions can proceed from the emitting plate is given by putting $\dot{x} = 0$, that is,

$$x_0 = \sqrt{-\frac{V_0}{\left(\dfrac{e}{2m}\right)\mu_0{}^2 H^2}}, \tag{83-6}$$

where V_0 is the potential at x_0. If the separation d of the plates is greater than this, no current flows, the ions curving back under the influence of the magnetic field and returning to the neighborhood of the plate from which they were emitted. Suppose we start with a fixed potential V_d across the plates and zero magnetic field. If we increase the magnetic field gradually, the current continues to flow until H reaches the value H_c given by the relation

$$V_d = -\left(\frac{e}{2m}\right)\mu_0{}^2 H_c{}^2 d^2 \tag{83-7}$$

and then the current ceases abruptly. Evidently (83-7) expresses the condition for *cut-off*, which can be attained as well by decreasing the potential difference of the plates as by increasing the magnetic field.

While the condition for cut-off is independent of space charge, the magnitude of the current density j as a function of the potential difference V_d between the plates and the magnetic intensity H can be determined only by solving the space charge equation as in art. 81. Hence we eliminate ρ between (83-1) and (83-2), and then get rid of $\dot{x}$ by means of (83-5). If we put

$$\omega \equiv -\frac{e}{m}\mu_0 H, \qquad \mathcal{J} \equiv \frac{j}{\kappa_0}\left(\frac{e}{m}\right),$$

$$W \equiv -\left(\frac{2e}{m}\right)V - \omega^2 x^2,$$

we obtain the differential equation

$$\frac{d^2 W}{dx^2} + 2\omega^2 = \frac{2\mathcal{J}}{\sqrt{W}}. \tag{83-8}$$

The first integral* of (83-8) is

$$\frac{dW}{dx} = (8\mathcal{J}\sqrt{W} - 4\omega^2 W)^{1/2},$$

* Page and Adams, *Phys. Rev.* **69**, 492 (1946).

since the electric field must vanish at the emitting plate.   To obtain
the second integral, put

$$W \equiv \frac{4\mathcal{J}^2}{\omega^4} \sin^4 \chi, \qquad x \equiv \frac{\mathcal{J}}{\omega^3} \xi,$$

taking χ positive when ω is positive.   The first integral above becomes

$$d\xi = 4 \sin^2 \chi d\chi,$$

and the second integral is

$$\xi = 2\chi - \sin 2\chi, \tag{83-9}$$

since ξ and χ must vanish together.   Evidently the zeros of W corresponding to the emitting plate and to the plane of cut-off come at

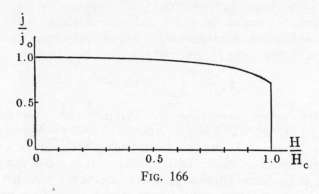

Fig. 166

$\chi = 0$ and at $\chi = \pi$, respectively, when ω is positive, as with electrons.
At cut-off, then, $\xi = 2\pi$.

Let j_0 be the current density which would exist with the specified
potential V_d at $x = d$ in the absence of a magnetic field, as given by
(81-7), and H_c the magnetic intensity necessary for cut-off at $x = $d, as
specified by (83-7).   From the defining equations for $\sin \chi$ and ξ it
follows that

$$\frac{j}{j_0} = \frac{1}{\frac{2}{9}\xi \left(1 + 4 \frac{\sin^4 \chi}{\xi^2}\right)^{3/2}},$$

$$\frac{H}{H_c} = \frac{1}{\left(1 + 4 \frac{\sin^4 \chi}{\xi^2}\right)^{1/2}}.$$

Calculating corresponding values of χ and ξ from (83-9) we can plot
j/j_0 against H/H_c.   The curve is shown in Fig. 166.   It should be

noted that the current decreases only slightly with increasing magnetic field until cut-off is reached, when it falls precipitously to zero. An investigation of the charge density shows that it becomes infinite at the plane of cut-off as well as at the emitting electrode.

Coaxial Cylinders. In this case ions in the form of electrons are emitted by the hot filament AB (Fig. 167) with negligible initial velocities. We shall neglect the magnetic field produced by the heating current in the filament, taking into account only the external magnetic field parallel to the axis of the tube and the radial electric field due to the difference in potential between the filament and the surrounding cylindrical electrode. It will be convenient to use cylindrical coordinates, r, θ, z, the last being measured parallel to the axis of the tube.

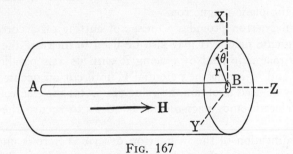

FIG. 167

Let a denote the radius of the filament and b that of the outer electrode. Evidently we have in place of (83-3)

$$\tfrac{1}{2}m(\dot{r}^2+r^2\dot{\theta}^2)+eV = 0. \tag{83-10}$$

The torque about the axis is due to the magnetic field alone and is equal to $-e\mu_0 r\dot{r}H$. Equating this to the rate of increase of angular momentum, we obtain

$$m\frac{d}{dt}(r^2\dot{\theta}) = -e\mu_0 r\dot{r}H,$$

that is,

$$r^2\dot{\theta} = -\frac{e}{m}\mu_0 H\int_a^r r\,dr$$

$$= -\frac{e}{m}\mu_0 H\left(\frac{r^2-a^2}{2}\right). \tag{83-11}$$

This may be combined with (83-10) to give

$$\dot{r}^2 = -\left(\frac{2e}{m}\right)V-\left(\frac{e}{m}\mu_0 H\right)^2\left(\frac{r^2-a^2}{2r}\right)^2. \tag{83-12}$$

If, now, we set $\dot{r} = 0$, we see that r_0, the greatest distance from the axis which the electrons can reach, is given by

$$\frac{r_0{}^2 - a^2}{2r_0} = \sqrt{-\frac{V_0}{\left(\dfrac{e}{2m}\right)\mu_0{}^2 H^2}}, \tag{83-13}$$

where V_0 is the potential at r_0.

Similarly, the cut-off field H_c is given by

$$V_b = -\left(\frac{e}{2m}\right)\mu_0{}^2 H_c{}^2\left(\frac{b^2 - a^2}{2b}\right)^2, \tag{83-14}$$

where V_b is the potential of the outer electrode. As in the case of the plane magnetron, the cut-off condition is independent of space charge. Cut-off here is found* to be even sharper than that illustrated in Fig. 166 for the plane magnetron.

The magnetron provides a means of cutting off a current by means of a magnetic field. It may also be used to measure the strength of a uniform magnetic field by placing it with its axis parallel to the lines of force and adjusting the potential V until cut-off occurs. Finally the tube may be used to obtain the value of e/m for the electron by adjusting known electric and magnetic fields so as to secure the condition of cut-off.

A modification of the magnetron described here is one of the most satisfactory sources of very high frequency electric oscillations.

Problem 83. A magnetron consists of a filament of 0.2 mm radius surrounded by a cylindrical electrode of 30 mm radius. It is observed that when the tube is placed with its axis parallel to the lines of force of a uniform magnetic field, cut-off takes place when the potential on the tube is 8.80 volts. Find the magnetic intensity. Ans. 531 amp/meter.

84. Diamagnetism. As pointed out in art. 75 the Ampèrian circuits responsible for the magnetic properties of matter may be rings of electrons revolving about the nuclei of the atoms. Consider one such circular ring; suppose it to consist of N electrons of charge e revolving in a circle of radius a with angular velocity ω under a force directed toward the center of the circle. As a charge Ne passes each point of the circumference in a time $2\pi/\omega$, the current is

$$i = \frac{Ne\omega}{2\pi}, \tag{84-1}$$

and the magnetic moment of the ring (art. 69) is

$$p = \mu_0 i(\pi a^2) = \frac{\mu_0 N e a^2 \omega}{2}. \tag{84-2}$$

* Page and Adams, *Phys. Rev.* **69**, 494 (1946).

In general an atom or molecule contains several such rings, the resultant magnetic moment being the vector sum of the magnetic moments of the individual rings. If the resultant magnetic moment is not zero, the atom or molecule has the properties of a small magnet and the medium of which it is a constituent is paramagnetic or ferromagnetic. In a great many cases, however, the resultant magnetic moment vanishes, and then the atom or molecule is subject to no torque when placed in an external magnetic field. In all cases, however, the application of an external field changes the magnetic moments of the rings of electrons, diminishing the moments of those whose axes lie in the direction of the field and increasing the moments of those whose axes are opposite to the field. This effect, known as *diamagnetism*, produces a resultant magnetic moment opposite to the applied field. It probably exists in all substances, although in paramagnetic and ferromagnetic media it is masked by the much greater opposite effect due to the orientation of the magnetic atoms or molecules.

To investigate the effect of an external magnetic field on the magnetic moment of a ring of electrons, consider the motion of a single electron (Fig. 168). In the absence of a magnetic field the only force on the electron is a central force $\mathscr{F}$, and its angular velocity ω_0 is given by the equation of motion

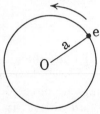

FIG. 168

$$m\omega_0{}^2 a = \mathscr{F}. \qquad (84\text{-}3)$$

If, now, a uniform magnetic field H_1 is applied at right angles to the plane of the figure, the lines of force being directed toward the reader, a magnetic force $e\mu_0 a\omega H_1$ directed away from O is brought into being and the equation of motion becomes

$$m\omega^2 a = \mathscr{F} - e\mu_0 a\omega H_1. \qquad (84\text{-}4)$$

This means that

$$\omega^2 - \omega_0{}^2 = -\frac{e}{m}\mu_0 H_1 \omega.$$

Hence, if we put $\Delta\omega$ for the increase in the angular velocity,

$$\Delta\omega = -\frac{e}{m}\mu_0 H_1\left(\frac{\omega}{\omega + \omega_0}\right) = -\frac{e}{2m}\mu_0 H_1 \qquad (84\text{-}5)$$

to a sufficient degree of approximation, since ω differs very little from ω_0 even in the strongest fields available in the laboratory.

From (84-2) and (84-5) we find for the change in the magnetic moment of the ring

$$\Delta p = \frac{\mu_0 N e a^2 \Delta\omega}{2} = -\frac{N e^2 a^2}{4m}\mu_0{}^2 H_1. \qquad (84\text{-}6)$$

Therefore, the change in the magnetic moment is in opposition to the applied field. Consider, for example, an atom which contains two rings of electrons of equal moments oppositely oriented, so that in the absence of a magnetic field it has zero resultant moment. The effect of a field, parallel to the axis of the first ring, is to decrease the moment of this ring and to increase that of the oppositely oriented ring. Thus, a resultant magnetic moment opposite to the field is imparted to the atom.

If the plane of the ring is not at right angles to the field, it is evident that only the component of H_1 parallel to p is effective in altering the angular velocity and the magnetic moment of the ring. If, then, the angle between p and H_1 is denoted by θ,

$$\Delta p = -\frac{Ne^2a^2}{4m} \mu_0{}^2 H_1 \cos \theta, \tag{84-7}$$

and the component of the added magnetic moment in the direction of the field is

$$\Delta p \cos \theta = -\frac{Ne^2a^2}{4m} \mu_0{}^2 H_1 \cos^2 \theta.$$

To find the magnetization I in a diamagnetic medium, we must sum up over all the n rings in a unit volume. Assuming that the axes of the rings are directed at random, the number making angles between θ and $\theta + d\theta$ with H_1 is

$$dn = \frac{2\pi \sin \theta d\theta}{4\pi} n = \tfrac{1}{2} n \sin \theta d\theta,$$

and

$$I = \int \Delta p \cos \theta dn = -\frac{nNe^2a^2}{12m} \mu_0{}^2 H_1. \tag{84-8}$$

The field H_1 in (84-8) is not the total field in the medium but rather the field external to the atom under consideration. It corresponds to the E_1 of art. 17. In fact, it may be shown that $H_1 = H + I/3\mu_0$, an expression analogous to (17-3).

As nN is just the total number of electrons per unit volume, (84-8) can be used to calculate a mean radius of the atom from measured values of the susceptibility of diamagnetic substances, or, if a is taken as known, the number of electrons revolving in rings can be computed. The results are in fair accord with expectations.

The phenomenon of diamagnetism constitutes the strongest kind of evidence for Ampère's theory of magnetism. For if magnetic properties were due to the presence of actual magnetic dipoles in the atom instead of Ampèrian circuits it is difficult to see how a medium could be diamagnetic. In the electrostatic analog, for instance, where true dipoles are responsible for the properties of the medium, we never find a value of the permittivity less than unity.

Problem 84a. From (84-8) find the susceptibility and the permeability of a diamagnetic medium in terms of $\delta \equiv (nNe^2a^2/12m)\mu_0$.

$$\text{Ans. } \chi = -\frac{\delta}{1+\dfrac{\delta}{3}}, \quad \mu = \frac{1-\dfrac{2\delta}{3}}{1+\dfrac{\delta}{3}}.$$

Problem 84b. Show that the field acting on an atom in a magnetic medium is $H + I/3\mu_0$, though the true field in the medium (art. 75) is B/μ_0.

85. Unipolar Induction. Finally we shall consider an example of the motion of ions in a magnetic medium. Let M (Fig. 169a) be a

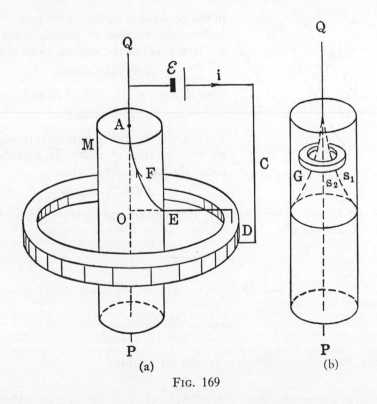

FIG. 169

symmetrically magnetized steel cylinder arranged so that it can rotate about its axis PQ and provided with a side arm ED the end D of which dips into a coaxial trough of mercury. The trough and the portion

ACD of the circuit are held fixed.   If a current passes from the trough through the side arm into the magnet, emerging along the axis at *A*, the magnet experiences a torque which causes it to rotate in the positive sense about its axis.

To calculate the torque on the current passing through the side arm and magnet, we have for the force per unit volume

$$\mathscr{F}_\tau = \mathbf{j} \times \mathbf{B},$$

from (75-4).   If α (Fig. 170) is taken as the angle between $\mathbf{j}$ and $\mathbf{B}$ and ϕ as the azimuth measured around the axis of the magnet, the force on the volume element $rd\phi dldn$ at a distance r from the axis is

$$jB \sin \alpha r d\phi dldn$$

directed away from the reader.   Thus the torque is

$$d^2\mathscr{L} = jB \sin \alpha r^2 d\phi dldn$$

in the positive sense about the axis.

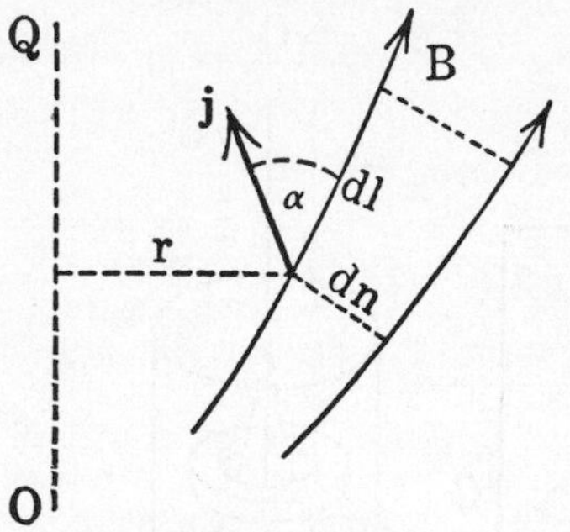

Now the current di passing through the face $rd\phi dl$ of the volume element is

$$di = j \sin \alpha r d\phi dl,$$

since dl has the direction of B, and hence

$$d^2\mathscr{L} = rB\, didn.$$

But if dN is the flux of induction through an annular ring of width dn described about the axis of the magnet,

$$dN = B \cdot 2\pi r dn,$$

Fig. 170

since the magnet is symmetrically magnetized and dn is perpendicular to B.   Consequently,

$$d^2\mathscr{L} = \frac{didN}{2\pi}.$$

Summing up dl and $d\phi$ is equivalent to summing up di without change in N, giving

$$d\mathscr{L} = \frac{idN}{2\pi}.$$

Finally, summing up dN gives for the total torque

$$\mathscr{L} = \frac{iN}{2\pi},\tag{85-1}$$

where N is the flux of induction through the circle of radius OD (Fig. 169a) at right angles to the axis of the magnet.   Evidently we have made no error in taking **j** in the plane through PQ since the component of the current density at right angles to this plane contributes nothing to the torque. As the lines of induction outside the magnet have the opposite sense to those in its interior, the torque is greatest when the side arm is shortest.

The torque expressed by (85-1) is that produced by the magnetic field on the portion of the current circuit lying in the movable part of the system. Before we can conclude that this is the total torque, we must show that there is no torque exerted by the current circuit on the poles of the magnet.

The spreading of the current in the interior of the magnet may be taken into account by replacing the current by a number of closed current filaments which follow the same path outside the magnet but separate in its interior. Let the circuit $ACDEFA$ (Fig. 169a) be one such elementary circuit, the current flowing in it being di. Construct a surface of revolution (Fig. 169b) by rotating the curve EFA about the axis of the magnet. This surface divides the magnet into two parts: an upper and outer part bounded above by the upper surface of the magnet and below by the conical surface s_1, and a lower and inner part bounded above by the surface s_2 coincident with s_1 and below by the lower surface of the magnet. Let us calculate first the torque on the upper and outer portion. It contains the positive pole-strength spread over the upper surface of the magnet and an equal amount of negative pole-strength spread over the surface s_1. Consider an annular ring G of radius r lying in this portion of the magnet, which may contain some of the pole-strength on the one or the other surface. If λ is the pole-strength per unit length of the ring, and H_ϕ is the component of the magnetic intensity in the direction of increasing ϕ due to the current filament di, the torque on the annular ring due to the current filament is

$$d^2\mathscr{L}' = r \int_0^{2\pi} \lambda H_\phi r d\phi. \tag{85-2}$$

As the magnet is symmetrically magnetized λ is not a function of ϕ and may be placed in front of the integral sign. Furthermore,

$$\int_0^{2\pi} H_\phi r d\phi = di \tag{85-3}$$

by Ampère's law (71-3). Hence

$$d^2\mathscr{L}' = r\lambda di = \frac{dm\, di}{2\pi}, \tag{85-4}$$

where $dm = 2\pi r \lambda$ is the total pole strength in the annular ring under consideration. Summing up over the portion of the magnet above s_1, we find that the torque vanishes, since the total pole-strength on any isolated body is zero.

Turning now to the inner and lower portion of the magnet, we note that the right-hand member of (85-3) is zero since an annular ring lying in this portion of the magnet does not encircle the current filament under consideration. Therefore, the torque is zero.

We conclude, then, that (85-1) represents the total torque on the movable part of the system. This formula is well verified by experiment,* and substitution of a brass cylinder in the magnetic field of a coaxial solenoid for the magnet verifies the theoretical deduction that the poles of the magnet are in no way responsible for the torque. The fact that the formula deduced on the basis of Ampère's theory of magnetism accords with the experimental measure of the torque shows the correctness of Ampère's conception of the nature of magnetism. For if the molecules of a magnetic medium owed their magnetic properties to the presence of actual dipoles instead of Ampèrian circuits, the flux in (85-1) would be that of $\mu_0 H$ rather than that of B and the calculated torque would be only a small fraction of that actually observed.

The mechanism in Fig. 169 is, in effect, a simple form of electric motor. It may also be operated as a generator. To show this, let $\mathscr{E}$ be the external electromotive force producing the current i and R the resistance of the circuit, and suppose that the magnet rotates with constant angular velocity ω against a frictional torque equal in magnitude to (85-1). Then the rate at which work is done by the external electromotive force is

$$\mathscr{E}i = Ri^2 + \frac{iN}{2\pi}\,\omega,$$

or

$$\left\{\mathscr{E} - \frac{N\omega}{2\pi}\right\}i = Ri^2.$$

As Ri^2 must equal the product of the total electromotive force by the current, we see that the rotation of the magnet gives rise to a reverse electromotive force

$$\mathscr{E}_r' = \frac{N\omega}{2\pi}. \tag{85-5}$$

Hence, if we remove $\mathscr{E}$ and rotate the magnet mechanically, the electromotive force (85-5) will be generated.

Problem 85. A current 0.05 amp passes through a magnet as indicated in Fig. 169. The flux through the circle of radius OD is $1.05(10)^{-5}$ weber. Compute the torque. Ans. $0.84(10)^{-7}$ newton meter.

* Zeleny and Page, *Phys. Rev.* **24**, 544 (1924).

Chapter IX

ELECTROMAGNETIC INDUCTION

86. Faraday's Law. Inasmuch as a current gives rise to a magnetic field, it occurred to Faraday in 1831 that a magnet might induce a current in a neighboring fixed circuit. Although he found that the proximity of a stationary magnet gives rise to no current, he noticed that a galvanometer in the circuit suffers a momentary deflection while the magnet is approaching or receding. Further investigation showed that the same effect is produced by moving a second circuit in which a current is flowing toward or away from the first, or by holding the second circuit fixed and varying the current in it. The phenomenon of current induction had been observed by Henry in America even earlier, but the discovery is generally attributed to Faraday since he was the first to publish his results.

Faraday's experiments indicate that a change in the flux of magnetic induction through a fixed circuit gives rise to an electromotive force which lasts as long as the flux is changing, the magnitude of the induced e.m.f. being proportional to the time rate of change of flux. If the flux through the circuit is decreasing, the sense of the induced electromotive force is found to be that of rotation of a right-handed screw advancing in the direction of the flux passing through the circuit, as illustrated in Fig. 171a, whereas if the flux is increasing, the induced electromotive force is in the opposite sense as in Fig. 171b. Now suppose we take the upper face of the circuit shown in the figure as positive so as to make the flux through it positive. Then, according to the convention relating the positive sense of describing the periphery of a surface to the positive direction of the normal, the periphery is traversed in the positive sense when we pass from a to b to c. Consequently, the induced electromotive force is positive in the case of decreasing flux and negative in the case of increasing flux. As a current in the circuit would have to flow in the sense a to b to c to produce a flux in the same direction as that of the external field, the induced e.m.f. acts in such a sense as to produce additional flux in the *same* direction as the flux due to external sources if the latter is decreasing, and in the sense to produce

271

additional flux in the *opposite* direction to the flux due to external sources if the latter is increasing. In each case the induced e.m.f. acts in the sense to *oppose* the change in flux which produces it.

If B is the magnetic induction, ds an element of area of any surface s having the circuit as its periphery, and γ the angle between the lines of induction and the positive normal to the surface element, the flux of induction through the surface is

$$N = \int_s B \cos \gamma ds = \int_s \mathbf{B} \cdot d\mathbf{s}.$$

Taking account of the relation between the positive face of the circuit and the positive sense of describing the periphery, *Faraday's law states that the electromotive force $\mathscr{E}$ induced by changing the flux of induc-*

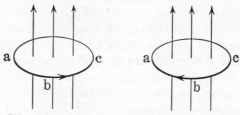

(a) Flux decreasing (b) Flux increasing

Fig. 171

tion through a fixed circuit is proportional to the time rate of decrease of the flux. In analytical form Faraday's law must contain a constant of proportionality. However, this constant is not arbitrary, since both the electromotive force and the rate of change of flux are known quantities. Resorting to experiment, we find that the constant has the magnitude unity. Evidently it is a pure number, inasmuch as the physical dimensions of the volt (art. 7) are the same as those of the weber per second (art. 43). Thus, we have

$$\mathscr{E} = -\frac{dN}{dt}. \tag{86-1}$$

In terms of the magnetic induction, (86-1) may be written

$$\mathscr{E} = -\int_s \frac{\partial}{\partial t} (B \cos \gamma) ds, \tag{86-2}$$

where we must differentiate $\cos \gamma$ as well as B since the direction as well as the magnitude of the induction may change with the time. To express this in vector notation (art. 67), let $\mathbf{B}$ in Fig. 172 be the induction at the time t and $\mathbf{B}'$ that at the time $t+\Delta t$, the angle which $\mathbf{B}'$ makes with the normal n to the surface element ds being denoted by γ'. The increase in $\mathbf{B}$ during the time Δt is then $\Delta \mathbf{B} = \mathbf{B}' - \mathbf{B}$ in the direction PQ, and the time rate of increase of $\mathbf{B}$ at the time t is the vector

$$\frac{\partial \mathbf{B}}{\partial t} = \lim_{\Delta t \to 0} \frac{\Delta \mathbf{B}}{\Delta t}$$

in the limiting direction assumed by PQ as Δt approaches zero. If, now, we represent the magnitude of the vector $\Delta \mathbf{B}$ by $|\Delta \mathbf{B}|$, we have from the figure

$$|\Delta \mathbf{B}| \cos \alpha = B' \cos \gamma' - B \cos \gamma,$$

so that

$$\left| \frac{\Delta \mathbf{B}}{\Delta t} \right| \cos \alpha = \frac{B' \cos \gamma' - B \cos \gamma}{\Delta t}.$$

Hence

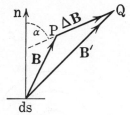

Fig. 172

$$\left| \frac{\partial \mathbf{B}}{\partial t} \right| \cos \alpha = \frac{\partial}{\partial t}(B \cos \gamma), \quad (86\text{-}3)$$

the angle α between PQ and the normal now having its limiting value, and (86-2) becomes

$$\mathscr{E} = -\int_s \left| \frac{\partial \mathbf{B}}{\partial t} \right| \cos \alpha \, ds = -\int_s \frac{\partial \mathbf{B}}{\partial t} \cdot d\mathbf{s}. \quad (86\text{-}4)$$

Note that the magnitude of the derivative of $\mathbf{B}$ must be distinguished from the derivative of the magnitude of $\mathbf{B}$, that is, from the derivative of B, since in general these quantities are not equal.

In differentiating $\mathbf{B}$ with respect to the time we use the notation for partial rather than for total differentiation for the reason that $\mathbf{B}$ is generally a function of the coordinates as well as of the time. In (86-4) we are dealing with a fixed circuit and are concerned solely with the time rate of change of $\mathbf{B}$ at each point. As the electromotive force in this case is the line integral (48-5) of the electric intensity $\mathbf{E}$ around the circuit, we can write (86-4) in the form

$$\mathscr{E} \equiv \oint \mathbf{E} \cdot d\mathbf{l} = -\int_s \frac{\partial \mathbf{B}}{\partial t} \cdot d\mathbf{s}. \quad (86\text{-}5)$$

It is important to note that Faraday's law applies to any closed curve whether or not a conducting wire coincides with it, although only when a conducting circuit is present does the electromotive force give rise to a current. *In all cases Faraday's law tells us that the line integral of the electric intensity around any fixed closed curve is equal to the time rate of decrease of the flux of magnetic induction through the curve.* Equation (86-5) should be compared with the circuital form (71-3) of Ampère's law, to which it is quite analogous, particularly if the latter is written in the form

$$\mathscr{H} \equiv \oint \mathbf{H} \cdot d\mathbf{l} = \int_s \mathbf{j} \cdot d\mathbf{s}, \qquad (86\text{-}6)$$

obtained by expressing i in terms of the current density $\mathbf{j}$ over any surface s whose periphery coincides with the path along which the line integral of $\mathbf{H}$ is taken.

Faraday's law implies that the lines of electric force due to changing magnetic induction form closed curves much as do the lines of magnetic force produced by a current in a wire. Consider, for instance, a magnet

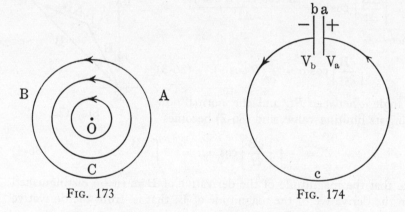

FIG. 173   FIG. 174

(Fig. 173) held above the plane of the figure with its axis on the perpendicular through O, the positive pole being the nearer to O. If, now, the magnet is moved toward the figure, the lines of electric force in the plane of the figure are, on account of symmetery, circles with O as center, the sense of the electric intensity being that of the arrowheads. Reversal of the direction of motion of the magnet merely reverses the sense of the electric intensity. If a wire coincides with the line ABC, the electric field exerts a force on the free electrons in a direction everywhere tangent to the wire, and consequently a current is produced. Evidently no scalar potential exists in an electric field of this type, for such a potential would have to decrease as we pass in the direction of the electric intensity from A to B to C to A, so that after passing completely around the circuit we would come back to the starting point with a different value of the potential from that with which we had begun.

In the case under consideration no part of the wire ABC is charged electrically. If, however, we cut the wire and insert a parallel plate capacitor as in Fig. 174, the situation is altered. Now the electric field due to the changing induction causes positive charge to accumulate at a and negative charge at b until the difference of potential $\mathscr{E}_{ab} \equiv V_a - V_b$ between the two plates of the capacitor due to these charges is equal to the electromotive force $\mathscr{E}'$ represented by the line integral of the induced electric intensity $\mathbf{E}$ along the wire from b to c to a. That is,

$$\mathscr{E}_{ab} = \int_{bca} \mathbf{E} \cdot d\mathbf{l},$$

for only when this condition is satisfied is the total work performed in carrying an electron from b to a through the wire equal to zero and only then can the flow of electrons stop. If the distance d between the plates of the capacitor is small compared with the distance l around the circuit, $\mathscr{E}' = E(l-d) = (1-d/l)\mathscr{E}$, where $\mathscr{E} = El$ is the total induced electromotive force, and we have

$$\mathscr{E}_{ab} = \left(1 - \frac{d}{l}\right)\mathscr{E}.$$

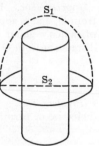

Fig. 175

Note that the total electric intensity between the plates is not $\mathscr{E}_{ab}/d$, but rather $\mathscr{E}_{ab}/d + E = \mathscr{E}/d$, since the E field is continuous around the circuit. In this connection it must be remembered that a field due to static charges can never give rise to an electromotive force around a closed circuit. For every electrostatic field possesses a potential, and therefore the line integral of the electric intensity around any closed curve vanishes, as shown in art. 48. Consequently, the electromotive force around a closed curve when there is changing magnetic flux is not altered by the presence of charges such as those on the capacitor plates of Fig. 174.

If a circuit is located in empty space, where B and $\mu_0 H$ are the same, the flux of magnetic induction through the circuit is equal to the flux of μ_0 times the magnetic intensity. However, if the circuit embraces a magnetic core, as in Fig. 175, we may determine the flux either by integrating over a surface s_1 lying entirely in empty space or by integrating over a surface s_2 cutting the core. In this case the flux of B, but not that of $\mu_0 H$, is the same through s_1 as through s_2 (art. 43). Hence we see that, when the surface of integration passes through a permeable medium, the induced electromotive force must depend upon the rate of change of flux of B, as expressed by (86-2) and (86-4). The same conclusion may be reached from Ampère's theory of magnetism (art. 75), which shows that the actual magnetic intensity inside a permeable medium is B/μ_0.

Problem 86a. A long solenoid of n_l turns per unit length and cross section A carries an alternating current $i = i_0 \sin \omega t$. The solenoid is wound on a core of permeability μ. Find the flux N through a closed curve which encircles the solenoid and calculate the e.m.f. $\mathscr{E}$ around the curve.

Ans. $N = \mu_0 \mu n_l i_0 A \sin \omega t$, $\quad \mathscr{E} = -\mu_0 \mu n_l i_0 A\omega \cos \omega t$.

Problem 86b. A current $i = i_0 \sin \omega t$ flows in a very long straight wire. Calculate the flux N through and e.m.f. $\mathscr{E}$ around a rectangle of dimensions h and d which lies in a plane through the wire, the sides of length h being parallel to the wire and at distances R and $R + d$ from it.

$$\text{Ans. } N = \frac{\mu_0 i_0 h}{2\pi} \log\left(1 + \frac{d}{R}\right) \sin \omega t,$$

$$\mathscr{E} = -\frac{\mu_0 i_0 h}{2\pi} \log\left(1 + \frac{d}{R}\right) \omega \cos \omega t.$$

Problem 86c. If the magnet of Fig. 173 has a moment p, is at a distance h from O, and is approaching O with a velocity v, find the flux N through a circle of radius a about O and the electric intensity E in the plane of the figure at a distance a from O.

$$\text{Ans. } N = \frac{pa^2}{2(a^2 + h^2)^{3/2}}, \quad E = -\frac{3pahv}{4\pi(a^2 + h^2)^{5/2}}.$$

Problem 86d. The plates of the capacitor of Fig. 174 are separated by a dielectric of permittivity κ. Show that the polarization is

$$\text{P} = \kappa_0(\kappa - 1)\frac{\mathscr{E}}{d}.$$

87. The Betatron. A very illuminating application of Faraday's law is found in the *betatron*. This device, developed by D. W. Kerst in 1940, is used to produce electron beams of energies so great that the mass m of each electron is many times its rest mass m_0 (art. 79). The instrument consists of a large electromagnet (Fig. 176) between the pole pieces of which is placed an evacuated toroidal chamber DD known as a *doughnut*, a top view of which is shown in the upper part of the figure. The magnet is actuated by an alternating current so as to produce a sinusoidally varying magnetic field. The changing magnetic flux gives rise to circular electric lines of force, such as pictured in Fig. 173, lying in planes perpendicular to the axis of the magnet with their centers on this axis. During the quarter cycle in which the magnetic field increases from zero to its maximum value, the induced electric field accelerates, along a circular path lying inside the doughnut, electrons which have been injected at P. The electrons are kept in this circular path by the deflecting force (68-11) due to the magnetic field.

Let r_0 be the constant radius of the equilibrium circular orbit which the electrons follow and let $B_0 = \mu_0 H_0$ be the varying magnetic induction in the median plane at this distance from the axis of the magnet. The varying magnetic induction at any point in the median plane, given as a function of the distance r from the axis, we shall designate by B. Then the varying flux through the area bounded by the equilibrium path is

$$N_0 = \int_0^{r_0} B \cdot 2\pi r dr \qquad (87\text{-}1)$$

and the varying electric field E_0 along this path is given by

$$2\pi r_0 E_0 = -\frac{dN_0}{dt} \qquad (87\text{-}2)$$

from Faraday's law. Since the force exerted on an electron by this field is eE_0, the equation governing the motion tangent to the circle is

$$\frac{d}{dt}(mv) = -\left(\frac{e}{2\pi r_0}\right)\frac{dN_0}{dt} \qquad (87\text{-}3)$$

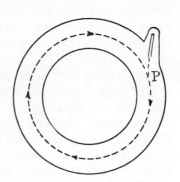

from (79-4), where m is the variable mass (79-2). The minus sign indicates that the motion would be in the negative sense relative to the flux for a positive e while N_0 is increasing, as indicated by the arrow in the figure. Actually the motion is in the positive sense, as e is negative.

Since the transverse acceleration is $f_t = v^2/r_0$, the motion at right angles to the path toward the centre of curvature is specified by

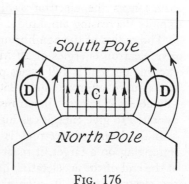

FIG. 176

$$m\frac{v^2}{r_0} = -evB_0. \qquad (87\text{-}4)$$

Now the integral of (87-3), subject to the initial condition that $v=0$ when $N_0=0$, is

$$mv = -\frac{eN_0}{2\pi r_0}, \qquad (87\text{-}5)$$

whereas (87-4) gives

$$mv = -er_0 B_0. \qquad (87\text{-}6)$$

Consequently, the device will operate in the desired manner only if the flux has the value

$$N_0 = 2\pi r_0^2 B_0 \qquad (87\text{-}7)$$

instead of the smaller value $\pi r_0^2 B_0$ which would result from a uniform field over the entire median plane. The equilibrium orbit is that circle whose radius r_0 satisfies this equation. Evidently the magnetic field must be stronger at the axis of the magnet than at the distance r_0, as indicated by the lines of force in the figure. This is accomplished in part by a proper shaping of the pole pieces and in part by the insertion of the soft iron cylinder C in the center of the gap. The non-uniform character of the field is actually an advantage in holding the beam to the proper path. First, the deflecting force (68-11) is in such a direction as to bring back to the median plane any electron which may have strayed from this plane. Second, the required weakening of the magnetic field near the periphery can be utilized to produce focusing in the median plane. For this purpose the pole pieces are designed so that B falls off less rapidly than $1/r$ in the neighborhood of the equilibrium path. Then, as the centrifugal reaction is proportional to $1/r$, the electron is brought back to the equilibrium path if it deviates to either side of it. Actually a more detailed analysis shows that in such circumstances the electron oscillates about the equilibrium path with rapidly decreasing amplitude.

The radius of the equilibrium circle in a typical betatron designed to give electron energies of 20 Mev is 18.8 cm and the frequency of the exciting current is 180 cycles per second. In a quarter cycle the electrons make approximately 250,000 revolutions and travel about 300 kilometers. Larger betatrons have been built and successfully operated to give energies as high as 100 Mev.

If the beam of electrons is to be used to produce hard X-rays by impinging on a target, it must be swerved out of the equilibrium path at the end of the accelerating quarter cycle, for in the next quarter cycle the electric field is in such a direction as to decelerate the electrons. This may be done by an additional coil, which is excited near the end of the accelerating period.

Contrasting the betatron with the cyclotron, we notice that the magnetic and electric fields in the former vary together at a relatively low frequency, whereas in the latter the magnetic field is constant and the electric field alternates at a very high frequency. Furthermore, the action of the electric field is continuous in the first case and intermittent in the second.

88. Motional Electromotive Force and Neumann's Law. In art. 86 we confined our attention to the electromotive force in a circuit which is fixed relative to the observer. Now we shall determine the electromotive force along a conducting wire of length l which is moving with velocity v relative to the observer across the lines of force of a magnetic field. In this case we do not need to appeal to experiment, for the electromotive force is deducible at once from the general expression (76-2) for the force on each of the free electrons in the moving wire. From this equation the force per unit charge due to the magnetic field is seen to be

$$\mathbf{E}_v = \mathbf{v} \times \mathbf{B},$$

where $\mathbf{v}$ represents the velocity of the wire. So, if $d\mathbf{l}$ is a vector element of length of the wire, the *motional electromotive force* is

$$\mathscr{E} = \int_l \mathbf{E}_v \cdot d\mathbf{l} = \int_l (\mathbf{v} \times \mathbf{B}) \cdot d\mathbf{l} \qquad (88\text{-}1)$$

in the sense of the component of $\mathbf{v} \times \mathbf{B}$ along the wire.

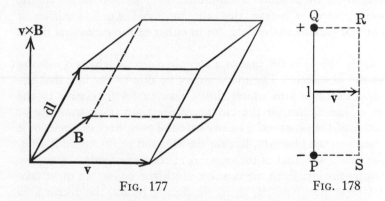

Fig. 177   Fig. 178

Consider the parallelepiped (Fig. 177) formed by the vectors $\mathbf{v}$, $\mathbf{B}$ and $d\mathbf{l}$. The vector $\mathbf{v} \times \mathbf{B}$ is equal in magnitude to the area of the base and has the direction of the altitude. Consequently, the scalar $(\mathbf{v} \times \mathbf{B}) \cdot d\mathbf{l}$ is equal to the area of the base multiplied by the component of $d\mathbf{l}$ normal to the base, that is, equal to the volume of the parallelepiped. If, now, we chose the face of the parallelepiped of which $\mathbf{v}$ and $d\mathbf{l}$ are edges as base, the volume of the parallelepiped is given by $(d\mathbf{l} \times \mathbf{v}) \cdot \mathbf{B} = \mathbf{B} \cdot (d\mathbf{l} \times \mathbf{v})$. Therefore,

$$(\mathbf{v} \times \mathbf{B}) \cdot d\mathbf{l} = \mathbf{B} \cdot (d\mathbf{l} \times \mathbf{v}),$$

and the electromotive force under consideration may be written

$$\mathscr{E} = \int_l \mathbf{B} \cdot (d\mathbf{l} \times \mathbf{v}). \qquad (88\text{-}2)$$

Now $d\mathbf{l} \times \mathbf{v}$ is the area swept over per unit time by the length $d\mathbf{l}$ of wire and $\mathbf{B} \cdot (d\mathbf{l} \times \mathbf{v})$ is the flux of induction through this area.   Therefore, *the motional electromotive force is equal to the flux of induction cut by the wire per unit time.   It acts in the direction of the component of* $\mathbf{v} \times \mathbf{B}$ *along the wire.*

Consider, for instance, a straight wire PQ (Fig. 178) of length l with a metal knob on either end moving with velocity $\mathbf{v}$ to the right through a uniform field the lines of force of which are directed perpendicular to the plane of the figure away from the reader.   The electromotive force acts in the direction of the vector $\mathbf{v} \times \mathbf{B}$, that is, from P to Q. The flux of induction cut by the wire per unit time is the flux Bvl passing through the area $PQRS$.   Therefore,

$$\mathcal{E} = Bvl$$

acting from P toward Q.   This electromotive force urges positive electricity toward Q and negative toward P until the knobs acquire sufficient charges to produce a difference of potential equal to the electromotive force.   Observe that the motional e.m.f. vanishes if either $d\mathbf{l}$ or $\mathbf{v}$ is parallel to the field, for in either of these cases no flux is cut.

Let us apply (88-2) to the case of a complete circuit which is moving relative to the observer.   The motion may be due to the fact that the circuit has a movable arm which slides back or forth relative to the remainder of the circuit, or the circuit, while rigid, may translate or rotate relative to the observer.   In any case the periphery or a part of it moves relative to the observer, having the location of the curve l_1 (Fig. 179) at the time t and that of the curve l_2 at the time $t + dt$.   Since we are describing the circuit in the counter-clockwise sense, we must take the front face as positive.   If, then, we denote by $d\mathbf{s}_l$ the vector area which is added to the circuit per unit length in the time dt, the area $PQRS$ added to the length dl in the time dt is

$$d\mathbf{s}_l dl = -d\mathbf{l} \times \mathbf{v} dt,$$

the negative sign being due to the fact that the positive sense of $d\mathbf{s}_l$ is toward the reader, and (88-2) becomes

$$\mathcal{E} = -\oint \mathbf{B} \cdot \frac{\partial \mathbf{s}_l}{\partial t} \, dl = -\oint B \cos \gamma \left| \frac{\partial \mathbf{s}_l}{\partial t} \right| dl, \qquad (88\text{-}3)$$

the angle γ being that between $\mathbf{B}$ and the positive normal to the area $PQRS$ and the integral being taken all the way around the circuit. The integral alone represents the amount of flux of B through the area added to the circuit per unit time on account of the motion of the periphery.   Therefore, *the motional electromotive force around a closed cir-*

cuit is equal to the rate of decrease of the flux of induction through the circuit due to the motion of the periphery relative to the observer.

Finally let us compute the total electromotive force around a closed circuit when **B** at every point is changing with the time and also the circuit is moving relative to the observer. Referring again to Fig. 179, if the circuit remains fixed in the position l_1 we have an e.m.f. proportional to the rate of decrease of flux of induction through the fixed curve l_1 as specified by Faraday's law. In addition, however, we have in the case of a moving circuit a motional e.m.f. proportional to the rate of decrease of flux due to the motion of the periphery. Adding the two together, *the total electromotive force $\mathscr{E}$ is equal to the total rate of decrease of flux of induction through the circuit, due in part to the change of* **B** *with the time and in part to the motion of the circuit relative to the observer.* In analytical form,

$$\mathscr{E} = -\frac{dN}{dt}, \qquad (88\text{-}4)$$

where

$$N = \int_s B \cos \gamma ds = \int_s \mathbf{B} \cdot d\mathbf{s},$$

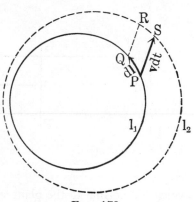

FIG. 179

integrated over the entire area bounded by the circuit at the instant considered. This law was formulated by F. E. Neumann in 1845. It is equivalent to Faraday's law for the case of a fixed circuit, but is more general in that it applies also to a moving circuit.

Two cautionary remarks are called for by the preceding discussion. In the first place, although an e.m.f. acts around a fixed closed curve through which the flux of induction is changing, whether a conducting circuit coincides with the curve or not, we cannot suppose a motional e.m.f. to exist in the absence of moving charges, such as the electrons carried along by a moving conductor. Secondly, the statement often made that the motional e.m.f. along a moving wire is equal to the number of tubes of induction cut per unit time is correct only if the tubes of induction are considered to be stationary relative to the observer, for only in this case is the number of tubes cut equal to the flux of induction through the area swept over by the wire. The concept of moving tubes of induction is one which should be avoided as it often leads to erroneous conclusions.

A simple example of motional electromotive force is afforded by the circuit of Fig. 180a. The arms AC, CD, DE are fixed, whereas the wire FG slides to the right with velocity v through a magnetic field directed perpendicular to the plane of the figure away from the reader. The positive sense of describing the circuit is $FDCG$ and the e.m.f. is

$$\mathscr{E} = -\frac{dN}{dt} = -Bvl, \tag{88-5}$$

where l is the width of the circuit. The negative sign indicates that the e.m.f. acts in the sense $GCDF$. It is generated entirely in the moving wire FG, and the present method of computing it leads to the same result as that obtained in the case of the isolated wire of Fig. 178.

Next consider the plane coil abc (Fig. 180b) of one turn rotating about a line PQ lying in its plane. We shall suppose that there is a uniform magnetic field at right angles to the axis PQ. If θ is the angle

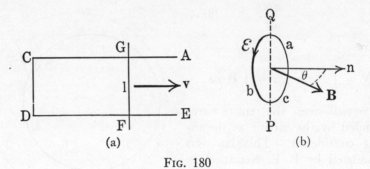

(a)   (b)

FIG. 180

which the normal to the plane of the circuit makes with B, the flux of induction is

$$N = BA \cos \theta,$$

where A represents the area of the circuit, and the induced e.m.f. is

$$\mathscr{E} = -\frac{dN}{dt} = BA \sin \theta \frac{d\theta}{dt}. \tag{88-6}$$

If the coil consists of n turns, each of which embraces the same flux, the e.m.f. is n times as great. Both the flux and the induced e.m.f. reverse their senses relative to the circuit twice each revolution. If the rotation is uniform, the one is maximum when the other is zero and vice versa, as illustrated in Fig. 181. In this case $\theta = \omega t$, where ω is the constant angular velocity of the coil, and

$$\mathscr{E} = nBA\omega \sin \omega t. \tag{88-7}$$

The ends of the coil may be connected to *collector rings*, C, C (Fig.

182), located on the axis of rotation PQ, from which the current is carried by means of brushes through an external circuit R.   We have here the essentials of an *alternating-current generator*.   The magnetic field in which the *armature coil* rotates is supplied by the *field magnet* whose poles are indicated.

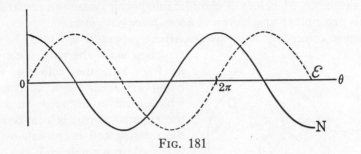

FIG. 181

If the lines of force are not perpendicular to the axis of rotation of the coil, we must replace B in (88-6) by the component of the magnetic induction at right angles to the axis, for the component of the magnetic induction parallel to the axis does not contribute to the flux through the circuit at any time during the course of a revolution.

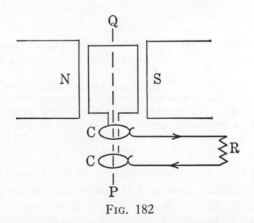

FIG. 182

A simple type of *direct-current generator* making use of motional electromotive force is the *Faraday disk machine*.   It consists of a copper disk D (Fig. 183) of radius a rotated with angular velocity ω between the poles, N, S of a magnet, the external circuit being brought into electrical contact with the disk by brushes at the axis A and at the rim P.   If, for simplicity, we assume the magnetic field to be uniform between A and P and perpendicular to the plane of the disk, (88-2) gives for the induced e.m.f.

$$\mathscr{E} = \int_0^a Bv\,dl = B\omega \int_0^a l\,dl = \frac{B\omega a^2}{2}, \qquad (88\text{-}8)$$

since $v = l\omega$ is the linear velocity of a point on the disk at a distance l from the axis. Machines of considerable power have been constructed on this principle, being known as *homo-polar generators*.

A more commonly used direct-current generator is similar in con-struction to the alternator illustrated in Fig. 182, the collector rings being replaced by a *commutator* which reverses the sense in which the external circuit is connected to the rotating coil every half-revolu-tion. With a single coil, as shown in the figure, this arrangement gives a unidirectional but fluctuating cur-rent. By using a number of arma-ture coils uniformly oriented about the axis PQ and connecting each to the external circuit only during that part of its revolution when the e.m.f. is near its maximum, an effectively constant current may be produced.

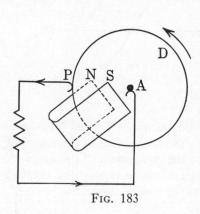

Fig. 183

Problem 88a. Twelve Faraday disks of radius 10 cm connected in series rotate at 50 r.p.s. If $B = 1$ weber/meter², find the induced e.m.f. Ans. 18.8 volt.

Problem 88b. A straight wire 1 meter long provided with a metal knob on each end as in Fig. 178 is carried by an airplane traveling at a speed of 720 kilo-meters per hour. The wire moves at right angles to the earth's magnetic field, whose magnitude is 40 amperes per meter. What is the e.m.f. along the wire as determined by an observer on the earth? To what does the pilot of the plane ascribe the charge appearing on the knobs? Ans. 0.01 volt.

89. Circuit with Self-Inductance and Resistance.

A current gives rise to a magnetic field and therefore contributes to the flux of induction through the circuit in which it is flowing. If the current changes, the flux is altered and an electromotive force is induced. This phenomenon is known as *self-induction*. As the flux produced by a current is positive relative to the sense in which it is flowing, the induced electromotive force is in the direction of the current if the latter is decreasing and in the opposite direction if the current is increasing. Therefore, the e.m.f. of self-induction opposes any change in the magnitude of the current.

According to Ampère's law (68-6) the magnetic field and consequently the flux of induction in a paramagnetic or diamagnetic medium are proportional to the current. Hence let us write for the flux of induction through a circuit in which a current i is flowing

$$N = Li. \qquad (89\text{-}1)$$

The positive coefficient L, known as the *self-inductance* of the circuit, represents the flux of induction through the circuit per unit current. Provided the permeability of the surrounding medium is constant, L is a constant characteristic of the circuit.

If the current i changes, an electromotive force

$$\mathscr{E}_i = -\frac{dN}{dt} = -L\frac{di}{dt} \qquad (89\text{-}2)$$

is induced in a circuit of constant self-inductance. From this equation we may define the self-inductance L more conveniently as the e.m.f. induced per unit time rate of decrease of current. The unit of inductance is called the *henry*. It is the self-inductance of a circuit in which an e.m.f. of one volt is induced when the current decreases at the rate of one ampere per second. Since inductance is measured basically in volt seconds per ampere, the henry expressed in terms of the fundamental units is 1 meter.

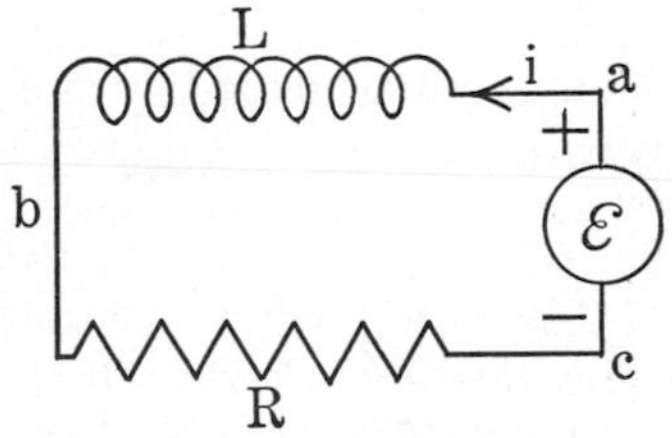

FIG. 184

Although the self-inductance of a single turn of wire is small, that of a coil of a number of closely wound turns may be quite large, especially if the wire is wound on a core of high permeability. For multiplying the turns by n multiplies the flux through each turn by n and the flux through the entire coil by n^2. Such a coil is often called an *inductor*.

Consider a circuit (Fig. 184) consisting of an applied electromotive force $\mathscr{E}$, a coil of self-inductance L, and a resistance R connected in series. The applied e.m.f., acting in the direction c to a, builds up a positive charge at a and a negative charge at c. If the resistance between c and a is zero the potential difference due to such charges must at every instant be equal to $\mathscr{E}$, for the resultant electric intensity must vanish in the interior of a perfect conductor. So if we denote by $\mathscr{E}_A$ the drop in potential between c and a due to the charges on the circuit,

$$\mathscr{E} + \mathscr{E}_A = 0. \qquad (89\text{-}3)$$

If the current is varying, an electromotive force $\mathscr{E}_i$ (taken as positive when acting from a to b) is induced in the coil L on account of its self-inductance. This e.m.f. likewise gives rise to a separation of charge until a potential drop $\mathscr{E}_L$ is established between the ends a and b of the coil such that

$$\mathscr{E}_i + \mathscr{E}_L = 0. \tag{89-4}$$

Finally the charges on the wire give rise to a difference of potential between the ends b and c of the resistance. Denoting the drop of potential in passing from b to c by $\mathscr{E}_R$ we have

$$\mathscr{E}_R = Ri \tag{89-5}$$

from Ohm's law.

Adding equations (89-3), (89-4) and (89-5),

$$\mathscr{E} + \mathscr{E}_i + (\mathscr{E}_A + \mathscr{E}_L + \mathscr{E}_R) = Ri. \tag{89-6}$$

But the electromotive force taken all the way around the circuit due to the static charges vanishes, that is,

$$\mathscr{E}_A + \mathscr{E}_L + \mathscr{E}_R = 0.$$

Hence, replacing $\mathscr{E}_i$ by the right-hand side of (89-2) and rearranging terms,

$$L\frac{di}{dt} + Ri = \mathscr{E}. \tag{89-7}$$

This relation is known as the *equation of the circuit*.

It should be observed that the effect of the charges on the circuit is to transfer the place at which work is done on the electrons constituting the current from the region of the external electromotive force and the coil L to the resistance. As the resultant e.m.f. through the external source is zero by (89-3) no work is done there on the current, and the same is true of the coil on account of (89-4). The entire work done on the current is expended in the resistance, being dissipated there in the form of heat.

If a voltmeter V (Fig. 185) is connected across the coil of the circuit under consideration in such a way that there is no varying flux through the space between the leads, the voltmeter measures the potential drop $\mathscr{E}_L$ between the terminals a and b of the coil. According to (89-4) this potential drop is

$$\mathscr{E}_L = -\mathscr{E}_i = L\frac{di}{dt}.$$

The voltmeter reading, therefore, is equal to the negative of the electromotive force due to self-induction in the coil. If, for instance, the current is increasing, the e.m.f. of self-induction is directed from b to a whereas the voltmeter registers the equal potential drop from a to b. We may refer to $\mathscr{E}_L$ as the electromotive force *across* the coil.

Heretofore we have supposed the resistance of the circuit to exist entirely outside the applied e.m.f. and the inductance. Suppose now that a resistance R_1 is associated with the applied e.m.f. $\mathscr{E}$ and a resistance R_2 with the coil L, the remaining resistance of the circuit being denoted by R_3. Then equations (89-3), (89-4) and (89-5) become

$$\mathscr{E} + \mathscr{E}_A = R_1 i,$$
$$\mathscr{E}_i + \mathscr{E}_L = R_2 i,$$
$$\mathscr{E}_R = R_3 i,$$

respectively, and adding we get

$$\mathscr{E} + \mathscr{E}_i + (\mathscr{E}_A + \mathscr{E}_L + \mathscr{E}_R) = (R_1 + R_2 + R_3)i.$$

If we put R for the total resistance $R_1 + R_2 + R_3$ of the circuit and remember that $\mathscr{E}_A + \mathscr{E}_L + \mathscr{E}_R$ is zero, we are led to (89-7) again. Therefore, this equation is valid no matter how the resistance may be distributed in the circuit.

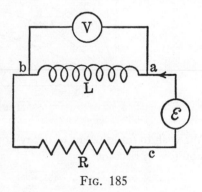

FIG. 185

Growth and Decay of Current. Suppose that the applied electromotive force $\mathscr{E}$ is a constant e.m.f. such as might be supplied by a cell, and let the circuit be suddenly completed by closing a key or switch. We wish to investigate the rate of growth of the current. Separating the variables i and t in (89-7),

$$\frac{di}{i - \dfrac{\mathscr{E}}{R}} = -\frac{R}{L} dt,$$

of which the integral is

$$i - \frac{\mathscr{E}}{R} = A e^{-(R/L)t}.$$

If we determine the constant of integration A by taking $t=0$ when $i=0$,

$$i = \frac{\mathscr{E}}{R}\{1 - e^{-(R/L)t}\}. \tag{89-8}$$

The current approaches asymptotically the value $\mathscr{E}/R$ given by Ohm's law (49-7) for the steady state. It reaches the fraction $(1-1/e)$ of its final value, that is, $0.632\,\mathscr{E}/R$, in the time L/R. This ratio,

$$\lambda \equiv \frac{L}{R}, \tag{89-9}$$

is called the *time constant* of the circuit. The smaller λ, the more rapidly the current grows. In Fig. 186 the current is plotted against the time for several different values of the time constant. As t and λ each represent a time, the units employed on the diagram are arbitrary.

Next let us suppose that the applied e.m.f. is suddenly removed from the circuit while a current i_0 is flowing, without breaking the circuit.

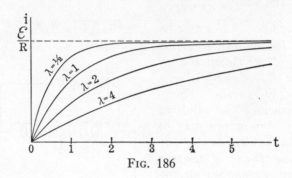

Fig. 186

We wish to find the law of decay of the current. In this case $\mathscr{E}$ vanishes and (89-7) becomes

$$\frac{di}{i} = -\frac{R}{L}\,dt,$$

leading to the integral

$$i = i_0 e^{-(R/L)t}, \tag{89-10}$$

if we count the time from the instant at which the applied e.m.f. is removed. The current decays exponentially, falling to the fraction $1/e$ of its original value, that is, $0.368i_0$, in a time λ. The decay curves for the values of λ appearing in Fig. 186 are obtained by inverting the figure. The smaller λ, the more rapidly the current falls off.

Simple Harmonic Electromotive Force. If the applied electromotive force $\mathscr{E}$ is a simple harmonic function of the time of the form

$$\mathscr{E} = \mathscr{E}_0 \sin \omega t,$$

such as might be produced by a coil rotating with constant angular velocity ω in a uniform magnetic field, the equation of the circuit becomes

$$L \frac{di}{dt} + Ri = \mathscr{E}_0 \sin \omega t. \qquad (89\text{-}11)$$

Evidently in the steady state the current alternates with the same frequency as the applied e.m.f.   Therefore, we should expect a solution of (89-11) of the form

$$i = i_0 \sin (\omega t - \phi).$$

Substituting in (89-11) and arranging terms,

$$(L\omega i_0 \cos \phi - Ri_0 \sin \phi) \cos \omega t + (L\omega i_0 \sin \phi + Ri_0 \cos \phi - \mathscr{E}_0) \sin \omega t = 0,$$

and the differential equation is satisfied for all values of t provided the coefficients of $\cos \omega t$ and $\sin \omega t$ vanish, that is,

$$\tan \phi = \frac{L\omega}{R}, \qquad i_0 = \frac{\mathscr{E}_0}{L\omega \sin \phi + R \cos \phi}.$$

Consequently, if we put the values of $\sin \phi$ and $\cos \phi$ obtained from the first of these relations in the second,

$$i = \frac{\mathscr{E}_0}{\sqrt{R^2 + L^2\omega^2}} \sin (\omega t - \phi), \qquad \tan \phi \equiv \frac{L\omega}{R}. \qquad (89\text{-}12)$$

The current in this case is out of phase with the applied e.m.f., *lagging* behind it by an angle ϕ, that is, by $\phi/2\pi$ of a period.   The tangent of the *lag* is proportional to the frequency of $\omega/2\pi$ as well as to the self-inductance, the lag increasing from 0 for a steady e.m.f. to $\pi/2$ for infinite frequency.

The quantity $Z = \sqrt{R^2 + L^2\omega^2}$ is known as the *impedance* of the circuit.   The amplitude i_0 of the current is related to the amplitude $\mathscr{E}_0$ of the applied e.m.f. by the equation

$$i_0 = \frac{\mathscr{E}_0}{\sqrt{R^2 + L^2\omega^2}}. \qquad (89\text{-}13)$$

Therefore, impedance plays much the same part in this a-c (alternating-current) circuit that resistance does in a d-c (direct-current) circuit. It is to be noted that the impedance increases with the frequency. The quantity $X = L\omega$ contained in the impedance is called the circuit *reactance*.   At low frequency the reactance may be relatively unimportant as compared with the resistance, whereas at high frequency the reactance may be so great as to make the effect of the resistance quite negligible.   The unit of impedance and of reactance is, of course, the same as the unit of resistance.

Equation (89-12) is a particular solution of the equation of the circuit in that it contains no arbitrary constant. As (89-11) is a differential equation of the first order, the complete solution must contain one constant of integration. For the moment let us denote the particular solution (89-12) by i_2 and the solution of the equation obtained by making the right-hand member of (89-11) equal to zero by i_1. Then

$$i = i_1 + i_2$$

is a solution of (89-11). For, if we substitute in the differential equation,

$$\left(L\frac{di_1}{dt} + Ri_1\right) + \left(L\frac{di_2}{dt} + Ri_2 - \mathscr{E}_0 \sin \omega t\right) = 0,$$

which is satisfied identically since each of the two expressions within parentheses vanishes. Now i_1 is the solution (89-10) already obtained.

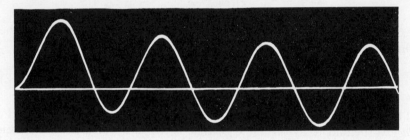

FIG. 187

So if we replace the coefficient i_0 in (89-10) by A to indicate that it represents an arbitrary constant of integration,

$$i = A e^{-(R/L)t} + \frac{\mathscr{E}_0}{\sqrt{R^2 + L^2\omega^2}} \sin (\omega t - \phi), \quad \tan \phi \equiv \frac{L\omega}{R}, \quad (89\text{-}14)$$

is the complete solution of the equation of the circuit. The constant A is to be determined by the initial conditions, for instance by the current at the time $t = 0$. The current represented by the first term is known as a *transient*. On account of the negative sign in the exponent the magnitude of this term decreases exponentially with the time, so that after a sufficiently long interval it becomes negligible as compared with the second term, and the current becomes that of the *steady state* represented by (89-12). The oscillogram (art. 116) shown in Fig. 187, which represents the current from the instant of connecting the circuit with a simple harmonic e.m.f., illustrates the decay of the transient and the establishment of a sinusoidal current.

Problem 89a. A circuit consists of two concentric cylindrical shells of radii a and b $(b > a)$ and common length l connected by flat end plates, the current flowing out along one shell and back along the other. The space between the shells contains a medium of permeability μ. Find the self-inductance of the circuit   Ans. $\dfrac{\mu_0 \mu l}{2\pi} \log \dfrac{b}{a}$.

Problem 89b. Find the self-inductance of a ring solenoid of mean radius b and cross-sectional radius a containing n turns of wire wound on a ring of permeability μ.   Ans. $\mu_0 \mu n^2 (b - \sqrt{b^2 - a^2})$.

Problem 89c. A circuit contains a ring solenoid of mean radius 20 cm and cross section 5 cm². The solenoid consists of 2000 turns wound on an iron core of permeability 2000 and it has a resistance 10 ohms. Find its inductance and its time constant.   Ans. 4.0 henry, 0.4 sec.

Problem 89d. A circuit has a resistance 2 ohms and a self-inductance 0.01 henry. At what frequency is the reactance equal to the resistance? What is the lag of the current at this frequency?   Ans. 31.8 cycle/sec, $\pi/4$ rad.

Problem 89e. In the circuit of problem *89c*, how long does it take a transient to fall to 1% of its initial value?   Ans. 1.8 sec.

Problem 89f. If a part R_2 of the resistance of the circuit discussed in this article is associated with the coil L, what is the reading on a voltmeter connected across the coil?   Ans. $\mathscr{E}_L + R_2 i$.

Problem 89g. A simple a-c generator such as illustrated in Fig. 182 is connected to an external resistance 1 ohm. The armature coil has a self-inductance 2 millihenrys and negligible resistance. It rotates 60 times a second, has an area of 100 cm² and contains 100 turns. The magnetic field in which it rotates is $0.8(10)^5$ amperes per meter. Find the current.   Ans. $30.26 \sin (\omega t - 0.65)$ amp.

Problem 89h. A circuit contains a constant applied e.m.f. and an inductance but no resistance. According to what law does the current grow?   Ans. $i = \dfrac{\mathscr{E}}{L} t$.

90. Circuit with Capacitance and Resistance.

Consider a capacitance C (Fig. 188) in series with an applied electromotive force $\mathscr{E}$ and a resistance R, the self-inductance of the circuit being so small as to be negligible. If $\mathscr{E}$ is a constant e.m.f. acting from c to a, the plate a of the capacitor C will acquire a positive charge and the plate b an equal negative charge of magnitude sufficient to produce a difference of potential between the plates equal to $\mathscr{E}$, the current ceasing to flow as soon as this state has been attained. On the other hand, if $\mathscr{E}$ is an alternating e.m.f., current will flow back and forth through the circuit from the one to the other plate of the capacitor, the charge on each plate reversing sign with every alternation of the electromotive force.

Let us analyze the circuit. If the resistance associated with $\mathscr{E}$ is negligible the charges present must give rise to a drop of potential $\mathscr{E}_A$ between c and a just sufficient to neutralize $\mathscr{E}$, so that at every instant

$$\mathscr{E} + \mathscr{E}_A = 0. \tag{90-1}$$

Next there is a potential drop $\mathscr{E}_C$ across the capacitor due to the charges q and $-q$ on the plates given by

$$\mathscr{E}_C = \frac{q}{C}. \tag{90-2}$$

Finally the charges present on the circuit give rise to a difference of potential $\mathscr{E}_R$ between the ends b and c of the resistance amounting to

$$\mathscr{E}_R = Ri. \tag{90-3}$$

Adding (90-1), (90-2) and (90-3),

$$\mathscr{E} + (\mathscr{E}_A + \mathscr{E}_C + \mathscr{E}_R) = \frac{q}{C} + Ri.$$

But the electromotive force $(\mathscr{E}_A + \mathscr{E}_C + \mathscr{E}_R)$ around the entire circuit due to the static charges vanishes. Hence, as

$$i = \frac{dq}{dt},$$

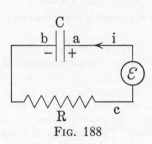

C

b | a   i

$-$ | $+$

$\mathcal{E}$

R   c

FIG. 188

$$R\frac{dq}{dt} + \frac{q}{C} = \mathscr{E} \tag{90-4}$$

is the equation of the circuit under consideration. This equation is identical in form with the equation (89-7) of a circuit containing self-inductance and resistance only, q taking the place of i, R that of L and $1/C$ that of R.

Growth and Decay of Charge. Suppose that $\mathscr{E}$ is a constant e.m.f. and that the circuit has just been completed by closing a key, the capacitor having previously been discharged. We wish to investigate the rate at which charge accumulates on the plates. As the equation of the circuit is of the same form as (89-7), we have at once from (89-8)

$$q = C\mathscr{E}\{1 - e^{-(1/RC)t}\}, \tag{90-5}$$

by substituting $1/C$ for R and R for L. The charge increases exponentially to the final value $C\mathscr{E}$. The time constant,

$$\lambda \equiv RC, \tag{90-6}$$

represents the time necessary for the charge to attain the fraction $(1 - 1/e)$ of its final value. The smaller λ the more rapidly the charge accumulates. If we interpret the ordinates in Fig. 186 as charge on the capacitor instead of current in the circuit, the curves there drawn show the accumulation of charge for various values of the time constant.

To get the current in the circuit, (90-5) must be differentiated with respect to the time, giving

$$i = \frac{dq}{dt} = \frac{\mathscr{E}}{R} e^{-(1/RC)t}. \tag{90-7}$$

The current starts with the value $\mathscr{E}/R$, gradually decreasing and finally stopping when the capacitor has attained its full charge $C\mathscr{E}$.

Next let us see what occurs if the applied e.m.f. is removed from the circuit when the capacitor has a charge q_0, without breaking the circuit. Evidently this is equivalent to charging the capacitor separately and then allowing it to discharge through the resistance. To find the way in which the discharge takes place it is only necessary to make the appropriate substitutions in (89-10). These give

$$q = q_0 e^{-(1/RC)t}. \tag{90-8}$$

We note that the capacitor discharges exponentially, the rate of discharge or the current being

$$i = \frac{dq}{dt} = -\frac{q_0}{RC}\, e^{-(1/RC)t}, \tag{90-9}$$

where the negative sign indicates that the current is in the sense to decrease the charge on the capacitor. The discharge is more rapid the smaller the time constant.

Simple Harmonic Electromotive Force. If the applied electromotive force $\mathscr{E}$ in the circuit of Fig. 188 is a simple harmonic function of the time of the form $\mathscr{E} = \mathscr{E}_0 \sin \omega t$, the equation of the circuit is

$$R\frac{dq}{dt} + \frac{q}{C} = \mathscr{E}_0 \sin \omega t. \tag{90-10}$$

As this equation is of the same form as (89-11) we obtain the solution for the steady state from (89-12) by means of the substitutions previously employed. Thus,

$$q = \frac{\mathscr{E}_0}{\sqrt{\dfrac{1}{C^2} + R^2\omega^2}} \sin (\omega t - \psi),$$

$$= \frac{\dfrac{\mathscr{E}_0}{\omega}}{\sqrt{R^2 + \dfrac{1}{C^2\omega^2}}} \sin (\omega t - \psi), \quad \tan \psi \equiv RC\omega, \tag{90-11}$$

and the current is

$$i = \frac{dq}{dt} = \frac{\mathscr{E}_0}{\sqrt{R^2 + \dfrac{1}{C^2\omega^2}}} \cos (\omega t - \psi)$$

$$= \frac{\mathscr{E}_0}{\sqrt{R^2 + \dfrac{1}{C^2\omega^2}}} \sin (\omega t - \phi), \quad \tan \phi \equiv -\frac{1}{RC\omega}. \tag{90-12}$$

As in the case of a circuit containing self-inductance and resistance the current is out of phase with the applied e.m.f., but here the current *leads* the e.m.f. instead of lagging behind it since ϕ is negative. For high frequency the angle ϕ is very nearly zero, decreasing to $-\pi/2$ for zero frequency. Note that this is quite different from the case of a circuit containing self-inductance.

The *impedance* of the circuit is

$$Z = \sqrt{R^2 + \frac{1}{C^2\omega^2}},$$

the amplitude i_0 of the current being related to that of the e.m.f. by the equation

$$i_0 = \frac{\mathscr{E}_0}{\sqrt{R^2 + \frac{1}{C^2\omega^2}}}. \tag{90-13}$$

Contrary to what was found in the case of self-inductance, the impedance of the circuit under consideration here decreases as the frequency is increased, approaching the limiting value R for very high frequencies. For zero frequency, that is a steady e.m.f., the impedance is infinite and no current can flow. Obviously this must be true, for the capacitor constitutes a break in the circuit and no steady current can flow under the action of a constant e.m.f.

The *reactance* of the circuit is $X = -1/C\omega$. It is important only at low frequencies, becoming negligible at high enough frequencies. In fact the insertion of a capacitance in a circuit has no appreciable effect upon either the amplitude or the phase of the current at sufficiently high frequency.

So far we have omitted the transient. The complete solution of the equation of the circuit may be obtained from (89-14) by means of the substitutions already employed. It is

$$i = Ae^{-(1/RC)t} + \frac{\mathscr{E}_0}{\sqrt{R^2 + \frac{1}{C^2\omega^2}}} \sin(\omega t - \phi), \qquad \tan\phi \equiv -\frac{1}{RC\omega}, \tag{90-14}$$

the constant of integration A being determined from the initial value of the current. The transient current, represented by the first term, falls off with the time, leaving the second term alone after the steady state has been attained.

Problem 90a. A capacitance 2 microfarads is connected in series with a high resistance and a quadrant electrometer. It is found that the capacitor loses half its charge in 120 sec. Find the resistance. Ans. 86.6 megohm.

Problem 90b. By integrating (90-4), find (90-5), (90-8) and (90-11) directly, without reference to art. 89.

Problem 90c. Express A (90-14) in terms of the steady state constants i_0 and ϕ, for the condition $i=0$ at $t=0$. Plot i/i_0 against ωt for the three cases $RC\omega=0.1, 1.0, 10.0$. Ans. $A=i_0 \sin \phi$.

91. Circuit with Self-Inductance, Capacitance and Resistance. A more general type of circuit, which includes both those considered heretofore, is one in which a self-inductance L (Fig. 189), a capacitance C and a resistance R are connected in series with an applied electromotive force $\mathscr{E}$. Denoting the potential drop from d to a due to the static charges on the circuit by $\mathscr{E}_A$, that from a to b by $\mathscr{E}_L$, that

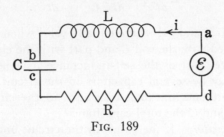

Fig. 189

between the plates b and c of the capacitor by $\mathscr{E}_C$ and that across the resistance by $\mathscr{E}_R$,

$$\mathscr{E} + \mathscr{E}_A = 0,$$
$$\mathscr{E}_i + \mathscr{E}_L = 0,$$
$$\mathscr{E}_C = \frac{q}{C},$$
$$\mathscr{E}_R = Ri,$$

where, as before,

$$\mathscr{E}_i = -L \frac{di}{dt} \tag{91-1}$$

is the induced e.m.f. due to the inductance of the coil L. Adding the preceding equations,

$$\mathscr{E} + \mathscr{E}_i + (\mathscr{E}_A + \mathscr{E}_L + \mathscr{E}_C + \mathscr{E}_R) = Ri + \frac{q}{C}.$$

As the e.m.f. around the complete circuit due to the static charges vanishes, the expression within parentheses is zero. So, making use of (91-1) and rearranging terms,

$$L \frac{di}{dt} + Ri + \frac{q}{C} = \mathscr{E}. \tag{91-2}$$

It should be noted that the left-hand side of this equation is equal to the sum of the potential drops *across* the three circuit elements L, R and C.

To obtain the differential equation for q we put $\frac{dq}{dt}$ for i getting

$$L\frac{d^2q}{dt^2}+R\frac{dq}{dt}+\frac{q}{C} = \mathscr{E}, \qquad (91\text{-}3)$$

or, if we wish to use i as dependent variable, we differentiate (91-2) with respect to the time, so as to have the equation of the circuit in the form

$$L\frac{d^2i}{dt^2}+R\frac{di}{dt}+\frac{1}{C}i = \frac{d\mathscr{E}}{dt}. \qquad (91\text{-}4)$$

Equations (91-3) and (91-4) are equally valid when part of the resistance is associated with the coil L and part with the electromotive force $\mathscr{E}$. Furthermore, part of the self-inductance may be associated with $\mathscr{E}$, and there may be several capacitors in the circuit. In every case, however, R represents the total resistance in the circuit, L the total self-inductance and C the total capacitance.

Charging Capacitor. If the e.m.f. in the circuit under consideration is constant, we can find the rate at which charge accumulates on the capacitor plates after the circuit is completed by closing a key. To do so we integrate (91-3), remembering that the right-hand member is a constant. The equation is put in more convenient form if we introduce a new dependent variable,

$$Q \equiv q-C\mathscr{E}.$$

Then (91-3) becomes

$$L\frac{d^2Q}{dt^2}+R\frac{dQ}{dt}+\frac{Q}{C} = 0. \qquad (91\text{-}5)$$

As this equation is linear and homogeneous in Q, the solution is of the form

$$Q = Ae^{\gamma t},$$

where A is an arbitrary constant. Substituting in (91-5),

$$L\gamma^2+R\gamma+\frac{1}{C} = 0,$$

giving

$$\gamma = -\frac{R}{2L}\pm\sqrt{\frac{R^2}{4L^2} - \frac{1}{LC}}. \qquad (91\text{-}6)$$

Each value of γ gives a solution. If we put

$$\alpha \equiv \frac{R}{2L}, \qquad \beta \equiv \sqrt{\frac{R^2}{4L^2} - \frac{1}{LC}},$$

so that $\gamma = -\alpha \pm \beta$, we have for the complete solution of (91-5)

$$q = C\mathscr{E} + e^{-\alpha t}\{A_1 e^{\beta t} + A_2 e^{-\beta t}\}, \tag{91-7}$$

where A_1 and A_2 are constants to be determined by the initial conditions. The current, obtained by differentiating (91-7) with respect to the time, is

$$i = e^{-\alpha t}\{(\beta - \alpha)A_1 e^{\beta t} - (\beta + \alpha)A_2 e^{-\beta t}\}. \tag{91-8}$$

If the capacitor is uncharged when the key is closed, $q = i = 0$ when $t = 0$. Consequently,

$$A_1 + A_2 = -C\mathscr{E}$$

from (91-7), and

$$(\beta - \alpha)A_1 - (\beta + \alpha)A_2 = 0$$

from (91-8). Solving for A_1 and A_2, we have

$$A_1 = -\frac{\alpha + \beta}{2\beta} C\mathscr{E}, \qquad A_2 = \frac{\alpha - \beta}{2\beta} C\mathscr{E},$$

and hence

$$q = C\mathscr{E}\left[1 - \frac{1}{2\beta} e^{-\alpha t}\{(\alpha + \beta)e^{\beta t} - (\alpha - \beta)e^{-\beta t}\}\right]. \tag{91-9}$$

The constant β is real if

$$\frac{R^2}{4L^2} > \frac{1}{LC},$$

that is, if the resistance is larger than twice the square root of the ratio of self-inductance to capacitance. In this case $\beta < \alpha$ by (91-6), the term involving the exponentials decreases continuously with the time, and q approaches the limiting value $C\mathscr{E}$. The broken curve in Fig. 190 shows how q increases with the time. Evidently the charging of the capacitor is aperiodic.

If the resistance of the circuit is less than twice the square root of the ratio of self-inductance to capacitance, β becomes imaginary and the solution (91-9) is not in convenient form. In this case oscillations are set up in the circuit, and we may proceed by assuming a solution of (91-5) of the form

$$Q = A_0 e^{-\alpha t} \sin(\omega_0 t + \epsilon). \tag{91-10}$$

Substituting in the differential equation,

$$\left\{(\alpha^2-\omega_0{}^2)L-\alpha R+\frac{1}{C}\right\}\sin{(\omega_0 t+\epsilon)}+\{-2\alpha\omega_0 L+\omega_0 R\}\cos{(\omega_0 t+\epsilon)}=0,$$

which is satisfied for all values of t provided the coefficients of the sine and cosine vanish, that is,

$$\alpha=\frac{R}{2L}, \qquad \omega_0=\sqrt{\frac{1}{LC}-\frac{R^2}{4L^2}}. \tag{91-11}$$

Consequently, the complete solution of (91-3) is

$$q=C\mathcal{E}+A_0 e^{-\alpha t}\sin{(\omega_0 t+\epsilon)}, \tag{91-12}$$

A_0 and ϵ being arbitrary constants to be determined by the initial conditions. As α is positive, the amplitude of the oscillations given by the

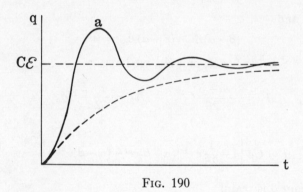

Fig. 190

second term falls off with the time and q approaches the same final value $C\mathcal{E}$ as in the previous case. The current

$$i=A_0 e^{-\alpha t}\{\omega_0\cos{(\omega_0 t+\epsilon)}-\alpha\sin{(\omega_0 t+\epsilon)}\}, \tag{91-13}$$

is also oscillatory, becoming, however, of smaller and smaller amplitude as time elapses.

Instead of solving the differential equation of the circuit anew for the oscillatory case, we may write

$$\beta=i\omega_0, \qquad \omega_0\equiv\sqrt{\frac{1}{LC}-\frac{R^2}{4L^2}},$$

in (91-7), where $i\equiv\sqrt{-1}$, and obtain (91-12) immediately by means of the identity

$$e^{\pm i\omega_0 t}\equiv\cos{\omega_0 t}\pm i\sin{\omega_0 t}.$$

For then the expression inside the braces in the second term of (91-7) becomes

$$(A_1 + A_2) \cos \omega_0 t + i(A_1 - A_2) \sin \omega_0 t,$$

which reduces to

$$A_0 \sin (\omega_0 t + \epsilon),$$

if we put

$$A_0 \equiv 2\sqrt{A_1 A_2}, \qquad \tan \epsilon \equiv i\frac{A_2 + A_1}{A_2 - A_1}.$$

Under the same initial conditions as considered previously, $q = i = 0$ when $t = 0$ in (91-12) and (91-13). Hence

$$A_0 \sin \epsilon = -C\mathscr{E},$$

$$\omega_0 \cos \epsilon - \alpha \sin \epsilon = 0,$$

giving

$$\tan \epsilon = \frac{\omega_0}{\alpha}, \qquad A_0 = -\frac{C\mathscr{E}}{\sin \epsilon} = -\frac{\sqrt{\omega_0{}^2 + \alpha^2}}{\omega_0} C\mathscr{E}.$$

Therefore,

$$q = C\mathscr{E}\left\{1 - \frac{\sqrt{\omega_0{}^2 + \alpha^2}}{\omega_0} e^{-\alpha t} \sin (\omega_0 t + \epsilon)\right\}, \qquad \tan \epsilon \equiv \frac{\omega_0}{\alpha}; \quad (91\text{-}14)$$

and the current is

$$i = \frac{\sqrt{\omega_0{}^2 + \alpha^2}}{\omega_0} C\mathscr{E} e^{-\alpha t}\{\alpha \sin (\omega_0 t + \epsilon) - \omega_0 \cos (\omega_0 t + \epsilon)\}$$

$$= \frac{\omega_0{}^2 + \alpha^2}{\omega_0} C\mathscr{E} e^{-\alpha t} \sin \omega_0 t,$$

which we may write

$$i = i_0 e^{-\alpha t} \sin \omega_0 t, \qquad i_0 \equiv \frac{\omega_0{}^2 + \alpha^2}{\omega_0} C\mathscr{E}. \qquad (91\text{-}15)$$

The charge on the capacitor in this case is shown by the solid curve in Fig. 190. During the oscillations the charge may become considerably greater than the final value $C\mathscr{E}$, and consequently the potential difference between the plates may exceed $\mathscr{E}$, as at the point a on the curve. This sometimes results in a breakdown of the dielectric between the plates, entailing destruction of the capacitor. Therefore, care must be exercised in connecting a circuit containing a capacitance and a self-inductance in series to a source of potential in order to avoid excessive oscillations. This may be done by including in the circuit sufficient resistance. If the resistance is great enough, the charge increases aperiodically in conformity with the broken curve and never becomes greater than $C\mathscr{E}$.

The factor $e^{-\alpha t}$ in the equation (91-15) causes the amplitude of the current oscillations to become smaller and smaller as time goes on. This factor is known as a *damping factor*. The larger α the more rapidly the current is damped out.

Discharging Capacitor. If there is no applied e.m.f. in the circuit, $\mathscr{E}=0$ in (91-3). This is the case of a charged capacitor connected in series with an inductance, resistance and key. The solution of (91-3) now specifies the rate of discharge of the capacitor through the inductance and resistance after the key is closed.

If the resistance is large, the discharge is aperiodic, and the charge q, obtained from (91-7) by taking $\mathscr{E}$ equal to zero, is

$$q = e^{-\alpha t}\{A_1 e^{\beta t} + A_2 e^{-\beta t}\}. \tag{91-16}$$

The current is still given by (91-8). To determine A_1 and A_2 we have $q=q_0$ and $i=0$ when $t=0$. Therefore,

$$A_1 + A_2 = q_0,$$

$$(\beta-\alpha)A_1 - (\beta+\alpha)A_2 = 0,$$

giving

$$A_1 = \frac{\alpha+\beta}{2\beta}q_0, \qquad A_2 = -\frac{\alpha-\beta}{2\beta}q_0.$$

Consequently, (91-16) becomes

$$q = \frac{q_0}{2\beta} e^{-\alpha t}\{(\alpha+\beta)e^{\beta t} - (\alpha-\beta)e^{-\beta t}\}. \tag{91-17}$$

When the resistance is so small as to make β imaginary, we need the periodic solution obtained from (91-12) by making $\mathscr{E}$ zero. In this case

$$q = A_0 e^{-\alpha t} \sin(\omega_0 t + \epsilon), \tag{91-18}$$

the current still being given by (91-13). Making use of the initial conditions employed above,

$$A_0 \sin \epsilon = q_0,$$

$$\omega_0 \cos \epsilon - \alpha \sin \epsilon = 0,$$

and

$$\tan \epsilon = \frac{\omega_0}{\alpha}, \qquad A_0 = \frac{q_0}{\sin \epsilon} = \frac{\sqrt{\omega_0{}^2 + \alpha^2}}{\omega_0}q_0.$$

Consequently,

$$q = \frac{\sqrt{\omega_0{}^2 + \alpha^2}}{\omega_0} q_0 e^{-\alpha t} \sin(\omega_0 t + \epsilon), \tag{91-19}$$

and the current is

$$i = \frac{\sqrt{\omega_0{}^2 + \alpha^2}}{\omega_0} q_0 e^{-\alpha t}\{\omega_0 \cos(\omega_0 t + \epsilon) - \alpha \sin(\omega_0 t + \epsilon)\}$$

$$= -\frac{\omega_0{}^2 + \alpha^2}{\omega_0} q_0 c^{-\alpha t} \sin \omega_0 t,$$

which we will write in the more convenient form

$$i = i_0 e^{-\alpha t} \sin \omega_0 t, \qquad i_0 \equiv -\frac{\omega_0{}^2 + \alpha^2}{\omega_0} q_0. \qquad (91\text{-}20)$$

The current is plotted against the time in Fig. 191, the broken lines representing the enveloping curves

$$i = \mp i_0 e^{-\alpha t}.$$

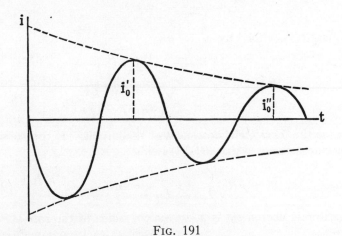

FIG. 191

The *natural frequency* of the circuit is

$$v_0 = \frac{\omega_0}{2\pi} = \frac{1}{2\pi}\sqrt{\frac{1}{LC} - \frac{R^2}{4L^2}}, \qquad (91\text{-}21)$$

the *natural* or *free period* P_0 being the reciprocal of this. If R is small compared with $2\sqrt{L/C}$, which is usually the case,

$$v_0 = \frac{\omega_0}{2\pi} = \frac{1}{2\pi\sqrt{LC}} \qquad (91\text{-}22)$$

to a sufficient degree of approximation.

To find the time t_s when the current has a stationary value, we place the derivative of (91-20) with respect to t equal to zero, getting

$$\tan \omega_0 t_s = \frac{\omega_0}{\alpha}.$$

Evidently there is a series of stationary values (Fig. 191), which are alternately minima and maxima. If τ_0 is the time elapsing between successive maxima,

$$\omega_0(t_s + \tau_0) = \omega_0 t_s + 2\pi,$$

or

$$\tau_0 = \frac{2\pi}{\omega_0} = P_0. \qquad (91\text{-}23)$$

The maxima recur, then, at intervals equal to the free period of oscillation. If i_0' and i_0'' are two successive maxima,

$$\frac{i_0'}{i_0''} = \frac{e^{-\alpha t}}{e^{-\alpha(t+P_0)}} = e^{\alpha P_0}.$$

The quantity δ defined by

$$\delta = \log \frac{i_0'}{i_0''} = \alpha P_0 = \frac{2\pi \left(\frac{R}{2L}\right)}{\sqrt{\frac{1}{LC} - \frac{R^2}{4L^2}}} \qquad (91\text{-}24)$$

is known as the *logarithmic decrement* of the circuit. If the resistance of the circuit is small so that (91-22) holds,

$$\delta = \pi R \sqrt{\frac{C}{L}} = \pi \frac{R}{L\omega_0} = \pi R C \omega_0. \qquad (91\text{-}25)$$

The logarithmic decrement is a convenient index of the rate at which the oscillations are damped out.

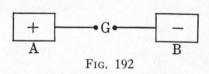

A   B

FIG. 192

The oscillator used by Hertz to produce electromagnetic waves in his famous experiments of 1888 consisted essentially of a capacitor discharging through an inductance and resistance. The apparatus is shown in Fig. 192. The two metal plates A and B form the capacitor, the self-inductance of the circuit being that of the two short wires connecting the plates to the spark gap G. As the first discharge ionizes the air in the gap, the resistance becomes so small that oscillations are set up. The potential difference existing between A and B in the first place may be produced by connecting the two sides of the gap to the secondary of an induction coil (art. 99). Each time the primary current in the coil is broken, an oscillatory discharge passes across the gap, as illustrated in Fig. 193 for two breaks of the primary. The impedance of the secondary of the coil is so great for the high frequency discharge taking place across the gap that no appreciable part of the current passes through the coil. As is shown in Chapter XVI, an oscillatory discharge

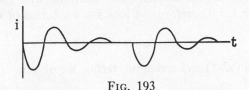

FIG. 193

such as that described here acts as a source of electromagnetic waves which travel out from it through the surrounding space.

Problem 91a. A circuit has an inductance 10 millihenrys, capacitance 0.1 microfarad and resistance 1000 ohms. Is it periodic? If there is an applied e.m.f. $(10)^5$ volts in the circuit, what is the final charge on the capacitor? Ans. No, 0.01 coulomb.

Problem 91b. A capacitor of capacitance 1 microfarad is connected in series with an inductance 10 millihenrys and a resistance 10 ohms. Initially the capacitor has a charge 1 coulomb. Find the natural frequency of the circuit and the charge at the end of 10 oscillations. Ans. 1590 cycle/sec, 0.0431 coulomb.

Problem 91c. An oscillatory circuit is connected to a constant e.m.f. Show that the greatest charge acquired by the capacitor is

$$q_{max} = C\mathscr{E}\{1 + e^{-\pi\alpha/\omega_0}\}.$$

If C, L and R have the values given in problem *91b*, find the ratio of q_{max} to the final charge. Ans. 1.85.

Problem 91d. A circuit in which

$$\frac{R^2}{4L^2} = \frac{1}{LC}$$

is said to be *critically damped*. Show that in this case the capacitor discharges aperiodically according to the law,

$$q = q_0(1 + \alpha t)e^{-\alpha t}.$$

Problem 91e. Find the logarithmic decrement of a circuit containing an inductance 10 millihenrys, a capacitance 1 microfarad and a resistance 1 ohm. By what percent does the current diminish per oscillation on discharge? Ans. 0.0314, 3.09%.

Problem 91f. Plot on a single diagram the aperiodic discharge curve given by (91-17) and the periodic discharge given by (91-19).

Problem 91g. Find the current occurring during the discharge specified by (91-17) and draw a graph showing how it varies with the time.

92. Alternating Current. If the circuit discussed in the last article is connected to the simple harmonic applied electromotive force $\mathscr{E} = \mathscr{E}_0 \sin \omega t$, the equation of the circuit becomes, from (91-4),

$$L \frac{d^2i}{dt^2} + R \frac{di}{dt} + \frac{1}{C} i = \mathscr{E}_0 \omega \cos \omega t. \tag{92-1}$$

In the steady state the current must alternate with the frequency of the applied e.m.f. Therefore, we look for a solution of the form

$$i = i_0 \sin (\omega t - \phi).$$

Substituting in (92-1) and arranging terms, we obtain

$$\left\{ -L\omega^2 \cos \phi + R\omega \sin \phi + \frac{1}{C} \cos \phi \right\} i_0 \sin \omega t$$

$$+ \left\{ \left(L\omega^2 \sin \phi + R\omega \cos \phi - \frac{1}{C} \sin \phi \right) i_0 - \mathscr{E}_0 \omega \right\} \cos \omega t = 0,$$

showing that to satisfy the differential equation we must have

$$\tan \phi = \frac{L\omega - \dfrac{1}{C\omega}}{R}, \quad i_0 = \frac{\mathscr{E}_0}{R \cos \phi + \left(L\omega - \dfrac{1}{C\omega} \right) \sin \phi}.$$

Putting in the expression for i_0 the values of $\sin \phi$ and $\cos \phi$ obtained from the expression for $\tan \phi$, we find

$$i = \frac{\mathscr{E}_0}{\sqrt{R^2 + \left(L\omega - \dfrac{1}{C\omega} \right)^2}} \sin (\omega t - \phi), \quad \tan \phi \equiv \frac{L\omega - \dfrac{1}{C\omega}}{R}; \tag{92-2}$$

the relation between the amplitude of the current and that of the applied e.m.f. being

$$i_0 = \frac{\mathscr{E}_0}{\sqrt{R^2 + \left(L\omega - \dfrac{1}{C\omega} \right)^2}}. \tag{92-3}$$

At low frequency the dominating term in the impedance,

$$Z = \sqrt{R^2 + \left(L\omega - \dfrac{1}{C\omega} \right)^2}, \tag{92-4}$$

is the one involving capacitance, whereas at high frequency the term containing inductance is the important one. The impedance is a minimum and therefore the current greatest for the frequency ν_r which makes the reactance $X = L\omega - 1/C\omega$ vanish, that is, for

$$\nu_r = \frac{\omega_r}{2\pi} = \frac{1}{2\pi\sqrt{LC}}. \tag{92-5}$$

By analogy with the simple harmonic oscillator this frequency is known as the *frequency of resonance*. In a circuit of negligible resistance it is equal to the natural frequency (91-22). In Fig. 194 the amplitude of the current is plotted against the logarithm of the frequency for constant $\mathscr{E}_0$, the point a on the curve corresponding to the state of

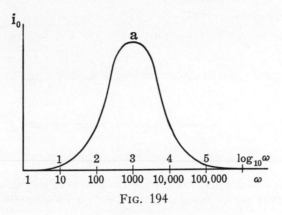

FIG. 194

resonance. If we denote the ratio ω/ω_r by k, equation (92-4) becomes

$$Z = \sqrt{R^2 + \frac{L}{C}\left(k - \frac{1}{k}\right)^2},$$

showing that the impedance is the same for the frequency $k\omega_r$ as for ω_r/k. Therefore, the curve of Fig. 194 is symmetrical about the frequency of resonance.

For frequencies less than resonance ϕ is negative, indicating that the current leads the applied e.m.f., the amount of lead, however, always being less than $\pi/2$. At resonance $\phi = 0$ and the current is in phase with the electromotive force. For frequencies greater than resonance ϕ is positive, the current lagging behind the e.m.f. by an angle between 0 and $\pi/2$. In terms of $k \equiv \omega/\omega_r$,

$$\tan\phi = \frac{\sqrt{\dfrac{L}{C}}\left(k - \dfrac{1}{k}\right)}{R},$$

showing that ϕ has the same absolute value (although opposite sign) for the frequency $k\omega_r$ as for ω_r/k. Therefore, if we plot ϕ against the logarithm of ω, we get the symmetrical curve shown in Fig. 195.

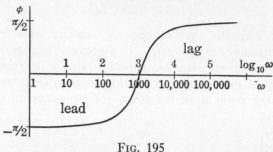

FIG. 195

The power delivered to the circuit by the applied e.m.f. at any instant t is

$$\mathscr{P} = \mathscr{E}i = \frac{\mathscr{E}_0^2}{\sqrt{R^2+\left(L\omega-\dfrac{1}{C\omega}\right)^2}} \sin \omega t \sin (\omega t - \phi). \qquad (92\text{-}6)$$

Evidently the power fluctuates during the course of an oscillation, and, as the current is not in phase with the e.m.f., it even becomes negative

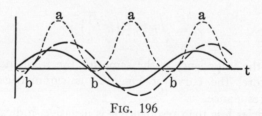

FIG. 196

for part of the time. If we represent the electromotive force by a solid curve (Fig. 196) and the current by a broken curve, we can find the power at any instant by taking the product of the ordinates of the two curves, the power being positive when the ordinates have the same sign and negative when they have opposite signs. In this way we get the dotted curve on the diagram. At $a, a, \cdots$ the power is positive, that is, the circuit is drawing energy from the source of electromotive force, whereas at $b, b, \cdots$ the power is negative, the circuit returning energy to the external source. As ϕ is always less than $\pi/2$ in absolute value the mean power, averaged over a period, is always positive. It is

$$\overline{\mathscr{P}} = \frac{\omega}{2\pi}\int_0^{2\pi/\omega} \mathscr{E}i\,dt$$

$$= \frac{\omega}{2\pi}\frac{\mathscr{E}_0{}^2}{\sqrt{R^2+\left(L\omega-\dfrac{1}{C\omega}\right)^2}}\left\{\cos\phi\int_0^{2\pi/\omega}\sin^2\omega t\,dt\right.$$

$$\left.-\sin\phi\int_0^{2\pi/\omega}\sin\omega t\cos\omega t\,dt\right\}$$

$$= \frac{1}{2}\frac{\mathscr{E}_0{}^2}{\sqrt{R^2+\left(L\omega-\dfrac{1}{C\omega}\right)^2}}\cos\phi. \tag{92-7}$$

The net energy supplied is all converted into heat in the resistance element, since there is no dissipation of energy in the inductance or the capacitance.

The *effective current* $\hat{\imath}$ is the steady current which will develop the same amount of heat in the resistance R as the alternating current actually flowing. We have from (49-8) for the energy converted into heat per unit time

$$R\hat{\imath}^2 \equiv R\left\{\frac{\omega}{2\pi}\int_0^{2\pi/\omega}i^2dt\right\} = Ri_0{}^2\left\{\frac{\omega}{2\pi}\int_0^{2\pi/\omega}\sin^2(\omega t-\phi)dt\right\}$$

$$= \tfrac{1}{2}Ri_0{}^2.$$

Consequently,

$$\hat{\imath} = \frac{1}{\sqrt{2}}i_0 = \frac{\dfrac{1}{\sqrt{2}}\mathscr{E}_0}{\sqrt{R^2+\left(L\omega-\dfrac{1}{C\omega}\right)^2}}. \tag{92-8}$$

As $\hat{\imath}$ is the square root of the mean value of the square of i, it is also known as the *root-mean-square* (r.m.s.) value of the current.

We define the *effective* or *root-mean-square* (r.m.s.) *electromotive force* $\hat{\mathscr{E}}$ in analogous manner by

$$\hat{\mathscr{E}}^2 \equiv \frac{\omega}{2\pi}\int_0^{2/\pi\omega}\mathscr{E}^2dt = \mathscr{E}_0{}^2\left\{\frac{\omega}{2\pi}\int_0^{2\pi/\omega}\sin^2\omega t\,dt\right\}$$

$$= \tfrac{1}{2}\mathscr{E}_0{}^2,$$

giving

$$\hat{\mathscr{E}} = \frac{1}{\sqrt{2}}\mathscr{E}_0.$$

Hence, from (92-4) and (92-8),

$$\hat{i} = \frac{\hat{\mathscr{E}}}{Z}, \qquad\qquad (92\text{-}9)$$

and from (92-7),

$$\bar{\mathscr{P}} = \hat{\mathscr{E}}\hat{i} \cos \phi. \qquad\qquad (92\text{-}10)$$

The quantity $\cos \phi$ is known as the *power factor*. At resonance it is equal to unity and maximum power is delivered to the circuit. At frequencies far from resonance the power factor becomes very small, and nearly as much work is done against the applied e.m.f. during the course of an oscillation as by it.

The current given by (92-2) is that existing in the steady state. In addition we may have transients. These, however, are rapidly damped out if there is any appreciable resistance in the circuit.

Problem 92a. Derive the a-c formulas of art. 89 and art. 90 from the corresponding formulas of this article.

Problem 92b. A circuit has an alternating e.m.f. in volts $100 \sin \omega t$, a resistance 2 ohms, a self-inductance 0.001 henry and a capacitance 1000 microfarads, all connected in series. Find the effective current for the following values of ω: 1 rad/sec, 10 rad/sec, 100 rad/sec, 1000 rad/sec, 10,000 rad/sec, 100,000 rad/sec, 1,000,000 rad/sec. Also find the frequency of resonance. Ans. 0.071 amp, 0.707 amp, 6.93 amp, 35.3 amp, 6.93 amp, 0.707 amp, 0.071 amp; 159 cycle/sec.

Problem 92c. A 60-cycle a-c circuit has resistance 2 ohms and inductance 10 millihenrys. What is the power factor? What capacitance, placed in the circuit, will make the power factor unity? By how much does the insertion of this capacitance increase the current? Ans. 0.47, 704 microfarad, 113%.

Problem 92d. Show that the mean power expended by the applied e.m.f. in the circuit under consideration in this article is equal to the rate at which heat is developed in the resistance.

REFERENCES

Duckworth, *Electricity and Magnetism* (Holt, Rinehart and Winston, 1960). Pp. 194–225, 230–236, 331–362.

Kip, *Electricity and Magnetism* (McGraw-Hill, 1962). Chap. 6, pp. 176–185, 256–275.

Winch, *Electricity and Magnetism* (Prentice-Hall, 1963). Chap. III–V, pp. 323–337, 344–358, 367–385.

Chapter X

INTERACTION OF CURRENTS AND FIELDS

93. Energy of an Isolated Circuit. The equation (91–3) of a circuit containing self-inductance, capacitance and resistance has the same form as that of a damped simple harmonic oscillator. Consider, for instance, a mass m (Fig. 197) suspended from O by means of a spring S. When displaced vertically a distance x from its equilibrium position, it experiences a force of restitution $-kx$ because of the spring, a damping force $-b\dfrac{dx}{dt}$ on account of air resistance, and in addition it may be subject to an external force $\mathcal{F}$. So its equation of motion is

$$m\frac{d^2x}{dt^2}+b\frac{dx}{dt}+kx = \mathcal{F}.$$

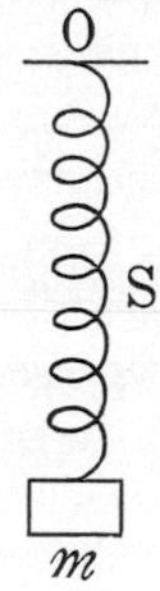

Comparing this equation with (91-3), we see that the self-inductance of the circuit corresponds to the mass of the oscillator, the resistance to the damping constant b and the reciprocal of the capacitance to the stiffness k of the spring. We can carry the analogy farther if we choose, likening i to the velocity and Li to the momentum of the oscillator. Thus, once the current is established, its momentum tends to keep it flowing even in the absence of an applied e.m.f. This momentum, however, is dissipated in part in overcoming resistance and the remainder is used up in charging the capacitor just as that of the oscillator is lost in extending or compressing the spring. After all the momentum has been dissipated or absorbed and the current has ceased to flow, the capacitor starts to discharge, giving rise to a current in the opposite sense, exactly as in the mechanical analog the oscillating mass comes to rest after extending the spring and then starts to move in the opposite direction as the spring contracts.

The rate at which work W is done by the applied e.m.f. in the circuit under consideration is obtained by multiplying (91-3) by $i=\dfrac{dq}{dt}$, which

FIG. 197

gives

$$\frac{dW}{dt} = \mathscr{E}\frac{dq}{dt} = Li\frac{di}{dt} + Ri^2 + \frac{1}{C}q\frac{dq}{dt}.$$

Integrating from time t_1 to time t_2 the total work done in the time $t_2 - t_1$ is

$$W = \tfrac{1}{2}Li_2{}^2 - \tfrac{1}{2}Li_1{}^2 + R\int_{t_1}^{t_2} i^2 dt + \frac{q_2{}^2}{2C} - \frac{q_1{}^2}{2C}, \qquad (93\text{-}1)$$

where i_1 is the current in the circuit at the time t_1 and i_2 that at the time t_2, q_1 and q_2 being the charges on the capacitor at the same times. As the integrand in the term involving R is always positive, this term becomes greater and greater the longer the interval of time. It represents an irreversible dissipation of energy, which is transformed into heat in the resistance. On the other hand, the remaining terms specify an increase of energy of the circuit which is reconverted to its original form when the current and charge resume their initial values. The quantity $\tfrac{1}{2}q^2/C$ has already (art. 21) been shown to be the potential energy of the charged capacitor. The expression $\tfrac{1}{2}Li^2$ represents energy possessed by the circuit on account of its self-inductance. As self-inductance is a consequence of the magnetic field of the current, we can interpret this as *magnetic energy*. By analogy with the oscillator we may describe it as *kinetic* rather than *potential* in character. In fact it represents the kinetic energy of the electrons constituting the current.

In the case of an alternating current the magnetic energy is

$$U_H = \tfrac{1}{2}Li^2 = \frac{L\mathscr{E}_0{}^2}{2Z^2}\sin^2(\omega t - \phi)$$

$$= \frac{L\mathscr{E}_0{}^2}{4Z^2}\{1 - \cos 2(\omega t - \phi)\}$$

from (92-2). Substituting (92-2) in (91-2), we find that the charge on the capacitor is

$$q = -\frac{\mathscr{E}_0}{Z\omega}\cos(\omega t - \phi),$$

so that the electric energy is

$$U_E = \frac{1}{2}\frac{q^2}{C} = \frac{\mathscr{E}_0{}^2}{2CZ^2\omega^2}\cos^2(\omega t - \phi)$$

$$= \frac{\mathscr{E}_0{}^2}{4CZ^2\omega^2}\{1 + \cos 2(\omega t - \phi)\}.$$

The energy of the circuit, therefore, passes from the kinetic to the potential form and back again with a frequency double that of the applied e.m.f., just as in the analogous case of the mechanical oscillator.

If we calculate the work done during a complete period, we see from (93-1) that it is entirely accounted for by the heat developed in the resistance.

Problem 93a. Show that only at resonance is the mean kinetic energy equal to the mean potential energy in the circuit treated in the latter part of this article.

Problem 93b. Find the kinetic and potential energies of the freely oscillating circuit discussed in art. 91. Show that, if the resistance of the circuit is negligible, the mean kinetic energy is equal to the mean potential energy.

Ans. $\dfrac{L(\omega_0{}^2 + \alpha^2)^2 q_0{}^2}{2\omega_0{}^2} e^{-2\alpha t} \sin^2 \omega_0 t,$ $\quad \dfrac{(\omega_0{}^2 + \alpha^2) q_0{}^2}{2C\omega_0{}^2} e^{-2\alpha t} \sin^2 (\omega_0 t + \epsilon).$

94. Energy of a System of Current Circuits.

In the preceding article we confined our attention to a single circuit. Now we shall consider the interactions of a number of circuits near one another and fixed relative to the observer. Although the method to be developed is applicable to any number of circuits, we shall confine the analysis to the case of three circuits designated by the numbers (1), (2) and (3). As we are interested only in the magnetic energy of the circuits, we shall suppose that they contain no capacitors.

The total flux of induction through (1) is made up of three parts, the flux due to the current i_1 in circuit (1) itself, the flux due to the current i_2 in circuit (2), and the flux due to the current i_3 in circuit (3). The first of these, as we have already seen, is $L_1 i_1$, where L_1 is the self-inductance of (1). As the magnetic field due to the current in (2) is proportional to i_2, the flux through (1) occasioned by it may be written $M_{12} i_2$. The coefficient M_{12} is a function of the coordinates specifying the relative positions of the two circuits but is independent of i_2, assuming that the permeability of the medium surrounding the circuits is constant. It is smaller in absolute magnitude the farther apart the circuits are placed. We call M_{12} the *mutual inductance* of circuit (1) with respect to circuit (2). It represents the flux through (1) due to a unit current in (2). It is positive or negative according as the flux passes through the two circuits in the same or in opposite senses. Evidently mutual inductance is measured in the same units as self-inductance.

Finally we have the flux $M_{13} i_3$ through circuit (1) due to the current i_3 in (3), M_{13} being the mutual inductance of (1) with respect to (3). So the entire flux through circuit (1) is

$$N_1 = L_1 i_1 + M_{12} i_2 + M_{13} i_3, \tag{94-1}$$

and, if the currents change, the circuits being held fixed in position, an electromotive force

$$\mathscr{E}_1{}' = -\frac{dN_1}{dt} = -L_1 \frac{di_1}{dt} - M_{12} \frac{di_2}{dt} - M_{13} \frac{di_3}{dt} \tag{94-2}$$

is induced in circuit (1).   From this equation we can define M_{12} as the e.m.f. induced in (1) per unit time rate of decrease of current in (2), and so on.   Expressions similar to (94-2) give the induced electromotive forces in circuits (2) and (3).

The magnetic energy of the system of circuits is equal to the work done against the induced e.m.f.'s as in the case of the single circuit discussed in the last article.   Therefore, we do not need to write down the complete equations of the circuits in order to calculate the magnetic energy of the system, but can obtain the desired result by computing the work done against the induced electromotive forces $\mathscr{E}_1'$, $\mathscr{E}_2'$, $\mathscr{E}_3'$ in the three circuits by the currents i_1, i_2, i_3 flowing in them.   In a time dt this work is

$$dU = -\mathscr{E}_1'i_1dt - \mathscr{E}_2'i_2dt - \mathscr{E}_3'i_3dt. \tag{94-3}$$

By starting with zero current in each circuit and gradually building the current up to its final value we can calculate the magnetic energy of the system of circuits.   Denote by I_1, I_2, I_3 the final values of the currents in the three circuits and suppose that the currents increase in such a way that at any instant each current is the same fraction α of its final value.   Then $i_1 = \alpha I_1$, $i_2 = \alpha I_2$, $i_3 = \alpha I_3$, where α increases from 0 to 1 during the process of building up the currents.   Putting (94-2) and similar expressions for the electromotive forces in the other circuits into (94-3), we find for the total work done against the induced e.m.f.'s in establishing the currents

$$U = \{L_1I_1{}^2 + M_{12}I_1I_2 + M_{13}I_1I_3$$
$$+ M_{21}I_2I_1 + L_2I_2{}^2 + M_{23}I_2I_3$$
$$+ M_{31}I_3I_1 + M_{32}I_3I_2 + L_3I_3{}^2\}\int_{a=0}^{a=1} \alpha \frac{d\alpha}{dt}\,dt$$

giving

$$U = \tfrac{1}{2}\{L_1I_1{}^2 + M_{12}I_1I_2 + M_{13}I_1I_3$$
$$\left.+ M_{21}I_2I_1 + L_2I_2{}^2 + M_{23}I_2I_3 \right\} \tag{94-4}$$
$$+ M_{31}I_3I_1 + M_{32}I_3I_2 + L_3I_3{}^2\}.$$

This expression represents the entire energy of the system of circuits, since no capacitors are present.   However, it does not represent all the work which has to be performed to establish the currents, since energy has to be supplied to overcome the resistances R_1, R_2, R_3 of the circuits at the rate

$$R_1i_1{}^2 + R_2i_2{}^2 + R_3i_3{}^2,$$

and this expenditure of energy continues after the currents have attained their final steady values.   The energy used in overcoming resistance is all dissipated in heat and does not add to the energy of the system of circuits.

If, now, we vary the current I_1 keeping the other currents constant, the change in the magnetic energy of the circuits is

$$\frac{\partial U}{\partial I_1}\, dI_1 - \{L_1 I_1 + \tfrac{1}{2}(M_{12} + M_{21})I_2 + \tfrac{1}{2}(M_{13} + M_{31})I_3\}\, dI_1. \quad (94\text{-}5)$$

But when I_1 alone is changed,

$$\mathscr{E}_1' = -L_1 \frac{dI_1}{dt}, \quad \mathscr{E}_2' = -M_{21}\frac{dI_1}{dt}, \quad \mathscr{E}_3' = -M_{31}\frac{dI_1}{dt},$$

and the work done against the induced electromotive forces is

$$\frac{\partial U}{\partial I_1}\, dI_1 = \left\{ L_1 I_1 \frac{dI_1}{dt} + M_{21} I_2 \frac{dI_1}{dt} + M_{31} I_3 \frac{dI_1}{dt} \right\} dt$$

$$= \{ L_1 I_1 + M_{21} I_2 + M_{31} I_3 \} dI_1. \quad (94\text{-}6)$$

The expressions (94-5) and (94-6) are equal whatever values we choose to give I_1, I_2 and I_3. If, for instance, we make I_1 and I_3 zero, we find that $M_{12} = M_{21}$. Similarly we find that the other mutual inductances are equal in pairs. In all we have

$$M_{12} = M_{21}, \quad M_{23} = M_{32}, \quad M_{31} = M_{13}. \quad (94\text{-}7)$$

Hence we conclude that the flux through circuit (1) due to unit current in (2) is equal to the flux through (2) due to unit current in (1) and so on. Instead of six independent mutual inductances we have but three.

Since the expression (94-4) holds for any values of the currents, it is no longer necessary to distinguish final values by special symbols. Hence, if we make use of (94-7), we have finally

$$U = \tfrac{1}{2}(L_1 i_1^2 + L_2 i_2^2 + L_3 i_3^2) + M_{12} i_1 i_2 + M_{23} i_2 i_3 + M_{31} i_3 i_1. \quad (94\text{-}8)$$

In the case of two neighboring circuits (94-8) reduces to

$$U = \tfrac{1}{2}L_1 i_1^2 + M i_1 i_2 + \tfrac{1}{2}L_2 i_2^2, \quad (94\text{-}9)$$

where $M \equiv M_{12}$, the middle term representing the mutual energy of the pair. If we separate the circuits, keeping the currents constant, the mutual energy becomes smaller and smaller in absolute value, approaching zero for infinite separation.

Although the mutual energy term may be negative as well as positive, U itself can never be negative. This enables us to establish an important relation between the mutual and the self-inductances of the circuits. Putting $x \equiv i_1/i_2$, we see that $U \geqslant 0$ requires that $L_1 x^2 + 2Mx + L_2$

should be greater than or equal to zero for all values of x. Evidently $x = -M/L_1$ gives this expression its minimum value $L_2 - M^2/L_1$, so that

$$M^2 \leqslant L_1 L_2, \tag{94-10}$$

no matter how the circuits are placed or oriented. Usually in practice the maximum value of M^2 obtainable is considerably less than $L_1 L_2$, although in special cases this limiting value may be very nearly reached.

Problem 94. A current 5 amperes flows in the solenoid of problem *89c*. Find its energy. Ans. 50 joule.

95. Forces and Torques on Rigid Circuits.

For simplicity we shall confine ourselves to a pair of circuits and calculate the force or torque on one due to the other. Each circuit will be supposed to be rigid, the only motion considered being that of the one relative to the other. If one circuit is fixed relative to the observer and the other suffers a small displacement $d\xi$, the work done by the magnetic force exerted by the first circuit on the second is $\mathscr{F}_\xi \, d\xi$, where $\mathscr{F}_\xi$ is the component of the force in the direction of the displacement.

As each circuit is rigid, the relative motion of the two circuits changes the mutual inductance M but not the self-inductances L_1 and L_2 of the two circuits. The change in mutual inductance means that the flux through each circuit changes, resulting in an induced e.m.f. and a change in current. The flux through the first circuit is

$$N_1 = L_1 i_1 + M i_2,$$

and the e.m.f. induced when both the currents and the mutual inductance change as a result of the displacement is

$$\mathscr{E}_1{}' = -L_1 \frac{di_1}{dt} - M \frac{di_2}{dt} - i_2 \frac{dM}{dt}.$$

If, then, $\mathscr{E}_1$ is the applied e.m.f. and R_1 the resistance of circuit (1), the equation of the circuit is

$$\mathscr{E}_1 + \mathscr{E}_1{}' = R_1 i_1,$$

or

$$L_1 \frac{di_1}{dt} + M \frac{di_2}{dt} + i_2 \frac{dM}{dt} + R_1 i_1 = \mathscr{E}_1. \tag{95-1}$$

Writing down a similar expression for circuit (2), the rate at which work is done on the two circuits by the applied electromotive forces $\mathscr{E}_1$ and $\mathscr{E}_2$ is

$$\frac{dW}{dt} = \mathscr{E}_1 i_1 + \mathscr{E}_2 i_2$$

$$= L_1 i_1 \frac{di_1}{dt} + L_2 i_2 \frac{di_2}{dt} + M i_1 \frac{di_2}{dt} + M i_2 \frac{di_1}{dt} + 2 i_1 i_2 \frac{dM}{dt} + R_1 i_1{}^2 + R_2 i_2{}^2.$$

$$\tag{95-2}$$

The rate of increase of magnetic energy obtained by differentiating (94-9) with respect to the time is

$$\frac{dU}{dt} = L_1 i_1 \frac{di_1}{dt} + L_2 i_2 \frac{di_2}{dt} + M i_1 \frac{di_2}{dt} + M i_2 \frac{di_1}{dt} + i_1 i_2 \frac{dM}{dt},$$

where we have kept L_1 and L_2 constant since the circuits are rigid. Now the work performed per unit time by the external sources of energy is equal to the sum of the rate $\mathscr{F}_\xi \frac{d\xi}{dt}$ at which mechanical work is done by the magnetic forces between the two circuits, the rate $\frac{dU}{dt}$ at which the magnetic energy of the pair of circuits increases, and the rate $R_1 i_1{}^2 + R_2 i_2{}^2$ at which energy is dissipated in heat. Consequently,

$$\frac{dW}{dt} = \mathscr{F}_\xi \frac{d\xi}{dt} + L_1 i_1 \frac{di_1}{dt} + L_2 i_2 \frac{di_2}{dt} + M i_1 \frac{di_2}{dt} + M i_2 \frac{di_1}{dt}$$

$$+ i_1 i_2 \frac{dM}{dt} + R_1 i_1{}^2 + R_2 i_2{}^2. \quad (95\text{-}3)$$

Equating (95-2) and (95-3),

$$\mathscr{F}_\xi \frac{d\xi}{dt} = i_1 i_2 \frac{dM}{dt}, \quad (95\text{-}4)$$

from which

$$\mathscr{F}_\xi = i_1 i_2 \frac{\partial M}{\partial \xi}. \quad (95\text{-}5)$$

If we are concerned with a torque instead of a force, the rate at which mechanical work is done when one of the circuits rotates through an angle $d\theta$ is $\mathscr{L}_\theta \frac{d\theta}{dt}$, where $\mathscr{L}_\theta$ is the torque about the axis of rotation. In this case we are led to the relation

$$\mathscr{L}_\theta \frac{d\theta}{dt} = i_1 i_2 \frac{dM}{dt},$$

or

$$\mathscr{L}_\theta = i_1 i_2 \frac{\partial M}{\partial \theta}, \quad (95\text{-}6)$$

for a pair of rigid circuits.

From these equations it is clear that the force or torque on the movable circuit is in such a direction as to increase M. Therefore, a circuit tends to move in such a way as to increase the flux of induction through it, the flux being taken as positive when in the direction of advance of a right-handed screw rotated in the sense in which the current is flowing. The position of stable equilibrium of the circuit is that for which the flux is a maximum, subject to whatever mechanical constraints may be imposed.

As the flux through the movable circuit (2), say, due to the other is

$$N = Mi_1,$$

we can put $i \equiv i_2$ and write (95-5) and (95-6) in the forms

$$\mathscr{F}_\xi = i\,\frac{\partial N}{\partial \xi}, \tag{95-7}$$

$$\mathscr{L}_\theta = i\,\frac{\partial N}{\partial \theta}, \tag{95-8}$$

where the change in flux represented by the derivative is that due to motion of the circuit alone and does not include any change in flux produced by time variation of the field. In other words, the change in flux involved is that which takes place when the current in the fixed circuit is kept constant.

Since the force or torque on the movable circuit may be considered as due to the magnetic field in its neighborhood, it makes no difference whether the flux N is produced by another circuit as we have supposed or by a magnet. In fact it may be due to a number of neighboring circuits and magnets acting together. Therefore, formulas (95-7) and (95-8)

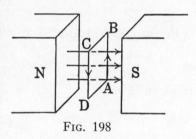

FIG. 198

are quite general in their applicability. If, for instance, a rectangular circuit $ABCD$ (Fig. 198) in which a current is flowing in the sense of the arrowheads is free to rotate in the gap between the poles of a magnet, the position of stable equilibrium is that in which the positive face of the circuit is turned toward the south pole and the negative face toward the north pole, as in the illustration. Hence the positive face of the circuit acts like the north pole of a magnet and the negative face like a south pole.

If the permeability of the medium in which the circuits are immersed is unity, $B = \mu_0 H$ and N in (95-7) and (95-8) is equal to μ_0 times the flux of magnetic intensity. Comparing with (41-5) and (41-6), we see that the force or torque on a current circuit in empty space is the same as that on a magnetic shell whose periphery coincides with the circuit and whose strength is equal to μ_0 times the current. From art. 70 such a magnetic shell produces the same field as the current at all outside points. Therefore, we have established the equivalence of a magnetic shell and a current circuit in empty space both as regards the field produced and the force or torque experienced under the action of an external field.

On the other hand, if a surrounding medium of permeability different from unity is present, N in (95-7) and (95-8) represents the flux of B whereas F in (41-5) and (41-6) stands for the flux of H. Nevertheless, the normal component of $\mu_0 H$ in the disk-shaped cavity in the medium occupied by the shell is equal to the normal component of B in the medium just outside the shell, and therefore to the component of B normal to the surface bounded by the circuit in the absence of the equivalent shell. So in this case too we have an exact equivalence both in the field produced and in the force or torque experienced.

Finally let us return to the problem of the interaction of two current circuits and consider the case where the electromotive forces $\mathscr{E}_1$ and $\mathscr{E}_2$ are chosen so as to keep the currents constant during the displacement $d\xi$ of the movable circuit. Then

$$\frac{dU}{dt} = i_1 i_2 \frac{dM}{dt},$$

and, comparing with (95-4), we conclude that the magnetic energy of the circuits increases at the same rate as that at which work is done by the mechanical force acting on the movable circuit. Hence, in addition to the work necessary to overcome resistance, the external e.m.f.'s supply energy at double the rate at which mechanical work is performed. This is known as *Kelvin's law*. The phenomenon is quite analogous to that discussed in art. 22 for the case of charged conductors, where it was shown that if the potentials of a set of conductors are kept constant during a displacement of one of them the electrostatic energy of the system increases at the same rate as that at which mechanical work is done, the sources of potential furnishing a double amount of energy.

Problem 95a. The center of a plane circular circuit of radius a consisting of one turn lies on the X axis at a distance x from the origin, the positive normal to the circuit being in the X direction. Find the force exerted on it by a radial field diverging from the origin of intensity $H = m/4\pi\mu_0 r^2$.

$$\text{Ans. } -\frac{mia^2}{2(a^2+x^2)^{3/2}}.$$

Problem 95b. Find the torque on the circuit of Fig. 198 for any angle θ between the normal to the circuit and the lines of force of the field. Assume that the coil has n turns of area A. Ans. $\mathscr{L}_\theta = -\mu_0 niHA \sin\theta$.

Problem 95c. The center O of a circular current of radius a lies at a distance R from the center C of a thin bar magnet of pole-strength m and length l, the line OC being parallel to the axis of the magnet and perpendicular to the plane of the circuit. Find the force between them.

$$\text{Ans. } -\frac{mia^2}{2}\left[\frac{1}{\left\{\left(R-\frac{l}{2}\right)^2+a^2\right\}^{3/2}} - \frac{1}{\left\{\left(R+\frac{l}{2}\right)^2+a^2\right\}^{3/2}}\right].$$

96. Calculation of Inductances. Both self and mutual inductance are manifestations of the interaction of currents and fields. Precise calculations of inductance in most practical cases are quite involved. Numerous examples of such calculations are given in publications of the Bureau of Standards, particularly in Scientific Papers No. 169 and in Circular No. 74. However, we may obtain approximate values of the inductance without difficulty in a number of useful cases.

Self-Inductance. We can deduce an approximate expression for the self-inductance of a straight solenoid of radius a and length l (Fig. 199) having n_l turns per unit length if we suppose that the field is uniform across the cross section of the solenoid and has the value given by (69-4)

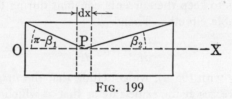

FIG. 199

for a point on the axis. Then at a point P at a distance x from the left end of the coil,

$$H = \frac{n_l i}{2} \{\cos \beta_2 + \cos (\pi - \beta_1)\}$$

$$= \frac{n_l i}{2} \left\{ \frac{x}{\sqrt{x^2 + a^2}} + \frac{l - x}{\sqrt{(l-x)^2 + a^2}} \right\},$$

and the flux through the $n_l dx$ turns in a length dx is

$$dN = \mu_0 H \cdot \pi a^2 n_l dx$$

$$= \frac{\pi \mu_0 n_l^2 a^2 i}{2} \left\{ \frac{x\,dx}{\sqrt{x^2 + a^2}} + \frac{(l-x)dx}{\sqrt{(l-x)^2 + a^2}} \right\}.$$

Integrating from 0 to l,

$$N = \frac{\pi \mu_0 n_l^2 a^2 i}{2} \left| \sqrt{x^2 + a^2} - \sqrt{(l-x)^2 + a^2} \right|_0^l$$

$$= \pi \mu_0 n_l^2 a^2 i \{\sqrt{l^2 + a^2} - a\}.$$

This gives for the self-inductance of the solenoid

$$L = \pi \mu_0 n_l^2 a^2 \{\sqrt{l^2 + a^2} - a\}, \tag{96-1}$$

an expression which is correct to within 2 percent if l is greater than $10a$.

For solenoids which are shorter in proportion to their radii Nagaoka has given the formula

$$L = \pi\mu_0 n_l{}^2 a^2 l K,$$ (96-2)

where K is a function of a/l which decreases from 1 to 0 as the argument increases from 0 to ∞ in accord with the curve of Fig. 200. A table

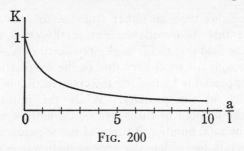

Fig. 200

of values of K may be found on page 283 of the Bureau of Standards Circular No. 74.

For the limiting case of a single circular turn of wire, which requires special treatment, the inductance is given by Kirchhoff's formula

$$L = \mu_0 a\left(\log \frac{8a}{w} - 1.75\right),$$ (96-3)

where a is the radius of the turn and w is the radius of the wire.

Mutual Inductance. Consider two solenoids one of which is wound outside the other as in Fig. 201. Suppose that the inner solenoid (*primary*) is very long whereas the outer (*secondary*) consists of a number of turns situated near the center of the primary. If i is the current in the primary and n_l the number of turns per unit length, the field far from the ends is

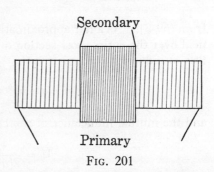

Fig. 201

$$H = n_l i$$

from (69-5), and if μ is the permeability of the core on which the primary is wound,

$$B = \mu_0\mu H = \mu_0\mu n_l i.$$

Consequently, if A is the cross section of the primary, the flux through each turn of the secondary is

$$N_c = BA = \mu_0\mu n_l A i,$$

and if the secondary has m turns the total flux linked is

$$N = mN_c = \mu_0\mu mn_l Ai.$$

Hence the (positive) mutual inductance of the two coils is

$$M = \mu_0\mu mn_l A. \tag{96-4}$$

This gives the flux through either coil due to unit current in the other. Observe that M is independent of the cross section of the secondary, for the field due to i is negligibly small outside the primary, and the flux through the secondary due to the current in the primary is not changed appreciably by making the cross section of the secondary greater than that of the primary. While the mutual inductance depends upon the number of turns per unit length of the primary, it depends upon the total number of turns of the secondary.

A pair of circuits for which the approximate value of the mutual inductance is easily calculated consists of two parallel coaxial circles (Fig. 202) a distance x apart, one of which has a radius b small compared with the radius a of the other. If a current i flows in the larger circuit, the field at the center P of the smaller is

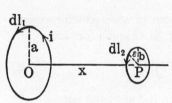

FIG. 202

$$H = \frac{ia^2}{2(a^2 + x^2)^{3/2}}$$

from (69-3). As a fair approximation we can take this to represent the field over the entire cross section of the smaller circle. Therefore, the flux of induction through it is

$$N = \mu_0 H \cdot \pi b^2 = \frac{\pi\mu_0 a^2 b^2}{2(a^2 + x^2)^{3/2}} i,$$

and the mutual inductance of the circuits is

$$M = \frac{\pi\mu_0 a^2 b^2}{2(a^2 + x^2)^{3/2}}. \tag{96-5}$$

If the coils contain more than one turn, this expression must be multiplied by the product of the number of turns in the two circuits.

In deducing (96-5) the currents have been supposed to flow in the same sense. This makes the mutual inductance, and therefore the flux through either circuit due to the other, positive in sign. Thus, as the circuits tend to move in such a direction as to increase the flux, the two currents attract each other. In general, *parallel currents flowing in the same direction attract, in opposite directions repel.*

A general expression which is fundamental in the calculation of inductances has been given by Neumann.   To deduce this formula we shall first compute the force exerted by one circuit on another.   Let dl_1 and dl_2 (Fig. 203) be elements of two circuits carrying currents i_1 and i_2 respectively.   Let θ be the angle between dl_1 and the position vector $\mathbf{r}$ of dl_2 relative to dl_1, and ϕ the angle between dl_2 and the plane of dl_1 and $\mathbf{r}$, which we shall take as the XY plane with the X axis in the direction of dl_1.   Further, let ψ be the angle which the projection

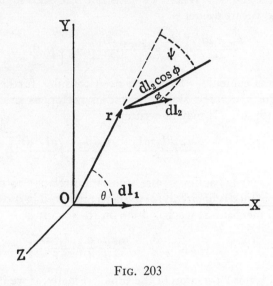

FIG. 203

$dl_2 \cos \phi$ of dl_2 on the XY plane makes with $\mathbf{r}$.   Then the magnetic field at dl_2 due to the current element $i_1 dl_1$ is

$$dH = k\,\frac{i_1 dl_1 \sin \theta}{4\pi r^2}$$

in the Z direction.

The force which this field exerts on the second current element is

$$d^2\mathscr{F} = \mu_0 i_2 dl_2 \times dH.$$

As $dl_2 = dl_2\{\boldsymbol{i}\cos\phi\cos(\theta-\psi) + \boldsymbol{j}\cos\phi\sin(\theta-\psi) + \boldsymbol{k}\sin\phi\}$ this expression becomes

$$d^2\mathscr{F} = \frac{\mu_0 i_1 i_2 dl_1 dl_2 \cos\phi}{4\pi r^2}\{\boldsymbol{i}\sin\theta\sin(\theta-\psi) - \boldsymbol{j}\sin\theta\cos(\theta-\psi)\}$$

$$= \frac{\mu_0 i_1 i_2 dl_1 dl_2 \cos\phi}{4\pi r^2}\{-\boldsymbol{i}\cos\theta\cos(\theta-\psi)$$

$$-\boldsymbol{j}\sin\theta\cos(\theta-\psi) + \boldsymbol{i}\cos\psi\}.$$

Now the angle ϵ between the two current elements is given by $\cos \epsilon = \cos \phi \cos (\theta - \psi)$ and the vector $\mathbf{r}$ is $\mathbf{r} = r \, (i \cos \theta + j \sin \theta)$. Also $dl_2 \cos \phi \cos \psi = dr$.   Hence

$$d^2\mathscr{F} = -\frac{\mu_0 i_1 i_2 dl_1 dl_2 \cos \epsilon}{4\pi r^2}\left(\frac{\mathbf{r}}{r}\right) + \frac{\mu_0 i_1 i_2 dl_1 dr}{4\pi r^2}i. \qquad (96\text{-}6)$$

To obtain the total force on the circuit of which dl_2 is an element due to the one of which dl_1 is an element, we must integrate this expression around both circuits.   When we integrate the second term around circuit (2), however, we get

$$\frac{\mu_0 i_1 i_2 dl_1}{4\pi}\oint \frac{dr}{r^2} = \frac{\mu_0 i_1 i_2 dl_1}{4\pi}\left| -\frac{1}{r} \right| = 0,$$

since the limits coincide.   Hence we need consider further only $d^2\mathscr{F}_r$, the portion of the force along the radius vector, as specified by the first term in (96-6).   It may be written

$$d^2\mathscr{F}_r = -\frac{\mu_0 i_1 i_2 d\mathbf{l}_1 \cdot d\mathbf{l}_2}{4\pi r^2} = \frac{\mu_0 i_1 i_2}{4\pi}\frac{\partial}{\partial r}\left(\frac{d\mathbf{l}_1 \cdot d\mathbf{l}_2}{r}\right). \qquad (96\text{-}7)$$

Now let circuit (2) suffer a pure translation relative to circuit (1) so that every element $d\mathbf{l}_2$ of circuit (2) remains unaltered in direction.   The rate at which mechanical work is done on the circuit is

$$d^2\mathscr{P}_m = d^2\mathscr{F}_r\frac{dr}{dt} = \frac{\mu_0 i_1 i_2}{4\pi}\frac{d}{dt}\left(\frac{d\mathbf{l}_1 \cdot d\mathbf{l}_2}{r}\right),$$

since $d\mathbf{l}_1 \cdot d\mathbf{l}_2$ is not a function of the time.   Finally, if we integrate first around one circuit and then around the other

$$\mathscr{P}_m = \frac{\mu_0 i_1 i_2}{4\pi}\frac{d}{dt}\oint\oint \frac{d\mathbf{l}_1 \cdot d\mathbf{l}_2}{r}.$$

Comparing this with (95-4), we obtain *Neumann's formula*

$$M = \frac{\mu_0}{4\pi}\oint\oint \frac{d\mathbf{l}_1 \cdot d\mathbf{l}_2}{r}. \qquad (96\text{-}8)$$

The symmetry of this expression shows at once that two circuits have but a single mutual inductance, i.e. $M_{12} = M_{21}$.   This formula enables us to calculate not only the mutual inductance of two circuits but also the self-inductance of a single circuit.   For we can consider a circuit to be made up of a bundle of current filaments, the self-inductance being the mutual inductance of the filaments with respect to one another.

By the use of Neumann's formula we may obtain a closer approximation than (96-5) for the mutual inductance of two parallel coaxial circles (Fig. 202) of radii a and b, without limiting ourselves to the case where b is small compared with a. From the figure we have

$$d\mathbf{l_1} \cdot d\mathbf{l_2} = dl_1 dl_2 \cos \epsilon = dl_1 b \cos \epsilon d\epsilon = b dl_1 \left(2 \cos^2 \frac{\epsilon}{2} - 1 \right) d\epsilon,$$

and the distance r between dl_1 and dl_2 is given by

$$r^2 = x^2 + (a - b \cos \epsilon)^2 + b^2 \sin^2 \epsilon$$

$$= x^2 + (a+b)^2 - 4ab \cos^2 \frac{\epsilon}{2}.$$

Putting

$$h^2 \equiv x^2 + (a+b)^2,$$

we have

$$r^2 = h^2 \left(1 - \frac{4ab}{h^2} \cos^2 \frac{\epsilon}{2} \right),$$

and expanding by the binomial

$$\frac{1}{r} = \frac{1}{h} \left(1 + 2 \frac{ab}{h^2} \cos^2 \frac{\epsilon}{2} + 6 \frac{a^2 b^2}{h^4} \cos^4 \frac{\epsilon}{2} + 20 \frac{a^3 b^3}{h^6} \cos^6 \frac{\epsilon}{2} + \cdots \right).$$

Therefore

$$M = \frac{\mu_0 b}{4\pi h} \oint dl_1 \oint \left(2 \cos^2 \frac{\epsilon}{2} - 1 \right) d\epsilon \left(1 + 2 \frac{ab}{h^2} \cos^2 \frac{\epsilon}{2} \right.$$

$$\left. + 6 \frac{a^2 b^2}{h^4} \cos^4 \frac{\epsilon}{2} + 20 \frac{a^3 b^3}{h^6} \cos^6 \frac{\epsilon}{2} + \cdots \right).$$

Integrating term by term,

$$M = \frac{\mu_0 ab^2}{4h^3} \oint dl_1 \left(1 + 3 \frac{ab}{h^2} + \frac{75}{8} \frac{a^2 b^2}{h^4} + \cdots \right)$$

$$= \frac{\pi \mu_0 a^2 b^2}{2h^3} \left(1 + 3 \frac{ab}{h^2} + \frac{75}{8} \frac{a^2 b^2}{h^4} + \cdots \right). \tag{96-9}$$

If b is neglected as compared with a, the first term of (96-9) is identical with (96-5).

Inductance of Straight Conductors. Fundamentally, inductance is a property of a complete circuit. However, it is often convenient to ascribe inductance to finite lengths of straight conductors in such a way that the inductance of a complete rectangular circuit, for instance, may be found by simple addition or subtraction of the component inductances.

To accomplish this, we may take as the self-inductance L of a straight conductor of length l and radius a (Fig. 204a) the flux per unit current which passes through a rectangular strip extending from the surface of the conductor to infinity.   Let this strip lie in the YZ plane as shown in the figure.   Expressing (69-7) in terms of the rectangular coordinates used here, the magnetic field normal to the YZ plane at the point P is

$$\frac{1}{4\pi z}\left\{\frac{l-y}{\sqrt{(l-y)^2+z^2}}+\frac{y}{\sqrt{y^2+z^2}}\right\}$$

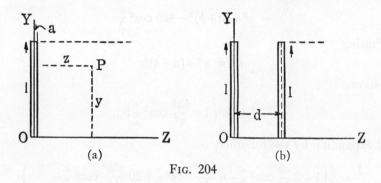

(a)   (b)

FIG. 204

per unit current.   Hence

$$L = \frac{\mu_0}{4\pi}\int_a^\infty\int_0^l\left\{\frac{l-y}{\sqrt{(l-y)^2+z^2}}+\frac{y}{\sqrt{y^2+z^2}}\right\}\frac{dy\,dz}{z}$$

$$= \frac{\mu_0}{2\pi}\int_a^\infty(\sqrt{l^2+z^2}-z)\frac{dz}{z}$$

$$= \frac{\mu_0}{2\pi}\left|\sqrt{l^2+z^2}-l\log\frac{l+\sqrt{l^2+z^2}}{z}-z\right|_a^\infty$$

$$= \frac{\mu_0 l}{2\pi}\left\{\log\frac{l+\sqrt{l^2+a^2}}{a}+\frac{a-\sqrt{l^2+a^2}}{l}\right\}. \tag{96-10}$$

Strictly speaking, (96-10) is correct for a thin tube of radius a rather than a solid conductor, since we have not included the flux inside the conductor.   Calculation shows that the mean value of this internal flux is $\mu_0 l/8\pi$ if the current is distributed uniformly over the cross section of the conductor, so we have more exactly

$$L = \frac{\mu_0 l}{2\pi}\left\{\log\frac{l+\sqrt{l^2+a^2}}{a}+\frac{a-\sqrt{l^2+a^2}}{l}+\frac{1}{4}\right\}. \tag{96-11}$$

Similarly, we may take as the mutual inductance M of two thin parallel conductors of length l and separation d (Fig. 204b) the flux per unit current in one which passes through a strip of width l extending from the other to infinity.   To find the flux we need only replace a by d in (96-10), obtaining

$$M = \frac{\mu_0 l}{2\pi}\left\{\log\frac{l+\sqrt{l^2+d^2}}{d}+\frac{d-\sqrt{l^2+d^2}}{l}\right\}. \tag{96-12}$$

As an application of (96-11) and (96-12) we shall calculate the self-inductance of a square circuit whose sides are conductors of length l and radius $a \ll l$.   Since the currents in opposite sides of the square are in opposite directions the mutual inductance of each side must be subtracted from the self-inductance of the opposite side.   Setting $d=l$ in (96-12), the total inductance of the square is

$$L_S = 4(L-M) = \frac{2\mu_0 l}{\pi}\left(\log\frac{l}{a}+\frac{a}{l}-0.52\right) \tag{96-13}$$

to a sufficient degree of approximation.   Formulas (96-11) and (96-12) are useful also in estimating the amount of inductance in a circuit due to connecting wires and instrument leads, a matter of importance at high frequencies.

The form of the inductance formulas above is of interest in connection with the physical dimensions of the quantity μ_0.   Although μ_0 is a pure number according to our definition (art. 37), it is clear that its unit can be called the *henry per meter*.   This designation has the advantage that it is similar to the corresponding designation in the case of κ_0 (art. 18).

Problem 96a.   An air solenoid of radius 2 cm and length 50 cm has 400 turns. A secondary of 200 turns, radius 2.5 cm and length 25 cm is wound around it so that the centers of the two windings coincide.   Find the self-inductance of each coil and the mutual inductance of the pair.   Ans. 0.49 millihenry, 0.36 millihenry, 0.25 millihenry.

Problem 96b.   A ring of mean radius b and cross-sectional radius a is surrounded by two windings: a primary of n turns and a secondary of m turns. Find the mutual inductance of the two circuits, using the result of problem *89b*. Ans. $M = \mu_0\mu nm(b-\sqrt{b^2-a^2})$.

Problem 96c.   Two parallel coaxial circles of the same radius a are a distance $7.75a$ apart.   Compute their mutual inductance.   Ans. $0.0101\frac{\mu_0 a}{\pi}$.

Problem 96d.   Find the force between two circular coaxial currents i_1 and i_2 of radii a and b a distance x apart, using (96-9).

Ans. $-\frac{3\pi\mu_0 a^2 b^2 i_1 i_2}{2h^5}x\left\{1+5\frac{ab}{h^2}+21.875\frac{a^2b^2}{h^4}+\cdots\right\}.$

Problem 96e.   Two square circuits constitute opposite faces of a cube each of whose edges has the length l.   Find the mutual inductance of the two circuits. Ans. $0.253\frac{\mu_0 l}{\pi}$.

97. Examples of Electromagnetic Reactions. Here we shall discuss some specific examples of the theory developed in the preceding articles. First we shall deduce Lenz's law.

Lenz's Law. Consider a turn of wire placed in a magnetic field. If we move it in such a way as to increase the flux through it as illustrated in Fig. 205a, a current is induced in such a sense as to give rise to an

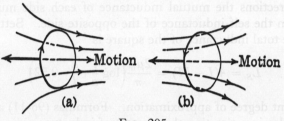

FIG. 205

oppositely directed flux. Therefore, the left-hand face of the circuit is positive relative to the sense in which the current is flowing and the force exerted on the circuit by the magnetic field is in the direction to produce a displacement which will increase the flux from right to left or decrease the flux from left to right. That is, the magnetic force is in the opposite sense to the motion. The same is true if the circuit is moved so as to decrease the flux as in Fig. 205b, and the reader can easily show that similar conclusions are reached regarding the torque in the case of rotation. *In all cases the induced current is in such a direction as to oppose the motion which generates it.* This is known as *Lenz's law.*

A striking application of Lenz's law is afforded by the copper pendulum (Fig. 206). This consists of a copper plate C suspended from O so that it can swing back and forth between the poles N, S of a large electromagnet. The pendulum is set swinging while the magnet is unexcited. If, now, the switch controlling the current in the magnet coils is closed, induced currents—known as *eddy currents*—are set up in the moving copper plate in such directions as to oppose the motion of the pendulum. Consequently the latter, which may be moving with considerable speed at the instant

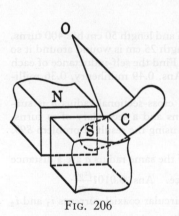

FIG. 206

the magnet is excited, is brought almost to a standstill and slowly sinks to its equilibrium position.

The energy of the pendulum is converted into heat through the agency of the eddy currents set up by its motion through the magnetic field. These eddy currents have the further effect of giving rise to a flux opposed to that of the magnet and thereby diminishing the flux which passes through the surface of the copper plate. This shielding effect is greater the less the resistance of the plate, a perfect conductor constituting a complete shield against variations in the magnetic field.

Electromagnetic Shielding. To illustrate more fully the phenomenon of *electromagnetic shielding*, consider a solenoid L (Fig. 207) through which an alternating current $i_0 \sin \omega t$ is flowing and a neighboring loop of wire A near which is placed a parallel metal plate C. If we suppose the latter to be a perfect conductor, the e.m.f. around every closed curve lying entirely inside it must vanish. Therefore, the change of flux through such a curve due to the varying current in L must be compensated by an equal and opposite change of flux produced by the eddy currents in the plate. As the resultant variation of flux is zero inside the plate, it is very small near the plate. So if A is placed close to C—it makes little difference whether it is on the one side or the other—there is very little variation of flux through A and therefore only a very small induced e.m.f.

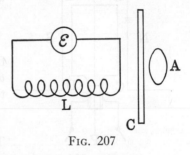

FIG. 207

If instead of a finite plate C a perfectly conducting shell is constructed so as to entirely surround L, the region outside is completely shielded from the varying flux produced by the alternating current in the solenoid. Actually the shielding is never complete since even the best conductors have some resistance.

On account of the dissipation of energy in heat through the production of eddy currents it is important to have no large pieces of metal in the neighborhood of electrical machines or instruments which make use of e.m.f.'s induced by varying flux. To avoid electromagnetic shielding and reduce eddy currents to a minimum, the iron cores used in transformers and in the armatures of a-c generators and motors are laminated, that is, cut into disks or sheets insulated from one another by shellac or paint. The particular type of lamination employed in each case is that which gives the least opportunity for the generation of eddy currents. Thus to reduce eddy currents in the copper pendulum, we might laminate the plate into narrow strips parallel to its longest edge.

Direct-Current Motor. In the simplest type of d-c motor an armature consisting of a number of rectangular coils wound at different orientations around a cylindrical soft iron core rotates in the space between the poles of a large magnet. By means of a commutator the current i is allowed to pass through only the one coil which is in a position to exert the greatest torque at the instant considered, that is, the one which has its face parallel to the field. We need, therefore, to consider only one rectangular coil *CDEF* (Fig. 208) rotating about an axis *PQ* between the two poles of the field magnet. If it contains n turns and has an area A, the flux through it due to the external field when the normal to the plane of the coil makes an angle θ with the lines of force is

$$N = nBA \cos \theta, \qquad (97\text{-}1)$$

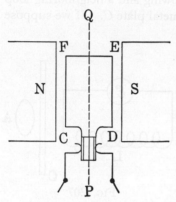

FIG. 208

and the torque is

$$i \frac{dN}{d\theta} = -niBA \sin \theta$$

from (95-8), which is greatest when $\theta = \pi/2$, as stated above. The steady torque on the armature, then, is

$$\mathscr{L} = -niBA. \qquad (97\text{-}2)$$

The minus sign indicates that the torque is in the opposite sense to that in which θ is measured.

On account of its motion through the field, however, an e.m.f.

$$-\frac{dN}{dt} = nBA\omega \sin \theta$$

is induced in the coil. Since the coil under consideration is connected to the external circuit through the commutator only when $\theta = \pi/2$, we have a steady e.m.f. generated of amount

$$\mathscr{E}' = nBA\omega. \qquad (97\text{-}3)$$

As the coil rotates in the sense of the torque, $\omega = \dfrac{d\theta}{dt}$ is negative and

the induced e.m.f. opposes the current, as might have been predicted from Lenz's law. Since $\mathscr{E}'$ is negative, it is more convenient to consider the positive reverse e.m.f. $\mathscr{E}_r' = -\mathscr{E}'$ acting in the opposite sense to the current. This e.m.f. is called the *counter electromotive force* of the motor. If $\mathscr{E}$ is the applied e.m.f. and R the resistance of the circuit, we have

$$\mathscr{E} - \mathscr{E}_r' = Ri \qquad (97\text{-}4)$$

from Ohm's law.   If R is small, the current is large when the motor is starting since ω and therefore $\mathscr{E}_r{}'$ are then small.   To avoid an excessive current, a starting rheostat is placed in the circuit.   By this means an additional resistance is connected in the circuit until the motor has come up to speed.   If the motor is carrying no load and the frictional resistance to the motion of the armature is negligible, the speed will increase until $\mathscr{E}_r{}'$ becomes equal to $\mathscr{E}$ and i vanishes.

Energy is developed by the applied e.m.f. at the rate $\mathscr{E}i$, converted into mechanical work in the motor at the rate $\mathscr{E}_r{}'i$ and dissipated in heat at the rate Ri^2.   To secure great efficiency the resistance of the circuit must be as little as possible.

Electromagnetic Repulsion.   Consider a circular ring C (Fig. 209) of heavy copper wire placed above an electromagnet K which is connected to an alternating electromotive force $\mathscr{E}$.   Denoting the current in K by

$$i_1 = i_0 \cos \omega t$$

and the mutual inductance of the two circuits by M, the flux through C due to the electromagnet is

$$N = Mi_1.$$

The induced e.m.f. in the ring, then, is

$$\mathscr{E}_2 = -\frac{dN}{dt} = M\omega i_0 \sin \omega t,$$

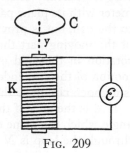

Fig. 209

and according to (89-12) this gives rise to a current

$$i_2 = \frac{M\omega i_0}{Z_2} \sin (\omega t - \phi_2), \qquad \tan \phi_2 \equiv \frac{L_2\omega}{R_2},$$

in C, where L_2 is the self-inductance, R_2 the resistance and Z_2 the impedance of the ring.   Making use of (95-5) the upward force on C is

$$\mathscr{F}_y = \frac{M\omega i_0{}^2}{Z_2} \sin (\omega t - \phi_2) \cos \omega t \frac{\partial M}{\partial y}. \qquad (97\text{-}5)$$

As the distance y of the ring from the electromagnet increases, M decreases.   Therefore $\dfrac{\partial M}{\partial y}$ is negative and we may write

$$\mathscr{F}_y = -A \sin (\omega t - \phi_2) \cos \omega t,$$

where A is a positive quantity.   Averaging over a period,

$$\overline{\sin (\omega t - \phi_2) \cos \omega t} = \overline{\sin \omega t \cos \omega t} \cos \phi_2 - \overline{\cos^2 \omega t} \sin \phi_2$$
$$= -\tfrac{1}{2} \sin \phi_2.$$

Therefore the mean force is positive. If R_2 is small and ω large, the force may easily be of such magnitude that the ring is thrown a meter or more up into the air when the alternating current is first turned on in the magnet coil. Decreasing R_2 increases the force both by making the impedance of the ring less and the lag ϕ_2 greater.

Problem 97a. How should the armature core of the d-c motor described in this article be laminated in order to minimize the production of eddy currents?

Problem 97b. Find the torque on the moving coil galvanometer of art. 73 by the method used in this article.

Problem 97c. Each coil in the armature of a d-c motor consists of 100 turns of 200 cm² cross section. The magnetic induction is 0.4 weber per meter² and the applied e.m.f. 110 volts. Find the counter e.m.f. at 1200 r.p.m. If the resistance of the circuit is 1 ohm what power is developed? Ans. 100.5 volt, 955 watt.

98. Galvanometer Damping.

A single loop of heavy copper wire is generally attached to the moving part of a d'Arsonval galvanometer with its plane parallel to the coil. It is not connected electrically to the coil, but is provided for the purpose of damping the oscillations of the moving part through the agency of the currents induced by its rotation in the field of the fixed magnet. We shall discuss first the motion of the suspended part of the instrument when the galvanometer is on open circuit so that there is no current in the coil.

If A is the area of the loop, H the field in which it swings, and α the angle which the plane of the loop makes with the lines of force, the flux through the loop is $N = \mu_0 HA \sin \alpha$. As the loop rotates an induced e.m.f.

$$\mathscr{E} = -\frac{dN}{dt} = -\mu_0 HA \cos \alpha \frac{d\alpha}{dt}$$

is set up in it. In calculating the induced current we can omit the term in the equation of the circuit which involves the self-inductance of the loop, for the time rate of change of current is so small for the slow oscillations we are concerned with here that this term is inappreciable as compared with the others. Hence the current is the quotient of $\mathscr{E}$ by the resistance R_0 of the loop, that is,

$$i = -\frac{\mu_0 HA}{R_0} \cos \alpha \frac{d\alpha}{dt}.$$

The torque due to the induced current is

$$\mathscr{L}_\alpha = i \frac{dN}{d\alpha} = -\frac{(\mu_0 HA)^2}{R_0} \cos^2 \alpha \frac{d\alpha}{dt}, \tag{98-1}$$

the negative sign indicating that the torque opposes the motion which produces it, in accord with Lenz's law.

In addition the moving coil is subject to a torque of restitution $-k\alpha$ due to the torsion of the suspension and a torque $-b\dfrac{d\alpha}{dt}$ due to air damping. So if $\mathscr{I}$ is the moment of inertia of the moving part, the equation of motion is

$$\mathscr{I}\frac{d^2\alpha}{dt^2} = -k\alpha - b\frac{d\alpha}{dt} - \frac{(\mu_0 HA)^2}{R_0}\cos^2\alpha\,\frac{d\alpha}{dt}.$$

If the deflection is small or the field radial (art. 73) we can replace $\cos^2\alpha$ by unity. Then,

$$\mathscr{I}\frac{d^2\alpha}{dt^2} + \left\{ b + \frac{(\mu_0 HA)^2}{R_0} \right\}\frac{d\alpha}{dt} + k\alpha = 0. \tag{98-2}$$

Since this equation is linear with constant coefficients, the solution is of the form $e^{\gamma t}$ multiplied by an arbitrary constant. On substituting this in (98-2) we find that γ is given by

$$\gamma = -\frac{b + \dfrac{(\mu_0 HA)^2}{R_0}}{2\mathscr{I}} \pm \frac{\sqrt{\left\{ b + \dfrac{(\mu_0 HA)^2}{R_0} \right\}^2 - 4\mathscr{I}k}}{2\mathscr{I}}.$$

As ordinarily designed the constants of the instrument are such that the expression under the radical is negative. Consequently, the two values of γ are complex, and, as shown in art. 91, the solution has the periodic form

$$\alpha = \alpha_0 e^{-lt}\sin(\omega_0 t + \epsilon), \tag{98-3}$$

where

$$l \equiv \frac{1}{2\mathscr{I}}\left\{ b + \frac{(\mu_0 HA)^2}{R_0} \right\}. \tag{98-4}$$

The moving part of the galvanometer, then, oscillates about its position of equilibrium with rapidly decreasing amplitude. Since air resistance is small, by far the greater part of the damping is due to electromagnetic action in the loop. That this is so can easily be observed by removing the loop from the instrument, when it is found that the coil, upon being set into motion, takes much longer to come to rest. If the coil, instead of being on open circuit, is connected to a constant source of e.m.f., the damping under consideration brings it rapidly to rest in the position for reading. In this case induced currents are set up in the coil as well as in the loop, thus increasing the electromagnetic damping.

If the loop is removed and the instrument is connected to an external resistance, electromagnetic damping is produced by the currents induced in the oscillating coil alone.   If the coil has n turns of area A, (98-4) becomes

$$l \equiv \frac{1}{2\mathscr{I}}\left\{b+\frac{(\mu_0 nHA)^2}{R}\right\}, \qquad (98\text{-}5)$$

where R is the resistance of the coil and the external circuit.   The coefficient $(\mu_0 nHA)^2$ of $1/R$ is just $(k/K_i)^2$ in terms of the symbols of (73-8).   Although the resistance of the coil of a d'Arsonval galvano-meter is generally about 100 ohms, the number of turns is so great that the electromagnetic damping due to the short-circuited coil alone is of the same order of magnitude as that due to the loop.   By putting different external resistances in series with the coil after the loop has been removed and determining l experimentally, the straight line of

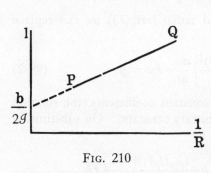

FIG. 210

Fig. 210 is obtained, confirming the formula (98-5) for l.   Extending PQ to the axis of ordinates, the damping due to air resistance only is obtained.

So far we have confined our attention to the moving coil galvano-meter.   Now we shall calculate the damping of the moving needle type. The change in flux through the fixed coil to be considered in this case is that due to the motion of the needle at its center.   First we must compute the flux N_c through a circle AB (Fig. 211) of radius a due to a pole m lying near the axis of the circle at a distance h from its plane.   Provided $h \ll a$, we may perform the calculation as if m lay exactly on the axis of the circle without appreciable error.   The field at P is

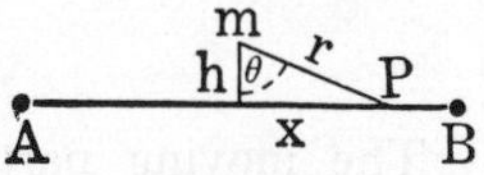

FIG. 211

$$H = \frac{m}{4\pi\mu_0 r^2} = \frac{m}{4\pi\mu_0(x^2+h^2)},$$

and, as we want the flux from below to above,

$$N_c = -\int_0^a (\mu_0 H \cos\theta)2\pi x\,dx = -\frac{mh}{2}\int_0^a \frac{x\,dx}{(x^2+h^2)^{3/2}}$$

since $\cos\theta = h/\sqrt{x^2+h^2}$.   Consequently

$$N_c = -\frac{m}{2}\left\{1-\frac{h}{\sqrt{a^2+h^2}}\right\}.$$

The south pole being an equal distance below AB, the flux through the circle due to the two poles is $2N_c$. In addition to this there is an upward flux m in the interior of the needle. Hence the total flux through the n turns in the coil is

$$N = \frac{nmh}{\sqrt{a^2 + h^2}},$$

and the induced e.m.f. is

$$\mathcal{E} = -\frac{dN}{dt} = -\frac{nma^2}{(a^2 + h^2)^{3/2}} \frac{dh}{dt}$$

$$= -\frac{nm}{a} \frac{dh}{dt},$$

since h is negligible compared with a. Now if d is the length of the needle and α the angle which it makes with the plane of the coil,

$$h = \frac{d}{2} \sin \alpha, \qquad \frac{dh}{dt} = \frac{d}{2} \cos \alpha \frac{d\alpha}{dt},$$

and

$$\mathcal{E} = -\frac{np}{2a} \cos \alpha \frac{d\alpha}{dt},$$

where p is the magnetic moment md of the needle. The current induced by this e.m.f. in the fixed coil is

$$i = \frac{\mathcal{E}}{R} = -\frac{np}{2aR} \cos \alpha \frac{d\alpha}{dt},$$

where R is the resistance of the coil and the external circuit.

This gives rise to a field

$$H = \frac{ni}{2a} = -\frac{n^2 p}{4a^2 R} \cos \alpha \frac{d\alpha}{dt}$$

at the center of the coil, which exerts a damping torque

$$\mathcal{L}_\alpha = pH \cos \alpha = -\left(\frac{np}{2a}\right)^2 \frac{1}{R} \cos^2 \alpha \frac{d\alpha}{dt} \qquad (98\text{-}6)$$

on the needle.

This relation applies directly to the tangent galvanometer but it holds also for the astatic galvanometer, provided n represents the total number of turns in both coils and R includes the total resistance.

Comparing (98-6) with (98-1), we see that for the astatic galvanometer

$$l \equiv \frac{1}{2\mathcal{I}} \left\{ b + \left(\frac{np}{2a}\right)^2 \frac{1}{R} \right\}. \qquad (98\text{-}7)$$

The coefficient $(np/2a)^2$ of $1/R$ is the ratio $(k/K_i)^2$ of the symbols appearing in (73-7). Expressed in terms of the galvanometer constant, then, equation (98-7) is identical with (98-5). However, the magnitude of the damping constant is not the same in the two cases. It is, in general, much smaller for astatic galvanometers than for d'Arsonval galvanometers.

Problem 98. Show that (98–6) is valid for the astatic galvanometer, as stated in the text.

99. Induction Coil.

This instrument consists essentially of a primary and a secondary, the latter wound outside the former on a longitudinally laminated iron core. A constant electromotive force $\mathscr{E}_1$ is suddenly inserted in the primary circuit and then suddenly removed. By making the number of turns in the secondary much greater than in the primary a momentary e.m.f. much greater than $\mathscr{E}_1$ may be induced in the former. We have here a special case of coupled circuits, which are discussed in more detail in Chapter XV.

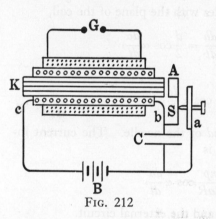

FIG. 212

The induction coil is illustrated schematically in Fig. 212. The primary circuit contains the battery B and the capacitor C which is placed in parallel with a *current interrupter*. The capacitor is employed primarily to prevent the formation of a spark when the circuit is broken. However, it also has the important function of making the discharge current oscillatory. The interrupter consists of a soft iron armature A on the end of the spring S. When growing, the primary current follows the path $cbSa$, but after it has reached a certain magnitude the soft iron core K of the coil becomes sufficiently magnetized to draw A toward it and break the circuit at S. The primary current now is constrained to follow the path cbC, charging the capacitor. In this way oscillations are set up which last until the current has decayed to the point where K loses enough of its magnetization to release A and allow contact at S to be renewed.

Generally the growth of the primary current is not sufficiently rapid to produce an e.m.f. in the secondary great enough to cause a spark to jump the gap G. On the other hand the decay, because of the action of the interrupter, is much more rapid, resulting in a greater rate of change of current in the primary and therefore a sufficiently great e.m.f. in the secondary to cause a spark.

In order to investigate the essential characteristics of the circuits after the break of the primary current without becoming involved in too lengthy an analysis, we shall neglect the small resistance of the primary. The resistance of the secondary, on the other hand, is large and must be taken into account. We have then for the equation of the primary after the break

$$L_1\frac{di_1}{dt} + M\frac{di_2}{dt} + \frac{q_1}{C_1} = \mathscr{E}_1, \tag{99-1}$$

where M is the mutual inductance. This can be expressed in terms of the currents alone if we differentiate with respect to the time and put i_1 for $\frac{dq_1}{dt}$. Then we have for the two circuits

$$L_1\frac{d^2i_1}{dt^2} + M\frac{d^2i_2}{dt^2} + \frac{1}{C_1}i_1 = 0, \tag{99-2}$$

$$L_2\frac{di_2}{dt} + M\frac{di_1}{dt} + R_2i_2 = 0, \tag{99-3}$$

since $\mathscr{E}_1$ in (99-1) is the constant e.m.f. of the battery B.

Differentiating (99-2) with respect to the time,

$$L_1\frac{d^3i_1}{dt^3} + M\frac{d^3i_2}{dt^3} + \frac{1}{C_1}\frac{di_1}{dt} = 0,$$

and from (99-3),

$$M\frac{di_1}{dt} = -L_2\frac{di_2}{dt} - R_2i_2,$$

$$M\frac{d^3i_1}{dt^3} = -L_2\frac{d^3i_2}{dt^3} - R_2\frac{d^2i_2}{dt^2}.$$

Using the last pair to eliminate i_1 from the previous equation,

$$(L_1L_2 - M^2)\frac{d^3i_2}{dt^3} + R_2L_1\frac{d^2i_2}{dt^2} + \frac{L_2}{C_1}\frac{di_2}{dt} + \frac{R_2}{C_1}i_2 = 0.$$

The solution is of the form $e^{\gamma t}$ multiplied by an arbitrary constant, where γ is a root of the equation

$$a\gamma^3 + b\gamma^2 + c\gamma + d = 0, \tag{99-4}$$

the positive constants a, b, c, d being

$$a \equiv L_1L_2 - M^2, \qquad b \equiv R_2L_1, \qquad c \equiv \frac{L_2}{C_1}, \qquad d \equiv \frac{R_2}{C_1}.$$

Now the cubic (99-4) has one real negative root, as the function of γ on the left changes sign between $\gamma = -\infty$ and $\gamma = 0$. The magnitudes of the constants involved in the problem under consideration are such that the two remaining roots are conjugate complex quantities, the real part of each being negative. So if we denote the three roots by $-\gamma_1$, $-\alpha + i\omega_0$, $-\alpha - i\omega_0$,

$$i_2 = Ae^{-\gamma_1 t} + e^{-\alpha t}(A_1 e^{i\omega_0 t} + A_2 e^{-i\omega_0 t}).$$

As is shown in art. 91 this can be written

$$i_2 = Ae^{-\gamma_1 t} + A_0 e^{-\alpha t} \sin(\omega_0 t + \epsilon). \tag{99-5}$$

If we count time from the instant of breaking the primary circuit,

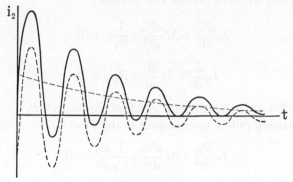

FIG. 213

$i_2 = 0$ when $t = 0$. Therefore $A + A_0 \sin \epsilon = 0$. The current is given by (99-5) as the sum of an exponentially decreasing term and a damped harmonic oscillation. These two components are represented by broken lines in Fig. 213, their sum being given by the solid line. Actual oscillograms of the current in the secondary of an induction coil conform quite closely to the theoretical curve which we have deduced, when the secondary terminals are connected by a constant high resistance. When they are not so connected and a spark is produced, the resistance of the gap decreases materially after the initial discharge and the current curve is somewhat distorted although it retains the essential features of the graph depicted in the figure.

REFERENCE

Shire, *Classical Electricity and Magnetism* (Cambridge Univ. Press, 1960). Pp. 173–181.

Chapter XI

FLUX MEASUREMENTS

100. Ballistic Galvanometers. It is often desirable to measure the total quantity of electricity passing through a circuit due to a momentary current. For instance, if a capacitor of capacitance C charged to a potential difference V is allowed to discharge, a quantity of electricity $Q = CV$ passes through the circuit connecting its plates. By measuring Q we may determine C, if V is known.

A more important case occurs in measurements involving magnetic induction. Consider a coil through which the flux of induction due to external sources changes suddenly from N_1 to N_2. During the short interval in which the flux is changing there is an induced e.m.f. $-\dfrac{dN}{dt}$ and if the coil forms part of a circuit whose total self-inductance is L and total resistance is R there is a momentary current i given by

$$L\frac{di}{dt} + Ri = -\frac{dN}{dt}.$$

Therefore, integrating over the time during which the current flows, the charge passing through the circuit is

$$Q = \int i\,dt = -\frac{1}{R}\left\{ L \int_0^0 di + \int_{N_1}^{N_2} dN \right\}.$$

This reduces to

$$Q = \frac{N_1 - N_2}{R}, \tag{100-1}$$

so that determination of flux may be made to depend on measurement of charge.

A *ballistic galvanometer* is one designed to measure the quantity of electricity passing through it in terms of the amplitude of the mechanical oscillation produced by the momentary current. An ordinary instrument of either the moving needle or the moving coil type, such as are described in art. 73, may be used ballistically provided it has a period of oscillation long compared with the duration of the momentary

337

current, and provided the damping of the moving element is not too great. On account of the second requirement the damping loop (art. 98) of a d'Arsonval galvanometer must be removed before it is used to measure charge. Also, if the galvanometer is used in a low resistance circuit, it may be necessary to break the circuit immediately after the passage of the charge and before the moving element has suffered an appreciable deflection. Although ordinary galvanometers are usually satisfactory for the measurement of charge as well as of current, special ballistic galvanometers with longer period are available for precise work.

To investigate the ballist behavior of a galvanometer, let $\mathcal{I}$ be the moment of inertia of the moving part and α its angular deflection.   Then its equation of motion is

$$\mathcal{I}\frac{d^2\alpha}{dt^2} = -f(\alpha) - b'\frac{d\alpha}{dt} + g(\alpha)\,i, \qquad (100\text{-}2)$$

where $f(\alpha)$ is the restoring torque, $b'\frac{d\alpha}{dt}$ is the total damping torque, and $g(\alpha)\,i$ is the deflecting torque due to the current i.   In the case of the tangent galvanometer $f(\alpha)$ is the torque $pH_t \sin \alpha$ exerted by the control field on the needle, whereas with the astatic or the moving coil galvanometer $f(\alpha)$ is the torque $k\alpha$ due to the suspension.   The quantity b', which includes both mechanical and electromagnetic damping, reduces to b (art. 98) when the latter effect is absent.

We consider first the short interval τ during which the momentary current i passes through the instrument.   During this time the moving part acquires momentum from the impulse given to it by the current, but, on account of its long period, its deflection $\Delta\alpha$ is only a negligible fraction of that which it acquires after the current ceases to flow.   So, integrating (100-2),

$$\mathcal{I}\frac{d\alpha}{dt} = -\int_\tau f(\alpha)\,dt - b'\Delta\alpha + \int_\tau g(\alpha)\,idt$$

$$= -f(0)\int_\tau dt - b'\Delta\alpha + g(0)\int_\tau idt,$$

where we have replaced α by 0 in the functions f and g since the deflection during the short interval of time under consideration is quite negligible.   Now $f(0)$ is zero for all types of instrument.   Therefore the first term on the right vanishes.   Next, the second term is inappreciable on account of the smallness of $\Delta\alpha$.   So, as the charge passing through the instrument is

$$Q = \int_\tau idt,$$

we have for the angular velocity acquired

$$\frac{d\alpha}{dt} = GQ, \qquad G \equiv \frac{g(0)}{\mathscr{I}}. \qquad (100\text{-}3)$$

For the tangent galvanometer $g(0) = np/2a \equiv pH_t/K_i$ by (73-1), K_i being the galvanometer constant, and

$$G = \frac{pH_t}{K_i\mathscr{I}}. \qquad (100\text{-}4)$$

For the astatic moving needle galvanometer, on the other hand, $g(0) = np/2a \equiv k/K_i$ in accord with (73-7). Hence

$$G = \frac{k}{K_i\mathscr{I}}. \qquad (100\text{-}5)$$

Finally, for the moving coil type, $g(0) = \mu_0 nHA \equiv k/K_i$ by (73-8), where n is the number of turns in the moving coil, A the area of each and H the field of the fixed magnet. So the constant G is given by (100-5) for this instrument as well.

Next we must consider the motion after the current has ceased to flow. As $i = 0$, (100-2) becomes

$$\mathscr{I}\frac{d^2\alpha}{dt^2} + b'\frac{d\alpha}{dt} + f(\alpha) = 0, \qquad (100\text{-}6)$$

subject to the initial conditions $\alpha = 0$ and $\dfrac{d\alpha}{dt} = GQ$ when $t = 0$. In discussing this part of the motion we must treat the different types of galvanometer separately, since $f(\alpha)$ has different functional forms in the different cases.

Tangent Galvanometer. In order to arrive at a simple solution we shall suppose that the damping is negligible. Then (100-6) becomes

$$\mathscr{I}\frac{d^2\alpha}{dt^2} + pH_t \sin\alpha = 0. \qquad (100\text{-}7)$$

Multiplying by $\dfrac{d\alpha}{dt}dt$ and integrating we get

$$\frac{1}{2}\mathscr{I}\left(\frac{d\alpha}{dt}\right)^2 = pH_t \cos\alpha + \text{cons.}$$

Determining the constant of integration then by means of the initial conditions given in connection with (100-6), we obtain

$$G^2Q^2 - \left(\frac{d\alpha}{dt}\right)^2 = 2\frac{pH_t}{\mathscr{I}}(1 - \cos\alpha)$$

$$= 4\frac{pH_t}{\mathscr{I}}\sin^2\frac{\alpha}{2}.$$

We observe the amplitude α_0 of the oscillation, which is known technically as the *throw* of the galvanometer. Since $\frac{d\alpha}{dt} = 0$ when $\alpha = \alpha_0$, the charge Q which has passed through the instrument is given in terms of the throw by the equation

$$Q = \frac{2}{G}\sqrt{\frac{pH_t}{\mathscr{I}}}\sin\frac{\alpha_0}{2}$$

$$= 2K_i\sqrt{\frac{\mathscr{I}}{pH_t}}\sin\frac{\alpha_0}{2}. \tag{100-8}$$

Now, for small oscillations of the needle (100-7) becomes

$$\mathscr{I}\frac{d^2\alpha}{dt^2} + pH_t\alpha = 0,$$

since we may replace $\sin\alpha$ by α itself. This is simple harmonic motion with the period

$$P_0 = 2\pi\sqrt{\frac{\mathscr{I}}{pH_t}}.$$

Therefore, we may write (100-8) in the form

$$Q = \frac{P_0 K_i}{\pi}\sin\frac{\alpha_0}{2}, \tag{100-9}$$

which becomes

$$Q = K_q\alpha_0, \qquad K_q \equiv \frac{P_0 K_i}{2\pi}, \tag{100-10}$$

if the throw is small. This type of ballistic galvanometer is an absolute instrument since K_i and the period P_0 may be determined by direct measurement. It must be remembered that P_0 is the period for small oscillations; if the amplitude is considerable, the period observed is greater than P_0.

Astatic and Moving Coil Instruments. In either of these cases (100-6) becomes

$$\mathscr{I}\frac{d^2\alpha}{dt^2} + b'\frac{d\alpha}{dt} + k\alpha = 0. \tag{100-11}$$

Dividing by $\mathscr{I}$ and putting

$$2l \equiv \frac{b'}{\mathscr{I}}, \qquad \kappa^2 \equiv \frac{k}{\mathscr{I}},$$

it takes the simpler form

$$\frac{d^2\alpha}{dt^2} + 2l\frac{d\alpha}{dt} + \kappa^2\alpha = 0. \tag{100-12}$$

This second order differential equation is of precisely the same form as (91-5). In the present instance we want the periodic solution corresponding to (91-10), that is,

$$\alpha = \alpha_0 e^{-lt} \sin(\omega_0 t + \epsilon), \qquad \omega_0 \equiv \sqrt{\kappa^2 - l^2};$$

the constant ω_0 being determined by replacing L, R and C in (91-11) by 1, $2l$ and $1/\kappa^2$ respectively.

To determine α_0 and ϵ, we have $\alpha = 0$ when $t = 0$ showing that $\epsilon = 0$, and

$$GQ = \left(\frac{d\alpha}{dt}\right)_{t=0} = \frac{2\pi}{P_0} \alpha_0,$$

since $2\pi/\omega_0$ is the period P_0. Hence

$$\alpha = \alpha_0 e^{-lt} \sin \omega_0 t, \qquad \alpha_0 \equiv \frac{GP_0}{2\pi} Q; \qquad (100\text{-}13)$$

which is the equation of *damped harmonic motion*, shown in Fig. 214.

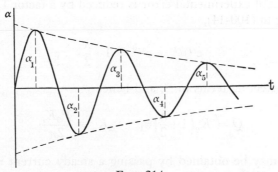

FIG. 214

The curve representing the motion lies between the broken line curves corresponding to $\alpha = \pm \alpha_0 e^{-lt}$, being tangent to them when $\sin \omega_0 t = \pm 1$.

When the damping is so small that l^2 may be neglected in comparison with κ^2, as is often the case, Q is easily expressed in terms of measurable quantities. For then the period P_0 reduces to $2\pi/\kappa = 2\pi\sqrt{\mathscr{I}/k}$ and the time of the first throw α_1 may be taken as that of the first tangency in the figure, that is, $P_0/4$. Replacing G by its value $k/K_i\mathscr{I}$, (100-13) gives

$$Q = \frac{P_0 K_i}{2\pi} e^{lP_0/4} \alpha_1 \qquad (100\text{-}14)$$

and it remains only to evaluate the exponential factor.

Since the amplitudes of successive throws are

$$\alpha_1 = \alpha_0 e^{-lP_0/4}, \qquad \alpha_2 = \alpha_0 e^{-3lP_0/4}, \qquad \alpha_3 = \alpha_0 e^{-5lP_0/4}, \cdots$$

each is in the constant ratio $e^{lP_0/2}$ to the next. Denoting by λ the logarithm of this quantity,

$$\lambda \equiv \frac{lP_0}{2} = \log \frac{\alpha_1}{\alpha_2} = \log \frac{\alpha_2}{\alpha_3} = \cdots. \tag{100-15}$$

This is one-half the logarithmic decrement as defined in art. 91, the half logarithmic decrement being more convenient here.

To obtain λ experimentally, it is only necessary to observe any two successive throws. However, when the damping is small, the ratio of successive throws is nearly unity, and a more accurate value is obtained by observing throws separated by several half periods. Evidently, if r is the number of half periods, we may express λ in the form

$$\lambda = \frac{1}{r} \log \frac{\alpha_n}{\alpha_{n+r}}, \tag{100-16}$$

and the effect of experimental error is reduced by a factor $1/r$.

Returning to (100-14),

$$e^{lP_0/4} = e^{\lambda/2} = 1 + \frac{\lambda}{2},$$

as we are neglecting terms in l^2, and hence

$$Q = K_q \left(1 + \frac{\lambda}{2}\right) \alpha_1, \qquad K_q \equiv \frac{P_0 K_i}{2\pi}. \tag{100-17}$$

Since K_i may be obtained by passing a steady current through the instrument, and P_0 and λ may be observed, the ballistic galvanometer is an absolute device, that is, it does not require calibration. However, it is often simpler to pass a known charge through it, from a capacitor, for example, and to observe the first throw, thereby obtaining the constant $K_q' \equiv K_q(1 + \lambda/2)$ at once.

When the damping is not small enough to permit the neglect of terms in l^2, the analysis is slightly more involved. This case occurs quite frequently in the measurement of the magnetic induction B. Here a small closely wound *flux coil* of area A and $\hat{n}$ turns is connected to the galvanometer and placed in the field at the point at which B is to be measured, with its plane perpendicular to the lines of induction. The coil is now suddenly moved to a place where the field is zero, or the field at the coil is reduced to zero by removing its source. The charge passing through the galvanometer due to change of flux through the coil is given by (100-1), where $N_1 = \hat{n}BA$ and $N_2 = 0$, so that

$$B = \frac{RQ}{\hat{n}A}.$$ (100-18)

Now the electromagnetic damping (art. 98) varies inversely with R, in this case the combined resistance of galvanometer and external coil. Usually R is not very great and the damping, at least for a moving coil instrument, is relatively large. It is, of course, possible to open the circuit just as the galvanometer swing begins, but this is often troublesome in practice. A moving needle instrument does not suffer from excessive damping but is much less convenient to use.

To obtain the exact relation between Q and α_1, we return to (100-13). As before $G = k/K_i \mathscr{I}$, but now

$$P_0 = \frac{2\pi}{\sqrt{\kappa^2 - l^2}} = \frac{2\pi}{\sqrt{\dfrac{k}{\mathscr{I}} - l^2}},$$

so that

$$\frac{k}{\mathscr{I}} = \frac{4\pi^2}{P_0^2} + l^2,$$

and

$$\alpha_0 = \frac{P_0}{2\pi K_i}\left(\frac{4\pi^2}{P_0^2} + l^2\right)Q = \frac{2\pi}{P_0 K_i}\left(1 + \frac{\lambda^2}{\pi^2}\right)Q.$$ (100-19)

The times t_s at which the throws $\alpha_1, \alpha_2, \alpha_3, \cdots$ occur are obtained by setting $\dfrac{d\alpha}{dt}$ equal to zero, which gives

$$\tan \omega_0 t_s = \frac{\omega_0}{l}.$$ (100-20)

As the period of this function is π/ω_0, it is evident that successive throws are separated by a half period as before, and that the ratio of any two successive throws is $e^{lP_0/2}$. Thus λ is determined exactly as in the previous case. However, the time T of the first throw α_1 is not $P_0/4$ but somewhat earlier, as indicated by (100-20).

Since

$$\sin \omega_0 T = \frac{1}{\sqrt{1 + \dfrac{l^2}{\omega_0^2}}} = \frac{1}{\sqrt{1 + \dfrac{\lambda^2}{\pi^2}}}$$

we have for the initial throw

$$\alpha_1 = \frac{2\pi}{P_0 K_i}\left(1 + \frac{\lambda^2}{\pi^2}\right)\frac{e^{-lT}}{\sqrt{1 + \dfrac{\lambda^2}{\pi^2}}}Q,$$

and hence

$$Q = \frac{P_0 K_i}{2\pi} \frac{e^{lT}}{\sqrt{1 + \frac{\lambda^2}{\pi^2}}} \alpha_1. \tag{100-21}$$

All quantities in the coefficient of α_1 are known, for (100-20) may be put in the form

$$lT = \frac{\lambda}{\pi} \arctan \frac{\pi}{\lambda}$$

to determine lT, but usually we write $Q = K_q'\alpha_1$ and determine the constant by calibration.

The expression (100-21) is valid for any magnitude of damping provided the motion of the galvanometer element is oscillatory. If the damping is made sufficiently great, the motion becomes non-oscillatory, but even in this case it may be shown that the single throw is proportional to the charge. Thus an equation of the form $Q = K_q'\alpha_1$ holds for a ballistic galvanometer under all circumstances.

Problem 100a. A tangent galvanometer having a period 8 sec deflects 15° when a steady current 0.1 amp passes through it. What charge will produce a throw 30° when the instrument is used ballistically, assuming negligible damping? Ans. 0.246 coulomb.

Problem 100b. A secondary of m turns is wound around the middle of a long air core solenoid of n_l turns per unit length and cross section A. The secondary is connected to an astatic ballistic galvanometer, the resistance of the circuit being R. Find the quantity of electricity passing through the galvanometer when the current i in the primary is reversed. If the throws are $\alpha_1 = 10$ scale division, $\alpha_2 = 9.5$ scale division, etc., and $i = 10$ amp, $R = 500$ ohm, $m = 100$ turn, $n_l = 1000$ turn/meter, $A = 0.002$ meter^2, find the ballistic constant K_q of the galvanometer in coulombs per scale division.

$$\text{Ans. } Q = \frac{2\mu_0 m n_l A i}{R},$$
$$K_q = 0.980(10)^{-6} \text{ coulomb/scale div.}$$

Problem 100c. The coil of a moving coil ballistic galvanometer has a period 10 sec for free oscillation, and throws $\alpha_1 = 12$ scale division, $\alpha_2 = 11$ scale division, etc. A steady current $(10)^{-4}$ amp produces a deflection 10 scale divisions. Find the capacitance of a capacitor which, when charged to 100 volts and then discharged through the galvanometer, produces an initial throw 8 scale divisions. Ans. 1.33 microfarad.

101. The Grassot Fluxmeter.

This instrument is essentially a moving coil galvanometer in which both mechanical damping and restoring torque are made negligibly small, connected by flexible leads to an external flux coil, sometimes called a *search coil*, similar to that used with an ordinary ballistic galvanometer.

Let us suppose that the search coil is moved from a position where the magnetic induction is B and the flux linkage, that is, the total flux passing through the circuit of the coil, is $N_0 = \hat{n}BA$ to a position where the flux linkage is zero. It is immaterial whether or not the motion is sudden. The induced e.m.f. gives rise to a current and hence to a torque on the moving element of the fluxmeter. This torque is of the form gi, as noted in art. 100, where g represents the flux cut by the galvanometer coil per unit angular deflection. The equation of motion of the moving element is therefore

$$\mathcal{I}\frac{d^2\alpha}{dt^2} = gi, \tag{101-1}$$

if $\mathcal{I}$ is its moment of inertia.

In order to express i in terms of the flux linkage N, it is necessary to write the electrical equation of the circuit composed of the search coil and the moving element. Let L be the total inductance of this circuit and R the total resistance. Then

$$L\frac{di}{dt} + Ri = -\frac{dN}{dt} - g\frac{d\alpha}{dt}, \tag{101-2}$$

the last term representing the e.m.f. induced in the galvanometer coil as it turns in the field of the fixed magnet. Eliminating the term in i between (101-1) and (101-2) gives

$$\mathcal{I}\frac{d^2\alpha}{dt^2} = \frac{g}{R}\left\{-\frac{dN}{dt} - g\frac{d\alpha}{dt} - L\frac{di}{dt}\right\}.$$

Let us integrate this equation over a period of time which includes the entire action, that is, over a period at the beginning and end of which both i and $\dfrac{d\alpha}{dt}$ are zero. Then,

$$\mathcal{I}\int_0^0 d\left(\frac{d\alpha}{dt}\right) = \frac{g}{R}\left\{-\int_{N_0}^0 dN - g\int_{\alpha_1}^{\alpha_2} d\alpha - L\int_0^0 di\right\},$$

or

$$0 = \frac{g}{R}\left\{N_0 - g(\alpha_2 - \alpha_1) - 0\right\}. \tag{101-3}$$

As the moving element has no restoring torque and therefore no zero position, the deflection interval $\alpha_2 - \alpha_1$ may fall anywhere on the scale with which the instrument is provided. Putting $\alpha_0 \equiv \alpha_2 - \alpha_1$, (101-3) gives

$$N_0 = g\alpha_0, \tag{101-4}$$

and

$$B = K_B\alpha_0, \qquad K_B \equiv \frac{g}{\hat{n}A}. \tag{101-5}$$

The constant g must be obtained by calibration. In practice the scale is usually arranged to give N_0 directly rather than B, so that different search coils may be used.

102. Magnetic Standards. Several methods are employed for the calibration of flux measuring apparatus. When calibration is to be made directly in terms of the induction B, a standard is necessary. This is obtained by means of a long air-core solenoid (art. 69), at the center of which $B = \mu_0 n_l i$ very closely, where n_l is the number of turns per unit length and i is the current. By tapering the ends of the solenoid or by using auxiliary windings at the ends the end effect can be much reduced and the field made essentially uniform over a considerable region on either side of the center.

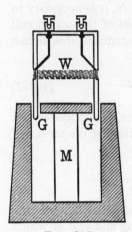

Fig. 215

Often it is only necessary to calibrate in terms of flux. In this case a standard mutual inductance may be used. Such an inductance usually consists of a standard solenoid of the sort described above with a small closely wound secondary coil about its central portion. If there are m turns in this coil and the cross section of the solenoid is A, a current i in the latter evidently produces a total flux linkage equal to $\mu_0 m n_l A i$. Therefore, a known change in current produces a known change in flux. In calibrating a Grassot fluxmeter the search coil may be replaced by the secondary of the mutual inductance as the deflection does not depend in any way on the resistance in the circuit. In the case of a ballistic galvanometer provided with a flux coil, however, both the damping of the instrument and the charge passing through it corresponding to a given change of flux depend on the resistance. Hence the secondary coil of the mutual inductance must be permanently included in the circuit of the galvanometer and its external coil to assure the use of the galvanometer under the exact conditions of calibration. An example of this procedure appears in the next article.

It is sometimes useful to have a standard source of flux which does not depend on a current. The *Hibbert magnetic standard*, shown in section in Fig. 215, is of this type. A permanent magnet M is set in a cylindrical iron yoke which provides a continuous path for the magnetic flux with the exception of a narrow circular gap GG. A thin brass cylinder, carrying a winding W, is arranged to drop through the gap, cutting the flux as it does so. The total flux linkage is found by multiplying the number of turns in the winding by the flux across the gap, which is usually of the order of $2(10)^{-4}$ weber. By using cylinders with different windings different amounts of flux linkage are obtained.

The device just described is, of course, a secondary standard, as the flux across the gap must be determined originally by comparison with an absolute standard such as the mutual inductance described above. It is, however, compact and very convenient, especially in cases where a calibration must be checked frequently.

103. Magnetic Properties of Materials. The behavior of almost all electrical machinery and apparatus depends on the magnetic properties of some ferromagnetic material. It is therefore very im-

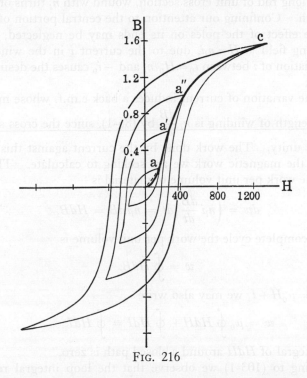

Fig. 216

portant to be able to determine these properties experimentally. There are several types of measurement which may be made. The most significant of these is the determination of the hysteresis loop, described in art. 36. As explained in that article the value of the magnetization I in a ferromagnetic material depends not only on H but also on the magnetic history of the given specimen. Unless this history has a definite character there is in general no definite relation between I and H. The same is true of B and H since $B = \mu_0 H + I$. We find it more convenient to deal with B than with I since B is usually the quantity measured. A repeated cyclic variation of H between limiting values H_0 and $-H_0$ provides a definite history and therefore establishes a definite relation—the hysteresis loop—between the variables. A family of loops for sheet iron corresponding to different values of H_0 is shown in Fig. 216.

Suppose now we calculate the energy expended in a complete cycle, that is, the work done in carrying a specimen of magnetic material around a given hysteresis loop. As magnetizing fields are usually produced electromagnetically it is interesting to make the calculation from that point of view. For convenience let the specimen be in the form of a long rod of unit cross section, wound with n_l turns of wire per unit length. Confining our attention to the central portion of the rod, where the effect of the poles on its ends may be neglected, the total magnetizing field is $H = n_l i$, due to the current i in the winding. A cyclic variation of i between $i_0 = H_0/n_l$ and $-i_0$ causes the desired variation in H.

Now the variation of current induces a back e.m.f. whose magnitude per unit length of winding is $n_l \dfrac{dB}{dt}$ by (86-1), since the cross section of the rod is unity. The work done by the current against this e.m.f. is evidently the magnetic work we are seeking to calculate. Thus for a time dt the work per unit volume of material is

$$dw = \left(n_l i \frac{dB}{dt} \right) dt = n_l i \, dB = H \, dB,$$

and for a complete cycle the work per unit volume is

$$w = \oint H \, dB. \tag{103-1}$$

Since $B = \mu_0 H + I$, we may also write

$$w = \mu_0 \oint H \, dH + \oint H \, dI = \oint H \, dI, \tag{103-2}$$

for the integral of $H \, dH$ around a closed path is zero.

Returning to (103-1) we observe that the loop integral represents exactly the area A_{BH} of the $B \sim H$ hysteresis loop, expressed in proper $B \sim H$ units. Thus,

$$w = A_{BH}. \tag{103-3}$$

When a hysteresis loop is plotted from experimental data, its area is ordinarily measured in square centimeters by a planimeter or some such device. The value thus obtained must be multiplied by the proper *scale factors*, that is, the number of B units per cm and the number of H units per cm, to obtain A_{BH}.

As the energy represented by (103-3) is dissipated in the form of heat, the hysteresis loop is of basic importance in the choice of materials for electrical machinery of all sorts from an economic as well as from a technical point of view. Care must be taken to distinguish between

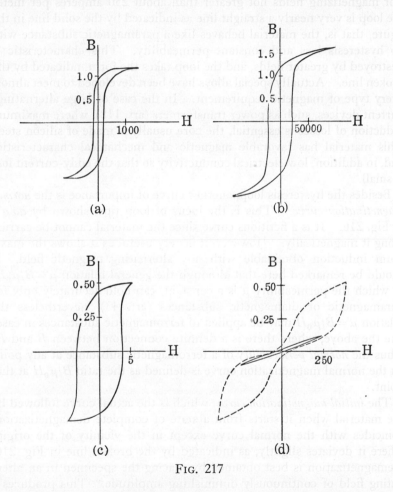

Fig. 217

energy losses due to hysteresis and those due to eddy currents (art. 97), which may be reduced by lamination.

To illustrate the manner in which the magnetic characteristics of materials are revealed by their hysteresis loops several loops are shown in Fig. 217. The first loop (a) is for soft iron and shows a large saturation value without excessive hysteresis loss. The next loop (b) applies to a specimen of cobalt steel. Because of the high retentiveness and large coercive force this material is excellent for permanent magnets but it is not at all suitable for cyclic use. Loop (c) is for an iron-nickel alloy known as *permalloy*. Its chief characteristic is the high degree of magnetization produced by a very small magnetizing force. Loop (d) for *perminvar*, an iron-nickel-cobalt alloy, is of particular interest. For magnetizing fields not greater than about 250 amperes per meter the loop is very nearly a straight line as indicated by the solid line in the figure, that is, the material behaves like a paramagnetic substance with no hysteresis loss and constant permeability. This characteristic is destroyed by greater fields, and the loop takes the form indicated by the broken line. Actually special alloys have been developed to meet almost every type of magnetic requirement. In the case of large alternating-current devices, such as power transformers (art. 118), where maximum reduction of losses is essential, the core usually is made of silicon steel. This material has favorable magnetic and mechanical characteristics and, in addition, low electrical conductivity so that the eddy-current loss is small.

Besides the hysteresis loop, another curve of importance is the *normal magnetization curve*. This is the locus of loop tips, shown by $aa'a''c$ in Fig. 216. It is a fictitious curve since the material cannot be carried along it magnetically. However, it is very useful as it shows the maximum induction obtainable with any alternating magnetic field. It should be remarked here that although the general relation $\mu = B/\mu_0 H$, in which the permeability μ is a constant, can hold accurately only for paramagnetic or diamagnetic substances (art. 43), nevertheless the relation $\mu = B/\mu_0 H$ may be applied to ferromagnetic substances in cases like the above, where there is a definite connection between B and H. Thus the *normal permeability* of a ferromagnetic substance at any point on the normal magnetization curve is defined as the ratio $B/\mu_0 H$ at that point.

The *initial magnetization curve*, which is the actual curve followed by the material when it starts from a state of complete demagnetization, coincides with the normal curve except in the vicinity of the origin, where it deviates slightly, as indicated by the broken line in Fig. 216. Demagnetization is best obtained by placing the specimen in an alternating field of continuously diminishing amplitude. This produces a hysteresis loop that becomes smaller and smaller until it finally vanishes, leaving the material demagnetized. Demagnetization is also obtained by heating, ferromagnetic materials becoming practically non-magnetic at sufficiently high temperatures. However, heating may cause permanent changes in the magnetic characteristics of a substance, especially in the case of an alloy.

The *incremental permeability* μ_i is the effective permeability of a material to a small alternating field superposed on a larger constant one. This case occurs frequently in communication apparatus where coils carry direct and alternating currents simultaneously. Thus, if a small change ΔH in the magnetizing field causes a change ΔB in the induction, $\mu_i \equiv \dfrac{1}{\mu_0}\left(\dfrac{\Delta B}{\Delta H}\right)$. In general μ_i decreases continuously as the magnetization of the material is increased from zero to saturation. The limiting value of μ_i corresponding to a vanishingly small alternating field is called the *reversible permeability*, since in the limit hysteresis effects disappear.

Problem 103a. The core of a generator armature is made of iron whose hysteresis loop under operating conditions has an area of $(10)^4/2\pi$ $B \sim H$ units. The core is cylindrical, having a length of 40 cm and diameter of 20 cm. If it rotates at 1200 r.p.m., find the rate at which heat is developed in it. Ans. 400 joule/sec.

Problem 103b. A solenoid 1 meter long and 5 cm in diameter has 500 turns of wire. The solenoid is filled with an iron core whose magnetic characteristics are shown in Fig. 216. Starting with the core demagnetized, a current of 0.5 amp is allowed to flow through the winding, a number of reversals being made to establish a cyclic state. Then the current is increased to 1.0 amp and the process repeated. Find the flux of induction in the core in both cases, neglecting end effects. Ans. $0.98(10)^{-3}$ weber, $2.16(10)^{-3}$ weber.

104. Measurement of Magnetic Properties.

There are several methods by which the magnetic properties discussed in the previous article may be measured. Description of the more common follows.

Ring Method. A ring, usually of rectangular cross section, is cut from the material whose characteristics are to be determined. Two windings are placed on it, a magnetizing coil of n_l turns per unit length measured at the mean circumference, and a flux coil of m turns total. As the dimensions of the cross section A are made small in comparison with the mean radius and there are no end effects, a current i in the magnetizing coil produces a very nearly uniform field of magnitude $n_l i$ throughout the ring. The corresponding flux of induction is determined with the aid of the flux coil and an associated ballistic galvanometer or fluxmeter. Division by mA gives the induction B itself.

A typical experimental arrangement is shown in Fig. 218. Current for the magnetizing winding of the ring is supplied by a battery $\mathscr{E}$, the magnitude of the current, which is controlled by an adjustable resistance R_1, being indicated by an ammeter M. The direction of the current is readily reversed by means of a double-pole double-throw switch S connected as a *reversing switch*. A second resistance R_2 is included with the switch in such a way that it is in series with R_1 when the switch is in one position but not when it is in the other. The flux coil on the ring, with the secondary of a standard mutual inductance and an adjustable resistance R in series, is connected to a ballistic galvanometer G. The mutual inductance is used to calibrate the galvanometer, while R serves to control the sensitivity. Deflection of the galvanometer when not desired is prevented by means of a short-circuiting key K.

The exact experimental procedure depends on the type of measurement. To determine a hysteresis loop R_2 is set at zero and R_1 is

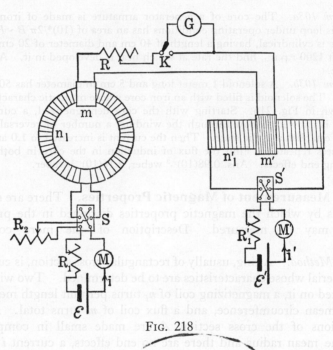

Fig. 218

adjusted until the magnetizing field $H = n_i i$ has the desired maximum value H_0 for the given loop. Then with the aid of S the field is reversed a number of times, perhaps fifteen or twenty, to establish a cyclic state. This is an important matter and it is well to ascertain the number of reversals necessary by comparing flux measurements made after different numbers. After the cyclic state is established, further reversals are without effect. Finally, R is set to give approximately a full scale throw of the galvanometer when the maximum field is reversed, and G is calibrated. Calibration is effected by observing the throw α_1', corresponding to a reversal of the current i' in the primary of the mutual inductance.   Then if a throw α_1 corresponds to a change of induction from B_1 to B_2 in the ring,

$$\frac{mA(B_1 - B_2)}{2\mu_0 m'n_l'A'i'} = \frac{\alpha_1}{\alpha_1'},$$

or

$$B_1 - B_2 = \frac{2\mu_0 m'n_l'A'i'}{mA\alpha_1'}\alpha_1, \qquad (104\text{-}1)$$

the primed quantities referring to the calibrating apparatus.   The galvanometer should be calibrated at several points along its scale, in case the latter is not quite linear.   Also, it must be recalibrated if the sensitivity is increased as is usually necessary in measuring the smaller values of B.

We are now ready to make the actual measurements.   Denoting the "up" position of S as plus and the "down" position as minus, we start at plus and observe the galvanometer throw caused by a reversal with $R_2 = 0$.   This corresponds to a change of induction equal to $2B_0$, the value of which is given by (104-1).   As $H_0 = n_l i_0$, we are able to plot the point a (Fig. 219) on the $B \sim H$ diagram.   To obtain the next point, we return S to plus, bringing the ring back to a on the loop, and then increase R_2 until the field is reduced to seven or eight-tenths of its former value, corresponding to point b.   A reversal of S now gives

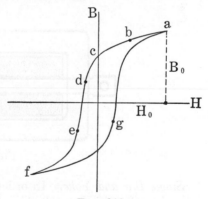

Fig. 219

the change of induction between b and f, from which the ordinate of b is obtained by subtracting B_0.   Other points on the portion ac of the loop are obtained in the same way.   Great care must be taken not to destroy the cyclic state during the measurements.   For instance, after the reversal from b to f just described, R_2 must be reduced to zero before S is returned to plus, and then set for the next point; otherwise the ring does not move along the path $fgab$ and subsequent observations are incorrect.   If the cyclic state is accidentally disturbed, it must be reestablished by a number of complete reversals between a and f.

Points between c and f are most readily obtained by moving the leads connected to R_1 and M to the other end of S, without changing the polarity.   Then R_2 is included in the circuit when S is in the minus position instead of the plus, and, starting at a with R_2 correctly set, a reversal carries the ring from a to d.   Subtracting the observed change of induction from B_0, we obtain the ordinate of d.   For the next point we reduce R_2 to zero, return S to plus and then reset R_2, in order to preserve the cyclic state.   As regards the lower branch fga of the loop, it is exactly like the upper branch inverted and may be plotted from the data already collected, provided the ring has no permanent magnetic set.   As a precaution a few points should be located experimentally for the lower branch even if the ring was originally demagnetized.

Measurements for the normal magnetization curve are relatively simple.   Having determined the coordinates of a for a loop in the manner just described, we readjust R_1 to give a different value of H_0 and establish a new cyclic state by repeated reversals.   The coordinates of the new loop tip are now obtained and so on until enough points are located to delineate a curve from the origin to the region of saturation.

The procedure in measuring incremental permeability is straight-forward and will suggest itself to the reader.

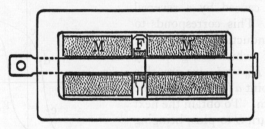

FIG. 220

Single Bar and Yoke.   In order to avoid the necessity of preparing ring-shaped specimens, Hopkinson devised a heavy yoke of soft iron (Fig. 220) in which a bar of the material to be tested may be placed. Magnetizing coils M, M' and a small flux coil F, all wound on brass bobbins, are slipped over the bar as shown in the figure.   The bar is cut at the center and arranged so that one end may be withdrawn a short distance, allowing the flux coil which is attached to a spring to fly out. All the flux in the bar is thereby cut by the coil and B can be measured directly.   The corresponding H is calculated from the magnetizing current and the mean turns per unit length of bar.   We use the mean turns, that is, the total number of turns divided by the length of bar between the inside surfaces of the yoke, rather than the actual turns per unit length on M and M', because of the small gap in which F lies.

This method is not highly accurate as there is some leakage of flux where the bar passes through the yoke and at the cut in the center. Moreover, as the yoke does not have infinite permeability, it does not entirely fulfill its purpose of joining the ends of the rod magnetically. Both effects tend to produce demagnetization, that is, to make H less than $n_l i$ by a few per cent.   We shall see how to calculate a correction for the effect of the yoke in the next article.

The experimental arrangements (Fig. 221) and procedure are very similar to those used with the ring.   No auxiliary resistance R_2 is required in this case and the induction is given directly by the formula

$$B = \frac{2\mu_0 m' n_l' A' i'}{m A \alpha_1'} \alpha_1, \tag{104-2}$$

the symbols having the same significance as before.   One additional precaution must be taken, however.   Since each time B is measured the

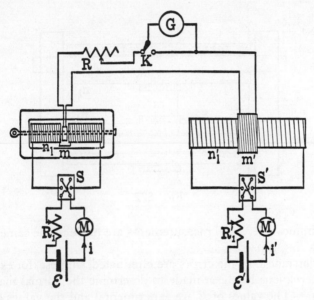

Fig. 221

parts of the bar are separated and free poles are exposed, the magnetic condition of the bar is disturbed, and must be restored before another measurement.   Thus for a hysteresis loop suppose the preliminary adjustments and galvanometer calibration have been made and the coordinates of the point a (Fig. 219) have been obtained.   To locate b the flux coil is returned to the measuring position, the field set at H_0 and a number of reversals made to re-establish the cyclic state destroyed by the previous measurement.   Then the field is reduced to the desired value H by adjustment of R_1, and B determined.   This process must be repeated for each point, reversals being made at H_0 before the field is adjusted to the measuring value. Points between c and f are most easily reached by adjusting the field to a positive value of the same magnitude as the desired negative value, and then throwing S from plus to minus. This fulfills the condition that the bar must always move from a to f on the upper branch of the loop.

The procedure for the normal magnetization curve is exactly the same with the yoke as with the ring, since it is necessary to establish a cyclic state before each measurement in either case.

Double Bar and Yoke. By modifying Hopkinson's method to use two bars instead of one (Fig. 222), Ewing succeeded in eliminating the errors due to demagnetizing effects. A bobbin with magnetizing and flux coils is slipped over each bar as shown in the figure. In this case the flux

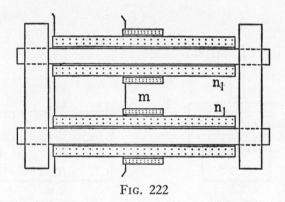

FIG. 222

coils are immovable, so all measurements are made in the same manner as when a ring is used.

To understand how the errors are eliminated, suppose, for example, a set of observations has been made to determine the normal magnetization curve. The values of B are experimental and the values of H are given by

$$H = H' - h, \tag{104-3}$$

where $H' = n_l i'$ and h is the demagnetizing field due to flux leakage and so forth. Let us plot B against H' obtaining curve (1), Fig. 223. The true $B \sim H$ curve (unnumbered) evidently lies to the left of (1) by the amount h, which is a function of H. To find h suppose we replace the two magnetizing coils by another pair each of which has the same number of turns per unit length as before, but is one-half as long. The yoke blocks are of course moved up to the ends of the coils, so the effective length of the bars is reduced to one-half its former value.

Repeating the measurements for the $B \sim H$ curve, we have now

$$H = H'' - 2h, \tag{104-4}$$

where $H'' = n_l i''$ and $2h$ is the demagnetizing field. This field is twice as great as before because the same sources of demagnetization become twice as effective with half-length bars, a fact demonstrated analytically in the next article. Plotting B against H'' gives curve (2). Now from (104-3) and (104-4) it appears that curves (1) and (2) are also separated by the amount h. Therefore, the true $B \sim H$ curve is simply derived from the other curves by laying off $ab = bc$ for various values of B.

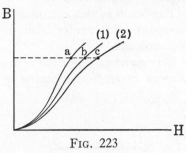

FIG. 223

The double bar method is rather laborious and is used in practice only to standardize certain bars for reference purposes.

Magnetometer. When the quantity of material available for testing is small, the specimen being in the form of a fine wire or thin film, for example, a magnetometer must be used. An ordinary instrument of the sort described in art. 47, with the earth's field as a control, will serve, but a double needle or astatic instrument, similar to the astatic galvanometer (art. 73), is preferable. The measurements may be made in a number of ways. An excellent method employing an astatic magnetometer is described by Bozorth.* Here two identical solenoids (Fig. 224) are symmetrically placed on either side of the magnetometer. The solenoids are connected in series with their fields in the same sense and the whole system carefully adjusted until the magnetometer deflection is entirely independent of the solenoids.

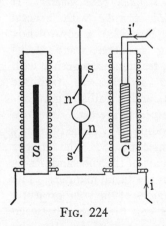

FIG. 224

The test specimen S is now placed in one solenoid and a very small compensating coil C of the same length as S is placed in the other. Because of the field of the solenoid, S becomes a small magnet and produces a deflection of the magnetometer. This deflection is reduced to zero by adjusting the current i' through C until the latter has an

* Bozorth, R. M. *Rev. Sci. Ins.* **10**, 591 (1925).

equivalent magnetic moment equal to that of S.   As this equivalent magnetic moment can be calculated in terms of i' and the dimensions of the coil, the magnetic moment of S becomes known and from this the magnetization I can be found. H is calculated in terms of the current i in the solenoid by (69-4), taking account of the demagnetizing effect of the ends of the specimen.   Finally, using $B = \mu_0 H + I$, we can plot B as a function of H.

For details of this and other magnetometer methods, which are rather laborious, the reader should consult some treatise on magnetic measurements.

Permeameters.   For commercial testing a number of complete assemblies of magnetic measuring apparatus have been produced, special care having been taken to insure flexibility, facility of operation, direct indication of B and H, and other convenient characteristics. Such units are called *permeameters*. With one or two exceptions their operation depends on the principle of the yoke.

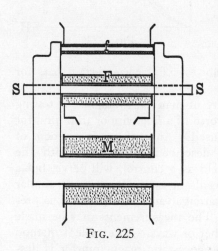

FIG. 225

One of the most widely used permeameters for general testing is the *Fahy simplex permeameter*.   It consists of a yoke with several windings (Fig. 225), a control box containing ammeter, standard inductance, resistances, together with keys and switches to facilitate operation, and a ballistic galvanometer.   The construction of the yoke is of especial interest.   Its form is shown in the figure.   The magnetizing winding M is placed directly on the yoke and does not surround the test specimen S.   The latter is clamped in a pair of heavy jaws which are a part of the yoke and passes through a flux coil F, so that B is measured in the usual manner.   The determination of H, however, is novel.   The sides of the yoke project a short distance beyond F and an air-core flux coil f is placed between them.   The field H_f through this coil is not in general equal to the field H in the specimen, which we wish to measure.   In fact, H_f is variable both in magnitude and direction, while H is essentially constant.   However, the flux of induction linking f is the same as for a constant field equal to H and therefore $\mu_0 H$ is measured with the aid of f in exactly the same way as B with the aid of F.   This gives H.

To demonstrate the equality of flux linkage under the conditions mentioned, we observe that the difference of magnetic potential between the ends of f is practically the same as the difference between the ends of the effective portion of S, since the magnetic intensity and hence the potential drop is very small in the projecting parts of the yoke. Thus if l is the distance between the sides of the yoke, and α is the angle which H_f makes at any point with the axis of f,

$$\int_0^l H_f \cos \alpha \, dx = Hl, \tag{104-5}$$

where dx is an element of length parallel to the axis. Now the flux linking f is

$$N_f = \mu_0 \int_0^l \left(\frac{n}{l}\right) dx \int_0^A H_f \cos \alpha \, ds,$$

n being the total number of turns and A the cross section of which ds is an element. Since the order of integration is immaterial, we have, with the aid of (104-5),

$$N_f = \mu_0\left(\frac{n}{l}\right) \int_0^A ds \int_0^l H_f \cos \alpha \, dx = \mu_0 nHA, \tag{104-6}$$

which is exactly the flux linkage corresponding to a constant field equal to H, as stated.

The general experimental procedure is the same as in other yoke methods.

105. The Magnetic Circuit. Having determined the magnetic properties of materials in general, it remains to translate these properties into the production of flux in electromagnetic apparatus and machinery, for all electromagnetic reactions depend in one way or another on flux. We may attack the problem in the same way as in art. 44 and art. 45, that is, by attempting to find a function specifying the field which satisfies the assigned boundary conditions. This is often difficult, however. Moreover, we are primarily interested in the amount of flux rather than in its exact distribution. The fact that the tubes of induction which comprise the flux are confined to a definite circuital path, composed largely or entirely of ferromagnetic materials, in almost all practical cases, suggests the point of view of a *magnetic circuit*.

To establish the necessary ideas consider the magnetized ring described in the previous article. If A is the cross section of the ring, l the mean distance around it, and n the total number of turns in the magnetizing winding, the flux in the ring, that is, in the magnetic circuit, is

$$N_c = BA = \left(\frac{\mu_0 \mu A}{l}\right) ni,$$

or

$$N_c = \frac{ni}{\dfrac{l}{\mu_0 \mu A}}. \tag{105-1}$$

The flux, being circuital, is the same through any cross section around the ring. Note that the flux in the magnetic circuit is not the same thing as the flux linking the electric circuit, the latter being n times the former in this case.

Now by Ampère's law ni is the work done in carrying a unit pole around the magnetic circuit, that is, the magnetomotive force $\mathscr{H}$ defined in art. 71. Evidently $l/\mu_0 \mu A$ measures the resistance of the circuit to the production of flux. If we call this magnetic resistance the *reluctance* $\mathscr{R}$ and write (105-1) in the form

$$N_c = \frac{\mathscr{H}}{\mathscr{R}},$$

we have an equation of exactly the same form as Ohm's law, namely,

$$i = \frac{\mathscr{E}}{R}.$$

The magnetic circuit is therefore analogous to an electric circuit, flux corresponding to current, m.m.f. to e.m.f. and reluctance to resistance. The analogy is even more close, for the resistance of a conductor whose length is l, cross section A and conductivity γ, is $l/\gamma A$, which compares exactly with $l/\mu_0 \mu A$. Thus $\mu_0 \mu$ corresponds to γ. The unit of reluctance is, properly, the *ampere per weber*. However, the unit is often called the *ampere-turn per weber*, since magnetomotive force is involved in its definition.

Equation (105-1) deduced from the uniform ring evidently applies with very little error to a ferromagnetic circuit of any shape in which μ and A are constant, even if the magnetizing winding is not uniformly distributed, for the flux is still almost entirely confined to the high permeability material of which the circuit is composed. We may easily generalize (105-1) to apply to a circuit of variable cross section and permeability, including air gaps. Carrying a unit pole around such a circuit,

$$\oint H dl = ni \tag{105-2}$$

by Ampère's law. Now $H = B/\mu_0 \mu = N_c/\mu_0 \mu A$, and, since N_c is constant around the circuit except for slight leakage, (105-2) becomes

$$\frac{N_c}{\mu_0} \oint \frac{dl}{\mu A} = ni,$$

so that

$$N_c = \frac{ni}{\frac{1}{\mu_0}\oint\frac{dl}{\mu A}}. \tag{105-3}$$

In practice a circuit usually consists of several distinct parts in each of which μ and A are constant. Then

$$\frac{1}{\mu_0}\oint\frac{dl}{\mu A} = \frac{1}{\mu_0}\left(\frac{l_1}{\mu_1 A_1}+\frac{l_2}{\mu_2 A_2}+\cdots\right).$$

This indicates that the reluctance of a magnetic circuit is the sum of the reluctances of its parts, just as the resistance of an electric circuit is the sum of its component resistances. In fact, since the basic equations of the two circuits are alike, all the properties which depend on these equations must be the same. Thus parallel reluctances combine in the same way as parallel resistances (art. 52) and flux divides between the former in the same way as current divides between the latter.

Neglecting leakage of flux through the air evidently introduces an error of the same sort as neglecting leakage of current from an electric circuit which is placed in a slightly conducting solution. This error is not very great except perhaps at an air gap, where, unless the gap is very small compared with the linear dimensions of the circuit at that point, there is some spreading of flux. In any case leakage factors are known for the common forms of magnetic circuit, and may be used if necessary.

As an example of the utility of magnetic circuit analysis let us find the effect of cutting a narrow gap of width a in the uniform ring discussed above. Using the same symbols as before, the reluctance is now

$$\mathscr{R} = \frac{1}{\mu_0}\left(\frac{l-a}{\mu A}+\frac{a}{A}\right) = \frac{l+a(\mu-1)}{\mu_0\mu A}.$$

Comparing this with the former value $l/\mu_0\mu A$, we see that the gap reduces the original flux by a factor $\dfrac{l}{l+a(\mu-1)}$. For instance, with $\mu-1=500$, a gap as small as $l/500$ reduces the flux by one-half, which shows the great effect of even very small gaps in a magnetic circuit.

Another useful application of (105-3) may be made to yokes used in magnetic measurements (art. 104). Denoting total length of path, cross section and permeability by l, A and μ, respectively, for the test material, and by l', A' and μ' for the yoke, we have

$$N_c = \frac{ni}{\frac{1}{\mu_0}\left(\frac{l}{\mu A}+\frac{l'}{\mu'A'}+\frac{a}{A}\right)}, \tag{105-4}$$

where a is the total equivalent air gap in the circuit. Now, as we have seen, B is measured in the determination of magnetic characteristics but H must be calculated. Since $H = N_c/\mu_0\mu A$, (105-4) becomes

$$H = \frac{n_l i}{1 + \dfrac{l'\mu A}{l\mu'A'} + \mu\dfrac{a}{l}}, \tag{105-5}$$

n_l being the mean number of turns in the magnetizing winding per unit length of the test bar. As the last two terms in the denominator are made as small as possible in practice, the equation may be written

$$H = n_l i\left(1 - \frac{l'\mu A}{l\mu'A'} - \mu\frac{a}{l}\right). \tag{105-6}$$

In applying this to the single bar and yoke it is customary to neglect the last term in the parentheses, as it is usually smaller than the second term and somewhat indeterminate. The field correction factor, due to the yoke, is then $(1 - l'\mu A/l\mu'A')$, which may differ from unity by several percent. Note that here A' represents twice the cross section of either side of the yoke, since the two sides are effectively in parallel.

Problem 105a. Let the core of a U-shaped electromagnet wound with n turns of wire have a permeability μ, a length l and a square cross section of area A. The pole separation is d. Using (43-12), show that the force with which it holds a bar of the same cross section and material against its poles is approximately

$$\frac{\mu_0\mu^2 n^2 i^2 A}{(l+d)^2}.$$

Problem 105b. Using (105-5), show that (104-3) and (104-4) have the correct form. Find the value of h. Ans. $\left(\dfrac{l'\mu A}{l\mu'A'} + \mu\dfrac{a}{l}\right)H$.

Problem 105c. Using (43-4) and (43-6) show that $I = [\mu_0\chi/(l+a\chi)]ni$ for the uniform ring with gap considered above (p. 361).

REFERENCES

Duckworth, *Electricity and Magnetism* (Holt, Rinehart and Winston, 1960). Pp. 287–299, 316–321.

Winch, *Electricity and Magnetism* (Prentice-Hall, 1963). Pp. 337–344, 444–453, 468–473.

Chapter XII

ABSOLUTE STANDARDS AND UNITS

106. Absolute Measurement of Current. By means of an *electrodynamometer* the absolute measurement of a current can be made in terms of the force between connected coils through which the current passes. A suitable electrodynamometer is the *Kelvin current balance* (Fig. 226) which consists of coils A and B attached to the ends of a beam

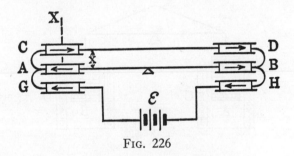

FIG. 226

balance, the first lying between the parallel fixed coils C and G and the second between D and H. The coils are connected in series so that the same current i passes through each coil in the sense of the arrow. Consequently, A is attracted by G and repelled by C and similarly B is attracted by D and repelled by H. By sliding a rider along the beam of the balance until the torque due to the forces on A and B is compensated, the latter can be measured in terms of the weight of the rider.

If M is the mutual inductance of A and C, the force between these two coils is

$$i^2 \frac{\partial M}{\partial x}$$

from (95-5), and as the total force $\mathscr{F}$ is four times as great,

$$i = \frac{1}{2} \sqrt{\frac{\mathscr{F}}{\frac{\partial M}{\partial x}}}. \tag{106-1}$$

363

In art. 96 we have seen how to calculate the mutual inductance of two parallel coaxial circles in terms of their dimensions.   Therefore, all the quantities on the right of (106-1) are readily determined.   Incidentally it may be noted that, as the force between the coils of an electrodynamometer is proportional to the square of the current, this instrument may be used to measure alternating as well as direct currents. When so used, the effective or root-mean-square current is given by (106-1).

An electrodynamometer designed by Ayrton and Jones for absolute measurements is capable of even greater precision than the Kelvin current balance.   This instrument (Fig. 227), considered to be accurate to 1 part in 50,000, consists of two coils A and B wound on marble cylinders suspended from the ends of a beam balance.   The suspended coils move inside the coaxial fixed coils C and D.   All four coils are connected in series in such a way that the force on one of the suspended

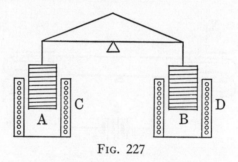

Fig. 227

coils is downward and that on the other upward.   The torque due to the current is balanced by a weight in much the same way as with the Kelvin balance.

If, now, a silver voltameter (art. 59) is connected in series with an electrodynamometer, the mass of silver deposited on the cathode by a current of one ampere flowing for one second can be measured.   In this way the electrochemical equivalent of silver, $1.118(10)^{-6}$ kg/coulomb, and the value of Faraday's constant, $9.649(10)^7$ coulomb/kg-equivalent, are determined in absolute measure.

Once the electrochemical equivalent of silver has been accurately determined, a given current can be measured in absolute units more simply by observing the rate at which it deposits silver in a voltameter than by the use of an electrodynamometer.   Furthermore, the calibration curve of a current measuring instrument which is not absolute may be obtained by connecting it in series with a silver voltameter and passing steady currents of various magnitudes through the two, measuring the current in each instance by the rate at which silver is deposited on the cathode of the voltameter.

107. Absolute Measurement of Resistance. The absolute measurement of the resistance of a standard coil of wire is of prime importance, since, once a resistance has been so determined, the value in absolute units of an electromotive force may be obtained from Ohm's law in terms of resistance and current.   Moreover, any other resistance may be accurately measured in terms of the standard by the use of a Wheatstone bridge.

One method of measuring the resistance of a coil AB of radius a (Fig. 228) consists in rotating the coil about a diameter in a uniform field H.   If the coil has n closely wound turns, and we take the positive normal to the circuit in the direction of the arrow perpendicular to its plane, the induced e.m.f. is

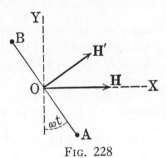

FIG. 228

$$\mathscr{E} = -\frac{dN}{dt} = \pi\mu_0 na^2\omega H \sin \omega t$$

when the coil is rotated about the Z axis with angular velocity ω.   This e.m.f. induces a current

$$i = \frac{\pi\mu_0 na^2\omega H}{\sqrt{R^2+L^2\omega^2}} \sin (\omega t - \phi), \qquad \tan \phi \equiv \frac{L\omega}{R},$$

in accord with (89-12).   This current in turn gives rise to a magnetic field

$$H' = \frac{ni}{2a} = \frac{\pi\mu_0 n^2 a\omega H}{2\sqrt{R^2+L^2\omega^2}} \sin (\omega t - \phi)$$

at the center O of the rotating coil.

Now if a magnetic needle is suspended at O, it will point in the direction of the resultant mean field.   The mean values of the components of H' along X and Y are

$$\bar{H}_x' = \frac{\pi\mu_0 n^2 a\omega H}{2\sqrt{R^2+L^2\omega^2}} \overline{\sin (\omega t - \phi) \cos \omega t} = -\frac{\pi\mu_0 n^2 a\omega H}{4\sqrt{R^2+L^2\omega^2}} \sin \phi,$$

$$\bar{H}_y' = \frac{\pi\mu_0 n^2 a\omega H}{2\sqrt{R^2+L^2\omega^2}} \overline{\sin (\omega t - \phi) \sin \omega t} = \frac{\pi\mu_0 n^2 a\omega H}{4\sqrt{R^2+L^2\omega^2}} \cos \phi,$$

where

$$\sin \phi \equiv \frac{L\omega}{\sqrt{R^2+L^2\omega^2}}, \qquad \cos \phi \equiv \frac{R}{\sqrt{R^2+L^2\omega^2}}.$$

Therefore, the deflection of the needle from the X axis due to the rotation of the coil is given by

$$\tan \alpha = \frac{\bar{H}_y'}{H + \bar{H}_x'} = \frac{\pi \mu_0 n^2 a \omega R}{4R^2 + (4L^2 - \pi \mu_0 n^2 aL)\omega^2}.$$

For the speeds of rotation ordinarily used the second term in the denominator is negligible compared with the first. Consequently,

$$R = \frac{\pi \mu_0 n^2 a \omega}{4 \tan \alpha}, \tag{107-1}$$

which gives the resistance in terms of easily measurable quantities. A small correction is necessary, however, to take account of the current induced in the coil by the magnetic field of the needle.

Alternative methods of measuring resistance involve comparison of a resistance with a known inductance. A detailed account of such methods may be found in Glazebrook's *Dictionary of Applied Physics*.

108. Other Absolute Measurements. The absolute value of an electromotive force cannot easily be obtained directly. Hence recourse is had to Ohm's law, the value of an electromotive force being obtained from the value of the current it produces in a circuit of known resistance. The Weston cell (art. 61), when made according to prescribed specifications, has very closely the e.m.f. 1.0186 volts at 20° C on open circuit. Other electromotive forces can be compared with this by the potentiometer method of art. 56.

We have seen that the capacitances of capacitors of simple form can be calculated from their dimensions. The capacitance of any other capacitor can be compared with that of a standard by the bridge method of art. 23.

Finally both self and mutual inductances may be calculated from their dimensions in many cases by the methods developed in art. 96. Once a standard of inductance has been obtained, any other inductance may be measured in terms of it by the bridge methods described in art. 121.

109. Systems of Units. Let us now consider systems of units, in general. We shall describe first the more important c.g.s. systems, since the m.k.s. practical system followed these historically and was to some extent developed from them.

One of the simplest c.g.s. systems is the *Gaussian system*, in which all electric quantities, including current, are expressed in electrostatic units (art. 6) and all magnetic quantities are expressed in electromagnetic units (art. 37). Collecting the fundamental equations so far developed and transforming them by means of the conversion relations given in art. 50, we have in g.u. (Gaussian units)

$$E_g = \frac{q_g}{r_g^2}, \quad (1g) \qquad H_g = \frac{m_g}{r_g^2}, \quad (2g)$$

$$\oint H_g \cdot dl_g = \frac{4\pi}{c_g} \int_s j_g \cdot ds_g, \quad (3g) \qquad \oint E_g \cdot dl_g = -\frac{1}{c_g} \int_s \frac{\partial B_g}{\partial t} \cdot ds_g, \quad (4g)$$

$$D_g = E_g + 4\pi P_g = \kappa E_g, \quad (5g) \qquad B_g = H_g + 4\pi I_g = \mu H_g, \quad (6g)$$

$$\mathscr{F}_{\tau g} = \rho_g E_g + \frac{1}{c_g} j_g \times B_g. \quad (7g)$$

Here $c_g \equiv 3(10)^{10}$ cm sec^{-1}, the dimensions being taken to make the equations dimensionally homogeneous. Note that it is not necessary to use a subscript with t, since the unit of time is the same in all systems, both c.g.s. and m.k.s.

Equations (1) and (2) are Coulomb's laws for electric charges and for magnetic poles, respectively; (3) is Ampère's law; (4) is Faraday's law; and (5) and (6) are the constitutive relations between displacement, electric intensity and polarization on the one hand, and between induction, magnetic intensity and magnetization on the other. Finally, (7) is the force per unit volume on free charge of density ρ_g in the electric field E_g and on current of density j_g in the magnetic field B_g. The current density j_g is, of course, due to such part of the charge density ρ_g as is in motion.

To pass to any other system of c.g.s. units, indicated by single accents, we may put $q_g = \alpha q'$, $m_g = \beta m'$, $D_g = \gamma D'$, $B_g = \delta B'$, where we agree to preserve the defining relations

$$\left. \begin{array}{c} \mathscr{F}_g = q_g E_g = q' E' = \mathscr{F}', \\ \mathscr{F}_g = m_g H_g = m' H' = \mathscr{F}', \\ t = \dfrac{q_g}{i_g} = \dfrac{q'}{i'}. \end{array} \right\} \quad (109\text{-}1)$$

Therefore, we have $E_g = (1/\alpha)E'$, $H_g = (1/\beta)H'$, $i_g = \alpha i'$, $j_g = \alpha j'$. Furthermore, since polarization is electric moment per unit volume, $P_g = \alpha P'$, and similarly $I_g = \beta I'$. The constants κ and μ, being pure ratios, are the same in all systems of units. Hence the fundamental equations become

$$E' = \alpha^2 \frac{q'}{r'^2}, \quad (1') \qquad H' = \beta^2 \frac{m'}{r'^2}, \quad (2')$$

$$\oint H' \cdot dl' = \frac{4\pi\alpha\beta}{c'} \int_s j' \cdot ds', \quad (3')$$

$$\oint E' \cdot dl' = -\frac{\alpha\delta}{c'} \int_s \frac{\partial B'}{\partial t} \cdot ds', \quad (4')$$

$$\mathbf{D'} = \frac{1}{\alpha\gamma}\,\mathbf{E'} + 4\pi\!\left(\frac{\alpha}{\gamma}\right)\!\mathbf{P'} = \frac{\kappa}{\alpha\gamma}\,\mathbf{E'}, \quad (5')$$

$$\mathbf{B'} = \frac{1}{\beta\delta}\,\mathbf{H'} + 4\pi\!\left(\frac{\beta}{\delta}\right)\!\mathbf{I'} = \frac{\mu}{\beta\delta}\,\mathbf{H'}, \quad (6')$$

$$\mathscr{F}_\tau' = \rho'\mathbf{E'} + \frac{\alpha\delta}{c'}\,\mathbf{j'} \times \mathbf{B'}. \quad (7')$$

The most convenient c.g.s. system for theoretical investigation, which has the advantage of eliminating the coefficient 4π in the more important equations, is the *Heaviside-Lorentz system*, the units of which are designated by the abbreviation h.l.u. In this system $\alpha = \beta = 1/\sqrt{4\pi}$, $\gamma = \delta = \sqrt{4\pi}$.

If we indicate Heaviside-Lorentz units by the subscript h, the fundamental equations in these units take the form

$$E_h = \frac{q_h}{4\pi r_h{}^2}, \quad (1h) \qquad\qquad H_h = \frac{m_h}{4\pi r_h{}^2}, \quad (2h)$$

$$\oint \mathbf{H}_h \cdot d\mathbf{l}_h = \frac{1}{c_h}\int_s \mathbf{j}_h \cdot d\mathbf{s}_h, \quad (3h) \qquad \oint \mathbf{E}_h \cdot d\mathbf{l}_h = -\frac{1}{c_h}\int_s \frac{\partial \mathbf{B}_h}{\partial t} \cdot d\mathbf{s}_h, \quad (4h)$$

$$\mathbf{D}_h = \mathbf{E}_h + \mathbf{P}_h = \kappa\mathbf{E}_h, \quad (5h) \qquad \mathbf{B}_h = \mathbf{H}_h + \mathbf{I}_h = \mu\mathbf{H}_h, \quad (6h)$$

$$\mathscr{F}_{\tau h} = \rho_h\mathbf{E}_h + \frac{1}{c_h}\,\mathbf{j}_h \times \mathbf{B}_h. \quad (7h)$$

It is to be noticed that the force between two charges measured in h.l.u. is

$$\mathscr{F}_h = \frac{q_h q_h{}'}{4\pi r_h{}^2}. \tag{109-2}$$

Therefore, the Heaviside-Lorentz unit charge is that charge which repels an equal like charge at a distance of 1 cm *in vacuo* with a force of $1/4\pi$ dyne. Similar remarks apply to the unit of pole-strength.

Gauss' law (14-4) takes the form

$$\int_s \mathbf{D}_h \cdot d\mathbf{s}_h = \int_\tau \rho_h\,d\tau_h \tag{109-3}$$

in h.l.u., so while we have introduced a factor $1/4\pi$ in Coulomb's law we have rid ourselves of 4π in Gauss' law. A system of units which removes the factor 4π from Gauss' law and the constitutive relations, as the Heaviside-Lorentz system does, is said to be *rationalized*.

The complete *electrostatic system*, in which not only electric but also magnetic quantities are expressed in e.s.u., is obtained by putting $\alpha = \gamma = 1$, $\beta = \delta = c_e$. This system has not been much used but it is included here, as a matter of interest, to show how it differs from the other systems. Indicating electrostatic units by the subscript e, we have for the fundamental equations

$$E_e = \frac{q_e}{r_e^2}, \quad (1e) \qquad H_e = c_e^2 \frac{m_e}{r_e^2}, \quad (2e)$$

$$\oint H_e \cdot dl_e = 4\pi \int_s j_e \cdot ds_e, \quad (3e) \qquad \oint E_e \cdot dl_e = -\int_s \frac{\partial B_e}{\partial t} \cdot ds_e, \quad (4e)$$

$$D_e = E_e + 4\pi P_e = \kappa E_e, \quad (5e) \qquad B_e = \frac{1}{c_e^2} H_e + 4\pi I_e = \frac{\mu}{c_e^2} H_e, \quad (6e)$$

$$\mathscr{F}_{\tau e} = \rho_e E_e + j_e \times B_e. \quad (7e)$$

The complete *electromagnetic system*, in which electric as well as magnetic quantities are expressed in e.m.u., is obtained by putting $\alpha = \gamma = c_m$, $\beta = \delta = 1$. This system, although much used in the past, is now giving way to the m.k.s. practical system employed in this book. When quantities are measured in electromagnetic units, indicated by the subscript m, the fundamental equations take the form

$$E_m = c_m^2 \frac{q_m}{r_m^2}, \quad (1m) \qquad\qquad H_m = \frac{m_m}{r_m^2}, \quad (2m)$$

$$\oint H_m \cdot dl_m = 4\pi \int_s j_m \cdot ds_m, \quad (3m) \qquad \oint E_m \cdot dl_m = -\int_s \frac{\partial B_m}{\partial t} \cdot ds_m, \quad (4m)$$

$$D_m = \frac{1}{c_m^2} E_m + 4\pi P_m = \frac{\kappa}{c_m^2} E_m, \quad (5m) \qquad B_m = H_m + 4\pi I_m = \mu H_m, \quad (6m)$$

$$\mathscr{F}_{\tau m} = \rho_m E_m + j_m \times B_m. \quad (7m)$$

When using any of the c.g.s. systems described above it must be remembered that in the case of the mechanical quantities the subscripts merely signify basic c.g.s. units. Thus $r_g = r_h = r_e = r_m$ (in cm), $c_g = c_h = c_e = c_m \equiv 3(10)^{10}$ cm sec^{-1}, and so on. Evidently the fundamental equations are simpler and more symmetrical in both g.u. and h.l.u. than in e.s.u. and e.m.u.

We are now ready to discuss m.k.s. systems, in particular, the practical system. The fundamental equations in pr.u. are

$$E = \frac{q}{4\pi\kappa_0 r^2}, \quad (1) \qquad H = \frac{m}{4\pi\mu_0 r^2}, \quad (2)$$

$$\oint H \cdot dl = \int_s j \cdot ds, \quad (3) \qquad \oint E \cdot dl = -\int_s \frac{\partial B}{\partial t} \cdot ds, \quad (4)$$

$$D = \kappa_0 E + P = \kappa_0 \kappa E, \quad (5) \qquad B = \mu_0 H + I = \mu_0 \mu H, \quad (6)$$

$$\mathscr{F}_\tau = \rho E + j \times B. \quad (7)$$

The practical system is rationalized, like the Heaviside-Lorentz system, to simplify the fundamental equations. It is based on the coulomb and on the practical unit pole. Historically, the coulomb followed the electromagnetic unit charge and it was chosen, as a matter of convenience, to have one-tenth the latter's magnitude. The physical dimensions of the coulomb are, of course, arbitrary, since the physical dimensions of κ_0 are arbitrary. We have taken these to be meter^{-2} sec^2 (art. 6) merely because this allows κ_0 to be expressed simply in terms of c. Finally, the unit pole is chosen so that $1/\sqrt{\kappa_0\mu_0}=c$ (art. 37).

To express the m.k.s. equations in generalized form, let us put
$$q=\sqrt{4\pi\kappa_0}\,\alpha q'', \quad m=\sqrt{4\pi\mu_0}\,\beta m'', \quad D=\sqrt{\kappa_0/4\pi}\,\gamma D'', \quad B=\sqrt{\mu_0/4\pi}\,\delta B'',$$
where, as in the c.g.s. case, we preserve the defining relations

$$\left.\begin{aligned}
\mathscr{F} &= qE = q''E'' = \mathscr{F}'', \\
\mathscr{F} &= mH = m''H'' = \mathscr{F}'', \\
t &= \frac{q}{i} = \frac{q''}{i''}.
\end{aligned}\right\} \quad (109\text{-}4)$$

Then, in the same way as before, we have $E=(1/\sqrt{4\pi\kappa_0}\,\alpha)E''$, $H=(1/\sqrt{4\pi\mu_0}\,\beta)H''$, $i=\sqrt{4\pi\kappa_0}\,\alpha i''$, $j=\sqrt{4\pi\kappa_0}\,\alpha j''$, with $P=\sqrt{4\pi\kappa_0}\,\alpha P''$, $I=\sqrt{4\pi\mu_0}\,\beta I''$, and the fundamental equations become

$$E'' = \alpha^2\frac{q''}{r''^2}, \quad (1'') \qquad\qquad H'' = \beta^2\frac{m''}{r''^2}, \quad (2'')$$

$$\oint \mathbf{H}''\cdot d\mathbf{1}'' = \frac{4\pi\alpha\beta}{c''}\int_s \mathbf{j}''\cdot d\mathbf{s}'', \quad (3'')$$

$$\oint \mathbf{E}''\cdot d\mathbf{1}'' = -\frac{\alpha\delta}{c''}\int_s \frac{\partial\mathbf{B}''}{\partial t}\cdot d\mathbf{s}'', \quad (4'')$$

$$\mathbf{D}'' = \frac{1}{\alpha\gamma}\mathbf{E}'' + 4\pi\left(\frac{\alpha}{\gamma}\right)\mathbf{P}'' = \frac{\kappa}{\alpha\gamma}\mathbf{E}'', \quad (5'')$$

$$\mathbf{B}'' = \frac{1}{\beta\delta}\mathbf{H}'' + 4\pi\left(\frac{\beta}{\delta}\right)\mathbf{I}'' = \frac{\mu}{\beta\delta}\mathbf{H}'', \quad (6'')$$

$$\mathscr{F}_\tau'' = \rho''\mathbf{E}'' + \frac{\alpha\delta}{c''}\mathbf{j}''\times\mathbf{B}''. \quad (7'')$$

We may use these equations to pass from the practical system of units to other m.k.s. systems, if we wish, but actually we are not concerned here with other m.k.s. systems. Nevertheless, equations $(1'')-(7'')$ are of interest because they are identical in form with equations $(1')-(7')$, so that the practical system, as well as the c.g.s. systems, can be derived from either group of equations. That is, only a single group is required to represent all the systems. The practical system is obtained by putting $\alpha=1/\sqrt{4\pi\kappa_0}$, $\beta=1/\sqrt{4\pi\mu_0}$, $\gamma=\sqrt{4\pi/\kappa_0}$, $\delta=\sqrt{4\pi/\mu_0}$.

Since the fundamental equations can be expressed in terms of the parameters α, β, γ, δ, relations derived from the fundamental equations can be similarly expressed. A list of the more important derived relations is given below. As it is not necessary to distinguish between practical units and c.g.s. units in the generalized form, the distinguishing accents have been omitted. However, appropriate subscripts are added to all quantities, as before, when α, β, γ, δ are given values corresponding to a system of c.g.s. units, or when α, β, γ, δ do not appear and it is desired to indicate c.g.s. units. Those relations, such as (21-1), which do not contain the parameters are, of course, independent of the units employed.

$$(6\text{-}2) \quad \mathscr{F} = \alpha^2 \frac{qq'}{r^2},$$

$$(7\text{-}4) \quad V = \alpha^2 \sum \frac{q}{r},$$

$$(8\text{-}5) \quad \int_s \mathbf{E} \cdot d\mathbf{s} = 4\pi\alpha^2 \int_\tau \rho d\tau,$$

$$(14\text{-}4) \quad \int_s \mathbf{D} \cdot d\mathbf{s} = 4\pi\left(\frac{\alpha}{\gamma}\right) \int_\tau \rho d\tau,$$

$$(15\text{-}10) \quad E = \frac{4\pi\alpha^2\sigma}{\kappa},$$

$$(16\text{-}8) \quad \mathscr{F}_s = \frac{\kappa E^2}{8\pi\alpha^2} = \frac{2\pi\alpha^2\sigma^2}{\kappa},$$

$$(18\text{-}9) \quad C = \frac{\kappa A}{4\pi\alpha^2 d},$$

$$(21\text{-}1) \quad U = \frac{1}{2}\frac{Q^2}{C} = \frac{1}{2}CV^2,$$

$$(21\text{-}9) \quad U = \frac{1}{8\pi\alpha^2} \int_\tau \kappa E^2 \, d\tau,$$

$$(37\text{-}2) \quad \mathscr{F} = \beta^2 \frac{mm'}{r^2},$$

$$(38\text{-}4) \quad V = \beta^2 \sum \frac{m}{r},$$

$$(39\text{-}6) \quad \int_s \mathbf{H} \cdot d\mathbf{s} = 4\pi\beta^2 \int_\tau \rho d\tau,$$

$$(43\text{-}3) \quad \int_s \mathbf{B} \cdot d\mathbf{s} = 0,$$

$$(46\text{-}3) \quad U = \frac{1}{8\pi\beta^2} \int_\tau \mu H^2 \, d\tau,$$

$$(49\text{-}8) \quad \mathscr{P} = Ri^2,$$

$$(68\text{-}6) \quad d\mathbf{H} = \frac{\alpha\beta}{c}\left(i\frac{d\mathbf{l}\times\mathbf{r}}{r^3}\right),$$

$$(68\text{-}12) \quad d\mathscr{F} = \frac{\alpha\delta}{c}\,\mathbf{i}\times\mathbf{B}dl,$$

$$(69\text{-}5) \quad H = \frac{4\pi\alpha\beta n_l i}{c},$$

$$(69\text{-}8) \quad H = \frac{2\alpha\beta i}{cR},$$

$$(88\text{-}4) \quad \mathscr{E} = -\frac{\alpha\delta}{c}\frac{dN}{dt},$$

$$(89\text{-}1) \quad N = \frac{c}{\alpha\delta}Li,$$

$$(91\text{-}3) \quad L\frac{di}{dt}+Ri+\frac{q}{C} = \mathscr{E},$$

$$(92\text{-}4) \quad Z = \sqrt{R^2+\left(L\omega-\frac{1}{C\omega}\right)^2},$$

$$(94\text{-}9) \quad U = \tfrac{1}{2}L_1 i_1{}^2 + M i_1 i_2 + \tfrac{1}{2}L_2 i_2{}^2,$$

$$(95\text{-}7) \quad \mathscr{F}_\xi = \frac{\alpha\delta}{c}\left(i\frac{\partial N}{\partial \xi}\right),$$

$$(96\text{-}4) \quad M = \frac{4\pi\alpha^2\mu m n_l A}{c^2},$$

$$(100\text{-}1) \quad Q = \frac{\alpha\delta}{c}\frac{N_1-N_2}{R},$$

$$(100\text{-}18) \quad B = \frac{c}{\alpha\delta}\frac{RQ}{\hat{n}A}.$$

The procedure explained above is illustrated by the following examples.

(1) $$C = \frac{\kappa A}{4\pi\alpha^2 d}.$$

In g.u., $\alpha = 1$, $\qquad\qquad C_g = \dfrac{\kappa A_g}{4\pi d_g};$

In h.l.u., $\alpha = \dfrac{1}{\sqrt{4\pi}}$, $\qquad C_h = \dfrac{\kappa A_h}{d_h};$

In e.s.u., $\alpha = 1$, $\qquad\qquad C_e = \dfrac{\kappa A_e}{4\pi d_e};$

In e.m.u., $\alpha = c_m$, $\qquad\quad C_m = \dfrac{\kappa A_m}{4\pi c_m{}^2 d_m};$

In pr.u., $\alpha = \dfrac{1}{\sqrt{4\pi\kappa_0}}$, $\qquad C = \dfrac{\kappa_0 \kappa A}{d}.$

(2) $$H = \frac{4\pi\alpha\beta n_l i}{c}.$$

In g.u., $\alpha\beta = 1$, $\qquad\qquad H_g = \dfrac{4\pi n_{lg} i_g}{c_g};$

In e.s.u., $\alpha\beta = c_e$, $\qquad\qquad H_e = 4\pi n_{le} i_e;$

In pr.u., $\alpha\beta = \dfrac{1}{4\pi\sqrt{\kappa_0\mu_0}} = \dfrac{c}{4\pi}$, $H = n_l i.$

(3) $$M = \frac{4\pi\alpha^2 \mu m n_l A}{c^2}.$$

In h.l.u., $\alpha = \dfrac{1}{\sqrt{4\pi}}$, $\qquad\qquad M_h = \dfrac{\mu m n_{lh} A_h}{c_h{}^2};$

In e.m.u., $\alpha = c_m$, $\qquad\qquad M_m = 4\pi\mu m n_{lm} A_m;$

In pr.u., $\alpha = \dfrac{1}{\sqrt{4\pi\kappa_0}} = c\sqrt{\dfrac{\mu_0}{4\pi}}$, $M = \mu_0 \mu m n_l A.$

Although it is convenient, it is not necessary to express a formula in generalized form in order to effect its transformation. We can transform any formula directly, as explained in art. 50, using the general conversion table at the front of the book. In fact, this is often the simpler method when only a single transformation is required. Certain equations, which are really definitions of one of the quantities involved, hold in all systems of units. In addition to (109-1) and (109-4) the following are among these:

$$E_l = -\frac{\partial V}{\partial l}, \qquad\qquad H_l = -\frac{\partial V}{\partial l},$$

$$\mathscr{E} = \oint \mathbf{E} \cdot d\mathbf{l}, \qquad\qquad \mathscr{H} = \oint \mathbf{H} \cdot d\mathbf{l},$$

$$R = \frac{\mathscr{E}}{i}, \qquad\qquad \mathscr{R} = \frac{\mathscr{H}}{N_c},$$

$$C = \frac{Q}{V}, \qquad\qquad N = \int_s \mathbf{B} \cdot d\mathbf{s},$$

$$i = \int_s \mathbf{j} \cdot d\mathbf{s}, \qquad\qquad L = -\frac{\mathscr{E}}{\dfrac{di}{dt}}.$$

Problem 109a. Derive any ten of the generalized relations listed in this article.

Problem 109b. Given the conversion equations in art. 50 for E, D, H, B, work out the complete set of conversion equations for these quantities as they appear in the table at the beginning of the book.

Problem 109c. Suppose that both κ_0 and μ_0 are given the physical dimensions meter^{-1} sec, rather than those specified in art. 6 and art. 37. Find the dimensions of q, E, P, D, m, H, I, B in this case and compare them with the corresponding dimensions in the text.

REFERENCES

Bleaney and Bleaney, *Electricity and Magnetism* (Oxford Univ. Press, 1965). Chap. 24.

Kip, *Electricity and Magnetism* (McGraw-Hill, 1962). Chap. 15.

Shire, *Classical Electricity and Magnetism* (Cambridge Univ. Press, 1960). Pp. 267–279.

Page, *Physics* **2**, 289 (1932); *N.R.C. Bull.* **93**, 39 (1933).

Page and Adams, *J. Franklin Inst.* **218**, 517 (1934); *Am. Phys. Teacher* **3**, 51 (1935).

Birge, *Am. Phys. Teacher* **3**, 102:171 (1935).

Chapter XIII

ALTERNATING CURRENTS

110. Simple A-C Circuits. When a periodic or alternating electromotive force is introduced into a circuit, an alternating current results. The e.m.f. need not be sinusoidal in form, although it very frequently is so in practice. We may restrict our analysis to the sinusoidal case, however, for a non-sinusoidal periodic e.m.f. may be expressed as an infinite series of sinusoidal terms whose frequencies are integral multiples of the fundamental frequency of the e.m.f. The current is then the sum of the currents corresponding to the separate terms in the infinite series. An infinite series of the sort just described is called a *Fourier series*.

We have already made a preliminary study of a simple series circuit with resistance, inductance and capacitance in art. 92. Denoting these quantities by R, L and C, respectively, an applied electromotive force $\mathscr{E}_0 \sin \omega t$ gives rise to a current

$$i = i_0 \sin(\omega t - \phi),$$

where

$$i_0 \equiv \frac{\mathscr{E}_0}{\sqrt{R^2 + \left(L\omega - \dfrac{1}{C\omega}\right)^2}}, \qquad \tan \phi \equiv \frac{L\omega - \dfrac{1}{C\omega}}{R}.$$

These equations were deduced on the assumption that each circuit element consists of a single unit, but, as pointed out in art. 91, R, L and C may also represent resultant values if each element is a combination of units. We know how to calculate these values for series and parallel arrangements of resistances (art. 52) and of capacitances (art. 18). When inductances are placed in series, the total induced e.m.f. is the sum of the separate e.m.f.'s. Hence, if i is the current flowing through the inductances and L is the resultant or equivalent inductance,

$$L \frac{di}{dt} = L_1 \frac{di}{dt} + L_2 \frac{di}{dt} + \cdots L_k \frac{di}{dt} = \left[\sum_1^k L_j\right]\frac{di}{dt},$$

and therefore

$$L = \sum_1^k L_j. \tag{110-1}$$

With inductances in parallel the induced e.m.f. is the same for each inductance, whereas the currents $i_1, i_2, \cdots i_k$ are in general different. Then

$$L\frac{di}{dt} = L_1\frac{di_1}{dt} = L_2\frac{di_2}{dt} = \cdots L_k\frac{di_k}{dt}, \tag{110-2}$$

where $i = i_1 + i_2 + \cdots i_k$ is the total current. Writing (110-2) in the form

$$\frac{L}{L_1}\frac{di}{dt} = \frac{di_1}{dt}, \qquad \frac{L}{L_2}\frac{di}{dt} = \frac{di_2}{dt}, \qquad \cdots \frac{L}{L_k}\frac{di}{dt} = \frac{di_k}{dt},$$

and adding, gives

$$\left(\frac{L}{L_1} + \frac{L}{L_2} + \cdots \frac{L}{L_k}\right)\frac{di}{dt} = \frac{di_1}{dt} + \frac{di_2}{dt} + \cdots \frac{di_k}{dt}.$$

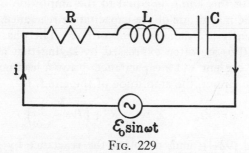

$$\mathscr{E}_0 \sin\omega t$$
Fig. 229

As the right-hand member of this equation is equal to $\dfrac{di}{dt}$, we must have

$$\frac{L}{L_1} + \frac{L}{L_2} + \cdots \frac{L}{L_k} = 1,$$

or, finally,

$$\frac{1}{L} = \sum_1^k \frac{1}{L_j}. \tag{110-3}$$

Thus self-inductances combine, when arranged in series or in parallel, in the same way as resistances.

Let us now return to the original circuit (Fig. 229) and consider the relation between current and e.m.f. across each element. These e.m.f.'s are the potential drops $\mathscr{E}_R$, $\mathscr{E}_L$ and $\mathscr{E}_C$ of art. 91.

The e.m.f. across the resistance is

$$\mathscr{E}_R = Ri = Ri_0 \sin{(\omega t - \phi)}, \qquad (110\text{-}4)$$

which is simply Ohm's law.

The e.m.f. across the inductance is, as shown in art. 89,

$$\mathscr{E}_L = L\frac{di}{dt} = L\omega i_0 \cos{(\omega t - \phi)}. \qquad (110\text{-}5)$$

The amplitude of this e.m.f. is therefore obtained by multiplying the amplitude of the current by the magnitude of the inductive reactance. This is analogous to Ohm's law for the resistance. In this case, however, there is a difference in phase between e.m.f. and current. In fact, since $\cos{(\omega t - \phi)} = \sin{(\omega t - \phi + \pi/2)}$, i lags $\pi/2$ radians behind $\mathscr{E}_L$. This means that the current in the inductance reaches its maximum value a quarter of a period after the e.m.f. across the inductance.

The e.m.f. across the capacitance,

$$\mathscr{E}_C = \frac{q}{C} = -\frac{1}{C\omega} i_0 \cos{(\omega t - \phi)}, \qquad (110\text{-}6)$$

is found from (91-2) by substituting for $\mathscr{E}$ and i their sinusoidal values. The amplitude of this e.m.f. is equal to the amplitude of the current multiplied by the magnitude of the capacitative reactance. As regards phase, i is evidently $\pi/2$ radians ahead of $\mathscr{E}_C$. The phase relations in (110-5) and (110-6) are often expressed by saying that an inductance draws a lagging current and a capacitance draws a leading current.

For the whole circuit, the amplitude of the e.m.f. is

$$\mathscr{E}_0 = Zi_0, \qquad Z \equiv \sqrt{R^2 + \left(L\omega - \frac{1}{C\omega}\right)^2}, \qquad (110\text{-}7)$$

from (92-3) and (92-4); and, denoting the reactance by X, the phase difference is given by

$$\tan{\phi} = \frac{X}{R}, \qquad X \equiv L\omega - \frac{1}{C\omega}. \qquad (110\text{-}8)$$

Evidently (110-7) and (110-8) include the previous results. For let us reduce the circuit to only a resistance by setting $L=0, C=\infty$. Then X and ϕ become zero, so that the amplitude of the e.m.f. across R is Ri_0 and the phase difference is zero. Similarly with $R=0, C=\infty$, the the amplitude of the e.m.f. is $L\omega i_0$ and the lag ϕ is $\pi/2$, while with $R=0, L=0$, the values are $(1/C\omega)i_0$ and $-\pi/2$.

We may also find the relation between current and e.m.f. for any pair of circuit elements. For example, putting $C=\infty$, we see that the amplitude of the e.m.f. across a resistance and an inductance in series is $\sqrt{R^2 + L^2\omega^2}\, i_0$ and the angle of lag is arc tan $(L\omega/R)$.

Problem 110a. Inductances 2 millihenrys and 5 millihenrys respectively are connected in parallel. The combination is placed in series with a resistance 10 ohms and a 1000-cycle e.m.f. whose amplitude is 100 volts. Find the amplitude and the angle of lag of the current in the resistance and in each inductance. Ans. 7.44 amp, 5.31 amp, 2.13 amp; 0.732 radian.

Problem 110b. Find the amplitude and the phase angle (relative to the applied e.m.f.) of the e.m.f.'s across the resistance and the inductances in the preceding problem. Ans. 74.4 volt, −0.732 radian; 66.8 volt, 0.839 radian.

111. Divided Circuits. Often circuits are divided into several branches. A simple illustration of a divided circuit is given in Fig. 230. To find the total current i in this circuit, denote the current through L by i_L and that through C by i_C. Also let the charge on C be q_C. Since

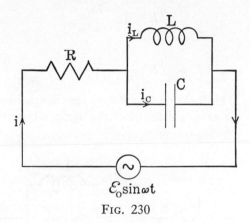

$$\mathscr{E}_0 \sin \omega t$$

Fig. 230

the circuit is divided there are two circuit equations, corresponding to (89-7) and (90-4), respectively. That is,

$$L\frac{di_L}{dt} + Ri = \mathscr{E}_0 \sin \omega t,$$

$$Ri + \frac{q_C}{C} = \mathscr{E}_0 \sin \omega t.$$

Differentiating the second equation twice, multiplying through by LC and adding to the first equation, we obtain

$$RLC\frac{d^2i}{dt^2} + L\frac{di}{dt} + Ri = \mathscr{E}_0(1 - LC\omega^2) \sin \omega t, \qquad (111\text{-}1)$$

since $i_L + i_C = i$. As in the case of (92-1) we know the solution of (111-1) has the form,

$$i = i_0 \sin (\omega t - \phi).$$

Substituting in the differential equation and arranging terms, we have

$$\{(-RLC\omega^2 \cos\phi + L\omega \sin\phi + R\cos\phi)i_0 - \mathscr{E}_0(1-LC\omega^2)\} \sin\omega t$$
$$+ \{RLC\omega^2 \sin\phi + L\omega \cos\phi - R\sin\phi\}i_0 \cos\omega t = 0,$$

showing that to satisfy (111-1) we must have

$$i_0 = \frac{\mathscr{E}_0}{R\cos\phi + \left(\dfrac{L\omega}{1-LC\omega^2}\right)\sin\phi}, \quad \tan\phi = \frac{1}{R}\left(\frac{L\omega}{1-LC\omega^2}\right).$$

The values of $\sin\phi$ and $\cos\phi$ may be obtained from the expression for $\tan\phi$, and we find that

$$i_0 = \frac{\mathscr{E}_0}{\sqrt{R^2 + \left(\dfrac{L\omega}{1-LC\omega^2}\right)^2}}, \tag{111-2}$$

and hence

$$Z = \sqrt{R^2 + \left(\frac{L\omega}{1-LC\omega^2}\right)^2}. \tag{111-3}$$

Inspection of (111-3) shows that $Z = \infty$ for the frequency $1/2\pi\sqrt{LC}$. Because this is the exact antithesis of the series circuit case where the

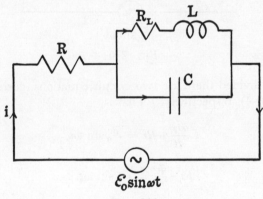

Fig. 231

impedance has a minimum value for this frequency, the circuit is said to be *antiresonant*. Antiresonant circuits are often useful when it is necessary to eliminate certain definite frequencies in a current supply.

Usually, divided circuits are more complicated than the one just discussed. For example, the resistance R_L of an inductance coil often cannot be neglected. Consider the circuit shown in Fig. 231. This may be solved by the same method as before, but, as the reader may easily convince himself, the analysis is quite involved. We, therefore, defer the solution of this and more elaborate circuits and turn our attention to the development of a new and more powerful method of attacking circuit problems which depends on the use of complex quantities.

112. Complex Quantities. Although the square roots of negative numbers have no existence in the domain of real quantities, we often find it necessary to deal with them in analytical problems. A quantity of this type, called an *imaginary*, may evidently be expressed in the form $\pm iy$ where $i \equiv \sqrt{-1}$ and y is the square root of the magnitude of the negative number. The combination of a real quantity and an imaginary is called a *complex quantity*. Thus $x + iy$ and its *conjugate* $x - iy$ are complex quantities. We shall use **black face** type, as in the case of vectors, to distinguish a complex quantity. For example,

$$\mathbf{z} = x + iy. \tag{112-1}$$

Complex numbers obey all the ordinary laws of algebraic manipulation. Thus to add, and to subtract,

$$\left.\begin{aligned} \mathbf{z} + \mathbf{z}' &= (x + iy) + (x' + iy') = (x + x') + i(y + y'), \\ \mathbf{z} - \mathbf{z}' &= (x + iy) - (x' + iy') = (x - x') + i(y - y'). \end{aligned}\right\} \tag{112-2}$$

To multiply, and to divide,

$$\left.\begin{aligned} \mathbf{z}\mathbf{z}' &= (x + iy)(x' + iy') = (xx' - yy') + i(xy' + x'y), \\ \frac{\mathbf{z}}{\mathbf{z}'} &= \frac{x + iy}{x' + iy'} = \frac{(x + iy)(x' - iy')}{x'^2 + y'^2} \\ &= \left(\frac{xx' + yy'}{x'^2 + y'^2}\right) - i\left(\frac{xy' - x'y}{x'^2 + y'^2}\right). \end{aligned}\right\} \tag{112-3}$$

It is important to observe that since the real and the imaginary parts of a complex equation are entirely independent, such an equation represents two real equations. If we set

$$\mathbf{z} + \mathbf{z}' = \mathbf{z}\mathbf{z}',$$

for instance, we must have

$$x + x' = xx' - yy',$$
$$y + y' = xy' + x'y.$$

We may represent $\mathbf{z}$ graphically by a point in the XY plane, taking the X axis as the *real axis* and the Y axis as the *imaginary axis*. In Fig. 232 are shown $\mathbf{z}$, $\mathbf{z}'$ and $\mathbf{z} + \mathbf{z}'$. Evidently, if we think of the lines from the origin to the given points rather than of the points themselves as representing the complex quantities, the addition of complex quantities is, graphically, exactly like the addition of vectors. That is, the directed lines are placed head to tail and a closing line drawn to obtain the sum. Similarly, subtraction is effected graphically by reversing the direction of the representative line and then adding.

The vector properties of complex quantities suggest that it may be

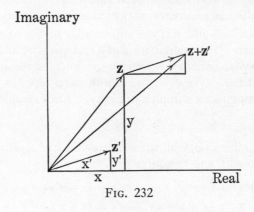

Fig. 232

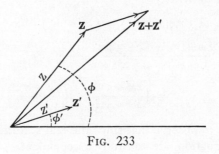

Fig. 233

convenient to express the latter in terms of amplitude and direction as well as in terms of real and imaginary parts. In polar coordinates z, ϕ,

$$x = z \cos \phi, \qquad y = z \sin \phi; \qquad (112\text{-}4)$$

and, conversely,

$$z = \sqrt{x^2 + y^2}, \qquad \tan \phi = \frac{y}{x}. \qquad (112\text{-}5)$$

These relations are illustrated in Fig. 233, which shows the same quantities as Fig. 232, in terms of z and ϕ.

The polar form $z = z(\cos \phi + i \sin \phi)$ leads us to an important result, for

$$\cos \phi + i \sin \phi = e^{i\phi}, \tag{112-6}$$

as may be seen by expanding all terms in infinite series, where $e = 2.718 \cdots$ is the base of the Napierian logarithms, as usual. Therefore

$$z = z e^{i\phi}. \tag{112-7}$$

The exponential form of complex quantities is very convenient for multiplication and division, just as the rectangular form is especially adapted to addition and subtraction. Thus,

$$\left. \begin{aligned} zz' &= (ze^{i\phi})(z'e^{i\phi'}) = zz'e^{i(\phi+\phi')}, \\ \frac{z}{z'} &= \frac{ze^{i\phi}}{z'e^{i\phi'}} = \frac{z}{z'} e^{i(\phi-\phi')}. \end{aligned} \right\} \tag{112-8}$$

Graphically, multiplication or division by a complex number is represented by a change of amplitude and a rotation of the quantity affected. For example, multiplying z' by z increases the amplitude of the former by a factor z and rotates it through an angle ϕ. A special case of interest is multiplication by i. Since $i = e^{i\pi/2}$, this merely causes rotation through $\pi/2$ radians. Similarly division by i causes a rotation of $-\pi/2$ radians.

From (112-2) and (112-8) we may formulate the rules for combining complex quantities:

(I) *In addition (subtraction) the components of the sum (difference) are equal respectively to the sum (difference) of the components.*

(II) *In multiplication (division) the amplitude of the product (quotient) is equal to the product (quotient) of the amplitudes, and the angle of the product (quotient) is equal to the sum (difference) of the angles.*

In the course of complex analysis we express quantities in rectangular or in exponential form according to convenience, passing from one to the other by means of (112-4) and (112-5). Numerous examples of this procedure will be found in following articles.

Problem 112a. Show that

$$\sqrt{x+iy} = \pm \frac{1}{\sqrt{2}} \left(\sqrt{\sqrt{x^2+y^2}+x} + i\sqrt{\sqrt{x^2+y^2}-x} \right).$$

Problem 112b. Prove that if n is an integer

$$\sqrt[n]{i} = \cos \left(\frac{\frac{\pi}{2}+2\pi p}{n} \right) + i \sin \left(\frac{\frac{\pi}{2}+2\pi p}{n} \right); \quad p = 0, 1, \cdots (n-1).$$

Problem 112c. Show that

$$(\cos \phi + i \sin \phi)^n = \cos n\phi + i \sin n\phi.$$

Problem 112d. Find the value of i^1. Ans. 0.208

Problem 112e. Find the real part and also the amplitude of

$$\left(\frac{1-2i}{4+2i}\right)(2+5i).$$

Ans. 5/2, $\sqrt{29}/2$.

113. Application of Complex Quantities to A-C Circuits. In order to see how complex quantities may be used in solving a-c circuit problems, consider again the differential equation of a simple series circuit (art. 92). This equation is

$$L\frac{d^2i}{dt^2}+R\frac{di}{dt}+\frac{1}{C}i = \frac{d\mathscr{E}}{dt}.$$

Suppose we indicate the solution corresponding to $\mathscr{E}=\mathscr{E}_0\cos\omega t$ by i_x and that corresponding to $\mathscr{E}=\mathscr{E}_0\sin\omega t$ by i_y. Then

$$L\frac{d^2i_x}{dt^2}+R\frac{di_x}{dt}+\frac{1}{C}i_x = \frac{d}{dt}(\mathscr{E}_0\cos\omega t),$$

$$L\frac{d^2i_y}{dt^2}+R\frac{di_y}{dt}+\frac{1}{C}i_y = \frac{d}{dt}(\mathscr{E}_0\sin\omega t).$$

Multiplying the second of these equations by i and adding it to the first gives

$$L\frac{d^2\mathbf{i}}{dt^2}+R\frac{d\mathbf{i}}{dt}+\frac{1}{C}\mathbf{i} = \frac{d}{dt}(\mathscr{E}_0 e^{i\omega t}), \qquad (113\text{-}1)$$

where $\mathbf{i}=i_x+ii_y$. Thus, in solving the circuit problem, if we replace the actual sinusoidal e.m.f. by a corresponding complex e.m.f., we obtain a complex current whose real part is the current due to an applied cosine e.m.f. and whose imaginary part is the current due to an applied sine e.m.f. The utility of this procedure lies in the fact that it is simpler to solve the differential equation in the complex form than in the real form. This is not of great importance in the case of (113-1), but the method is applicable to all a-c circuit problems and is of very great value in the more complicated cases.

Let us now solve (113-1). The solution must be of the form $\mathbf{i}_0 e^{i\omega t}$, since current and e.m.f. have the same frequency. Substituting in the differential equation,

$$\left(-L\omega^2+Ri\omega+\frac{1}{C}\right)\mathbf{i}_0 e^{i\omega t} = \mathscr{E}_0 i\omega e^{i\omega t},$$

so, in order that (113-1) may be satisfied, we must have

$$\mathbf{i}_0 = \frac{\mathscr{E}_0}{R+i\left(L\omega-\frac{1}{C\omega}\right)}. \qquad (113\text{-}2)$$

The denominator of the right-hand side of (113-2) is the *complex impedance* **Z** of the circuit.   Its amplitude

$$Z = \sqrt{R^2 + \left(L\omega - \frac{1}{C\omega}\right)^2}$$

is the real impedance to which we are accustomed, and its angle ϕ, given by

$$\tan \phi = \frac{L\omega - \dfrac{1}{C\omega}}{R},$$

is the angle of lag.

Expressing **Z** in exponential form,

$$\mathbf{i} = \frac{\mathscr{E}_0}{Z e^{i\phi}} e^{i\omega t} = \frac{\mathscr{E}_0}{Z} e^{i(\omega t - \phi)}. \tag{113-3}$$

The actual current corresponding to an applied e.m.f. $\mathscr{E}_0 \sin \omega t$ is the imaginary part of (113-3), that is,

$$i = \frac{\mathscr{E}_0}{Z} \sin (\omega t - \phi),$$

which is the value previously found in (92-2).   Since actual values are obtained so simply from the complex expressions, circuit problems often reduce merely to a calculation of impedance.

From (113-3) the relation in complex form between the applied e.m.f. and the current is seen to be

$$\mathscr{E} = \mathbf{Z}\mathbf{i}. \tag{113-4}$$

The quantity **Z**i is equal to the sum of the e.m.f.'s across the circuit elements R, L and C, since, in accord with (110-4), (110-5) and (110-6), these e.m.f.'s are, respectively,

$$\left.\begin{array}{l} \mathscr{E}_R = R\mathbf{i}, \\[2mm] \mathscr{E}_L = L\dfrac{d\mathbf{i}}{dt} = \mathbf{i}L\omega\mathbf{i}, \\[2mm] \mathscr{E}_C = \dfrac{\mathbf{q}}{C} = -\mathbf{i}\dfrac{1}{C\omega}\mathbf{i}. \end{array}\right\} \tag{113-5}$$

In each case the e.m.f. is equal to the impedance of the element multiplied by the current.   It should be borne in mind that $\mathscr{E}_R$, $\mathscr{E}_L$ and $\mathscr{E}_C$ are potential drops.

Evidently a relation of the form (113-4) holds not only for a simple series circuit, but for any circuit.   The value of **Z** depends, of course, on the arrangement of circuit elements involved, but it is always of the form

$$\mathbf{Z} = \hat{R} + i\hat{X},$$

where $\hat{R}$ is the equivalent series resistance, and $\hat{X}$ is the equivalent reactance. Comparing (113-4) with Ohm's law in real form, $\mathscr{E} = Ri$, it is evident that in an a-c circuit complex impedances behave exactly as real resistances do in a d-c circuit. Thus, impedances in series add directly, and impedances in parallel add by reciprocals. Since the impedances of the elements R, L and C are R, $iL\omega$ and $-i\dfrac{1}{C\omega}$, respectively, we can easily calculate the impedance of any series and parallel combination of them.

We are now able to deal with the circuit of Fig. 231. The impedance of the upper branch of the divided circuit is $R_L + iL\omega$ and that of the lower $-i\dfrac{1}{C\omega}$. Therefore, the impedance of the divided portion of the circuit is

$$\frac{1}{\dfrac{1}{R_L + iL\omega} + \dfrac{1}{-i\dfrac{1}{C\omega}}} = \frac{R_L + iL\omega}{(1 - LC\omega^2) + iR_L C\omega}.$$

Multiplying numerator and denominator by the conjugate of the latter reduces the expression to the standard form

$$\frac{R_L}{(1 - LC\omega^2)^2 + R_L^2 C^2\omega^2} + i\,\frac{L\omega(1 - LC\omega^2) - R_L^2 C\omega}{(1 - LC\omega^2)^2 + R_L^2 C^2\omega^2},$$

and $\mathbf{Z}$ is obtained by adding R. Setting

$$\left.\begin{aligned} \hat{R} &\equiv R + \frac{R_L}{(1 - LC\omega^2)^2 + R_L^2 C^2\omega^2}, \\[2mm] \hat{X} &\equiv \frac{L\omega(1 - LC\omega^2) - R_L^2 C\omega}{(1 - LC\omega^2)^2 + R_L^2 C^2\omega^2}, \end{aligned}\right\} \tag{113-6}$$

the amplitude and angle of $\mathbf{Z}$ are given by

$$Z = \sqrt{\hat{R}^2 + \hat{X}^2}, \qquad \tan\phi = \frac{\hat{X}}{\hat{R}}.$$

A divided circuit of the type under discussion is, by definition, antiresonant when its equivalent reactance vanishes. Hence, putting $\hat{X} = 0$, the antiresonant frequency is found to be

$$\nu_a = \frac{1}{2\pi}\sqrt{\frac{1}{LC} - \frac{R_L^2}{L^2}}. \tag{113-7}$$

Evidently this does not differ appreciably from the series resonant frequency $\nu_r = 1/2\pi\sqrt{LC}$ if R_L^2/L^2 is small compared with $1/LC$, which it usually is in practice. In this case we may take $\nu_a = \nu_r$. At antiresonance the impedance of the circuit is equal to $R + L/CR_L$, which becomes infinite if R_L is reduced to zero as in the ideal circuit of Fig. 230.

In the foregoing discussion we have assumed that the frequency can be adjusted to the value ν_a. Of course, if ν is fixed, antiresonance is obtained by varying L or C so as to make $\nu_a = \nu$.

Returning to (113-4), we observe that while this relation is of convenient form when circuit elements or parts of circuits are in series, an expression of the form

$$\mathbf{i} = \mathbf{Y}\mathscr{E}, \tag{113-8}$$

is better suited for parallel combinations. We therefore define the *complex admittance* $\mathbf{Y}$ as the reciprocal of $\mathbf{Z}$. As the admittances of the elements R, L and C are respectively $\dfrac{1}{R}$, $-i\,\dfrac{1}{L\omega}$ and $iC\omega$ the total admittance of R, L and C in parallel is

$$\mathbf{Y} = \frac{1}{R} - i\left(\frac{1}{L\omega} - C\omega\right) \equiv G - iB, \tag{113-9}$$

where G is called the *conductance* and B the *susceptance*. In the exponential form

$$\mathbf{Y} = Ye^{-i\phi}, \tag{113-10}$$

where

$$Y = \sqrt{G^2 + B^2}, \qquad \tan\phi = \frac{B}{G}.$$

The admittance for a more complicated combination of circuit elements always has the general form

$$\mathbf{Y} = \hat{G} - i\hat{B},$$

in which $\hat{G}$ is the equivalent parallel conductance and $\hat{B}$ is the equivalent susceptance. For example, the admittance corresponding to $\mathbf{Z} = R + iX$ is

$$\mathbf{Y} = \frac{1}{R + iX} = \frac{R - iX}{R^2 + X^2} = \frac{R}{Z^2} - i\,\frac{X}{Z^2}.$$

Hence, in this case,

$$\hat{G} = \frac{R}{Z^2}, \qquad \hat{B} = \frac{X}{Z^2}.$$

The relation between current and e.m.f. in any circuit may be determined by calculating either $\mathbf{Z}$ or $\mathbf{Y}$, of course. One calculation is usually found to be simpler than the other, however.

There is one restriction on the use of complex quantities in circuit analysis which must be mentioned. They cannot be used to calculate power directly, because the real or imaginary part of $\mathscr{E}\mathbf{i}$ is not equal to the product of the real or imaginary parts of $\mathscr{E}$ and $\mathbf{i}$ respectively. To find the power at any instant we must find the actual e.m.f. and the actual current and multiply these real quantities together.

Problem 113a. Deduce (110-4) to (110-6), inclusive, by means of complex quantities.

Problem 113b. Find the current in the circuit of Fig. 230, using complex analysis.

$$\text{Ans. } i = \frac{\mathscr{E}_0}{\sqrt{R^2 + \left(\dfrac{L\omega}{1 - LC\omega^2}\right)^2}} \sin(\omega t - \phi), \quad \tan\phi \equiv \frac{1}{R}\left(\frac{L\omega}{1 - LC\omega^2}\right).$$

Problem 113c. Given a current $i = i_0 \sin(\omega t + \epsilon)$ flowing through R and L in parallel. Find the e.m.f.

$$\text{Ans. } \frac{RL\omega i_0}{\sqrt{R^2 + L^2\omega^2}} \sin(\omega t + \epsilon + \phi), \quad \tan\phi \equiv \frac{R}{L\omega}.$$

Problem 113d. In the circuit of Fig. 231 the resistance R_L in series with L is removed, and an equal resistance R_C is placed in series with C. Find $\mathbf{Z}$. Also, show that $\mathbf{Z}$ has the same value at antiresonance for both circuits.

$$\text{Ans. } \mathbf{Z} = \left[R + \frac{R_C L^2 C^2 \omega^4}{(1 - LC\omega^2)^2 + R_C^2 C^2 \omega^2}\right] + i\left[\frac{L\omega(1 - LC\omega^2) + R_C^2 LC^2\omega^3}{(1 - LC\omega^2)^2 + R_C^2 C^2 \omega^2}\right].$$

Problem 113e. In the circuit of Fig. 231 an additional resistance R_C is included, in series with C. Find $\mathbf{Z}$ if $R_L = R_C = \sqrt{L/C}$. Ans. $\mathbf{Z} = R + \sqrt{L/C}$.

114. Graphical Representation of Electric Quantities.

Electric quantities in complex form may be represented graphically, according to the method illustrated in art. 112. Graphical representations are often of great value in understanding the behavior of complicated circuits and graphical analysis is particularly useful to the engineer in designing electrical machinery and other apparatus.

Figure 234 shows an impedance

$$\mathbf{Z} = R + i\left(L\omega - \frac{1}{C\omega}\right),$$

and Fig. 235 an admittance

$$\mathbf{Y} = \frac{1}{R} - i\left(\frac{1}{L\omega} - C\omega\right).$$

A more complicated case, the impedance of the circuit of Fig. 231, is shown in Fig. 236.   Line 1 is the impedance of the upper branch of the divided circuit, and its reciprocal (line 2) is the corresponding admittance.   Adding $iC\omega$ we obtain line 3, the admittance of the divided part of the circuit.   The reciprocal of this (line 4) is the corresponding impedance, to which we add R and obtain $\mathbf{Z}$.   The diagram as drawn indicates a frequency condition below antiresonance, since ϕ is positive. This follows from (113-6).

Often it is more instructive to show currents and e.m.f.'s directly on the diagram, rather than impedances and admittances.   In this case we usually dispense with the axes as we are interested only in the *relative* phases of the electric quantities.   A graphical representation of currents and e.m.f.'s is called a *vector diagram* although the quantities represented are not true vectors in the physical sense.

To illustrate such a diagram we may use again the divided circuit to

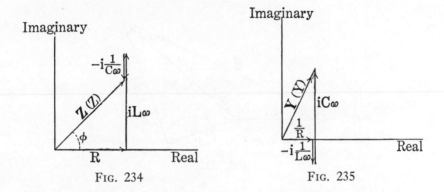

FIG. 234   FIG. 235

which Fig. 236 refers.   Denoting the current through the upper branch by i_L and that through the lower branch by i_C, the current and e.m.f. relations are represented by Fig. 237.   Angles measured counterclockwise indicate a lead in phase.   The diagram shows that the applied e.m.f. $\mathscr{E}$ is the sum of Ri and the e.m.f. across the divided portion of the circuit.   This last e.m.f. is, in turn, the sum of $R_L i_L$ and the e.m.f. across L.   As regards the currents, the total current $\mathbf{i}$, which is in phase with Ri, is the sum of i_L, which is in phase with $R_L i_L$, and i_C, which leads the condenser e.m.f. by $\pi/2$ radians.

Note that if we are interested in the actual or *instantaneous* values of the electric quantities, we may draw the real and the imaginary axes and project the entire diagram on them.   As $\mathscr{E} = \mathscr{E}_0 e^{i\omega t}$, the projection on the real axis at any instant gives the instantaneous values for an applied cosine e.m.f., and the projection on the imaginary axis gives the corresponding values for an applied sine e.m.f.   Since the phase of each of the electric quantities contains ωt, the angles of the vectors increase uniformly with time, which is equivalent to a rotation of the vector diagram about the origin. The variation of the projections due to the

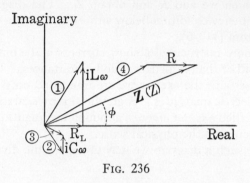

Fig. 236

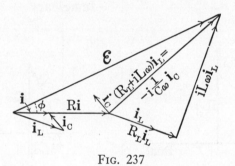

Fig. 237

rotation represents the actual sinusoidal variation of the instantaneous values.

Problem 114. Draw the vector diagram of a divided circuit with a resistance R_C in series with the capacitance instead of R_L in series with the inductance.

115. A-C Networks and Kirchhoff's Laws. When an a-c network is so arranged that it cannot be analyzed into series and parallel groups of circuit elements a fundamental treatment is required, as in the analogous d-c case (art. 52). Evidently Kirchhoff's laws can be generalized to apply to a-c networks. As in the d-c case there can be no continual accumulation of charge at a junction, so Law I of art. 52 remains unchanged. On the other hand, Law II assumes a more complicated form. Consider any closed path in the network, made up of three or more network branches each of which may contain an applied e.m.f. together with inductance, capacitance and resistance. Now, just as for the simple circuit of art. 91, we have for each branch a relation of the form

$$\mathcal{E}+\mathcal{E}_i+(\mathcal{E}_A+\mathcal{E}_L+\mathcal{E}_C+\mathcal{E}_R) = Ri+\frac{q}{C}$$

in the notation of that article. Here, however, the expression within parentheses does not vanish. But if we sum around the closed path, we have $\sum(\mathcal{E}_A+\mathcal{E}_L+\mathcal{E}_C+\mathcal{E}_R)=0$ since the summation represents the e.m.f. due to static charges around a complete circuit. Hence, replacing $\mathcal{E}_i$ by $-L\dfrac{di}{dt}$, we obtain

$$\sum\left(L\frac{di}{dt}+Ri+\frac{q}{C}\right) = \sum\mathcal{E}$$

for any closed path in the network, as the analytical form of Law II. In this form the law holds for any type of varying current, whether sinusoidal or not. The left-hand side of the equation is the sum of the e.m.f.'s across the various circuit elements included in the closed path and the right-hand side is the sum of the applied e.m.f.'s. In the case of sinusoidal currents, if we express the a-c network equations in terms of real currents and e.m.f.'s, they are awkward to solve, except in the case of a pure resistive network, because of the phase differences involved. In terms of complex quantities, however, the sum of the e.m.f.'s across the circuit elements is given simply by $\sum \mathbf{Z}i$, where the $\mathbf{Z}$'s are the branch impedances. This follows at once from (113-5). Thus we may state the generalized Kirchhoff's laws in the complex form:

LAW I. *The algebraic sum of all the complex currents meeting at a junction is zero.*

LAW II. *The algebraic sum of the $\mathbf{Z}i$ terms around any closed path equals the algebraic sum of the complex applied e.m.f.'s in the given path.*

Consider, for example, a network of the Wheatstone bridge type (Fig. 238), in which each branch, except the one with the e.m.f., contains an impedance of any form. Since the equations arising from Kirchhoff's laws have exactly the same form as for the d-c bridge (art. 53), the solutions also have the same form. Hence, referring to (53-1), we see that the complex current in the galvanometer arm is

$$\mathbf{i}_g = \frac{(\mathbf{Z}_2\mathbf{Z}_3-\mathbf{Z}_4\mathbf{Z}_1)\mathcal{E}}{\Delta+\mathbf{Z}_g(\mathbf{Z}_1+\mathbf{Z}_2)(\mathbf{Z}_3+\mathbf{Z}_4)}, \tag{115-1}$$

where

$$\Delta \equiv \mathbf{Z}_1\mathbf{Z}_2\mathbf{Z}_3+\mathbf{Z}_2\mathbf{Z}_3\mathbf{Z}_4+\mathbf{Z}_3\mathbf{Z}_4\mathbf{Z}_1+\mathbf{Z}_4\mathbf{Z}_1\mathbf{Z}_2.$$

The actual current i_g is found by taking the real or the imaginary part of (115-1), as usual.

When the bridge is balanced $\mathbf{i}_g = 0$, so that we must have

$$\frac{\mathbf{Z}_1}{\mathbf{Z}_2} = \frac{\mathbf{Z}_3}{\mathbf{Z}_4}. \tag{115-2}$$

This result may also be obtained by observing that, at balance,

$$\mathbf{Z}_1\mathbf{i}_1 = \mathbf{Z}_3\mathbf{i}_3, \qquad \mathbf{Z}_2\mathbf{i}_2 = \mathbf{Z}_4\mathbf{i}_4.$$

Dividing the first equation by the second gives (115-2), since $\mathbf{i}_1 = \mathbf{i}_2$, and $\mathbf{i}_3 = \mathbf{i}_4$.

A common variety of this bridge, the *inductance bridge*, is shown in

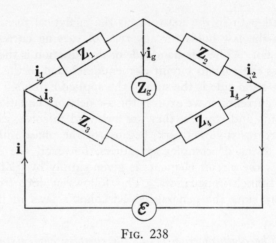

Fig. 238

Fig. 239. Usually L_1 is an unknown inductance of resistance R_1, while L_3 is a known adjustable inductance of resistance R_3. The resistances R_2 and R_4 are also known and adjustable. Equation (115-2), the condition for balance, reduces in this case to

$$\frac{R_1 + iL_1\omega}{R_2} = \frac{R_3 + iL_3\omega}{R_4}. \tag{115-3}$$

Equating real parts and imaginary parts, we find

$$\frac{R_1}{R_2} = \frac{R_3}{R_4}, \qquad \frac{L_1}{R_2} = \frac{L_3}{R_4}.$$

The double condition for balance is characteristic of a-c bridges. The first relation corresponds to an ordinary d-c balance and is established with the aid of a constant e.m.f. and a d-c current indicator, R_2

or R_4 being adjusted. Then an alternating e.m.f. and an a-c current indicator are put in place of the others and the second (inductive) relation is established by adjusting L_3, care being taken not to disturb the d-c balance. The unknown L_1 is now determined in terms of L_3, R_2 and R_4.

Although the simultaneous solution of the junction and the loop equations does not present any difficulty for a network such as shown in Fig. 238, it is desirable to write the circuit equations in a more compact and symmetrical form, especially when the number of branches is large. Since the circuit equations are linear, every branch current can be expressed as the algebraic sum of a number of loop currents each of

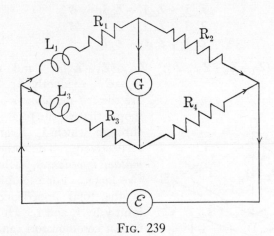

Fig. 239

which is continuous around a closed path in the network. The loop currents satisfy Law I individually, so that the junction equations are satisfied automatically and only the loop equations in terms of the loop currents remain to be solved.

To illustrate the use of loop currents, let us suppose that loop currents i_a, i_b and i_c flow in the network of Fig. 238, the relation between these currents and the branch currents being shown schematically in Fig. 240.

Since

$$\left.\begin{aligned} i_1 &= i_a + i_b, & i_2 &= i_a, \\ i_3 &= -i_a - i_b + i_c, & i_4 &= -i_a + i_c, \\ i &= i_c, & i_g &= i_b, \end{aligned}\right\} \quad (115\text{-}4)$$

the loop equations

$$\left.\begin{aligned} Z_1 i_1 + Z_2 i_2 - Z_4 i_4 - Z_3 i_3 &= 0, \\ Z_1 i_1 + Z_g i_g - Z_3 i_3 &= 0, \\ Z_3 i_3 + Z_4 i_4 &= \mathscr{E}, \end{aligned}\right\} \quad (115\text{-}5)$$

become

$$(Z_1+Z_2+Z_3+Z_4)i_a+(Z_1+Z_3)i_b+(-Z_3-Z_4)i_c = 0,$$
$$(Z_1+Z_3)i_a+(Z_1+Z_g+Z_3)i_b+(-Z_3)i_c = 0,$$
$$(-Z_3-Z_4)i_a+(-Z_3)i_b+(Z_3+Z_4)i_c = \mathscr{E}.$$

$$(115\text{-}6)$$

Solving these and using the simple relations contained in (115-4), we obtain the branch currents, but with less labor than before. When only one branch current, such as i_g, is required, the labor is reduced to a minimum by choosing the loop currents in such a way that one of them, i_b in this case, is identical with the required branch current.

Let us examine the constants appearing in the loop equations after writing them in the completely symmetrical form

$$Z_{aa}i_a+Z_{ab}i_b+Z_{ac}i_c = \mathscr{E}_a,$$
$$Z_{ba}i_a+Z_{bb}i_b+Z_{bc}i_c = \mathscr{E}_b,$$
$$Z_{ca}i_a+Z_{cb}i_b+Z_{cc}i_c = \mathscr{E}_c,$$

$$(115\text{-}7)$$

where $Z_{aa}\equiv(Z_1+Z_2+Z_3+Z_4)$, $Z_{ab}\equiv(Z_1+Z_2)$, $\cdots$ and $\mathscr{E}_a=\mathscr{E}_b\equiv0$, $\mathscr{E}_c\equiv\mathscr{E}$. Evidently Z_{aa}, Z_{bb} and Z_{cc} are the *self-impedances* of the three loops, that is, the total impedances through which i_a, i_b and i_c flow, respectively. The other Z's are *mutual impedances*, each shared by two loops. For example, $Z_{ab}=Z_{ba}$ is the total impedance traversed jointly by i_a and i_b, while $Z_{ac}=Z_{ca}$ is that common to i_a and i_c. Note in each case that the mutual impedance terms are positive if the two loop currents have the same direction through them, and nega-

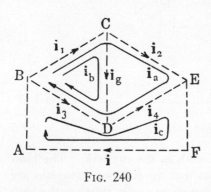

Fig. 240

tive if they have opposite directions. Finally, $\mathscr{E}_a$, $\mathscr{E}_b$ and $\mathscr{E}_c$ represent the algebraic sums of the applied e.m.f.'s contained in the three loops, respectively.

Evidently loop equations in the form (115-7), with the required number of independent loop currents, apply to any network, and it is unnecessary to write them down in the form corresponding to (115-5), since the self and mutual impedances are known as soon as the loop currents have been specified. It is particularly advantageous to use equations (115-7) for the investigation of general properties of networks. Either the fundamental branch current method or the derived loop current method may be used, as preferred, for the solution of any particular network.

When a network contains several applied e.m.f.'s of the same frequency, it is necessary that they all be given as cosines or all as sines, with appropriate phase angles, before they are expressed in complex form. Otherwise the actual solutions cannot be obtained by taking real parts of the complex solutions throughout or imaginary parts throughout. If some of the e.m.f.'s have different frequencies, actual solutions for each frequency must be obtained separately and added together to obtain the complete solution.

Problem 115. Obtain (115-1) by the loop current method.

116. A-C Measuring Instruments.

Alternating currents and e.m.f.'s cannot be measured with an ordinary instrument of the d'Arsonval type because even at low frequencies the inertia of the moving element is too great to permit the latter to follow the alternating torque, and the mean torque, to which any steady deflection must be due, is zero. We may, however, use the *dynamometer* type of instrument, in which both the fixed and the moving element consist of coils. The torque at any instant on the moving part is proportional to the product of the currents in the two elements from (95-6). If these currents are drawn from the same source, the mean torque is, in general, not zero, so that a steady deflection results.

When the elements are connected in series, so that the same current i flows in each, the deflection is proportional to the mean value of i^2, which by definition (art. 92) is $\hat{i}^2$, the square of the effective current. Alternating-current ammeters and voltmeters are often instruments of this sort. The ammeters are made with as low resistance as possible, so they may be included in a circuit without disturbing it appreciably. The voltmeters, on the other hand, are made with high resistance, so they may be placed across any part of a circuit with negligible effect. Both ammeters and voltmeters are calibrated to indicate effective (r.m.s.) values. Because the scale is of the "squared" type, small values are determined with less accuracy than large, which is often a serious defect.

In addition to the measurement of current and e.m.f., it is important to be able to determine the mean power supplied to a circuit or to part of a circuit. This can be done by means of a dynamometer instrument with one low resistance element and one high resistance element. The former is connected in series with the load, and the latter across it (Fig. 241). The instantaneous torque on the moving element is therefore proportional to $\mathscr{E}i$, where $\mathscr{E}$ is the e.m.f. across the load and i is the current through it. The mean torque—and hence the deflection— is proportional to the mean value of $\mathscr{E}i$, which is the mean power. The instrument just described is called a *wattmeter*. It is accurate and can be constructed for almost any power range desired, but, in common with all dynamometer type instruments, its use is limited to relatively low frequencies, not over a few hundred cycles per second.

There are other types of a-c instruments beside the dynamometer. One of the most widely used is the *moving iron* type in which two parallel pieces of soft iron, one fixed and one movable, are surrounded by a single coil coaxial with the moving element. Current in the coil produces a magnetic field which magnetizes the two pieces of iron. The resulting mutual repulsion causes the movable iron to be deflected. Moving iron instruments, like dynamometers, are restricted to low frequencies. For high frequencies thermocouple meters such as described in art. 64, or other special devices, must be employed.

For null measurements, such as are involved in balancing a-c bridges, an instrument sensitive to small currents is required. In the range of audio frequencies, that is, up to a few thousand cycles per second, a telephone receiver serves very well. For low frequencies a *vibration galvanometer* (Fig. 242) is more suitable. This resembles a d'Arsonval galvanometer in that it contains a fixed magnet and a moving coil. The method of suspending the coil, however is different. The coil, which is made very small, is held between two metal strips whose length and tension may be varied until the period of mechanical oscillation of the moving element is exactly equal to the period of the current in the coil. In this condition of resonance the periodic force due to a very small current builds up vibrations of considerable amplitude. A small mirror mounted on the coil reflects a spot of light on a scale. During vibration the spot of light is drawn out into a band. For greater convenience and wider frequency ranges electronic null indicators may be used.

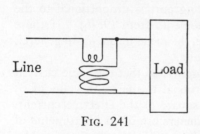

FIG. 241

Finally we shall describe an important instrument which is of an entirely different nature from those discussed above. This is the *cathode-ray oscillograph*, a device for examining the wave form of an e.m.f. It consists of an evacuated cathode-ray tube (Fig. 243) together with its external power and control circuits. Within the tube an "electron gun" G produces a sharply defined beam of electrons whose speed corresponds to an accelerating potential of several thousand volts. The beam, after passing between a pair of horizontal deflection plates H and a pair of vertical deflection plates V, impinges on a screen SS of fluorescent material placed on the glass which forms the end of the tube.   Impact of the electrons on the screen produces a luminous spot which moves when the beam is deflected.   In order that the spot may trace a curve showing the e.m.f. as a function of the time, a periodic potential difference called the *sweep voltage* is applied between

FIG. 242

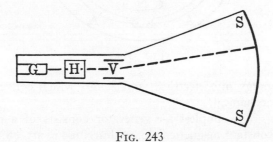

FIG. 243

the horizontal plates.   Because of the resulting field, the spot sweeps across the screen in a horizontal direction at a uniform rate.   When it reaches the edge of the screen, it returns in a negligibly small fraction of the sweep time to its starting point and begins the next sweep.   Simultaneously the e.m.f. whose wave form is required is applied between the vertical plates. Ordinarily the curve representing the wave form is traced in a small fraction of a second, too fast for the eye to follow. However, if the wave form is repeated periodically and the sweep frequency is properly adjusted, the curve is continually retraced. A steady picture of the wave form is then obtained, as a result of a slight persistence of the fluorescence of the screen. A permanent print or photograph of the wave form, such as that reproduced in Fig. 187, is called an *oscillogram*.

The cathode-ray oscillograph appears in a variety of forms depending on the service for which it is designed. It is of great value in the adjustment of complicated vacuum tube circuits, especially at high frequencies.

117. A-C Machinery. Alternating-current machinery may be divided into two classes—*generators* or *alternators* which convert

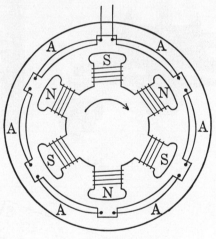

Fig. 244

mechanical energy into electrical, and *motors* which convert electrical energy into mechanical.

Generators. The simplest a-c generator consists of a coil of wire rotating in a constant magnetic field, as described in art. 88. However, in order to generate a sufficient e.m.f. several coils in series, wound on an iron frame, and an equal number of field magnets are usually employed. The former comprise the *armature* and the latter the *field*. Since the armature winding is more complicated and requires better insulation than the field, it is usual practice to keep it stationary and to rotate the field. In any case the stationary part is called the *stator*, and the rotating part the *rotor*.

A typical arrangement is shown in Fig. 244. The armature coils (A), each of which contains a number of turns, lie in slots in the frame while the field windings are placed on salient pole pieces attached to the rotating element. The direct current necessary to excite the field is supplied through brushes resting on *slip rings*.

The machine just illustrated is a *single-phase generator*. That is, it produces a single e.m.f. of the form $\mathscr{E} = \mathscr{E}_0 \sin \omega t$ between its terminals. For the efficient operation of motors, however, several e.m.f.'s of uniform phase difference are desirable. A *polyphase generator* is exactly like a single-phase generator except that it has as many independent sets of armature coils as there are phases, uniformly spaced

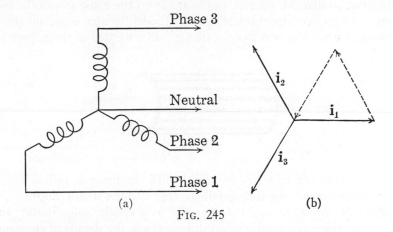

FIG. 245

around the armature frame. For example, a three-phase generator, which is the most common, produces e.m.f.'s.

$$\mathscr{E}_1 = \mathscr{E}_{10} \sin \omega t,$$

$$\mathscr{E}_2 = \mathscr{E}_{20} \sin \left(\omega t + \frac{2\pi}{3} \right),$$

$$\mathscr{E}_3 = \mathscr{E}_{30} \sin \left(\omega t + \frac{4\pi}{3} \right).$$

To transmit power from a three-phase machine, four wires are required, in general, one end of each phase being connected to *neutral* (Fig. 245a). However, when the loads are balanced so that the currents in the three phases have the same amplitude and uniform phase difference, the neutral wire is unnecessary. For the current in the neutral wire at any instant is the sum of the currents in the three phases and, under the conditions specified, this sum is zero, as shown by the vector diagram in Fig. 245b. When the neutral wire is not required for transmission, it is usually brought out of the machine and connected to ground to stabilize the system.

Motors. The simplest type of a-c motor to understand is the *synchronous motor*, which is, in effect, an alternator running backwards. Consider two identical machines connected electrically phase to phase and running at the same speed, one as a generator and the other as a motor. In the generator the reaction of the stator on the rotor is such as to oppose the motion of the latter, causing the machine to absorb energy mechanically. In the motor, conditions are exactly reversed, for current is everywhere in the opposite direction to that in the generator, so that the reaction of the stator on the rotor assists the motion and produces mechanical work. Evidently this state of affairs exists only when the speed of the motor is exactly that of the generator.

Fig. 246

If the load on the motor is increased until the latter is pulled out of synchronous speed, the torque falls to zero and the motor stops.

Although any alternator may be used as a synchronous motor, and vice versa, there are usually slight differences in the details of construction. For one thing, since the motor has no starting torque, it must be provided with an auxiliary winding or some other device by means of which it can be brought up to speed.

The most useful type of a-c motor is the *induction motor*. The stator of an induction motor is similar to that of a synchronous motor. The rotor, however, is entirely different, consisting merely of a core with some closed windings on it, or in its simplest form of a *squirrel cage* (Fig. 246) made by setting copper bars into the edges of two conducting disks. The rotor is thus energized by induction instead of by an auxiliary exciting current, a great practical advantage.

To investigate the means by which rotation is produced, let us take a simple case such as a three-phase machine with a single concentrated winding per phase (Fig. 247). We wish first to calculate the resultant magnetic field **H** in the region occupied by the rotor. This is due to three fields, $H_0 \sin \omega t$ in the direction AO, $H_0 \sin\left(\omega t + \dfrac{2\pi}{3}\right)$ in the direction BO and $H_0 \sin\left(\omega t + \dfrac{4\pi}{3}\right)$ in the direction CO.

Taking XY axes as shown in the figure, the components of the resultant field are

$$H_x = H_0\left\{\sin \omega t + \sin\left(\omega t + \frac{2\pi}{3}\right)\cos\frac{2\pi}{3} + \sin\left(\omega t + \frac{4\pi}{3}\right)\cos\frac{4\pi}{3}\right\}$$

$$= \frac{3}{2} H_0 \sin \omega t,$$

$$H_y = H_0\left\{0 + \sin\left(\omega t + \frac{2\pi}{3}\right)\sin\frac{2\pi}{3} + \sin\left(\omega t + \frac{4\pi}{3}\right)\sin\frac{4\pi}{3}\right\}$$

$$= \frac{3}{2} H_0 \cos \omega t.$$

Evidently then the resultant field has the constant magnitude $\frac{3}{2}H_0$. Its

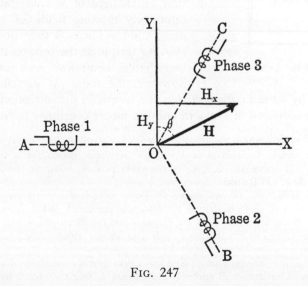

FIG. 247

direction is determined by $\tan \theta = \tan \omega t$, that is, $\theta = \omega t$, which indicates a uniform rotation in a direction opposite to the progression of phases.

Now consider the effect of a rotating field on a conductor or a closed coil placed in it. Induced currents, and hence forces, are the same as for a rotating conductor in a stationary field, and by Lenz' law (art.

97) motion of a conductor in a field is always opposed. Therefore, the motion of the field is opposed, which, of course, results in a torque on the conductor or coil.

Thus, in the machine described, there is a torque on the rotor in a direction opposite to the phase progression. The same thing is true in any polyphase induction motor, although when the windings for each phase are distributed around the stator the analysis of the rotating field may be very complex. The magnitude of this torque in any particular machine depends on the relative speed of field and rotor. A typical speed-torque curve is shown in Fig. 248. The torque at first increases with rotor speed, reaching a maximum at a little under synchronous speed. Thereafter the torque falls rapidly to zero as synchronism is approached. The fact that polyphase induction motors have a starting torque constitutes one of their major advantages.

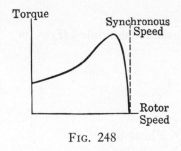

FIG. 248

Single-phase induction motors are more difficult to analyze as the stator field is not rotating, but merely oscillatory. However, an oscillatory field may be thought of as consisting of two oppositely rotating fields of the same magnitude. There is then no resultant starting torque as the torques due to the two fields neutralize each other. If, however, the motor is started in either direction by some auxiliary device, the torque in that direction becomes greater as indicated in Fig. 248 and the motor continues to run.

Problem 117a. Show by means of a vector diagram the relation between voltage of phases to neutral and voltage between phases for a three-phase alternator. If there are 220 volts between phases, what is the voltage to neutral? Ans. 127.0 volt.

Problem 117b. A single-phase six-pole synchronous motor (like the alternator in Fig. 244) is driven by 60-cycle current. What is its speed of rotation? If the armature coils are reconnected for three-phase operation with a two-pole rotor, at what speed will the motor run? Ans. 1200 r.p.m., 3600 r.p.m.

Problem 117c. Given a simplified induction motor consisting of a single flat coil of area A, resistance R and self-inductance L, free to revolve in a rotating magnetic field of magnitude H. Prove that the mean torque on the coil in the direction of rotation of the field is

$$\frac{\mu_0{}^2 H^2 A^2 R\Omega}{2(R^2 + L^2\Omega^2)},$$

where Ω is the angular velocity of the field relative to the coil. Show that this leads to a speed-torque curve like that in Fig. 248.

118. Transformers. It is often desirable to change the relative magnitudes of current and e.m.f. in a-c systems. For instance, the generation of electrical power is most conveniently effected at a few thousand volts with large currents. On the other hand, in the transmission of power, especially over long distances, high voltages and small currents must be used to avoid excessive ohmic losses, for the latter are of the form Ri^2 and so diminish rapidly as the current is decreased. Finally, devices using power, such as motors, are usually designed for a few hundred volts.

Transformations of current and e.m.f. of the sort indicated are readily made by means of *transformers*, which consist essentially of two coils wound on a laminated iron core, so arranged that the magnetic coupling between them is as nearly perfect as possible. Power is delivered to the *primary* winding and withdrawn from the *secondary*, being transferred from one to the other by electromagnetic induction. Figure 249 illustrates a common type of transformer construction in which the windings are superposed and the core is made in the form of a frame so designed that there is a double path for the flux outside the coils.

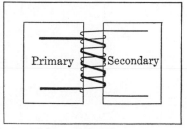

Let us first investigate the properties of an *ideal transformer*, in which there are no energy losses and no leakage of flux (that is, all the flux links every turn of both primary and secondary), and in which the

Fig. 249

numbers of turns are so large that the self-inductances of both windings as well as the mutual inductance between them are effectively infinite.

As all the flux links all the turns of both windings, an induced e.m.f. in one is always accompanied by an induced e.m.f. in the other, and the amplitudes of these e.m.f.'s are in the same ratio as the numbers of turns in the windings. Further, at any finite frequency the induced e.m.f.'s can be finite only if the total flux in the core is very small, since by hypothesis the numbers of turns in the windings are very large. Hence a current in the primary must always be accompanied by a current in the secondary such that the resulting fluxes are substantially equal and opposite. This requires that the amplitudes of the currents be in the inverse ratio of the numbers of turns in the windings. Thus, if $\mathscr{E}_p$ and $\mathscr{E}_s$ are the *terminal voltages* across the primary and secondary, respectively, and i_p and i_s are the currents, we have for the amplitudes

$$\frac{\mathscr{E}_{p0}}{\mathscr{E}_{s0}} = \frac{1}{a},$$

$$\frac{i_{p0}}{i_{s0}} = a,$$

$$\left.\right\}\quad (118\text{-}1)$$

where a is the ratio of the number of turns in the secondary to the number in the primary.

Suppose we couple two circuits (Fig. 250) by means of an ideal transformer, the coupling being taken *positive*. That is, having chosen positive directions for the currents in the circuits, we connect the circuits to the transformer in such a way that the flux in the transformer core links the two windings in the same sense (mutual inductance positive). Then the simultaneous induced e.m.f.'s in the windings are in the same sense. However, $\mathscr{E}_p$ has the sense opposite to the induced

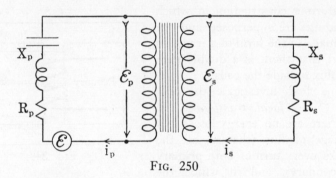

Fig. 250

e.m.f. in the primary since it is defined as the potential drop across the winding, whereas $\mathscr{E}_s$ has the same sense as the induced e.m.f. in the secondary since it is defined as the potential drop across the external part of the circuit. Therefore, the terminal voltages have opposite senses. The currents i_p and i_s also have opposite senses since they produce opposing fluxes. Thus the complete transformer equations for positive coupling are

$$\frac{\mathscr{E}_p}{\mathscr{E}_s} = -\frac{1}{a},$$

$$\frac{i_p}{i_s} = -a.$$

$$\left.\right\}\quad (118\text{-}2)$$

Actually, these equations apply to negative coupling also, if the turn ratio a in this case is taken to be negative.

In order to express the voltages and currents indicated in Fig. 250 in terms of the given circuit elements and the applied electromotive force $\mathscr{E}$, consider the impedance of the secondary circuit. The true impedance, exclusive of the transformer, is given by $Z_s = \mathscr{E}_{s0}/i_{s0}$. On the other hand, the equivalent impedance introduced into the primary through the transformer is $Z_{ps} = \mathscr{E}_{p0}/i_{p0} = Z_s/a^2$, using (118-1). Therefore, the characteristics of the primary circuit are the same as if the transformer was entirely removed and a resistance R_s/a^2 and a reactance X_s/a^2 were put in its place. This arrangement is equivalent to a simple series circuit with

$$\hat{R}_p = R_p + \frac{R_s}{a^2},$$

$$\hat{X}_p = X_p + \frac{X_s}{a^2},$$

for which calculations are easily made (art. 110). Having determined $\mathscr{E}_p$ and i_p we obtain $\mathscr{E}_s$ and i_s at once by means of (118-2). The property

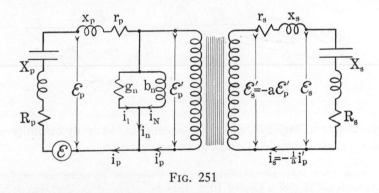

FIG. 251

of a transformer of effectively changing an impedance is of great value as it allows us to adapt apparatus and circuits to use with other apparatus and circuits of entirely different impedances.

A well-constructed transformer in practice approximates an ideal transformer but it has some losses due to resistance of the windings and to hysteresis and eddy currents in the core. Also there is some leakage of flux in both windings and the inductance of the windings, although large, is finite. These defects may be represented in a circuit diagram* by a fictitious ideal transformer of the given turn ratio with a small resistance and reactance in series with each winding and with a conductance and a susceptance shunted across the primary.

* Mass. Inst. Tech. Staff, *Magnetic Circuits and Transformers*, John Wiley & Sons, 1943, pp. 313–356.

Two circuits coupled by a real transformer are shown in Fig. 251. The terminal voltages are $\mathscr{E}_p$ and $\mathscr{E}_s$, as before, and the total currents are i_p and i_s. Primed quantities refer to the fictitious ideal transformer. The current i_l flowing through the conductance g_n represents the core losses, while i_N flowing through the susceptance b_n is the magnetizing current that produces the flux N_c in the core. The sum of i_l and i_N is the *exciting current* i_n, which added to $i_p{'}$ gives the total primary current i_p. The quantities r_p and r_s are the primary and secondary winding resistances; x_p and x_s are the primary and secondary *leakage reactances*. The relations of the various currents and e.m.f.'s are shown in the

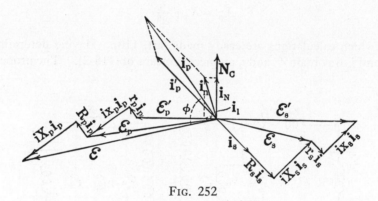

FIG. 252

vector diagram, Fig. 252, which the reader should study carefully as it is an excellent example of graphical representation.

Problem 118a. An a-c generator with a resistance 10 ohms and negligible reactance is coupled to a load of 1000 ohms by means of an ideal transformer. In order to deliver maximum power to the load, what turn ratio must the transformer have? Ans. 10.

Problem 118b. Referring to Fig. 250, suppose the primary circuit contains a resistance 60 ohms and an inductance $1/\pi$ henry while the secondary contains a resistance 900 ohms and an inductance $3/\pi$ henry. The turn ratio of the transformer is 3. If the applied e.m.f. has an amplitude 100 volts and a frequency 60 cycles per second, find the primary and secondary currents (amplitude and phase). Ans. 0.442 amp, $-\pi/4$ radian; 0.147 amp, $3\pi/4$ radian.

Problem 118c. The circuits of the preceding problem are tuned to resonance, first by placing a capacitor of appropriate size in the primary, then by placing one in the secondary. Find the ratio of the capacitances. Ans. 9.

Problem 118d. Two coupled circuits, such as shown in Fig. 250, include a 5-microfarad capacitor in the primary and a 1-microfarad capacitor in the secondary. If voltmeters connected across the capacitors indicate equal voltages, what turn ratio does the transformer have? Ans. 5.

Chapter XIV

MEASUREMENTS WITH VARYING CURRENTS

---

119. Types and Methods of Measurement. There are three fundamental quantities, resistance, inductance and capacitance, to be determined in circuits carrying varying currents. Pure ohmic resistance is independent of frequency, except at very high frequencies, and it may be measured by d-c methods when these are available. A special method for measuring very high resistance is given below. An inductance coil with an iron core has an apparent resistance, in addition to its ohmic resistance, due to hysteresis and eddy-current losses. Similarly a capacitor with a material dielectric has an apparent resistance due to dielectric losses (art. 20). These apparent resistances, which are often quite important, are usually measured in a-c bridges simultaneously with the inductance or capacitance with which they are associated.

Inductance and capacitance are measured in a-c bridges or by some special method, usually of a ballistic nature, depending on equipment available, accuracy required, and so forth. Measurements of inductance and capacitance, except at high frequencies where resonance methods are used, fall into two general classes; *comparison*, where the unknown quantity is determined in terms of known inductances and capacitances, and *absolute*, where the unknown is found in terms of some basic quantity, such as resistance.

120. Measurement of High Resistance. From (90-8) we see that if a capacitor of capacitance C with an initial charge q_0 is allowed to discharge through a resistance R the charge remaining after a time t is given by

$$q = q_0 e^{-(1/RC)t}.$$

This provides us with a method for measuring high resistance. With the aid of a ballistic galvanometer G the ratio q_0/q corresponding to any value of t may be found. This determines the value of RC experimentally, and, if C is known, we can calculate R. The method is usually limited to resistances greater than 10 megohms by the size of available capacitors, for RC should be equal to 10 seconds or more to give accurate results.

The experimental arrangements are shown in Fig. 253.   The known capacitance is shunted by the resistance to be measured.   A two-position key K connects the capacitor to a steady e.m.f. $\mathcal{E}$ of a few volts or to the ballistic galvanometer, as required.   It must be possible to leave the arm of this key midway between the contacts while the condenser is discharging through R.

A set of observations is begun by observing the galvanometer throw when K is snapped quickly from the lower to the upper contact.   This throw corresponds to q_0 and should be made approximately full scale by proper choice of $\mathcal{E}$.   The next observation is made by moving the arm of the key from the lower contact to the mid-position, allowing it to remain there for a measured time t, and then moving it to the upper position.   The throw now corresponds to the charge q remaining after the capacitor has discharged for a time t through R.   Other observations are made with successively greater intervals of discharge, until the throw is too small to be accurately determined.

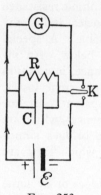

FIG. 253

Now, taking the ratio of the first throw to each of the following, we have the values of q_0/q corresponding to various values of t.   We may calculate RC for each case and take the mean, but it is simpler to find the average value of RC graphically. Taking the logarithm of the charge ratio, we have

$$t = RC \log \frac{q_0}{q}. \tag{120-1}$$

Thus, plotting t against $\log (q_0/q)$ gives a straight line whose slope is RC.   Having determined RC, we divide by the known value of C to obtain R.

The value of R just obtained applies actually to the parallel combination of the resistance to be measured and the insulation resistance of the capacitor.   The effect of the latter may not be entirely negligible, especially in measuring very high resistances, so we make another set of observations with the resistance element removed.   The former value of R may then be corrected, if necessary, by means of the ordinary formula for resistances in parallel.

In the measurements just described it is essential to use a capacitor entirely free from dielectric absorption, a condition usually satisfied by mica capacitors. Also, the key employed must have extremely good insulation between its contacts to avoid leakage from the source of potential.

121. A-C Bridges. A number of a-c bridge networks adapted to various measurements have been devised. Except under special conditions, they all involve a double balance. Usually one balance, called the d-c balance, can be made with a steady e.m.f. and a d'Arsonval galvanometer. The remaining balance is then established with an alternating e.m.f. and a telephone receiver or other a-c indicator, depending on the frequency. In practice double-pole double-throw switches in the battery and galvanometer arms are used to facilitate change from d-c to a-c condition and vice versa. However, these switching arrangements are not shown in the circuit diagrams of bridges described in this article for the sake of simplicity. The e.m.f. is designated in general by $\mathcal{E}$ and the appropriate current indicator by G. In this connection it is interesting to note that if the a-c balance is independent of frequency, as is almost always the case, it holds for any wave form of applied e.m.f., since the latter may be expressed as a sum of sinusoidal components. Thus the a-c balance may be obtained with the same steady e.m.f. and d'Arsonval galvanometer as the d-c balance by merely opening and closing a switch in the battery circuit. This procedure does not yield as accurate results as the other, however.

Certain precautions must be observed in the use of a-c bridges. In order to obtain a sharp a-c balance, care must be taken that no random e.m.f.'s are introduced into the bridge. That is, the source of the alternating e.m.f. should be shielded or located at some distance from the bridge, so that there is no magnetic coupling between the two. Inductive and capacitative coupling between different elements of the bridge should be reduced to a minimum by a careful arrangement of the parts. Capacitance effects become increasingly important with higher frequencies. When a telephone receiver is used, it is advisable to couple it to the bridge by means of a transformer with some point grounded, in order to eliminate the effect of the observer's capacitance. It is essential, of course, to employ only non-inductive resistance boxes designed for a-c use.

Self-Inductance Bridge. This bridge (Fig. 254) has been analyzed in art. 115. The conditions for balance are

$$\left.\begin{array}{l} \dfrac{R_1}{R_2} = \dfrac{R_3}{R_4}, \\[2mm] \dfrac{L_1}{R_2} = \dfrac{L_3}{R_4}. \end{array}\right\} \quad (121\text{-}1)$$

In order to minimize the effect of any small residual inductance in the resistance boxes and to avoid insensitive arrangements of the bridge, it is desirable to have R_2 and R_4 at least of the same order of magnitude. To establish the d-c balance under this condition it may be necessary to include a small external resistance in series with one of the inductances. For the a-c balance L_1 and L_3 must now also be of the same order of magnitude. Satisfactory use of this bridge is therefore limited to the measurement of inductances which do not differ greatly in magnitude from the extreme values at which the adjustable inductance L_3 can be set.

The accuracy of the results depends directly on the variable inductance or *inductometer* used. There are two standard types, the

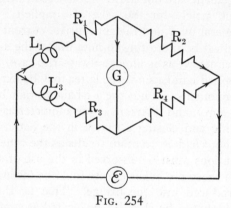

Fig. 254

Brooks-Weaver, in which several coils connected in series move relative to one another in parallel planes, and the *Ayrton-Perry*, in which one coil rotates inside another.

Maxwell's L ∼ C Bridge. A bridge for comparing a self-inductance and a capacitance, due to Maxwell, is shown in Fig. 255. To find the conditions of balance we observe that, as in (115-2),

$$\frac{Z_1}{Z_2} = \frac{Z_3}{Z_4},$$

that is,

$$\frac{R_1 + iL_1\omega}{R_2} = \frac{R_3}{\dfrac{R_4}{1 + iR_4C_4\omega}}.$$

Equating real parts and imaginary parts gives

$$\left.\begin{aligned} \frac{R_1}{R_2} &= \frac{R_3}{R_4}, \\ \frac{L_1}{R_2} &= R_3 C_4. \end{aligned}\right\} \quad (121\text{-}2)$$

If either the self-inductance or the capacitance is variable, the d-c balance may be made in the usual way and left undisturbed while the a-c balance is established. As variable capacitances are usually not available except in small sizes, Maxwell's bridge is adapted to the measurement of a capacitance in terms of a variable inductance or to the calibration of a variable inductance in terms of a capacitance. If the inductance and the capacitance are both fixed, the bridge can be

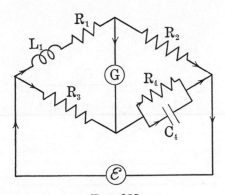

Fig. 255

balanced only by the laborious process of trying different d-c balances until one is found which is also an a-c balance. Under these circumstances some other more suitable bridge should be used for the measurement.

Anderson's L∼C Bridge. This is a modification of Maxwell's bridge which avoids the difficulties mentioned in the last paragraph. The capacitance C_4 (Fig. 256) is now bridged across R_4 and an adjustable resistance R in the galvanometer arm, instead of across R_4 alone.

Let us apply Kirchhoff's laws to this network. Denoting the complex currents in the main arms of the bridge by i_1, i_2, i_3 and i_4, and those flowing through R and C_4 by i_R and i_C, respectively, we have at balance the special relations

$$(R_1 + iL_1\omega)i_1 = R_3 i_3 + R i_R,$$

$$R_2 i_2 = -i\,\frac{1}{C_4\omega}\,i_C,$$

together with

$$\mathbf{i}_1 = \mathbf{i}_2, \qquad \mathbf{i}_R = \mathbf{i}_C.$$

Dividing the first equation by the second and using the current relations,

$$\frac{R_1 + iL_1\omega}{R_2} = \frac{R_3\left(\dfrac{\mathbf{i}_3}{\mathbf{i}_C}\right) + R}{-i\dfrac{1}{C_4\omega}}. \tag{121-3}$$

To find $\mathbf{i}_3/\mathbf{i}_C$ we note the general relations

$$R\mathbf{i}_R - i\frac{1}{C_4\omega}\mathbf{i}_C = R_4\mathbf{i}_4,$$

$$\mathbf{i}_3 = \mathbf{i}_R + \mathbf{i}_4.$$

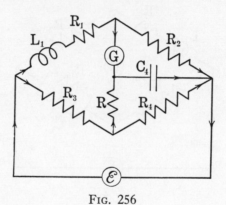

Fig. 256

With $\mathbf{i}_R = \mathbf{i}_C$ these reduce to

$$\left(R - i\frac{1}{C_4\omega}\right)\mathbf{i}_C = R_4\mathbf{i}_4,$$

$$\mathbf{i}_3 = \mathbf{i}_C + \mathbf{i}_4,$$

from which

$$\frac{\mathbf{i}_3}{\mathbf{i}_C} = \frac{R_4 + R - i\dfrac{1}{C_4\omega}}{R_4}.$$

Combining this with (121-3), we find

$$\frac{R_1 + iL_1\omega}{R_2} = \frac{\dfrac{R_3}{R_4}\left(R_4 + R - i\dfrac{1}{C_4\omega}\right) + R}{-i\dfrac{1}{C_4\omega}},$$

and the balance conditions are

$$\left.\begin{array}{l} \dfrac{R_1}{R_2} = \dfrac{R_3}{R_4}, \\[2ex] \dfrac{L_1}{R_2} = C_4\left[\dfrac{R_3}{R_4}(R_4+R)+R\right]. \end{array}\right\} \quad (121\text{-}4)$$

After the usual d-c adjustment has been made, the a-c balance is established by means of R, so neither inductance nor capacitance need be variable. It is usually desirable to have R_3 and R_4 of the same order of magnitude. Often they are made equal, in which case

$$L_1 = C_4 R_2 (2R + R_4).$$

The Anderson bridge does not suffer any serious restrictions, being

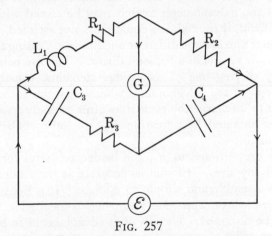

FIG. 257

capable of accurate measurements over a wide range of values. Its characteristics are described in detail by Rosa and Grover* who have used it in standardization work.

Owen's $L \sim C$ *Bridge.* This differs from the two preceding bridges in that two capacitances (Fig. 257) are involved, an adjustable resistance R_3 being placed in series with one of them.

The balance conditions are obtained from

$$\frac{Z_1}{Z_2} = \frac{Z_3}{Z_4},$$

* Bureau of Standards Bull. **1**, 291 (1905).

that is, from

$$\frac{R_1+iL_1\omega}{R_2} = \frac{R_3-i\dfrac{1}{C_3\omega}}{-i\dfrac{1}{C_4\omega}}.$$

Evidently we must have

$$\left.\begin{aligned}\frac{R_1}{R_2} &= \frac{C_4}{C_3}, \\[2mm] \frac{L_1}{R_2} &= C_4R_3.\end{aligned}\right\} \quad (121\text{-}5)$$

The first condition does not represent an ordinary Wheatstone bridge balance, since no direct current flows through the capacitors. However, the balance can be made by d-c means. Suppose that the galvanometer arm is opened and a steady e.m.f. is applied to the bridge. If $R_1/R_2 = C_4/C_3$, the ends of the galvanometer arm are at the same potential, and the galvanometer switch may be closed without effect. On the other hand, if the balance equation is not satisfied, the ends of the galvanometer arm assume different potentials. Closing the galvanometer switch now results in a ballistic throw. The d-c balance is thus established by varying one of the bridge elements, usually R_2, until there is no throw of the galvanometer when its switch is closed. Care must be taken to discharge the capacitors after each observation. The a-c balance is obtained by adjusting R_3, the other balance thereby remaining undisturbed.

Since L_1 is proportional to R_3, the bridge is useful for measuring inductances of any size. It is not as accurate as the Anderson bridge but is easy to assemble and simple to operate. It is necessary to use good capacitors whose apparent resistance is negligible, if a sharp balance is to be obtained. Usually it is advantageous to have C_3 and C_4 of the same order of magnitude, which may require some external resistance in series with L_1.

Mutual Inductance Bridge. A simple network for the comparison of mutual inductances is shown in Fig. 258. The equations for balance are readily found with the aid of Kirchhoff's laws. Denoting the currents in the bridge arms by $\mathbf{i}_1$ and $\mathbf{i}_2$, and the current in the generator circuit by $\mathbf{i}$, we must have

$$(R_1+iL_1\omega)\mathbf{i}_1+iM_1\omega\mathbf{i} = 0,$$
$$(R_2+iL_2\omega)\mathbf{i}_2+iM_2\omega\mathbf{i} = 0,$$

with $\mathbf{i}_1 = \mathbf{i}_2$. By division we obtain

$$\frac{R_1+iL_1\omega}{R_2+iL_2\omega} = \frac{iM_1\omega}{iM_2\omega},$$

which gives

$$\left.\begin{array}{c} \dfrac{M_1}{R_1} = \dfrac{M_2}{R_2}, \\[2mm] \dfrac{M_1}{L_1} = \dfrac{M_2}{L_2}. \end{array}\right\} \quad (121\text{-}6)$$

Both equations represent a-c conditions, so the two balances must be made simultaneously. Fortunately this is not as laborious as it might appear, for by making the resistances large the effect of the self-inductances is made small and the bridge can be approximately balanced without regard to the ratio L_1/L_2. The resistances are now reduced without changing their ratio, and the approximate balance improved by an adjustment of L_1/L_2. Hereafter slight readjustments of R_1/R_2 and

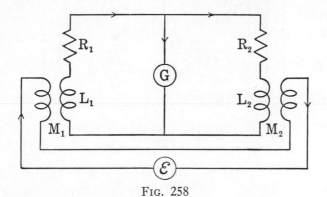

FIG. 258

L_1/L_2, made alternately, soon establish a complete balance. Note that the mutual inductances must be connected in the same sense to make this balance possible.

As ordinarily used the bridge consists of two fixed mutual inductances, one of which is known, with adjustable resistances in series. A variable, but not necessarily calibrated, self-inductance is placed in whichever arm of the bridge the self-inductance associated with the mutual inductance is too small to satisfy the balance condition. Since R_1 and R_2 are the total resistances of the bridge arms, the resistances of the coils must be found and added to the adjustable resistances.

Maxwell's $M \sim L$ Bridge. The comparison of a mutual inductance and the self-inductance of one of its coils is most simply made by means of the bridge illustrated in Fig. 259.

Analysis of the network is carried out in the usual manner. Distinguishing currents in the bridge arms by numerical subscripts and denoting the currents flowing through M and R by $\mathbf{i}_M$ and $\mathbf{i}_R$, respectively, we have under the conditions of balance

$$(R_1 + iL_1\omega)\mathbf{i}_1 + iM\omega\mathbf{i}_M = R_3\mathbf{i}_3,$$
$$R_2\mathbf{i}_2 = R_4\mathbf{i}_4,$$

together with

$$\mathbf{i}_1 = \mathbf{i}_2, \qquad \mathbf{i}_3 = \mathbf{i}_4.$$

In addition there are the general relations

$$R_3\mathbf{i}_3 + R_4\mathbf{i}_4 = R\mathbf{i}_R,$$
$$\mathbf{i}_1 + \mathbf{i}_3 + \mathbf{i}_R = \mathbf{i}_M.$$

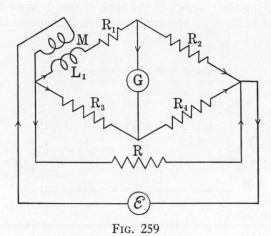

Fig. 259

Using $\mathbf{i}_3 = \mathbf{i}_4$, and eliminating $\mathbf{i}_R$, these give

$$\mathbf{i}_1 + \left(1 + \frac{R_3 + R_4}{R}\right)\mathbf{i}_3 = \mathbf{i}_M.$$

We can now eliminate $\mathbf{i}_M$ from the first condition equation and divide by the second, obtaining

$$\frac{(R_1 + iL_1\omega) + iM\omega}{R_2} = \frac{R_3 - iM\omega\left(1 + \dfrac{R_3 + R_4}{R}\right)}{R_4}.$$

The balance equations are thus

$$\left.\begin{aligned}
\frac{R_1}{R_2} &= \frac{R_3}{R_4}, \\[2mm]
\frac{L_1 + M}{R_2} &= \frac{-M\left(1 + \dfrac{R_3 + R_4}{R}\right)}{R_4}.
\end{aligned}\right\} \quad (121\text{-}7)$$

The a-c balance is made by adjustment of R, which does not disturb the previously obtained d-c balance. Rearrangement of the a-c balance equation gives

$$M = -L_1 \frac{R_4}{R_2\left(1+\dfrac{R_3}{R}\right)+R_4\left(1+\dfrac{R_2}{R}\right)},$$

which shows that the magnitude of L_1 must be greater than that of M. This is a distinct limitation on the usefulness of the bridge. The negative sign signifies, of course, that M must be connected to give negative coupling, so that the induced e.m.f. due to L_1 is opposed by that due to M.

Heaviside's $M \sim L$ Bridge.   This bridge (Fig. 260) is more sensitive

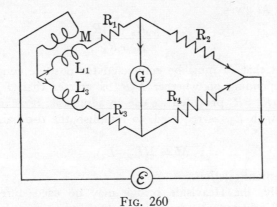

FIG. 260

than Maxwell's and it does not suffer from restrictions on the relative magnitudes of M and L_1. However, it involves a self-inductance L_3 in addition to that associated with the mutual inductance, and either the independent self-inductance or the mutual inductance must be adjustable.

Using the same notation as in the case of Maxwell's bridge just preceding, the condition equations at balance are

$$(R_1+iL_1\omega)i_1+iM\omega i_M = (R_3+iL_3\omega)i_3,$$

$$R_2 i_2 = R_4 i_4,$$

with

$$i_1 = i_2, \qquad i_3 = i_4.$$

Eliminating i_M from the first condition equation by means of the general relation $i_1 + i_3 = i_M$, and dividing by the second condition equation, we have

$$\frac{(R_1 + iL_1\omega) + iM\omega}{R_2} = \frac{(R_3 + iL_3\omega) - iM\omega}{R_4}.$$

The balance conditions are therefore

$$\left. \begin{array}{c} \dfrac{R_1}{R_2} = \dfrac{R_3}{R_4}, \\[2mm] \dfrac{L_1 + M}{R_2} = \dfrac{L_3 - M}{R_4}. \end{array} \right\} \quad (121\text{-}8)$$

The d-c balance is made as usual.   The a-c balance is established by adjusting L_3 or M.   In order to find either of these quantities in terms of the other, L_1 must be known, of course.   Solving the a-c balance equation for M gives

$$M = \frac{L_3 R_2 - L_1 R_4}{R_2 + R_4},$$

which shows that M must be connected for positive coupling or for negative, depending on whether $L_3 R_2$ is greater than $L_1 R_4$ or less. We may set $R_2 = R_4$ provided we use an adjustable resistance in series with L_1 or with L_3, as required, to establish the d-c balance.   This gives

$$M = \tfrac{1}{2}(L_3 - L_1),$$

a very convenient relation.

Incidentally, the Heaviside bridge may be used differentially to measure self-inductance in terms of mutual inductance alone.   Thus, suppose M is a variable calibrated mutual inductance, while L_1 and L_3 are fixed self-inductances, preferably of the same order of magnitude. First, let the bridge be balanced with $R_2 = R_4$, so that $M' = \tfrac{1}{2}(L_3 - L_1)$. Then, having placed the inductance L to be measured in series with L_3, let the bridge be rebalanced.   This time we must have

$$M'' = \tfrac{1}{2}([L_3 + L] - L_1).$$

Taking the difference of these equations, we see that

$$L = 2(M'' - M'),$$

where M' and M'' represent the two settings of the variable mutual inductance.   In addition to simplicity, this method of measuring self-inductance has the great advantage that errors due to residual inductance in R_2 and R_4, capacitance effects, and so forth, affect M' and M'' equally and so eliminate themselves.

Heydweiller's $M \sim C$ Bridge. A convenient method for comparing a mutual inductance and a capacitance is illustrated in Fig. 261. Both the inductance and the capacitance must have adjustable resistances in series with them, but no other variable elements are required.

When the bridge is balanced, we have

$$(R_1 + iL_1\omega)\mathbf{i}_1 + iM\omega\mathbf{i}_M = 0,$$

$$\left(R_2 - i\frac{1}{C_2\omega}\right)\mathbf{i}_2 = R_4\mathbf{i}_4,$$

with

$$\mathbf{i}_1 = \mathbf{i}_2,$$

where the notation is the same as that used for the two preceding

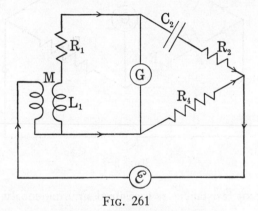

FIG. 261

bridges. Eliminating $\mathbf{i}_M$ from the first equation by means of the general relation $\mathbf{i}_1 + \mathbf{i}_4 = \mathbf{i}_M$, and dividing by the second equation, we obtain

$$\frac{(R_1 + iL_1\omega) + iM\omega}{R_2 - i\dfrac{1}{C_2\omega}} = \frac{-iM\omega}{R_4}.$$

The corresponding balance equations are

$$M = -L_1\frac{R_4}{R_2 + R_4},$$

$$M = -C_2 R_1 R_4,$$

$\left.\right\}$ (121-9)

the negative signs indicating the connection of the mutual inductance for negative coupling, as in the case of the Maxwell bridge. The balances are both a-c and must be made simultaneously. This is done simply by adjusting R_1 and R_2 alternately, since each of these appears in only one of the balance equations.   Note that L_1 must be greater in magnitude than M.   If necessary, a separate self-inductance can be placed in series with the appropriate coil of the mutual inductance to establish this condition.

Capacitance Bridge.   This bridge (Fig. 262) compares two capacitances and, incidentally, establishes a relation between their apparent resistances.   When the standard capacitance is supplied by a good capacitor with negligible apparent resistance, the unknown capacitance

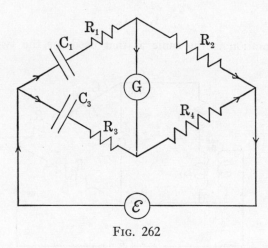

Fig. 262

and its apparent resistance are measured simultaneously, which is very convenient.

As in other bridges of the Wheatstone type, the balance conditions are obtained from

$$\frac{Z_1}{Z_2} = \frac{Z_3}{Z_4}.$$

In this case we have

$$\frac{R_1 - i\dfrac{1}{C_1\omega}}{R_2} = \frac{R_3 - i\dfrac{1}{C_3\omega}}{R_4},$$

and the balance equations are

$$\left.\begin{aligned} \frac{R_1}{R_2} &= \frac{R_3}{R_4}, \\[2mm] \frac{1}{C_1 R_2} &= \frac{1}{C_3 R_4}. \end{aligned}\right\} \quad (121\text{-}10)$$

As the bridge is ordinarily used, C_1 is the unknown capacitance and R_1 is its associated apparent resistance, while C_3 is the standard capacitance, with an adjustable resistance R_3 in series. No d-c current can flow, so the balances must be made simultaneously with a-c, C_3 and R_3 being varied alternately, beginning with C_3, until a complete balance is found. If C_3 is fixed, the capacitance balance is made by means of R_2 or R_4. When possible R_2 and R_4 should be of the same order of magnitude to minimize the effect of residual inductance.

From R_1 and C_1 we may determine the apparent power factor (art. 92) of the capacitor. Thus,

$$\cos \phi_1 = \frac{1}{\sqrt{1+\tan^2 \phi_1}} = \frac{1}{\sqrt{1+\dfrac{1}{R_1{}^2 C_1{}^2 \omega^2}}},$$

where $\omega/2\pi$ is the frequency at which the bridge is balanced. Actually,

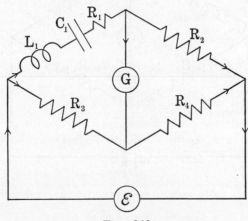

FIG. 263

with any usable capacitor, $R_1 C_1 \omega$ is very small compared with unity, so that, effectively,

$$\cos \phi_1 = R_1 C_1 \omega. \qquad (121\text{-}11)$$

The power factor of a capacitor is important because it is an excellent criterion of quality, the smaller the power factor, the better the capacitor, in general. Experiment shows that the power factor is practically independent of frequency, at least over moderate ranges of frequency variation.

Frequency Bridge. Any bridge in which the balance depends on frequency may be used to measure frequency. A simple but effective bridge for this purpose is shown in Fig. 263.

Evidently the balance conditions are

$$\left.\begin{array}{c} \dfrac{R_1}{R_2} = \dfrac{R_3}{R_4}, \\[2mm] 1 - L_1 C_1 \omega^2 = 0. \end{array}\right\} \quad (121\text{-}12)$$

Using a variable inductance or capacitance, the scale may be calibrated to read frequency directly, since the a-c balance is independent of the resistance ratios.

122. Absolute Measurements. It is demonstrated in art. 107 that resistance can be determined in absolute measure. Determinations of inductance and capacitance in which resistance is the only

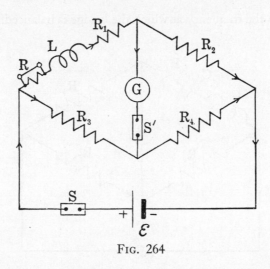

FIG. 264

electrical quantity involved are therefore regarded as absolute measurements. Examples of this type of measurement are given below.

Self-Inductance. The experimental arrangements for the absolute measurement of self-inductance (Fig. 264) consist essentially of a d-c Wheatstone bridge with the unknown inductance L included in one of the arms. In the same arm is a resistance R, very small compared with R_1, which can be short-circuited by a copper rod dipping into mercury cups or by some other device with negligible contact resistance. Switches S, S' are located as shown in the figure.

The galvanometer must have sufficiently small damping (including the effect of the external circuit) to allow ballistic observations to be made as well as steady current measurements. A moving needle galvanometer is preferable but a d'Arsonval galvanometer may be used if the galvanometer circuit is opened immediately after the ballistic impulse has been given. The resistance elements must have negligible self-inductance as compared with L.

To measure L, an ordinary d-c balance is established and then, with the galvanometer circuit still closed, the battery circuit is opened. The current i' through L falls from its steady value i_1 to zero within a short interval of time during which there is an induced e.m.f. $-L\dfrac{di'}{dt}$.

This e.m.f. produces a momentary current through the galvanometer, whose ballistic throw is proportional to the total charge passing. As in the case of (100-1), we find that this charge is proportional to the total flux change Li_1, independent of the self-inductance of the galvanometer. Hence the charge is equal to $\hat{k}Li_1$, where $\hat{k}$ is a constant. Expressing the charge in terms of the first throw α_1, we have

$$\hat{k}Li_1 = \frac{P_0 K_i}{2\pi}\left(1+\frac{\lambda}{2}\right)\alpha_1 \tag{122-1}$$

from (100-17), where P_0 is the period, λ is the half logarithmic decrement and K_i is the galvanometer constant.

Next, with battery and galvanometer circuits both closed and the previous d-c balance unchanged, the resistance R is short-circuited. This has the same effect as introducing an e.m.f. equal to Ri_1 and causes a steady current $\hat{k}Ri_1$ to flow through the galvanometer. We use the undisturbed value i_1 for the current because R_1 is always taken so large compared with R that the current in this arm of the bridge is practically unaffected. The galvanometer now has a steady deflection α given by

$$\hat{k}Ri_1 = K_i\alpha \tag{122-2}$$

according to (73-8).

Dividing (122-1) by (122-2) we have the desired absolute relation between L and R, namely,

$$\frac{L}{R} = \frac{P_0}{2\pi}\left(1+\frac{\lambda}{2}\right)\frac{\alpha_1}{\alpha}, \tag{122-3}$$

where P_0 and λ must be determined with the galvanometer under working conditions.

For accurate results R should be so chosen that α is of the same order of magnitude as α_1. It must be remembered that α_1/α is the ratio of the angular deflections. This is equal to the ratio of the corresponding scale readings if the scale is curved. If the scale is straight, the ratio of the scale readings may require slight correction.

Mutual Inductance. The absolute measurement of mutual inductance depends on the same principle as the corresponding measurement of self-inductance just described. Circuit arrangements are illustrated in Fig. 265. A double-pole double-throw switch S allows the galvanometer to be coupled to the battery circuit through the mutual inductance M alone or to be shunted across a very small resistance R. The resistance of the battery circuit exclusive of R is R_1. If variable, it may conveniently be used to control sensitivity, but it must always be large compared with R. The total resistance of the galvanometer circuit is R_2. As in the previous case the galvanometer should be of the moving needle type to avoid excessive damping, unless the circuit is opened immediately after a ballistic impulse.

To measure M, the switch S is placed in the "up" position with the key K closed. The battery circuit is then broken and the current i' in it falls from the steady value i_1 to zero, inducing in the galvanometer circuit an e.m.f. $-M\dfrac{di'}{dt}$. A momentary current flows through the galvanometer, whose resulting throw is proportional to the total charge passing. From (100-1) this charge is Mi_1/R_2, independent of the self-inductance of the galvanometer. Expressing the charge in terms of the first throw α_1 by means of (100-17), we have

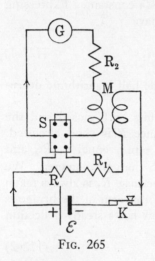

Fig. 265

$$\frac{Mi_1}{R_2} = \frac{P_0 K_i}{2\pi}\left(1+\frac{\lambda}{2}\right)\alpha_1, \quad (122\text{-}4)$$

where P_0 is the period, λ is the half logarithmic decrement and K_i is the galvanometer constant.

Next S is placed in the "down" position. With K closed there is a steady deflection α of the galvanometer corresponding to an e.m.f. Ri_1 in the galvanometer circuit. We use the same value i_1 as before for the current in the battery circuit, since R is so small compared with R_1 that the shunting effect of R_2 is negligible. The current through the galvanometer is evidently Ri_1/R_2 and hence, by (73-8),

$$\frac{Ri_1}{R_2} = K_i\alpha. \quad (122\text{-}5)$$

Dividing (122-4) by (122-5) gives the absolute relation between M and R,

$$\frac{M}{R} = \frac{P_0}{2\pi}\left(1+\frac{\lambda}{2}\right)\frac{\alpha_1}{\alpha}. \quad (122\text{-}6)$$

As in the case of the corresponding measurement of self-inductance above, P_0 and λ must be determined with the galvanometer under working conditions, and R should be chosen so that α and α_1 are of the same order of magnitude.

Capacitance. This absolute measurement is very similar to the preceding one, to which the reader should refer. The unknown capacitance C (Fig. 266) is charged to a potential difference $\mathscr{E}$ and then discharged through the galvanometer by means of a two-position key K. The first throw α_1 is therefore given by

$$C\mathscr{E} = \frac{P_0 K_i}{2\pi}\left(1+\frac{\lambda}{2}\right)\alpha_1.$$

Next, the switch S is closed, allowing a steady current to flow through the galvanometer which now has a very high resistance R in series with it. As the galvanometer resistance is negligible, the deflection α is determined by

$$\frac{\mathscr{E}}{R} = K_i\alpha.$$

Dividing the charge equation by the current equation, we obtain

$$RC = \frac{P_0}{2\pi}\left(1+\frac{\lambda}{2}\right)\frac{\alpha_1}{\alpha}. \qquad (122\text{-}7)$$

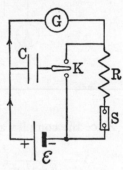

Fig. 266

As in the other absolute measurements R should be chosen so that α and α_1 are of the same order of magnitude. Note that in this case the galvanometer operates ballistically on open circuit, so the d'Arsonval type may be employed to advantage.

Problem 122. Denoting the galvanometer resistance by R_g, demonstrate by actual calculation for both (122-1) and (122-2) that the constant $\hat{k}$ is equal (very closely) to

$$\frac{R_2+R_4}{(R_1+R_3)(R_2+R_4)+R_g(R_1+R_2+R_3+R_4)},$$

where $R_2 R_3 = R_4 R_1$.

123. Measurement of Large Self-Inductance.

Iron-cored coils of large self-inductance, commonly called *choke coils*, are often used to separate direct currents from alternating currents. Such coils permit free passage of direct current but offer a high impedance to alternating current. It is difficult to determine the inductance L of a choke coil by any of the ordinary methods described in this chapter, both because of its magnitude, which may run to a number of henrys, and because of its dependence on the magnetic state of the iron core, that is, on the amount of direct current flowing simultaneously with the alternating current. To be of any value, measurements must be made on choke coils under the conditions in which the coils are to be used.

A simple method of measuring L under practical conditions has been devised by Turner.* The principle of the method is indicated in Fig. 267. The choke coil with a switch S in series is shunted by a variable capacitance C to form a divided circuit. An a-c ammeter A is included in the line to show the magnitude of the total current, which is proportional to the real admittance Y (art. 113) of the circuit.

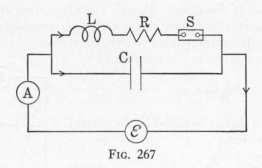

Fig. 267

Since the complex admittance is

$$\mathbf{Y} = \frac{1}{R+iL\omega} + iC\omega = \frac{R}{R^2+L^2\omega^2} - i\frac{L\omega - C\omega(R^2+L^2\omega^2)}{R^2+L^2\omega^2},$$

we have

$$Y = \sqrt{\left[\frac{R}{R^2+L^2\omega^2}\right]^2 + \left[\frac{L\omega - C\omega(R^2+L^2\omega^2)}{R^2+L^2\omega^2}\right]^2}$$

$$= \sqrt{\frac{1-2LC\omega^2}{R^2+L^2\omega^2} + C^2\omega^2}. \tag{123-1}$$

From this it appears that if

$$1 - 2LC\omega^2 = 0, \tag{123-2}$$

the admittance Y and hence the magnitude of the line current have the same values as if the capacitance alone was in the circuit. Therefore, to determine L we have only to adjust C until opening and closing S does not affect the ammeter reading. Then (123-2) is satisfied and we can calculate L if C and ω are known, irrespective of the resistance R of the choke coil.

* Turner, H. M., *Proc. I.R.E.* **16**, 1559 (1928).

In order to send direct current through the coil simultaneously with the alternating current, a battery may, of course, be introduced in series with the alternating e.m.f.   This is, however, objectionable in practice because it prevents a sensitive ammeter from being used in

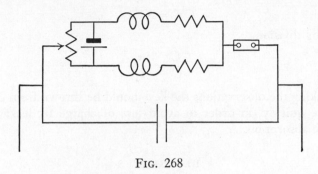

FIG. 268

the line.   A better plan is to use two identical choke coils, if available, in parallel, with a battery and potentiometer arranged to produce a circulating direct current which does not pass into the line.   Such an arrangement is shown schematically in Fig. 268.   The inductance now measured is one-half that possessed by either coil alone.

In making the measurements described above, care must be taken that the change of phase which takes place when S is opened or closed does not produce a change of voltage across the divided circuit and hence a change of total current even when (123-2) is satisfied.   This effect may be avoided by keeping the impedance of the ammeter and of the source of e.m.f. small.

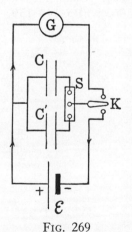

FIG. 269

124. Ballistic Comparison Measurements.   A ballistic galvanometer may be used to compare any two sources of charge, such as two mutual inductances, a mutual inductance and a capacitance, or two capacitances.   The latter comparison is particularly useful, as it provides a very simple means of finding an unknown capacitance in terms of a standard when measurement of the apparent resistance is not required.

The experimental arrangements (Fig. 269) consist of a single-pole double-throw switch S and a two-position key K so connected that either the unknown or the standard capacitance may be charged to a potential difference $\mathscr{E}$ and then discharged through the galvanometer.

If C and C' are the capacitances and α_1 and α_1' are the corresponding first throws, we have from art. 100

$$C\mathscr{E} = K_q'\alpha_1,$$
$$C'\mathscr{E} = K_q'\alpha_1'.$$

Hence, by division,

$$\frac{C}{C'} = \frac{\alpha_1}{\alpha_1'}. \tag{124-1}$$

In making the observations the key should be thrown from charge to discharge quickly, in order to avoid loss of charge by leakage or by dielectric absorption.

REFERENCES

Bleaney and Bleaney, *Electricity and Magnetism* (Oxford Univ. Press, 1965).   Pp. 227–236, 247–252, 414–429.

Duckworth, *Electricity and Magnetism* (Holt, Rinehart and Winston, 1960).   Pp. 365–382.

Kip, *Electricity and Magnetism* (McGraw-Hill, 1962).   Pp. 280–290.

Peck, *Electricity and Magnetism* (McGraw-Hill, 1953).   Chap. 11.

Winch, *Electricity and Magnetism* (Prentice-Hall, 1963).   Pp. 144–159, 166–174, Chap. 18.

Chapter XV

COUPLED CIRCUITS, FILTERS AND LINES

125. Types of Coupled Circuits. It is often convenient to couple two or more simple circuits by means of inductance or capacitance. The combination of circuits forms a network and may be treated as such. It is easier to obtain a physical insight into the behavior of the circuits, however, if their separate identities are maintained.

Confining ourselves to two circuits for the present, the simplest types of coupling are illustrated in Fig. 270. In (a) the coupling is *magnetic*, in (b) *inductive*, and in (c) *capacitative*.

The larger the fraction of the inductance or of the capacitance of each circuit that is mutual, the more the circuits react on one another. The square root of the product of these fractions for any pair of coupled circuits of the type illustrated is called the *coefficient of coupling* of the circuits. For example, in case (a) the coefficient of coupling is given by

$$k = \sqrt{\left(\frac{|M|}{L_1}\right)\left(\frac{|M|}{L_2}\right)} = \frac{|M|}{\sqrt{L_1 L_2}}, \qquad (125\text{-}1)$$

where $|M|$ denotes the absolute value of M, so that k is always positive. As the greatest possible magnitude of the mutual inductance is $\sqrt{L_1 L_2}$ from (94-10), we see that $0 \leqslant k \leqslant 1$. Similarly, in case (b),

$$k = \frac{L_M}{\sqrt{(L' + L_M)(L'' + L_M)}}, \qquad (125\text{-}2)$$

and in case (c),

$$k = \frac{\dfrac{1}{C_M}}{\sqrt{\left(\dfrac{1}{C'} + \dfrac{1}{C_M}\right)\left(\dfrac{1}{C''} + \dfrac{1}{C_M}\right)}}. \qquad (125\text{-}3)$$

The general behavior of all three types of coupled circuits is the same. Except under limiting conditions there are two characteristic frequencies, both for free oscillations and for forced oscillations. An

427

investigation of magnetically coupled circuits, the most common type, is carried out in the next two articles.

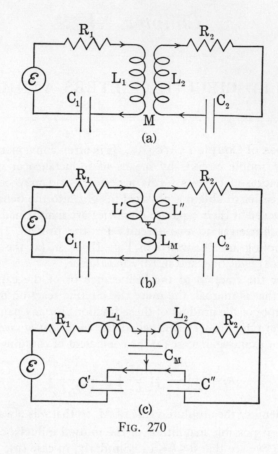

Fig. 270

Problem 125a. Show that inductive coupling between two circuits may be replaced by magnetic coupling such that

$$M = -L_M, \quad L_1 = L' + L_M, \quad L_2 = L'' + L_M,$$

without changing the electrical characteristics of the circuits.

Problem 125b. If C_1 and C_2 are the total series capacitances in two capacitatively coupled circuits, show that the coefficient of coupling may be put in the the form $\sqrt{C_1 C_2}/C_M$.

126. Coupled Circuits Freely Oscillating.

Suppose an electrical impulse is given to the coupled circuits of Fig. 271 by some means, such as allowing the capacitor C_1 in the primary circuit (1) to discharge, there being no applied e.m.f. in either circuit. Then, if the resistances are not too great, free oscillations take place as in the case of a single circuit (art. 91).

The circuit equations are

$$\left. \begin{aligned} L_1 \frac{di_1}{dt} + R_1 i_1 + \frac{q_1}{C_1} &= -M \frac{di_2}{dt}, \\ L_2 \frac{di_2}{dt} + R_2 i_2 + \frac{q_2}{C_2} &= -M \frac{di_1}{dt}, \end{aligned} \right\} \quad (126\text{-}1)$$

or, differentiating with respect to the time,

$$\left. \begin{aligned} L_1 \frac{d^2 i_1}{dt^2} + R_1 \frac{di_1}{dt} + \frac{1}{C_1} i_1 &= -M \frac{d^2 i_2}{dt^2}, \\ L_2 \frac{d^2 i_2}{dt^2} + R_2 \frac{di_2}{dt} + \frac{1}{C_2} i_2 &= -M \frac{d^2 i_1}{dt^2}. \end{aligned} \right\} \quad (126\text{-}2)$$

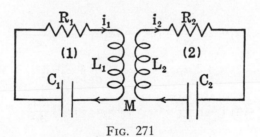

Fig. 271

The first step in solving these simultaneous differential equations is to express each in terms of one current only. Having multiplied either equation through by M and differentiated twice, we may substitute in the relation so obtained the value of the right-hand member of the other equation, getting

$$\left. \begin{aligned} (L_1 L_2 - M^2) \frac{d^4 i_1}{dt^4} + (R_1 L_2 + R_2 L_1) \frac{d^3 i_1}{dt^3} & \\ + \left(\frac{L_1}{C_2} + R_1 R_2 + \frac{L_2}{C_1} \right) \frac{d^2 i_1}{dt^2} + \left(\frac{R_1}{C_2} + \frac{R_2}{C_1} \right) \frac{di_1}{dt} + \frac{1}{C_1 C_2} i_1 &= 0, \\ (L_1 L_2 - M^2) \frac{d^4 i_2}{dt^4} + (R_1 L_2 + R_2 L_1) \frac{d^3 i_2}{dt^3} & \\ + \left(\frac{L_1}{C_2} + R_1 R_2 + \frac{L_2}{C_1} \right) \frac{d^2 i_2}{dt^2} + \left(\frac{R_1}{C_2} + \frac{R_2}{C_1} \right) \frac{di_2}{dt} + \frac{1}{C_1 C_2} i_2 &= 0. \end{aligned} \right\} \quad (126\text{-}3)$$

Since these equations are identical in form the currents must be of the same form. That is, damping constants α and frequencies of oscillation ω_0 (art. 91) must be the same in the two circuits.   Exact solutions of (126-3) are extremely complicated.   Fortunately in practical applications of oscillating circuits we always use circuits with small damping, so we shall restrict our analysis to this condition and obtain approximate solutions.   Thus, we shall refer to 1, α/ω_0, $(\alpha/\omega_0)^2$, $\cdots$ as quantities of the zero, first, second, $\cdots$ order, respectively, and shall neglect a quantity of any order in comparison with one of lower order. This enables us to neglect α in comparison with ω_0, $\alpha\omega_0$ in comparison with $\omega_0{}^2$, and so on.

Let us divide both equations of (126-3) by L_1L_2.   If we put

$$\alpha_1 \equiv \frac{R_1}{2L_1}, \qquad \alpha_2 \equiv \frac{R_2}{2L_2},$$

and

$$\omega_1 \equiv \frac{1}{\sqrt{L_1C_1}}, \qquad \omega_2 \equiv \frac{1}{\sqrt{L_2C_2}},$$

we obtain

$$\left.\begin{aligned}
(1-k^2)\frac{d^4i_1}{dt^4}+2(\alpha_1+\alpha_2)\frac{d^3i_1}{dt^3}+(\omega_1{}^2+4\alpha_1\alpha_2+\omega_2{}^2)\frac{d^2i_1}{dt^2} \\
+2(\alpha_1\omega_2{}^2+\alpha_2\omega_1{}^2)\frac{di_1}{dt}+\omega_1{}^2\omega_2{}^2i_1 = 0, \\
(1-k^2)\frac{d^4i_2}{dt^4}+2(\alpha_1+\alpha_2)\frac{d^3i_2}{dt^3}+(\omega_1{}^2+4\alpha_1\alpha_2+\omega_2{}^2)\frac{d^2i_2}{dt^2} \\
+2(\alpha_1\omega_2{}^2+\alpha_2\omega_1{}^2)\frac{di_2}{dt}+\omega_1{}^2\omega_2{}^2i_2 = 0,
\end{aligned}\right\} \quad (126\text{-}4)$$

where k is the coefficient of coupling considered in art. 125.   Evidently α_1 and α_2 are the damping constants of the two circuits taken separately, and ω_1 and ω_2 are the angular resonance frequencies (92-5) of applied e.m.f.'s for the individual circuits.   For small damping, however, the resonance frequencies do not differ appreciably from the natural frequencies of free oscillation, as indicated by (91-22), so we can regard ω_1 and ω_2 as the independent angular frequencies of free oscillation.

We may expect damped harmonic oscillations as in the case of the single oscillating circuit, so we take solutions of the form $e^{\gamma t}$ multiplied by an arbitrary constant and put $\gamma = -\alpha \pm i\omega_0$.   Substituting $e^{(-\alpha+i\omega_0)t}$ for the current in either equation of (126-4), we obtain

$$(1-k^2)(-\alpha+i\omega_0)^4+2(\alpha_1+\alpha_2)(-\alpha+i\omega_0)^3$$
$$+(\omega_1{}^2+4\alpha_1\alpha_2+\omega_2{}^2)(-\alpha+i\omega_0)^2$$
$$+2(\alpha_1\omega_2{}^2+\alpha_2\omega_1{}^2)(-\alpha+i\omega_0)+\omega_1{}^2\omega_2{}^2 = 0$$

after the common factor $e^{(-\alpha+i\omega_0)t}$ has been divided out, and this equation reduces to

$$(1-k^2)(4i\alpha\omega_0^3+\omega_0^4)+2(\alpha_1+\alpha_2)(-i\omega_0^3)$$
$$+(\omega_1^2+\omega_2^2)(-2i\alpha\omega_0-\omega_0^2)+2(\alpha_1\omega_2^2+\alpha_2\omega_1^2)(i\omega_0)+\omega_1^2\omega_2^2 = 0$$

when second and higher order terms are dropped. Separating real and imaginary parts, we have finally

$$(1-k^2)\omega_0^4-(\omega_1^2+\omega_2^2)\omega_0^2+\omega_1^2\omega_2^2 = 0, \tag{126-5}$$

and

$$\{2(1-k^2)\omega_0^2-(\omega_1^2+\omega_2^2)\}\alpha$$
$$-\{(\alpha_1+\alpha_2)\omega_0^2-(\alpha_1\omega_2^2+\alpha_2\omega_1^2)\} = 0. \tag{126-6}$$

Exactly the same questions are obtained, of course, if we substitute $e^{(-\alpha-i\omega_0)t}$ originally.

As there are two positive real roots of (126-5) namely,

$$\left.\begin{array}{l} \omega_0' = \sqrt{\dfrac{(\omega_1^2+\omega_2^2)-\sqrt{(\omega_1^2+\omega_2^2)^2-4(1-k^2)\omega_1^2\omega_2^2}}{2(1-k^2)}}, \\[3mm] \omega_0'' = \sqrt{\dfrac{(\omega_1^2+\omega_2^2)+\sqrt{(\omega_1^2+\omega_2^2)^2-4(1-k^2)\omega_1^2\omega_2^2}}{2(1-k^2)}}, \end{array}\right\} \tag{126-7}$$

there are two oscillation frequencies, both of which appear simultaneously in each circuit. From the form of (126-7) it is evident that these frequencies are always different from the characteristic frequencies ω_1 and ω_2 of the circuits oscillating independently. A special case of interest is when the circuits are *tuned* together; that is, when $\omega_1=\omega_2\equiv\Omega$. Then (126-7) reduces to

$$\left.\begin{array}{l} \omega_0' = \dfrac{\Omega}{\sqrt{1+k}}, \\[3mm] \omega_0'' = \dfrac{\Omega}{\sqrt{1-k}}. \end{array}\right\} \tag{126-8}$$

Corresponding to the two values of ω_0 there are two values of α, given by (126-6), which we may designate by α' and α'', respectively. These quantities have a simple form, independent of ω_1 and ω_2, only when the circuits are tuned together. In this case, using (126-8), we obtain from (126-6)

$$\left.\begin{array}{l} \alpha' = \dfrac{1}{1+k}\left(\dfrac{\alpha_1+\alpha_2}{2}\right), \\[3mm] \alpha'' = \dfrac{1}{1-k}\left(\dfrac{\alpha_1+\alpha_2}{2}\right). \end{array}\right\} \tag{126-9}$$

Let us return now to the differential equations. The complete solutions are obtained by adding together the four possible expressions of the required form. Hence,

$$i_1 = A_1'e^{(-\alpha'+i\omega_0')t} + B_1'e^{(-\alpha'-i\omega_0')t} + A_1''e^{(-\alpha''+i\omega_0'')t} + B_1''e^{(-\alpha''-i\omega_0'')t},$$
$$i_2 = A_2'e^{(-\alpha'+i\omega_0')t} + B_2'e^{(-\alpha'-i\omega_0')t} + A_2''e^{(-\alpha''+i\omega_0'')t} + B_2''e^{(-\alpha''-i\omega_0'')t},$$

where the A's and B's are arbitrary constants. In the usual way these equations may be put in trigonometric form and we have

$$\left. \begin{aligned} i_1 &= i_{10}'e^{-\alpha't}\sin{(\omega_0't+\epsilon_1')} + i_{10}''e^{-\alpha''t}\sin{(\omega_0''t+\epsilon_1'')}, \\ i_2 &= i_{20}'e^{-\alpha't}\sin{(\omega_0't+\epsilon_2')} + i_{20}''e^{-\alpha''t}\sin{(\omega_0''t+\epsilon_2'')}, \end{aligned} \right\} \quad (126\text{-}10)$$

the arbitrary constants now appearing as amplitudes and phase angles, represented by the i_0's and the ϵ's, respectively.

The arbitrary constants are not all independent, as may be seen by substituting (126-10) in either of the original differential equations. Thus, dividing the first equation of (126-2) by L_1 in order to introduce α_1, ω_1 and k, and substituting the values of the currents from (126-10), we find, if we take M to be positive,

$$(-\omega_0'^2 + \omega_1^2)i_{10}'e^{-\alpha't}\sin{(\omega_0't+\epsilon_1')}$$
$$+2(-\alpha'+\alpha_1)\omega_0'i_{10}'e^{-\alpha't}\cos{(\omega_0't+\epsilon_1')}$$
$$+(-\omega_0''^2 + \omega_1^2)i_{10}''e^{-\alpha''t}\sin{(\omega_0''t+\epsilon_1'')}$$
$$+2(-\alpha''+\alpha_1)\omega_0''i_{10}''e^{-\alpha''t}\cos{(\omega_0''t+\epsilon_1'')}$$

$$= k\sqrt{\frac{L_2}{L_1}}\,\omega_0'^2 i_{20}'e^{-\alpha't}\sin{(\omega_0't+\epsilon_2')}$$

$$+2k\sqrt{\frac{L_2}{L_1}}\,\alpha'\omega_0'i_{20}'e^{-\alpha't}\cos{(\omega_0't+\epsilon_2')}$$

$$+k\sqrt{\frac{L_2}{L_1}}\,\omega_0''^2 i_{20}''e^{-\alpha''t}\sin{(\omega_0''t+\epsilon_2'')}$$

$$+2k\sqrt{\frac{L_2}{L_1}}\,\alpha''\omega_0''i_{20}''e^{-\alpha''t}\cos{(\omega_0''t+\epsilon_2'')},$$

where the second order terms have been omitted as before. The equation holds for all values of t, so the parts of the equation in which ω_0' appears must represent one identity and the ω_0'' parts must represent another. Then, as the terms in α are negligible compared with those in ω,

$$(-\omega_0'^2 + \omega_1^2)i_{10}'e^{-\alpha't}\sin{(\omega_0't+\epsilon_1')}$$
$$= k\sqrt{\frac{L_2}{L_1}}\,\omega_0'^2 i_{20}'e^{-\alpha't}\sin{(\omega_0't+\epsilon_2')},$$
$$(-\omega_0''^2 + \omega_1^2)i_{10}''e^{-\alpha''t}\sin{(\omega_0''t+\epsilon_1'')}$$
$$= k\sqrt{\frac{L_2}{L_1}}\,\omega_0''^2 i_{20}''e^{-\alpha''t}\sin{(\omega_0''t+\epsilon_2'')},$$

from which we have

$$(-\omega_0'^2+\omega_1^2)i_{10}' = k\sqrt{\frac{L_2}{L_1}}\,\omega_0'^2 i_{20}', \qquad \epsilon_1' = \epsilon_2';$$

$$(-\omega_0''^2+\omega_1^2)i_{10}'' = k\sqrt{\frac{L_2}{L_1}}\,\omega_0''^2 i_{20}'', \qquad \epsilon_1'' = \epsilon_2''.$$

Hence, dropping unnecessary subscripts, the complete solutions of (126-4) for positive coupling become

$$\left.\begin{aligned}
i_1 &= i_0'e^{-\alpha't}\sin(\omega_0't+\epsilon')+i_0''e^{-\alpha''t}\sin(\omega_0''t+\epsilon''), \\
i_2 &= \frac{1}{k}\sqrt{\frac{L_1}{L_2}}\left[\left(\frac{\omega_1}{\omega_0'}\right)^2-1\right]i_0'e^{-\alpha't}\sin(\omega_0't+\epsilon') \\
&\quad -\frac{1}{k}\sqrt{\frac{L_1}{L_2}}\left[1-\left(\frac{\omega_1}{\omega_0''}\right)^2\right]i_0''e^{-\alpha''t}\sin(\omega_0''t+\epsilon'').
\end{aligned}\right\} \quad (126\text{-}11)$$

The arbitrary constants are now independent and are determined by the initial conditions under which the oscillations are set up.

The general character of the oscillations is apparent from (126-11). There are two damped harmonic oscillations in each circuit the simultaneous occurrence of which leads to a periodic rise and fall of amplitude superposed on a steady falling off due to damping, in a manner analogous to the production of acoustic beats between two musical notes. Since $\omega_0' < \omega_1$, while $\omega_0'' > \omega_1$, the low-frequency oscillations are in phase in the two circuits and the high-frequency oscillations are π radians out of phase, so the electrical beats in the circuits are out of phase, as illustrated in Fig. 272. Evidently energy surges back and forth from one circuit to the other at the *beat frequency*, which is $(\omega_0''-\omega_0')/2\pi$.

The graphs in the figure represent oscillations produced by discharging the primary condenser at time $t=0$. The values of the arbitrary constants for this case are found by setting

$$i_1 = 0, \qquad i_2 = 0,$$

$$q_1 = q_0, \qquad q_2 = 0,$$

for $t=0$ in (126-11) and (126-1). The current conditions give

$$0 = i_0'\sin\epsilon'+i_0''\sin\epsilon'',$$

$$0 = \frac{1}{k}\sqrt{\frac{L_1}{L_2}}\left[\left(\frac{\omega_1}{\omega_0'}\right)^2-1\right]i_0'\sin\epsilon'-\frac{1}{k}\sqrt{\frac{L_1}{L_2}}\left[1-\left(\frac{\omega_1}{\omega_0''}\right)^2\right]i_0''\sin\epsilon'',$$

from which we see that

$$\epsilon' = 0, \qquad \epsilon'' = 0. \qquad (126\text{-}12)$$

The charge conditions lead to

$$\omega_0'i_0'\cos\epsilon'+\omega_0''i_0''\cos\epsilon''+\omega_1{}^2q_0$$

$$= -\left[\left(\frac{\omega_1}{\omega_0'}\right)^2-1\right]\omega_0'i_0'\cos\epsilon'+\left[1-\left(\frac{\omega_1}{\omega_0''}\right)^2\right]\omega_0''i_0''\cos\epsilon'',$$

$$\left[\left(\frac{\omega_1}{\omega_0'}\right)^2-1\right]\omega_0'i_0'\cos\epsilon'-\left[1-\left(\frac{\omega_1}{\omega_0''}\right)^2\right]\omega_0''i_0''\cos\epsilon''$$

$$= -k^2\omega_0'i_0'\cos\epsilon'-k^2\omega_0''i_0''\cos\epsilon'',$$

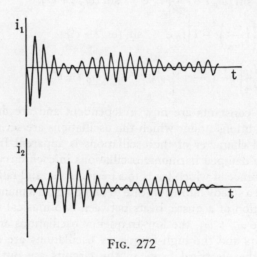

Fig. 272

after terms in α have been dropped.   Using (126-12) and combining, these equations reduce to

$$\frac{1}{\omega_0'}\,i_0'+\frac{1}{\omega_0''}\,i_0''+q_0 = 0,$$

$$\omega_0'i_0'+\omega_0''i_0''+\frac{\omega_1{}^2}{1-k^2}\,q_0 = 0,$$

so that

$$i_0'(\omega_0''^2-\omega_0'^2) = -\left(\omega_0''^2-\frac{\omega_1{}^2}{1-k^2}\right)\omega_0'q_0,$$

$$i_0''(\omega_0''^2-\omega_0'^2) = -\left(\frac{\omega_1{}^2}{1-k^2}-\omega_0'^2\right)\omega_0''q_0.$$

Now, if we eliminate $\omega_2{}^2$ between the equations (126-7), we have the relation

$$\cdot\ \frac{\omega_1{}^2}{1-k^2} = \omega_0'^2+\omega_0''^2-\frac{\omega_0'^2\omega_0''^2}{\omega_1{}^2},$$

which allows us to put the constants in the final form

$$i_0' = -\frac{1 - \left(\dfrac{\omega_1}{\omega_0''}\right)^2}{\left(\dfrac{\omega_1}{\omega_0'}\right)^2 - \left(\dfrac{\omega_1}{\omega_0''}\right)^2} \omega_0' q_0,$$

$$i_0'' = -\frac{\left(\dfrac{\omega_1}{\omega_0'}\right)^2 - 1}{\left(\dfrac{\omega_1}{\omega_0'}\right)^2 - \left(\dfrac{\omega_1}{\omega_0''}\right)^2} \omega_0'' q_0.$$

(126-13)

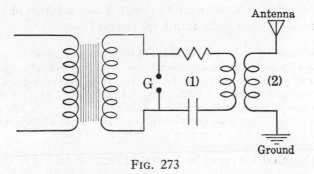

FIG. 273

When the circuits are tuned together, the complete solutions corresponding to the initial conditions given above become

$$i_1 = -\frac{1}{2}\frac{\Omega}{\sqrt{1+k}} q_0 e^{-\alpha' t} \sin\frac{\Omega}{\sqrt{1+k}} t - \frac{1}{2}\frac{\Omega}{\sqrt{1-k}} q_0 e^{-\alpha'' t} \sin\frac{\Omega}{\sqrt{1-k}} t,$$

$$i_2 = -\frac{1}{2}\sqrt{\frac{L_1}{L_2}}\frac{\Omega}{\sqrt{1+k}} q_0 e^{-\alpha' t} \sin\frac{\Omega}{\sqrt{1+k}} t$$

$$+ \frac{1}{2}\sqrt{\frac{L_1}{L_2}}\frac{\Omega}{\sqrt{1-k}} q_0 e^{-\alpha'' t} \sin\frac{\Omega}{\sqrt{1-k}} t,$$

the damping constants being given by (126-9) above. Tuned coupled circuits of this sort may be used to produce damped radio waves. The circuit arrangements are of interest, although in modern practice continuous rather than damped waves are used for radio communication. A spark gap G (Fig. 273), connected to the secondary of a high-voltage transformer, is included in the primary circuit (1). As the transformer voltage increases in magnitude the primary capacitor charges until finally a spark passes, effectively short-circuiting the gap, and oscillations ensue. Since the frequencies are very high, the oscillations die away long before the transformer voltage has passed through a half cycle. When the transformer voltage has reversed direction and again reaches sufficient magnitude, another set of oscillations results, and so on, the number of wave trains generated per second being equal to twice the frequency of the transformer power supply. In the secondary circuit (2) the capacitance is supplied by an antenna and ground system, from which energy is *radiated* in the form of electromagnetic waves, described in Chapter XVI.

The approximations made in the above treatment of free oscillations are valid only if the coupling between the circuits is not so small that terms involving k are of the same order of smallness as terms which are neglected. In particular, if $(\omega_2 - \omega_1)/\omega_0$ as well as k is of the first order or smaller, it is necessary to obtain a new solution of (126-4) in which at least all first order terms are retained.

Problem 126a. Given an oscillogram of the current in either of two coupled circuits tuned together to the angular frequency Ω, find a simple expression for k in terms of quantities which may be obtained from the oscillogram, assuming k^2 to be negligible compared with unity. Ans. $k = n/N$, where n is the beat frequency and N is the mean oscillation frequency.

Problem 126b. Taking ω_2 constant, plot ω_0' and ω_0'' as a function of ω_1 for k equal to 0.1, 0.5 and 0.9. Compare the three sets of curves.

127. Coupled Circuits in Forced Oscillation. Let us now investigate the behavior of coupled circuits (Fig. 274) when an alter-

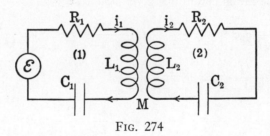

Fig. 274

nating e.m.f. $\mathscr{E} = \mathscr{E}_0 \sin \omega t$ is included in the primary circuit (1). The circuit equations are

$$\left. \begin{array}{l} L_1 \dfrac{di_1}{dt} + R_1 i_1 + \dfrac{q_1}{C_1} = -M \dfrac{di_2}{dt} + \mathscr{E}_0 \sin \omega t, \\[3mm] L_2 \dfrac{di_2}{dt} + R_2 i_2 + \dfrac{q_2}{C_2} = -M \dfrac{di_1}{dt}. \end{array} \right\} \quad (127\text{-}1)$$

Assuming that the e.m.f. has been acting long enough for a steady state to have been reached, the currents are sinusoidal in form with an angular frequency ω. Hence we may conveniently use the complex method of analysis, as explained in art. 113, to obtain the solutions of (127-1). Replacing $\mathscr{E}$ by $\mathscr{E} = \mathscr{E}_0 e^{i\omega t}$ and introducing complex currents we have, after differentiation,

$$\left.\begin{aligned}
L_1 \frac{d^2 i_1}{dt^2} + R_1 \frac{di_1}{dt} + \frac{1}{C_1} i_1 &= -M \frac{d^2 i_2}{dt^2} + \frac{d}{dt}(\mathscr{E}_0 e^{i\omega t}), \\
L_2 \frac{d^2 i_2}{dt^2} + R_2 \frac{di_2}{dt} + \frac{1}{C_2} i_2 &= -M \frac{d^2 i_1}{dt^2},
\end{aligned}\right\} \quad (127\text{-}2)$$

corresponding to (113-1) for a single circuit.

The complex currents must have the form

$$i_1 = i_{10} e^{i\omega t}, \qquad i_2 = i_{20} e^{i\omega t}.$$

Substituting these in (127-2) and removing common factors, we have

$$\left.\begin{aligned}
\left[R_1 + i\left(L_1\omega - \frac{1}{C_1\omega}\right)\right] i_{10} + iM\omega i_{20} &= \mathscr{E}_0, \\
\left[R_2 + i\left(L_2\omega - \frac{1}{C_2\omega}\right)\right] i_{20} + iM\omega i_{10} &= 0,
\end{aligned}\right\} \quad (127\text{-}3)$$

which give

$$\left.\begin{aligned}
i_{10} &= \frac{\mathscr{E}_0}{(R_1 + iX_1) + \dfrac{M^2\omega^2}{R_2 + iX_2}} = \frac{\mathscr{E}_0}{Z_1 + \dfrac{M^2\omega^2}{Z_2}}, \\
i_{20} &= \frac{-iM\omega\mathscr{E}_0}{(R_2 + iX_2)\left[(R_1 + iX_1) + \dfrac{M^2\omega^2}{R_2 + iX_2}\right]} = \frac{-iM\omega\mathscr{E}_0}{Z_2\left[Z_1 + \dfrac{M^2\omega^2}{Z_2}\right]},
\end{aligned}\right\} \quad (127\text{-}4)$$

where X_1, X_2 are the reactances of the separate circuits, and Z_1, Z_2 are the corresponding complex impedances. The same result may be obtained by applying Kirchhoff's laws to the coupled circuits regarded as a network. In this case we have

$$Z_1 i_1 + iM\omega i_2 = \mathscr{E},$$
$$Z_2 i_2 + iM\omega i_1 = 0,$$

which are equivalent to (127-3).

In order to find the actual currents we must take the imaginary parts of i_1 and i_2. Setting

$$Z_1' e^{i\phi_1'} \equiv Z_1 + \frac{M^2\omega^2}{Z_2},$$

equations (127-4) become

$$\mathbf{i}_{10} = \frac{\mathscr{E}_0}{Z_1'} e^{-i\phi_1'},$$

$$\mathbf{i}_{20} = \frac{-iM\omega\mathscr{E}_0}{Z_2 Z_1'} e^{-i(\phi_2+\phi_1')} = \frac{M\omega\mathscr{E}_0}{Z_2 Z_1'} e^{-i(\phi_2+\phi_1'+\pi/2)},$$

where

$$Z_1' = \sqrt{\left(R_1 + \frac{M^2\omega^2}{Z_2^2} R_2\right)^2 + \left(X_1 - \frac{M^2\omega^2}{Z_2^2} X_2\right)^2},$$

$$\tan\phi_1' = \frac{X_1 - \dfrac{M^2\omega^2}{Z_2^2} X_2}{R_1 + \dfrac{M^2\omega^2}{Z_2^2} R_2}. \qquad (127\text{-}5)$$

Hence

$$\left.\begin{aligned}
i_1 &= \frac{\mathscr{E}_0}{Z_1'} \sin(\omega t - \phi_1'), \\
i_2 &= \frac{M\omega\mathscr{E}_0}{Z_2 Z_1'} \sin\left(\omega t - \phi_2 - \phi_1' - \frac{\pi}{2}\right).
\end{aligned}\right\} \qquad (127\text{-}6)$$

We are concerned chiefly with the current amplitudes,

$$i_{10} = \frac{\mathscr{E}_0}{Z_1'}, \qquad i_{20} = \frac{M\omega\mathscr{E}_0}{Z_2 Z_1'}.$$

As these are functions both of the applied frequency and of the constants of the circuits, we shall investigate their behavior when ω alone is varied and also when X_1 and X_2 are changed with ω constant. In practice the resistances are almost always small compared with the reactances, except near the independent resonance points where the latter vanish.

Frequency Variation. We shall confine our analysis to the case of small resistances. Consider first i_{20} as it is the more important of the two amplitudes. We can write

$$Z_2 Z_1' = \sqrt{(R_1^2 + X_1^2)(R_2^2 + X_2^2) + 2M^2\omega^2(R_1 R_2 - X_1 X_2) + M^4\omega^4}. \qquad (127\text{-}7)$$

Neglecting the resistances in comparison with the reactances, this vanishes when

$$X_1 X_2 - M^2\omega^2 = 0,$$

that is, when

$$(1-k^2)\omega^4 - (\omega_1^2 + \omega_2^2)\omega^2 + \omega_1^2\omega_2^2 = 0, \qquad (127\text{-}8)$$

the constants k, ω_1 and ω_2 having the same significance as in (126-5). Evidently equation (127-8) has the same roots as (126-5), since the equations are identical in form.

Now, maximum values of i_{20} correspond, very closely at least, to minimum values of $Z_2 Z_1'$. Thus there are two *resonance frequencies* for the secondary circuit, given by

$$\left.\begin{aligned}
\omega_r' &= \sqrt{\frac{(\omega_1{}^2+\omega_2{}^2)-\sqrt{(\omega_1{}^2+\omega_2{}^2)^2-4(1-k^2)\omega_1{}^2\omega_2{}^2}}{2(1-k^2)}}, \\
\omega_r'' &= \sqrt{\frac{(\omega_1{}^2+\omega_2{}^2)+\sqrt{(\omega_1{}^2+\omega_2{}^2)^2-4(1-k^2)\omega_1{}^2\omega_2{}^2}}{2(1-k^2)}},
\end{aligned}\right\} \quad (127\text{-}9)$$

and these are identical with the frequencies of free oscillation. When

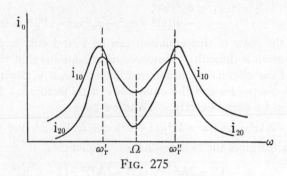

FIG. 275

the circuits are tuned together, as is often the case, so that $\omega_1 = \omega_2 \equiv \Omega$, we have simply

$$\left.\begin{aligned}
\omega_r' &= \frac{\Omega}{\sqrt{1+k}}, \\
\omega_r'' &= \frac{\Omega}{\sqrt{1-k}}.
\end{aligned}\right\} \quad (127\text{-}10)$$

Maximum values of i_{10} occur at very nearly the same values of ω as maximum values of i_{20}. The factor $M\omega/Z_2$ is increasing at ω_r' and decreasing at ω_r'', so that the primary maxima are slightly farther apart than the secondary. The chief effect of $M\omega/Z_2$ is, however, to make i_{10} decrease more rapidly than i_{20} between the maxima and less rapidly outside. The forms of the *resonance curves* for two circuits tuned together are shown in Fig. 275. With the resistances small, as assumed, the maxima in the secondary circuit are effectively equal, and those in the primary very nearly so. Note that, in accord with (127-10), the resonance peaks are not symmetrically placed relative to Ω.

If the coupling is made small, the foregoing results are somewhat modified, for the resonance values of ω approach ω_1 and ω_2 so that the reactances are no longer large compared with the resistances. To investigate this case, with the circuits tuned together, we express the secondary current amplitude in terms of the independent damping constants $\alpha_1 \equiv R_1/2L_1$ and $\alpha_2 \equiv R_2/2L_2$. After arranging and collecting terms, we find

$$i_{20} = \frac{k\omega^3 \mathscr{E}_0}{\sqrt{\begin{array}{l}[\{(1-k^2)\omega^4 - 2(\Omega^2 - \alpha_1{}^2 - \alpha_2{}^2)\omega^2 + \Omega^4\}^2 \\ \quad - 4(\alpha_1{}^2 - \alpha_2{}^2)^2\omega^4 + 4k^2(\alpha_1 + \alpha_2)^2\omega^6]L_1L_2\end{array}}}. \qquad (127\text{-}11)$$

To find the angular frequencies at which i_{20} is a maximum, or a minimum, we set $\dfrac{di_{20}}{d\omega}$ equal to zero and obtain

$$[(1-k^2)\omega^4 - \Omega^4]^2 + 4(\alpha_1{}^2 - \alpha_2{}^2)^2\omega^4 \\ - 4[(\Omega^2 - \alpha_1{}^2 - \alpha_2{}^2)\omega^2 - \Omega^4]^2 = 0. \qquad (127\text{-}12)$$

In general the roots of this equation can be found only approximately and the solution is difficult. However, if it happens that the damping constants of the circuits are equal, making $\alpha_1 = \alpha_2 \equiv A$, the middle term of (127-12) disappears and the equation can be factored. In this case the roots can be found exactly. Thus we have

$$[(1-k^2)\omega^4 - 2(\Omega^2 - 2A^2)\omega^2 + \Omega^4][(1-k^2)\omega^4 + 2(\Omega^2 - 2A^2)\omega^2 - 3\Omega^4] = 0.$$

The first factor gives the two resonance frequencies

$$\omega_r{}' = \sqrt{\frac{\Omega^2 - 2A^2 - \sqrt{(\Omega^2 - 2A^2)^2 - (1-k^2)\Omega^4}}{1-k^2}},$$

$$\omega_r{}'' = \sqrt{\frac{\Omega^2 - 2A^2 + \sqrt{(\Omega^2 - 2A^2)^2 - (1-k^2)\Omega^4}}{1-k^2}},$$

and the second factor gives the intermediate frequency of the minimum between the two resonance peaks

$$\omega_i = \sqrt{\frac{-(\Omega^2 - 2A^2) + \sqrt{(\Omega^2 - 2A^2)^2 + 3(1-k^2)\Omega^4}}{1-k^2}}.$$

Although these roots are exact, we are interested here in the case where k as well as A/Ω is a small quantity of the first order (art. 126). Hence, to the first approximation,

$$\left.\begin{array}{l} \omega_r{}' = \Omega\left[1 - \dfrac{1}{2}\sqrt{k^2 - 4\dfrac{A^2}{\Omega^2}}\right], \\[3mm] \omega_r{}'' = \Omega\left[1 + \dfrac{1}{2}\sqrt{k^2 - 4\dfrac{A^2}{\Omega^2}}\right], \\[3mm] \omega_i = \Omega. \end{array}\right\} \qquad (127\text{-}13)$$

Evidently as k diminishes the resonance peaks draw together. When k reaches the *transitional* value given by

$$k_t = 2\frac{A}{\Omega}, \tag{127-14}$$

the peaks merge. Up to this point the peaks have the same magnitude $\mathscr{E}_0/4A\sqrt{L_1L_2}$ independent of k, found by substituting $\omega_r{}'$ and $\omega_r{}''$ in (127-11), with $\alpha_1 = \alpha_2$. When k is less than k_t, there is only a single resonance frequency $\omega_r = \Omega$ and a single peak whose magnitude diminishes with k and vanishes, of course, when k becomes zero.

The behavior of the primary current is similar to that of the secondary except that the peaks merge a little less rapidly. Resonance curves for the transitional point are shown in Fig. 276. Actually the conclusions reached above on the assumption that α_1 equals α_2 are very nearly correct if α_1 and α_2 are not equal. The only difference of any importance in practice is the fact that in the first case i_{20} has a stationary maximum value for the entire range $k \geqslant k_t$, while in the second case it has a discrete maximum for a value of k less than k_t.

Circuit Tuning. When X_1 and X_2 are varied by means of the circuit elements, ω being kept constant, the exact conditions for resonance can be found without difficulty. Maximum values of i_{20}

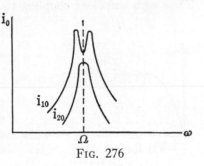

FIG. 276

occur at minimum values of Z_2Z_1', which may be found by setting the partial derivatives with respect to X_1 and X_2 equal to zero. Thus,

$$\left.\begin{aligned}
\frac{\partial}{\partial X_1}(Z_2Z_1') &= \frac{X_1(R_2{}^2 + X_2{}^2) - M^2\omega^2 X_2}{Z_2Z_1'} = 0, \\[2mm]
\frac{\partial}{\partial X_2}(Z_2Z_1') &= \frac{(R_1{}^2 + X_1{}^2)X_2 - M^2\omega^2 X_1}{Z_2Z_1'} = 0,
\end{aligned}\right\} \tag{127-15}$$

which are satisfied either by

$$X_1 = 0, \qquad X_2 = 0, \tag{127-16}$$

or by

$$\left.\begin{aligned}
X_1 &= \pm\sqrt{\frac{R_1}{R_2}(M^2\omega^2 - R_1R_2)}, \\[2mm]
X_2 &= \pm\sqrt{\frac{R_2}{R_1}(M^2\omega^2 - R_1R_2)}.
\end{aligned}\right\} \tag{127-17}$$

In the latter case both positive signs must be used or both negative, so there are only two possible sets of values.

Applying the usual tests for minima, we find that (127-16) represents the conditions for secondary resonance for the case $M^2\omega^2 < R_1R_2$, which we shall designate as *insufficient coupling*. The corresponding value of i_{20} is

$$(i_{20})_{max} = \frac{M\omega\mathscr{E}_0}{M^2\omega^2 + R_1R_2}, \tag{127-18}$$

which vanishes if $M = 0$ as is to be expected.

On the other hand (127-17) gives the resonance conditions for $M^2\omega^2 > R_1R_2$, which we shall call *sufficient coupling*. In this case, for either the positive or the negative set of values,

$$(i_{20})_{max} = \frac{\mathscr{E}_0}{2\sqrt{R_1R_2}}. \tag{127-19}$$

Thus with sufficient coupling the maximum current obtainable in the secondary is entirely independent of the coupling (Fig. 277) and, incidentally, of the frequency. Although in this case the circuits may be tuned for secondary resonance with their reactances either both positive or both negative, the latter is usually more convenient as smaller variable capacitances or inductances are required.

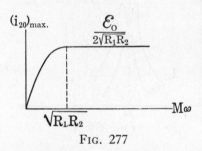

FIG. 277

As regards the primary circuit, there is no complete resonance, the maximum value of i_{10} increasing continuously as X_2 approaches infinity. There is, however, a partial resonance corresponding to adjustment of X_1 only, given by

$$\frac{\partial Z_1'}{\partial X_1} = \frac{X_1 - \frac{M^2\omega^2}{Z_2^2}X_2}{Z_1'} = 0.$$

This is equivalent to the first equation of (127-15), so the primary partial resonance for X_1 occurs at the same place as the secondary partial resonance for X_1.

The frequency $\nu = \omega/2\pi$ of a sinusoidal e.m.f. contained in a circuit (1) may be determined by coupling to this circuit an auxiliary adjustable circuit (2) composed of an inductance, a variable capacitor usually calibrated directly in terms of the independent resonance frequency $\nu_2 = \omega_2/2\pi$, and an alternating-current indicator such as a thermocouple type ammeter. An adjustable circuit of this sort, assembled as a unit, is called a *frequency meter*. When it is adjusted for maximum current indication, ν must equal the frequency ν_2 indicated by the capacitor setting, for with M small

$$i_{20} = \frac{M\omega\mathcal{E}_0}{\sqrt{(R_1{}^2+X_1{}^2)(R_2{}^2+X_2{}^2)}} \qquad (127\text{-}20)$$

and the maximum occurs when $X_2 = 0$, that is, when $\omega_2 = 1/\sqrt{L_2C_2}$ is made equal to the impressed angular frequency. Tuning the primary increases the meter deflection for any given coupling, but is not necessary to establish the secondary resonance relation.

Problem 127a. Referring to Fig. 274, suppose the e.m.f. is connected across C_1 instead of in series with it. Neglecting the resistances R_1 and R_2, find the condition under which the impedance of the network is (1) greatest, (2) least. In which case is the amplitude of the secondary current larger?

$$\text{Ans. (1) } X_1 = \frac{M^2\omega^2}{X_2}, \quad (2) \; L_1\omega = \frac{M^2\omega^2}{X_2}.$$

Problem 127b. Deduce the transformer equations (118-2) from (127-4).

Problem 127c. Given two identical series circuits with resistance 10 ohms, inductance 20 millihenrys and capacitance variable. They are coupled magnetically, the coefficient of couping being 0.1. If a sinusoidal e.m.f. of frequency $(10)^4$ cycles per second is introduced into one of the circuits, find how the capacitances must be adjusted to give a maximum current in the other circuit. Ans. $C_1 = C_2 = 0.0141$ microfarad, or $C_1 = C_2 = 0.0115$ microfarad.

128. Logarithmic Decrement and $\mathcal{Q}$ of a Circuit.

When dealing with free oscillations, we usually wish to know the logarithmic decrement δ of the circuit (art. 91), as the magnitude of δ determines the rapidity with which the oscillations are damped out. Similarly, in the case of forced oscillations, knowledge of the quantity $\mathcal{Q} \equiv L\omega/R$ is important since its value is an index of the sharpness of resonance as the circuit is tuned. For consider a series circuit which can be tuned by means of a variable capacitance to resonance with an applied e.m.f. of fixed angular frequency ω. The ratio of the amplitude of the current when the circuit is not adjusted to resonance to the amplitude at resonance is given by

$$\frac{i_0}{(i_0)_r} = \frac{R}{\sqrt{R^2+\left(L\omega-\dfrac{1}{C\omega}\right)^2}} = \frac{1}{\sqrt{1+\mathcal{Q}^2\left(1-\dfrac{\omega_0{}^2}{\omega^2}\right)^2}}, \qquad (128\text{-}1)$$

where $\omega_0 \equiv 1/\sqrt{LC}$ (the variable in the equation) is the angular frequency of resonance corresponding to the given adjustment, and also that of free oscillation since the damping is small. Thus the larger $\mathcal{Q}$ is, the more rapidly the current falls off as ω_0 is varied either side of resonance.

Ordinarily it is difficult to calculate the logarithmic decrement or the $\mathscr{Q}$ of a circuit accurately, particularly at high frequencies where the apparent values of the circuit elements may depend on the frequency, so we must resort to direct measurements. These may be made with either free oscillations or forced oscillations, that is, with damped waves or with undamped waves, but free oscillations are rarely used. Actually it is only necessary to measure $\mathscr{Q}$, since for the resonance adjustment $\omega_0 = \omega$ we have from (91-25) $\delta = \pi R/L\omega = \pi/\mathscr{Q}$.

As an example let us study the frequency meter circuit described in art. 127. This includes a device for measuring current, which is essential, and it is arranged so that it can be coupled loosely to a primary circuit (1) which contains an applied e.m.f. of the desired angular frequency ω. Now from (92-8) and (127-20) the mean-square current in the measuring circuit (2) is

$$\overline{i_2{}^2} = \tfrac{1}{2}i_{20}{}^2 = \frac{\tfrac{1}{2}M^2\omega^2\mathscr{E}_0{}^2}{(R_1{}^2 + X_1{}^2)(R_2{}^2 + X_2{}^2)}.$$

This is a function only of the adjustable resonance frequency ω_2 of the

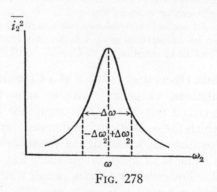

FIG. 278

measuring circuit, since both ω and the primary resonance frequency ω_1 are kept constant. Thus the maximum value $(\overline{i_2{}^2})_r$ occurs when $X_2 = 0$, that is, when ω_2 has its resonance value ω, and

$$\frac{\overline{i_2{}^2}}{(\overline{i_2{}^2})_r} = \frac{R_2{}^2}{R_2{}^2 + X_2{}^2} = \frac{1}{1 + \mathscr{Q}_2{}^2\left(1 - \dfrac{\omega_2{}^2}{\omega^2}\right)^2}. \qquad (128\text{-}2)$$

Let us vary ω_2 in the vicinity of resonance, putting $\omega_2 = \omega \pm \Delta\omega_2$. The corresponding resonance curve, shown in Fig. 278, is symmetrical about ω so that $\Delta\omega \equiv 2\Delta\omega_2$ is the interval between a pair of values giving the same value of $\overline{i_2{}^2}$ on either side of resonance. Finally, as we are interested only in circuits where the resonance is reasonably sharp,

$$\left(1 - \frac{\omega_2{}^2}{\omega^2}\right)^2 = \left(1 - \frac{\omega^2 \pm 2\omega\Delta\omega_2}{\omega^2}\right)^2 = \left(\frac{\Delta\omega}{\omega}\right)^2$$

to a sufficient degree of approximation. Substituting in (128-2), we have

$$\frac{\overline{i_2{}^2}}{(\overline{i_2{}^2})_r} = \frac{1}{1 + \mathcal{Q}_2{}^2\left(\dfrac{\Delta\omega}{\omega}\right)^2},$$

which gives

$$\mathcal{Q}_2 = \frac{\omega}{\Delta\omega}\sqrt{\frac{(\overline{i_2{}^2})_r - \overline{i_2{}^2}}{\overline{i_2{}^2}}}. \tag{128-3}$$

Hence the experimental procedure consists in tuning the measuring circuit to resonance to obtain $(\overline{i_2{}^2})_r$ and then detuning it to the same value $\overline{i_2{}^2}$ on either side. If the variable capacitor used in the tuning is calibrated in terms of actual frequency ν, we obtain $\omega/\Delta\omega = \nu/\Delta\nu$ directly. On the other hand, if the capacitor is calibrated in terms of capacitance only, we have

$$\frac{\omega}{\Delta\omega} = \frac{\dfrac{1}{\sqrt{L_2 C}}}{\sqrt{\dfrac{1}{L_2\left(C - \dfrac{\Delta C}{2}\right)}} - \sqrt{\dfrac{1}{L_2\left(C + \dfrac{\Delta C}{2}\right)}}} = 2\,\frac{C}{\Delta C},$$

where C is the resonance setting of the capacitor and ΔC is the capacitance difference corresponding to $\Delta\omega$. It is convenient to choose $\overline{i_2{}^2} = \frac{1}{2}(\overline{i_2{}^2})_r$ since then the radical in (128-3) reduces to unity. Care must be taken to note whether the ammeter scale gives mean-square or root-mean-square currents. In the latter case the scale readings must be squared.

Although here we have ascribed $\mathcal{Q}_2$ to the entire circuit, often the resistance of a circuit is almost completely associated with the inductance coil, in which case we may speak of "the $\mathcal{Q}$ of the coil."

Problem 128. Show how to measure the $\mathcal{Q}$ of a fixed circuit by varying the frequency of the applied e.m.f.

129. Filters.

We have investigated various simple a-c networks in which a limited number of impedance elements are used. Let us now turn our attention to a general type of network in which numbers of similar impedance elements are assembled to form a recurrent structure.   Networks of this sort are called *filters*, as they pass certain frequencies freely and stop others.

Various forms of structure may be employed.   We shall confine our

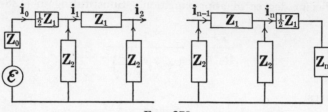

FIG. 279

discussion to the *ladder* type, illustrated in Fig. 279, which is one of the most common.   This filter consists of a number of identical series elements of complex impedance Z_1 and a number of shunt elements of complex impedance Z_2.   At the input end of the filter is a complex applied e.m.f. $\mathscr{E} = \mathscr{E}_0 e^{i\omega t}$, corresponding to an actual e.m.f. $\mathscr{E} = \mathscr{E}_0 \sin \omega t$, with a generator impedance Z_0, and at the output end is a complex load impedance Z_n.   As shown, the filter proper ends with half series elements and is said to have *mid-series* terminations.   We may think of the filter as composed of n T-sections (Fig. 280).   Sometimes, however, it is more convenient to arrange the filter as illustrated in Fig. 281, with *mid-shunt* terminations.   In this case we regard the filter as made up of n Π-sections (Fig. 282).   The type of termination affects the values of the currents in the different sections of the filter for given generator

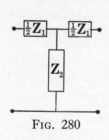

FIG. 280

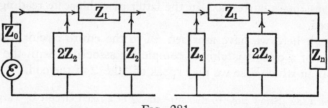

FIG. 281

and load impedances, of course, but it does not affect the general frequency characteristics of the filter.   Thus, to illustrate the principles involved, we need analyze only one case and we shall choose the mid-series.

Using Kirchhoff's laws in the complex form (art. 115), with positive directions of currents as indicated in Fig. 279, we have

$$\left.\begin{array}{c} \mathbf{Z}_0\mathbf{i}_0 + \tfrac{1}{2}\mathbf{Z}_1\mathbf{i}_0 - \mathbf{Z}_2(\mathbf{i}_1 - \mathbf{i}_0) = \mathscr{E}, \\ \mathbf{Z}_2(\mathbf{i}_1 - \mathbf{i}_0) + \mathbf{Z}_1\mathbf{i}_1 - \mathbf{Z}_2(\mathbf{i}_2 - \mathbf{i}_1) = 0, \\ \cdots\cdots\cdots\cdots\cdots\cdots \\ \mathbf{Z}_2(\mathbf{i}_{n-1} - \mathbf{i}_{n-2}) + \mathbf{Z}_1\mathbf{i}_{n-1} - \mathbf{Z}_2(\mathbf{i}_n - \mathbf{i}_{n-1}) = 0, \\ \mathbf{Z}_2(\mathbf{i}_n - \mathbf{i}_{n-1}) + \tfrac{1}{2}\mathbf{Z}_1\mathbf{i}_n + \mathbf{Z}_n\mathbf{i}_n = 0. \end{array}\right\} \quad (129\text{-}1)$$

As we assume that a steady state exists, the currents have the form $\mathbf{i}_0 = \mathbf{i}_{00}e^{i\omega t}$, $\mathbf{i}_1 = \mathbf{i}_{10}e^{i\omega t}$ and so on. Hence, removing the factors $e^{i\omega t}$ and arranging the equations symmetrically, (129-1) becomes

$$\left.\begin{array}{c} -\mathbf{Z}_2\mathbf{i}_{-10} + (\mathbf{Z}_1 + 2\mathbf{Z}_2)\mathbf{i}_{00} - \mathbf{Z}_2\mathbf{i}_{10} = 0, \\ -\mathbf{Z}_2\mathbf{i}_{00} + (\mathbf{Z}_1 + 2\mathbf{Z}_2)\mathbf{i}_{10} - \mathbf{Z}_2\mathbf{i}_{20} = 0, \\ \cdots\cdots\cdots\cdots\cdots\cdots \\ -\mathbf{Z}_2\mathbf{i}_{(n-2)0} + (\mathbf{Z}_1 + 2\mathbf{Z}_2)\mathbf{i}_{(n-1)0} - \mathbf{Z}_2\mathbf{i}_{n0} = 0, \\ -\mathbf{Z}_2\mathbf{i}_{(n-1)0} + (\mathbf{Z}_1 + 2\mathbf{Z}_2)\mathbf{i}_{n0} - \mathbf{Z}_2\mathbf{i}_{(n+1)0} = 0, \end{array}\right\} \quad (129\text{-}2)$$

where the quantities $\mathbf{i}_{-10}$ and $\mathbf{i}_{(n+1)0}$ are defined by

$$\left.\begin{array}{c} \mathbf{i}_{-10} = \dfrac{-(\mathbf{Z}_0 - \tfrac{1}{2}\mathbf{Z}_1 - \mathbf{Z}_2)\mathbf{i}_{00} + \mathscr{E}_0}{\mathbf{Z}_2}, \\[2mm] \mathbf{i}_{(n+1)0} = \dfrac{-(\mathbf{Z}_n - \tfrac{1}{2}\mathbf{Z}_1 - \mathbf{Z}_2)\mathbf{i}_{n0}}{\mathbf{Z}_2}. \end{array}\right\} \quad (129\text{-}3)$$

The equations of (129-2) are of the form

$$-\mathbf{Z}_2\mathbf{i}_{(m-1)0} + (\mathbf{Z}_1 + 2\mathbf{Z}_2)\mathbf{i}_{m0} - \mathbf{Z}_2\mathbf{i}_{(m+1)0} = 0, \qquad (129\text{-}4)$$

in which m takes all integral values from 0 to n, inclusive. We may expect a progressive change in the current as we pass from one section of the filter to the next, due to the recurrent structure. Let us, therefore, assume as a solution of (129-4)

$$\mathbf{i}_{m0} = \mathbf{A}e^{\Gamma m} + \mathbf{B}e^{-\Gamma m}, \qquad (129\text{-}5)$$

where $\mathbf{A}$, $\mathbf{B}$ and Γ are complex constants to be determined. Substituting (129-5) in (129-4) gives

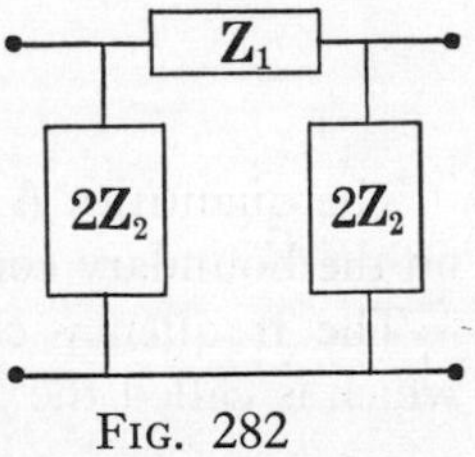

FIG. 282

$$-\mathbf{Z}_2[\mathbf{A}e^{\Gamma(m-1)} + \mathbf{B}e^{-\Gamma(m-1)}] + (\mathbf{Z}_1 + 2\mathbf{Z}_2)[\mathbf{A}e^{\Gamma m} + \mathbf{B}e^{-\Gamma m}]$$
$$-\mathbf{Z}_2[\mathbf{A}e^{\Gamma(m+1)} + \mathbf{B}e^{-\Gamma(m+1)}] = 0,$$

which reduces to

$$[(\mathbf{Z}_1 + 2\mathbf{Z}_2) - \mathbf{Z}_2(e^\Gamma + e^{-\Gamma})][\mathbf{A}e^{\Gamma m} + \mathbf{B}e^{-\Gamma m}] = 0.$$

Hence (129-5) is a solution of (129-4), provided only

$$e^{\Gamma}+e^{-\Gamma} = \frac{Z_1+2Z_2}{Z_2}.$$

Here we may use hyperbolic functions to advantage. The hyperbolic sine (sinh) and the hyperbolic cosine (cosh) are defined by

$$\sinh x = \frac{e^x-e^{-x}}{2}, \qquad \cosh x = \frac{e^x+e^{-x}}{2}.$$

Evidently sinh x is an odd function of x and cosh x is an even function. The graphs of these functions, assuming x real, are shown in Fig. 283. Note that cosh x is never less than unity, which is its value for $x=0$. When the argument of the functions is imaginary, we have

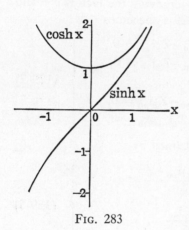

FIG. 283

$$\sinh (iy) = \frac{e^{iy}-e^{-iy}}{2} = i\sin y,$$

$$\cosh (iy) = \frac{e^{iy}+e^{-iy}}{2} = \cos y,$$

where y is real. It follows from these relations and from the general definition of the hyperbolic functions that

$$\cosh (x+iy) = \cosh x \cosh (iy) + \sinh x \sinh (iy)$$
$$= \cosh x \cos y + i \sinh x \sin y,$$

a result which we shall find useful.

In terms of hyperbolic functions the equation determining Γ is then

$$\cosh \Gamma = \frac{Z_1+2Z_2}{2Z_2}. \qquad (129\text{-}6)$$

The quantities $\mathbf{A}$ and $\mathbf{B}$ evidently are arbitrary constants depending on the boundary conditions, that is, on the values of $\mathbf{Z}_0$, $\mathbf{Z}_n$ and $\mathscr{E}_0$.

The frequency characteristics of the filter are controlled by $-\Gamma$, which is called the *propagation constant*. For let us write

$$-\Gamma \equiv \alpha+i\phi. \qquad (129\text{-}7)$$

Then, since the actual currents are obtained by multiplying (129-5) by $e^{i\omega t}$ and taking the imaginary part, there is an attenuation factor $e^{-\alpha}$ introduced into the amplitude of the first term by each section as we move away from the input end, and similarly for the second term as we move toward the input end. Hence if α differs from zero for any frequency and the filter has an appreciable number of sections, the current transmitted by the filter is effectively zero. On the other hand a current is freely transmitted if its frequency is such that $\alpha = 0$. The quantity α is called the *attenuation constant*. Similarly ϕ is called the *phase constant*, since it gives the change of phase per section (measured as a lag) in the currents as we move along the filter.

The physical significance of (129-5) is now clear. The first term represents *space waves* of current traveling away from the input end, attenuated from section to section much as the time waves of current due to free oscillations in a single circuit are attenuated from instant to instant. The second term represents similar waves traveling back toward the input end arising from reflections at the output end.

There are two separate points of interest to be considered, the dependence of the frequency characteristics upon the filter's construction, that is, upon the nature of Z_1 and Z_2, and the dependence of the general transmission characteristics upon the terminating impedances Z_0 and Z_n. The first matter involves only relations (129-6) and (129-7) already obtained, the second involves the determination of $\mathbf{A}$ and $\mathbf{B}$.

Frequency Characteristics. We shall neglect resistances in the filter as they are always made small compared with associated reactances. Then Z_1 and Z_2 are pure imaginaries and, in consequence, $\cosh \boldsymbol{\Gamma}$ is real. Expressing $\boldsymbol{\Gamma}$ in terms of α and ϕ,

$$\cosh \boldsymbol{\Gamma} = \cosh (-\boldsymbol{\Gamma}) = \cosh \alpha \cos \phi + i \sinh \alpha \sin \phi.$$

Since $\cosh \boldsymbol{\Gamma}$ is real, either α must be zero or ϕ must be an integral multiple of π. Hence, as $\cosh \alpha$ is never less than unity and $\cos \phi$ is never greater, we can distinguish three cases:

$$\left. \begin{array}{lll} -1 \leqslant \cosh \boldsymbol{\Gamma} \leqslant 1, & \alpha = 0, & \boldsymbol{\Gamma} = -i\phi; \\ \cosh \boldsymbol{\Gamma} > 1, & \phi = 0, & \boldsymbol{\Gamma} = -\alpha; \\ \cosh \boldsymbol{\Gamma} < -1, & \phi = \pm \pi, & \boldsymbol{\Gamma} = -\alpha \mp i\pi. \end{array} \right\} \quad (129\text{-}8)$$

In the frequency range corresponding to the first case, currents are transmitted freely without attenuation, so we have a *pass band*. Frequency ranges corresponding to the other two cases are *stop bands*. Thus, in terms of Z_1 and Z_2, pass bands are given by

$$-1 \leqslant \frac{Z_1 + 2Z_2}{2Z_2} \leqslant 1,$$

or

$$0 \leqslant \left(-\frac{Z_1}{Z_2}\right) \leqslant 4, \quad (129\text{-}9)$$

and stop bands by all other ranges of values.

The simplest filters of the type we are considering are illustrated in Fig. 284.   For the arrangement shown in (a),

$$\mathbf{Z}_1 = iL_1\omega, \qquad \mathbf{Z}_2 = -i\frac{1}{C_2\omega},$$

so that the pass band is given by

$$0 \leqslant L_1 C_2 \omega^2 \leqslant 4,$$

that is,

$$0 \leqslant \omega \leqslant \omega_c, \qquad \omega_c \equiv \frac{2}{\sqrt{L_1 C_2}}. \tag{129-10}$$

Since all frequencies from zero to a critical or *cut-off* frequency given

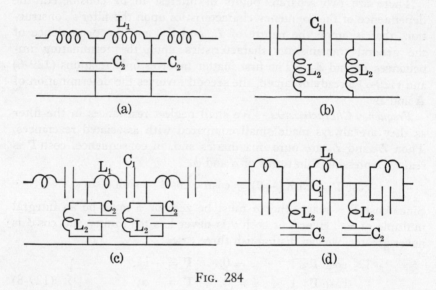

(a)   (b)

(c)   (d)

FIG. 284

by $\omega_c = 2/\sqrt{L_1 C_2}$ are passed without attenuation, we have a *low-pass* filter.

In (b) the filter elements are

$$\mathbf{Z}_1 = -i\frac{1}{C_1\omega}, \qquad \mathbf{Z}_2 = iL_2\omega,$$

and the pass band is determined by

$$0 \leqslant \frac{1}{L_2 C_1 \omega^2} \leqslant 4,$$

that is,

$$\omega_c \leqslant \omega \leqslant \infty, \qquad \omega_c \equiv \frac{1}{2\sqrt{L_2 C_1}}. \tag{129-11}$$

Here all frequencies above a critical frequency are passed without attenuation, so that we have a *high-pass* filter.

Arrangement (c) is slightly more complicated. As

$$\mathbf{Z}_1 = i\left(L_1\omega - \frac{1}{C_1\omega}\right), \qquad \mathbf{Z}_2 = i\frac{L_2\omega}{1-L_2C_2\omega^2},$$

we have the inequality

$$0 \leqslant \frac{(1-L_1C_1\omega^2)(1-L_2C_2\omega^2)}{L_2C_1\omega^2} \leqslant 4,$$

which is satisfied by two ranges of values of ω. We usually prefer to bring the two ranges together, however, by taking $L_1C_1 = L_2C_2$. Then, setting $\omega_c \equiv 1/\sqrt{L_1C_1} \equiv 1/\sqrt{L_2C_2}$, there is a single pass band given by

$$\left.\begin{array}{l}\omega_c{}' \leqslant \omega \leqslant \omega_c{}'', \\[2ex] \omega_c{}' \equiv \omega_c\left[\sqrt{\sqrt{\frac{L_2C_1}{L_1C_2}}+1} - \sqrt{\sqrt{\frac{L_2C_1}{L_1C_2}}}\right], \\[3ex] \omega_c{}'' \equiv \omega_c\left[\sqrt{\sqrt{\frac{L_2C_1}{L_1C_2}}+1} + \sqrt{\sqrt{\frac{L_2C_1}{L_1C_2}}}\right].\end{array}\right\} \quad (129\text{-}12)$$

This filter is called a *band-pass* filter.

In (d) we have

$$\mathbf{Z}_1 = i\frac{L_1\omega}{1-L_1C_1\omega^2}, \qquad \mathbf{Z}_2 = i\left(L_2\omega - \frac{1}{C_2\omega}\right).$$

The inequality

$$0 \leqslant \frac{L_1C_2\omega^2}{(1-L_1C_1\omega^2)(1-L_2C_2\omega^2)} \leqslant 4$$

is satisfied by two ranges of values of ω as in the previous case. Here we cannot bring the ranges together, but we will take $\omega_c \equiv 1/\sqrt{L_1C_1} \equiv 1/\sqrt{L_2C_2}$ as before, for simplicity. Then there are two pass bands:

$$\left.\begin{array}{ll}0 \leqslant \omega \leqslant \omega_c{}', & \omega_c{}' \equiv \frac{\omega_c}{4}\left[\sqrt{\sqrt{\frac{L_1C_2}{L_2C_1}}+16} - \sqrt{\sqrt{\frac{L_1C_2}{L_2C_1}}}\right]; \\[3ex] \omega_c{}'' \leqslant \omega \leqslant \infty, & \omega_c{}'' \equiv \frac{\omega_c}{4}\left[\sqrt{\sqrt{\frac{L_1C_2}{L_2C_1}}+16} + \sqrt{\sqrt{\frac{L_1C_2}{L_2C_1}}}\right].\end{array}\right\} \quad (129\text{-}13)$$

As there is a single stop band corresponding to $\omega_c{}' < \omega < \omega_c{}''$ this filter is usually called a *band-stop filter*.

In addition to the location of the cut-off frequencies, it is often important to know how α varies with frequency in a stop band or how

ϕ varies in a pass band. Using (129-6) to (129-8) inclusive, we see that in a stop band

$$\cosh \alpha = \pm \frac{Z_1 + 2Z_2}{2Z_2}, \tag{129-14}$$

the proper sign being used to make the right-hand side of the equation positive. Similarly, in a pass band,

$$\cos \phi = \frac{Z_1 + 2Z_2}{2Z_2}. \tag{129-15}$$

In Fig. 285 α and ϕ are shown as functions of the angular frequency for the four filters we have just discussed. To facilitate comparison the same value of ω_c is used in each case. The sign of ϕ is determined by including the resistance terms of Z_1 and Z_2 in the expanded form of (129-6) and observing that for $X_1 > 0$, $X_2 < 0$, ϕ is positive while for $X_1 < 0$, $X_2 > 0$, ϕ is negative. In other words ϕ always increases with frequency in pass bands.

In all the filters described the structure is such that $K \equiv \sqrt{Z_1 Z_2}$ is independent of the frequency. Hence they are usually termed *constant-K* filters.

Transmission Characteristics. The values of **A** and **B** are most simply expressed in terms of the *characteristic impedance* Z_K of the given filter, so we shall determine this quantity first. By definition Z_K is the impedance of a filter of the type in question having an infinite number of sections. For such a filter (129-5) may be written

$$\mathbf{i}_{m0} = \mathbf{A}_\infty e^{\Gamma m} + \mathbf{B}_\infty e^{-\Gamma m} = \mathbf{i}_{00} e^{\Gamma m} - \mathbf{B}_\infty (e^{\Gamma m} - e^{-\Gamma m})$$

since $\mathbf{i}_{00} = \mathbf{A}_\infty + \mathbf{B}_\infty$. But there can be no reflected waves, represented by the $e^{-\Gamma m}$ term, in an infinite filter, since the original transmitted wave is attenuated to zero before it reaches the output end of the filter. Hence $\mathbf{B}_\infty = 0$ and the complex current amplitudes are simply $\mathbf{i}_{m0} = \mathbf{i}_{00} e^{\Gamma m}$. The first equation in (129-2) then gives

$$[-Z_2(e^\Gamma - 1) + \tfrac{1}{2} Z_1 + Z_0] \mathbf{i}_{00} = \mathscr{E}_0.$$

But, for the infinite filter,

$$[Z_K + Z_0] \mathbf{i}_{00} = \mathscr{E}_0,$$

and hence

$$Z_K = -Z_2(e^\Gamma - 1) + \tfrac{1}{2} Z_1 = -Z_2 \left(\frac{e^\Gamma - e^{-\Gamma}}{2} \right). \tag{129-16}$$

Squaring this equation and using (129-6),

$$\left(\frac{Z_K}{Z_2} \right)^2 = \left(\frac{Z_1 + 2Z_2}{2Z_2} \right)^2 - 1 = \frac{Z_1}{Z_2} + \frac{Z_1^2}{4Z_2^2},$$

or, finally,

$$\mathbf{Z}_K = \sqrt{\mathbf{Z}_1\mathbf{Z}_2 + \tfrac{1}{4}\mathbf{Z}_1{}^2}. \tag{129-17}$$

We see that when we neglect the resistance terms in $\mathbf{Z}_1$ and $\mathbf{Z}_2$ as in

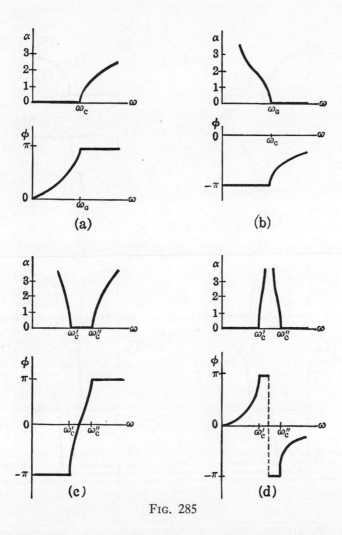

FIG. 285

(129-8), $\mathbf{Z}_K \equiv R_K$, a pure resistance, in the pass bands and $\mathbf{Z}_K \equiv iX_K$ in the stop bands. In Fig. 286 R_K and X_K are shown as functions of the angular frequency, the four cases corresponding to those of Fig. 285. To aid in comparison the same value of K is used in each case.

We are now ready to evaluate $\mathbf{A}$ and $\mathbf{B}$. Substituting (129-5) in the first and last equations of (129-1), we obtain

$$[-\mathbf{Z}_2(e^{\Gamma}-1)+\tfrac{1}{2}\mathbf{Z}_1+\mathbf{Z}_0]\mathbf{A}+[-\mathbf{Z}_2(e^{-\Gamma}-1)+\tfrac{1}{2}\mathbf{Z}_1+\mathbf{Z}_0]\mathbf{B} = \mathscr{E}_0,$$
$$e^{\Gamma n}[-\mathbf{Z}_2(e^{-\Gamma}-1)+\tfrac{1}{2}\mathbf{Z}_1+\mathbf{Z}_n]\mathbf{A}+e^{-\Gamma n}[-\mathbf{Z}_2(e^{\Gamma}-1)+\tfrac{1}{2}\mathbf{Z}_1+\mathbf{Z}_n]\mathbf{B} = 0.$$

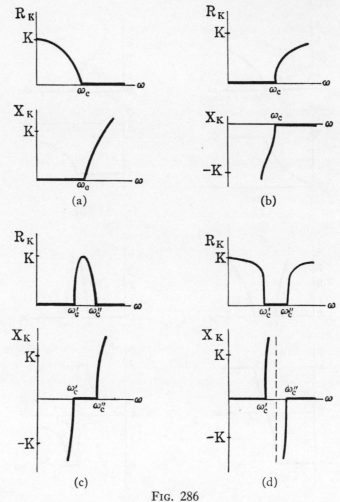

Fig. 286

From (129-16)

$$-\mathbf{Z}_2(e^{\Gamma}-1)+\tfrac{1}{2}\mathbf{Z}_1 = \mathbf{Z}_K.$$

Similarly, from (129-16) and (129-6),

$$-\mathbf{Z}_2(e^{-\Gamma}-1)+\tfrac{1}{2}\mathbf{Z}_1 = -\mathbf{Z}_K.$$

Hence we have

$$(\mathbf{Z}_K + \mathbf{Z}_0)\mathbf{A} - (\mathbf{Z}_K - \mathbf{Z}_0)\mathbf{B} = \mathscr{E}_0, \\ -e^{\Gamma n}(\mathbf{Z}_K - \mathbf{Z}_n)\mathbf{A} + e^{-\Gamma n}(\mathbf{Z}_K + \mathbf{Z}_n)\mathbf{B} = 0. \quad \Bigg\} \quad (129\text{-}18)$$

These equations can be solved for $\mathbf{A}$ and $\mathbf{B}$ immediately and the resulting values substituted in (129-5) to obtain the general expression for the complex current amplitudes, applicable to any filter with any terminating impedances. Then the actual current amplitudes i_{m0} and corresponding phase angles can be found in the usual manner. However, in the general form the current amplitudes are complicated functions of the frequency, and calculation of them is laborious, so we shall confine ourselves to special cases. Thus, suppose that there is an output *impedance match*, that is, $\mathbf{Z}_n = \mathbf{Z}_K$, while at the input end of the filter $\mathbf{Z}_0 = K \equiv \sqrt{\mathbf{Z}_1 \mathbf{Z}_2}$. In this case the filter with its load impedance behaves like an infinite filter. Reflections are absent, so that all the energy delivered to the filter at the input end is transmitted to $\mathbf{Z}_n$ and the filter operates at maximum efficiency. Setting $\mathbf{Z}_n = \mathbf{Z}_K$ in (129-18) gives

$$\mathbf{A} = \frac{\mathscr{E}_0}{\mathbf{Z}_K + K}, \qquad \mathbf{B} = 0,$$

and so

$$\mathbf{i}_{m0} = \frac{\mathscr{E}_0}{\mathbf{Z}_K + K} e^{\Gamma m}. \qquad (129\text{-}19)$$

Usually we are only interested in the input and output currents, determined by

$$\mathbf{i}_{00} = \frac{\mathscr{E}_0}{\mathbf{Z}_K + K}, \qquad \mathbf{i}_{n0} = \frac{\mathscr{E}_0}{\mathbf{Z}_K + K} e^{\Gamma n}. \qquad (129\text{-}20)$$

Both of these are functions of ω. Evidently in a pass band the actual currents i_0 and i_n have equal amplitudes but a phase difference $n\phi$, whereas in a stop band $i_{n0} = i_{00}e^{-n\alpha}$ and the phase difference is merely a multiple of π. These simple results hold, of course, only when $\mathbf{Z}_n = \mathbf{Z}_K$, and it should be observed that since $\mathbf{Z}_K$ is a function of the frequency no simple fixed load impedance can match the filter over a range of frequencies. For this reason it is often necessary in practice to use a special impedance matching section at the end of the filter.

Finally consider the reverse case where we have the input impedance match $\mathbf{Z}_0 = \mathbf{Z}_K$, while $\mathbf{Z}_n = K$. Here

$$\mathbf{A} = \frac{\mathscr{E}_0}{2\mathbf{Z}_K}, \qquad \mathbf{B} = \frac{\mathscr{E}_0}{2\mathbf{Z}_K} e^{\Gamma(2n)} \left(\frac{\mathbf{Z}_K - K}{\mathbf{Z}_K + K} \right),$$

so that

$$\mathbf{i}_{m0} = \frac{\mathscr{E}_0}{2\mathbf{Z}_K} \left[e^{\Gamma m} + e^{\Gamma(2n-m)} \left(\frac{\mathbf{Z}_K - K}{\mathbf{Z}_K + K} \right) \right]. \qquad (129\text{-}21)$$

and

$$
\left.
\begin{aligned}
\mathbf{i}_{00} &= \frac{\mathscr{E}_0}{2\mathbf{Z}_K}\left[1 + e^{\mathbf{\Gamma}(2n)}\left(\frac{\mathbf{Z}_K - K}{\mathbf{Z}_K + K}\right)\right] \\
&= \frac{\mathscr{E}_0}{\mathbf{Z}_K + K}\, e^{\mathbf{\Gamma}n}\left[\cosh \mathbf{\Gamma}n - \frac{K}{\mathbf{Z}_K}\sinh \mathbf{\Gamma}n\right], \\
\mathbf{i}_{n0} &= \frac{\mathscr{E}_0}{2\mathbf{Z}_K}\left[e^{\mathbf{\Gamma}n} + e^{\mathbf{\Gamma}n}\left(\frac{\mathbf{Z}_K - K}{\mathbf{Z}_K + K}\right)\right] = \frac{\mathscr{E}_0}{\mathbf{Z}_K + K}\, e^{\mathbf{\Gamma}n}.
\end{aligned}
\right\}
\qquad (129\text{-}22)
$$

Although the output current has the same form as before, due to the reciprocal nature of the two cases, the input current and, therefore, the relation between the currents are quite different.

Problem 129a. Show that the characteristic impedance $\mathbf{Z}_K{}'$ of a mid-shunt terminated filter (Fig. 281) is related to the corresponding mid-series characteristic impedance $\mathbf{Z}_K$ according to the equation $\mathbf{Z}_K\mathbf{Z}_K{}' = \mathbf{Z}_1\mathbf{Z}_2$.

Problem 129b. A low-pass filter with mid-series terminations is constructed of elements $L_1 = 1/\pi$ henry, $C_2 = 1/\pi$ microfarad. Find the cut-off frequency ν_c. Also express the characteristic impedance as a function of the frequency ν.

Ans. $\nu_c = 1000$ cycle/sec, $\mathbf{Z}_K = (10)^3\sqrt{1 - \left(\dfrac{\nu}{\nu_c}\right)^2}$ ohm.

Problem 129c. A high-pass filter with mid-series terminations has elements $C_1 = 1/4\pi$ microfarad, $L_2 = 1/4\pi$ henry. Make the same calculations as in the preceding problem.

Ans. $\nu_c = 1000$ cycle/sec, $\mathbf{Z}_K = (10)^3\sqrt{1 - \left(\dfrac{\nu_c}{\nu}\right)^2}$ ohm.

Problem 129d. Using (129-22) calculate and plot as a function of the frequency the actual output current (amplitude and phase) for (a) a two-section low-pass filter with elements as specified in problem *129b*, (b) a two-section high-pass filter with elements as specified in problem *129c*.

130. Lines. The a-c circuits and networks which we have considered up to this point are such that at any instant the current is the same all the way around a circuit or all the way along any branch of a network. Let us now consider a case in which the current varies along the circuit at every instant as well as varying in time at every point. Suppose we have two long parallel conductors of uniform, but not necessarily the same, cross section (Fig. 287). Although the two conductors are often separated as shown in the figure, one, in the form of a hollow cylinder, may surround the other. Let the long conductors be connected to an impedance $\mathbf{Z}_0$ and an e.m.f. $\mathscr{E} = \mathscr{E}_0 e^{i\omega t}$ at one end and to an impedance $\mathbf{Z}_S$ at the other. The pair of long conductors constitutes a *line*, and $\mathbf{Z}_0$ and $\mathbf{Z}_S$ are its associated generator and load impedances, respectively. Let the length of the line be S and the distance of any point on the line from the input end be s.   If R and L are the resistance and the inductance per unit length (including both sides of the line) and G and C are the leakage conductance and the capacitance between conductors per unit length, we have for the series impedance per unit length along the line $\mathbf{Z}_L = R + iL\omega$ and for the shunt impedance per unit length across the line $\mathbf{Z}_C = 1/(G + iC\omega)$.

Now consider an element ds of the line located at a distance s from

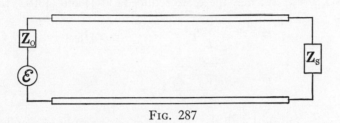

FIG. 287

the input end (Fig. 288), denoting the complex current along the conductors and the complex e.m.f. between them at this point by $\mathbf{i}_s$ and $\mathscr{E}_s$ respectively.   As we go from s to $s + ds$ the current along the line must diminish, in accord with Kirchhoff's first law, by an amount equal to the current across the line.   Since the shunt admittance for the length ds of line is $(Gds) + i(Cds)\omega$, the shunt current is equal to $[(Gds) + i(Cds)\omega]\mathscr{E}_s$ and we have

$$-\frac{\partial \mathbf{i}_s}{\partial s} ds = [(G\,ds) + i(C\,ds)\omega]\mathscr{E}_s$$

$$= \frac{\mathscr{E}_s}{\mathbf{Z}_C} ds.$$

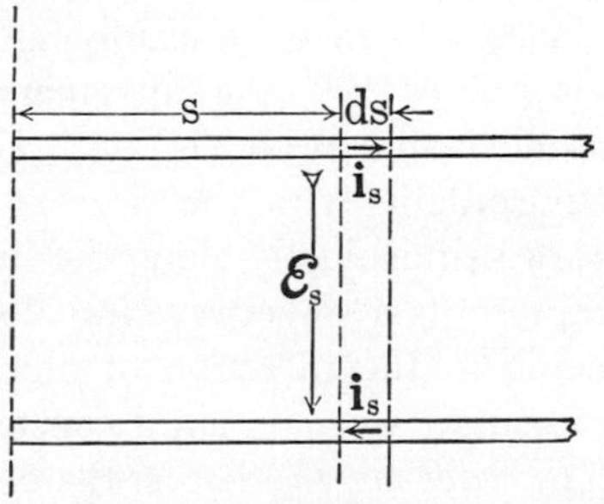

Similarly, as $(Rds) + i(Lds)\omega$ is the series impedance of the length ds of line, the e.m.f. across the line diminishes, as we go from s to $s + ds$, by an amount equal to $[(Rds) + i(Lds)\omega]\mathbf{i}_s$, giving

FIG. 288

$$-\frac{\partial \mathscr{E}_s}{\partial s} ds = [(R\,ds) + i(L\,ds)\omega]\mathbf{i}_s = \mathbf{Z}_L\mathbf{i}_s ds.$$

This follows from Kirchhoff's second law, since $-\left(\dfrac{\partial \mathscr{E}_s}{\partial s}\right)ds$ is, in effect, the e.m.f. applied to the elementary circuit formed by the length ds of the pair of conductors.

Hence

$$-\frac{\partial i_s}{\partial s} = \frac{\mathscr{E}_s}{Z_C}, \qquad -\frac{\partial \mathscr{E}_s}{\partial s} = Z_L i_s, \qquad (130\text{-}1)$$

and, eliminating $\mathscr{E}_s$,

$$\frac{\partial^2 i_s}{\partial s^2} - \frac{Z_L}{Z_C} i_s = 0. \qquad (130\text{-}2)$$

The frequency of the current is the same as that of the applied e.m.f. so that $i_s = i_{s0} e^{i\omega t}$. We may therefore reduce (130-1) and (130-2) to

$$-\frac{\partial i_{s0}}{\partial s} = \frac{\mathscr{E}_{s0}}{Z_C}, \qquad -\frac{\partial \mathscr{E}_{s0}}{\partial s} = Z_L i_{s0}, \qquad (130\text{-}3)$$

and

$$\frac{\partial^2 i_{s0}}{\partial s^2} - \frac{Z_L}{Z_C} i_{s0} = 0, \qquad (130\text{-}4)$$

respectively, and deal with the complex current amplitudes only.

The solution of (130-4) has the form

$$i_{s0} = A e^{\Gamma s} + B e^{-\Gamma s}, \qquad (130\text{-}5)$$

where $-\Gamma \equiv \alpha + i\phi$ is the *propagation constant* exactly as for the filters discussed in art. 129. Here, however, α is the attenuation constant per unit length of line and ϕ is the corresponding phase constant per unit length. The first term of (130-5) represents waves of current traveling away from the input end of the line, continuously attenuated because of the factor $e^{-\alpha s}$. To see this, express A in the exponential form $A e^{-ia}$. Then on multiplying through by $e^{i\omega t}$ the first term becomes $A e^{-\alpha s} e^{i(\omega t - \phi s - a)}$, the imaginary part of which, corresponding to an applied sine wave, is $A e^{-\alpha s} \sin(\omega t - \phi s - a)$. This expression varies sinusoidally with the time at every point along the line and it also varies sinusoidally along the line at every instant of time. It therefore represents a wave traveling along the line, the direction of propagation being in the direction of increasing s, since increasing s requires increasing t to maintain a constant value of the total phase $(\omega t - \phi s - a)$. The *wave length*, that is, the distance it is necessary to go along the line to find a phase difference of 2π radians at any instant, is given by

$$\lambda = \frac{2\pi}{\phi}, \qquad (130\text{-}6)$$

while the velocity v with which the waves travel is equal to the product of the wave length by the frequency, that is,

$$v = \lambda\left(\frac{\omega}{2\pi}\right) = \frac{\omega}{\phi}. \qquad (130\text{-}7)$$

The second term of (130-5) represents waves traveling back toward the input end, arising from reflections at the output end. A wave of the sort under discussion is depicted in Fig. 289, where the actual current i_s is shown as a function of distance for a particular instant of time. As time changes the wave crests move with the speed v keeping always between the broken line curves which represent the effect of the attenuation factor $e^{-\alpha s}$.

Frequency Characteristics. Substituting (130-5) in (130-4) shows us that

$$-\boldsymbol{\Gamma} = \sqrt{\frac{\mathbf{Z}_L}{\mathbf{Z}_C}} = \sqrt{(R+iL\omega)(G+iC\omega)}. \qquad (130\text{-}8)$$

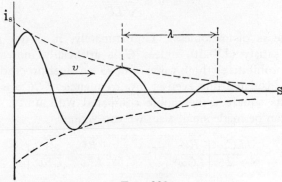

FIG. 289

Hence, squaring,

$$(\alpha+i\phi)^2 = (R+iL\omega)(G+iC\omega),$$

or

$$\alpha^2-\phi^2 = (RG-LC\omega^2),$$
$$2\alpha\phi = (GL+RC)\omega,$$

from which

$$\left.\begin{array}{l} \alpha = \sqrt{\dfrac{(RG-LC\omega^2)+\sqrt{(R^2+L^2\omega^2)(G^2+C^2\omega^2)}}{2}}, \\[3mm] \phi = \sqrt{\dfrac{-(RG-LC\omega^2)+\sqrt{(R^2+L^2\omega^2)(G^2+C^2\omega^2)}}{2}}. \end{array}\right\} \qquad (130\text{-}9)$$

Evidently both of these quantities have finite values over the entire range of frequencies between zero and infinity, so that current waves of any frequency suffer a steady attenuation and lag of phase during propagation along the line.

Lines are used both for the transmission of power and for communication. In the former case only one frequency is involved and the primary requisite is small attenuation. In the latter case, on the other hand, it is usually necessary to transmit an entire band of frequencies and the essential requirement is that attenuation and speed of propagation should be independent of frequency, in order to avoid distortion. Returning to (130-9) we see that, in general, this condition is not satisfied. If, however, we make

$$GL = RC, \tag{130-10}$$

then

$$\left. \begin{aligned} \alpha &= \sqrt{RG}, \\ v &= \frac{1}{\sqrt{LC}}, \end{aligned} \right\} \tag{130-11}$$

and the line is distortionless. Unfortunately, it is not possible in practice to satisfy (130-10) unless G is artificially increased. This results in a prohibitively high value of α, so we must proceed otherwise.

In a well-insulated line even at low frequencies $G/C\omega$ is usually so small that its square is negligible compared with unity. Assuming that $R/L\omega$ can be made small also, we can write

$$\begin{aligned} \alpha &= \sqrt{\frac{LC\omega^2}{2}\left[\frac{RG}{LC\omega^2} - 1 + \sqrt{1 + \frac{R^2}{L^2\omega^2} + \frac{G^2}{C^2\omega^2}}\right]} \\ &= \sqrt{\frac{LC\omega^2}{2}\left[\frac{RG}{LC\omega^2} - 1 + 1 + \frac{1}{2}\frac{R^2}{L^2\omega^2} + \frac{1}{2}\frac{G^2}{C^2\omega^2}\right]} \\ &= \sqrt{\frac{LC}{4}\left(\frac{R}{L} + \frac{G}{C}\right)^2}, \\ \phi &= \sqrt{\frac{LC\omega^2}{2}\left[-\frac{RG}{LC\omega^2} + 1 + \sqrt{1 + \frac{R^2}{L^2\omega^2} + \frac{G^2}{C^2\omega^2}}\right]} \\ &= \sqrt{\frac{LC\omega^2}{2}\left[-\frac{RG}{LC\omega^2} + 1 + 1 + \frac{1}{2}\frac{R^2}{L^2\omega^2} + \frac{1}{2}\frac{G^2}{C^2\omega^2}\right]} \\ &= \sqrt{LC\omega^2}. \end{aligned}$$

Hence

$$\left. \begin{aligned} \alpha &= \frac{R}{2}\sqrt{\frac{C}{L}} + \frac{G}{2}\sqrt{\frac{L}{C}}, \\ v &= \frac{1}{\sqrt{LC}}, \end{aligned} \right\} \tag{130-12}$$

and the line is again distortionless. To make $R^2/L^2\omega^2$ sufficiently small at audio frequencies, at least in telephone cable lines where the line conductors must be closely spaced, it is usually necessary to increase L as R cannot be reduced economically beyond a certain point. There are two practicable ways in which large values of L may be obtained. The first consists of enclosing the line conductors in a thin sheath of some highly permeable substance such as permalloy or perminvar (art. 103). This method is very expensive to employ and its use is confined commercially to long distance submarine cables. The second way of increasing L depends on the insertion of small inductance coils in the line at regular intervals. While this procedure introduces a recurrent structure which causes the line to cut off at some critical frequency like a low-pass filter, nevertheless at lower frequencies it is approximately equivalent to increasing the inductance of the line uniformly. For good results several coils per wave length must be used. This method is used for long distance cables on land. A line whose inductance has been increased above the normal by either of the means just described is said to be *loaded*. Note that loading not only eliminates distortion but also reduces attenuation, a very desirable circumstance.

Transmission Characteristics. Next let us determine the arbitrary constants $\mathbf{A}$ and $\mathbf{B}$ in (130-5). These are best expressed in terms of the *characteristic impedance* $\mathbf{Z}_K$ of the line, that is, the impedance of an infinitely long line of the given type. For such a line (130-5) may be put in the form

$$\mathbf{i}_{s0} = \mathbf{A}_\infty e^{\Gamma s} + \mathbf{B}_\infty e^{-\Gamma s} = \mathbf{i}_{00} e^{\Gamma s} - \mathbf{B}_\infty (e^{\Gamma s} - e^{-\Gamma s})$$

since $\mathbf{i}_{00} = \mathbf{A}_\infty + \mathbf{B}_\infty$. But in an infinite line, as in an infinite filter (art. 129), there can be no reflected waves. Consequently, $\mathbf{B}_\infty = 0$ and the complex current amplitude is given by $\mathbf{i}_{s0} = \mathbf{i}_{00} e^{\Gamma s}$. This may be substituted in the first equation of (130-3) giving

$$-\Gamma e^{\Gamma s} \mathbf{i}_{00} = \frac{\mathscr{E}_{s0}}{\mathbf{Z}_C}.$$

Taking $s = 0$ and using (130-8), we have

$$\sqrt{\mathbf{Z}_L \mathbf{Z}_C}\, \mathbf{i}_{00} = \mathscr{E}_{00}.$$

Hence, since $\mathbf{Z}_K \mathbf{i}_{00} = \mathscr{E}_{00}$ for the infinite line,

$$\mathbf{Z}_K = \sqrt{\mathbf{Z}_L \mathbf{Z}_C} = \sqrt{\frac{R + iL\omega}{G + iC\omega}}. \tag{130-13}$$

When $R/L\omega$ as well as $G/C\omega$ is small enough to make the line distortionless, $\mathbf{Z}_K$ reduces to the pure resistance

$$R_K = \sqrt{\frac{L}{C}}. \tag{130-14}$$

Returning now to (130-5), substitution in the first equation of (130-3) gives with the aid of (130-8)

$$\mathbf{Z}_K(\mathrm{e}^{\Gamma s}\mathbf{A} - \mathrm{e}^{-\Gamma s}\mathbf{B}) = \mathscr{E}_{s0}.$$

But

$$\mathscr{E}_{00} = \mathscr{E}_0 - \mathbf{Z}_0\mathbf{i}_{00} = \mathscr{E}_0 - \mathbf{Z}_0(\mathbf{A} + \mathbf{B}),$$

$$\mathscr{E}_{S0} = \mathbf{Z}_S\mathbf{i}_{S0} = \mathbf{Z}_S(\mathrm{e}^{\Gamma S}\mathbf{A} + \mathrm{e}^{-\Gamma S}\mathbf{B}),$$

so that

$$\left. \begin{aligned} (\mathbf{Z}_K + \mathbf{Z}_0)\mathbf{A} - (\mathbf{Z}_K - \mathbf{Z}_0)\mathbf{B} &= \mathscr{E}_0, \\ -\mathrm{e}^{\Gamma S}(\mathbf{Z}_K - \mathbf{Z}_S)\mathbf{A} + \mathrm{e}^{-\Gamma S}(\mathbf{Z}_K + \mathbf{Z}_S)\mathbf{B} &= 0. \end{aligned} \right\} \quad (130\text{-}15)$$

Solving for $\mathbf{A}$ and $\mathbf{B}$ we find

$$\left. \begin{aligned} \mathbf{A} &= \frac{\mathscr{E}_0}{(\mathbf{Z}_K + \mathbf{Z}_0)} \frac{1}{(1 - \mathrm{e}^{2\Gamma S}\mathbf{T}_0\mathbf{T}_S)}, \\ \mathbf{B} &= \frac{\mathscr{E}_0}{(\mathbf{Z}_K + \mathbf{Z}_0)} \frac{\mathrm{e}^{2\Gamma S}\mathbf{T}_S}{(1 - \mathrm{e}^{2\Gamma S}\mathbf{T}_0\mathbf{T}_S)}, \end{aligned} \right\} \quad (130\text{-}16)$$

where

$$\mathbf{T}_0 \equiv \frac{\mathbf{Z}_K - \mathbf{Z}_0}{\mathbf{Z}_K + \mathbf{Z}_0}, \qquad \mathbf{T}_S \equiv \frac{\mathbf{Z}_K - \mathbf{Z}_S}{\mathbf{Z}_K + \mathbf{Z}_S},$$

and, finally,

$$\mathbf{i}_{s0} = \frac{\mathscr{E}_0}{(\mathbf{Z}_K + \mathbf{Z}_0)} \frac{\mathrm{e}^{\Gamma s} + \mathrm{e}^{\Gamma(2S-s)}\mathbf{T}_S}{(1 - \mathrm{e}^{2\Gamma S}\mathbf{T}_0\mathbf{T}_S)}. \quad (130\text{-}17)$$

It is very instructive to expand (130-17) with the aid of the binomial theorem to the form

$$\mathbf{i}_{s0} = \frac{\mathscr{E}_0}{(\mathbf{Z}_K + \mathbf{Z}_0)} [\mathrm{e}^{\Gamma s} + \mathrm{e}^{\Gamma(2S-s)}\mathbf{T}_S + \mathrm{e}^{\Gamma(2S+s)}\mathbf{T}_0\mathbf{T}_S + \mathrm{e}^{\Gamma(4S-s)}\mathbf{T}_0\mathbf{T}_S{}^2$$
$$+ \mathrm{e}^{\Gamma(4S+s)}\mathbf{T}_0{}^2\mathbf{T}_S{}^2 + \mathrm{e}^{\Gamma(6S-s)}\mathbf{T}_0{}^2\mathbf{T}_S{}^3 + \cdots]. \quad (130\text{-}18)$$

Each term in this series has a definite physical significance. Since $\mathscr{E}_0/(\mathbf{Z}_K + \mathbf{Z}_0)$ gives the current flowing into an infinitely long line of the given type, the term $\dfrac{\mathscr{E}_0}{(\mathbf{Z}_K + \mathbf{Z}_0)} \mathrm{e}^{\Gamma s}$ represents a current wave of characteristic initial amplitude which has traveled directly from the input end of the line to the point s. Similarly $\dfrac{\mathscr{E}_0}{(\mathbf{Z}_K + \mathbf{Z}_0)} \mathrm{e}^{\Gamma(2S-s)}\mathbf{T}_S$ is the same current wave after it has traveled to the output end of the line, been reflected, and returned to the point s, a distance $2S - s$. Evidently $\mathbf{T}_S$, which represents the effect of the reflection itself, is just the *output reflection coefficient*. The third term in the series gives the current wave after it has returned to the input end, been reflected with an *input reflection coefficient* $\mathbf{T}_0$ and traveled down the line to the point s again. Thus we may regard the current at any point along the line as due to a current wave $\mathscr{E}_0/(\mathbf{Z}_K+\mathbf{Z}_0)$ which enters at the input end and is then reflected back and forth across the point in question.

The point of view adopted above is helpful in considering the transmission characteristics of the line as a whole. By giving $\mathbf{T}_0$ and $\mathbf{T}_S$ suitable values various special characteristics can be established, as will be shown below.

The actual current corresponding to an applied sine wave is obtained by multiplying (130-17) or (130-18) through by $e^{i\omega t}$ and taking the imaginary part, as usual. For example, consider the special case of a line matched at the input end but short-circuited at the output end, that is, $\mathbf{Z}_0=\mathbf{Z}_K$ so that $\mathbf{T}_0=0$, while $\mathbf{Z}_S=0$ so that $\mathbf{T}_S=1$. For simplicity we will assume that R and G are negligible, in which case there is no attenuation and $\mathbf{Z}_K$ reduces to R_K, a pure resistance. Then (130-18) becomes

$$\mathbf{i}_{s0} = \frac{\mathscr{E}_0}{2R_K}\left[e^{-i\phi s}+e^{-i\phi(2S-s)}\right],$$

and the actual current is

$$i_s = \frac{\mathscr{E}_0}{2R_K}\left[\sin\omega\left(t-\frac{s}{v}\right)+\sin\omega\left(t-\frac{2S-s}{v}\right)\right], \tag{130-19}$$

ϕ having been replaced by ω/v in accord with (130-7). The first term represents the primary current wave and the second the reflected wave from the closed end of the line. The combination of these waves results in a *standing wave*. That is, there is a fixed amplitude of oscillation at every point on the line, the amplitude varying sinusoidally between zero and a maximum, $\mathscr{E}_0/R_K$, as we pass along the line. Since $\omega/v=2\pi/\lambda$, the points of maximum oscillation, called *loops*, evidently occur at

$$s = S, \qquad S-\frac{\lambda}{2}, \qquad S-\lambda, \qquad \cdots,$$

while the points of zero oscillation, called *nodes*, occur at

$$s = S-\frac{\lambda}{4}, \qquad S-\frac{3\lambda}{4}, \qquad S-\frac{5\lambda}{4}, \qquad \cdots,$$

halfway between the loops. This standing wave may be shown graphically as in Fig. 290, the vertical distance between the curves representing the limiting magnitude of oscillation, that is, twice the amplitude, at each point. As nodes and loops may be located experimentally, standing waves afford a means of determining an unknown wave length directly.   The method is particularly valuable at very high frequencies where the wave lengths are small.

With the line open-circuited at the output end instead of short-circuited, $\mathbf{T}_S = -1$, and the current is

$$i_s = \frac{\mathscr{E}_0}{2R_K}\left[\sin\,\omega\!\left(t-\frac{s}{v}\right)-\sin\,\omega\!\left(t-\frac{2S-s}{v}\right)\right]. \qquad (130\text{-}20)$$

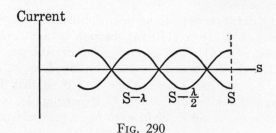

FIG. 290

In this case the standing wave is as shown in Fig. 291.   A standing wave is, in fact, produced by any termination of the line other than $\mathbf{Z}_S = \mathbf{Z}_K$.   However, in cases other than those mentioned above, the standing wave is combined with a progressive wave, so that the amplitude of the resultant wave does not fall to zero at its minimum. We shall refer to such a wave as an *incomplete* standing wave.   In all

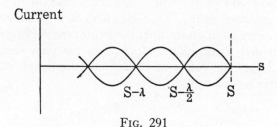

FIG. 291

cases the distance between successive maxima or successive minima is $\lambda/2$.

It remains, as a matter of some interest, to determine the values of v and R_K for some actual lines.   The common unloaded open-wire telephone line consists of two wires of circular cross section of radius a separated by a distance b large compared with a.

The inductance per unit length of line is found by calculating the flux which links a unit length of the line when a unit current is flowing.

Taking the origin of rectangular coordinates halfway between the wires as indicated in Fig. 292, we have

$$L = \frac{\mu_0}{2\pi} \int_{-(b/2)+a}^{(b/2)-a} \left(\frac{1}{\frac{b}{2}-x} + \frac{1}{\frac{b}{2}+x} \right) dx$$

$$= \frac{\mu_0}{2\pi} \left| \log \frac{\frac{b}{2}+x}{\frac{b}{2}-x} \right|_{-(b/2)+a}^{(b/2)-a} = \frac{\mu_0}{\pi} \log \frac{b}{a},$$

since b is large compared with a.

The corresponding capacitance per unit length is

$$C = \frac{\pi \kappa_0}{\log \frac{b}{a}}$$

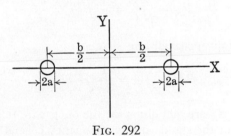

FIG. 292

from (32-3). Thus, assuming the resistance of the line is small enough so that the line is distortionless,

$$v = \frac{1}{\sqrt{LC}} = c, \tag{130-21}$$

from art. 37, regardless of the size of the wires or the spacing. This shows that for any unloaded open-wire telephone line the wave velocity is equal to the velocity of light. On the other hand, in a telephone cable, loading the line to the extent necessary for satisfactory voice transmission reduces v to about one-third c or less. That is, the velocity on an average loaded telephone line is of the order of $(10)^5$ kilometers per second. The corresponding wave length at a thousand cycles per second, for example, is a hundred kilometers.

For transmission of high frequencies the *coaxial* type of line is most commonly used as it is both self-shielding and convenient to handle.

It consists of a wire of circular cross section of radius a surrounded by a coaxial tubular conductor of inside radius b. Usually the wire is mechanically supported and insulated from the outer conductor by thin ceramic disks widely spaced, in which case we may consider the region between the conductors to be empty. Then, from the results of problem *89a* and problem *18a*,

$$L = \frac{\mu_0}{2\pi} \log \frac{b}{a}, \qquad C = \frac{2\pi\kappa_0}{\log \dfrac{b}{a}}.$$

Since the transmission frequencies are high, the line is distortionless and, as we might expect, we find $v = c$ again. Sometimes the space between the conductors is filled with a solid dielectric, which increases C, and then v is less than c, of course.

Unlike v, the characteristic impedance of a line depends both on the type of line and on the line constants. Thus, for the unloaded open-wire line

$$R_K = \sqrt{\frac{L}{C}} = \frac{1}{\pi}\sqrt{\frac{\mu_0}{\kappa_0}} \log \frac{b}{a}, \tag{130-22}$$

while for the (empty) coaxial line

$$R_K = \sqrt{\frac{L}{C}} = \frac{1}{2\pi}\sqrt{\frac{\mu_0}{\kappa_0}} \log \frac{b}{a}. \tag{130-23}$$

Usual values of R_K are 600 ohms for the open-wire telephone line and 50 to 70 ohms for the standard high-frequency coaxial line.

Special Applications at High Frequencies. In the high-frequency range where λ is small, short sections of line can be used conveniently for coupling, impedance matching and other special purposes, in addition to simple transmission. Consider a section of line of length S terminated at the output end by an impedance $\mathbf{Z}_S$. From (130-17) the *input impedance* of such a terminated section is

$$\mathbf{Z}_{\text{in}} \equiv \frac{\mathscr{E}_{00}}{\mathbf{i}_{00}} = \frac{\mathscr{E}_0 - \mathbf{Z}_0\mathbf{i}_{00}}{\mathbf{i}_{00}} = \frac{(\mathbf{Z}_K + \mathbf{Z}_0)(1 - e^{2\Gamma S}\mathbf{T}_0\mathbf{T}_S) - \mathbf{Z}_0(1 + e^{2\Gamma S}\mathbf{T}_S)}{1 + e^{2\Gamma S}\mathbf{T}_S}$$

$$= \mathbf{Z}_K \frac{(\mathbf{Z}_K + \mathbf{Z}_S) - (\mathbf{Z}_K - \mathbf{Z}_S)e^{2\Gamma S}}{(\mathbf{Z}_K + \mathbf{Z}_S) + (\mathbf{Z}_K - \mathbf{Z}_S)e^{2\Gamma S}}$$

$$= \mathbf{Z}_K \left[\frac{\mathbf{Z}_S(1 + e^{2\Gamma S}) + \mathbf{Z}_K(1 - e^{2\Gamma S})}{\mathbf{Z}_K(1 + e^{2\Gamma S}) + \mathbf{Z}_S(1 - e^{2\Gamma S})} \right].$$

As we are interested here in short lengths of line, the effects of attenuation are negligible and we may put $\mathbf{\Gamma} = -\mathbf{i}\phi = -\mathbf{i}(2\pi/\lambda)$. Also, at high frequencies, $\mathbf{Z}_K = R_K$. Making these substitutions and using the relation $(1 - e^{-i(4\pi S/\lambda)})/(1 + e^{-i(4\pi S/\lambda)}) = i \tan (2\pi S/\lambda)$, we find

$$\mathbf{Z}_{in} = R_K \frac{\mathbf{Z}_S + iR_K \tan 2\pi \left(\dfrac{S}{\lambda}\right)}{R_K + i\mathbf{Z}_S \tan 2\pi \left(\dfrac{S}{\lambda}\right)}. \tag{130-24}$$

There are several special cases of interest. Suppose we make $S = \lambda/2$ (or any number of half waves). Then

$$\mathbf{Z}_{in} = \mathbf{Z}_S, \tag{130-25}$$

independent of R_K. Hence a half-wave line may be used to couple elements of a high-frequency circuit without affecting the impedances involved. When so used, it performs the same function as a transformer (art. 118) of turn ratio unity in a low-frequency circuit. On the other hand, if we take $S = \lambda/4$ (or any odd number of quarter waves) we have

$$\mathbf{Z}_{in} = \frac{R_K{}^2}{\mathbf{Z}_S}. \tag{130-26}$$

Evidently a quarter-wave line provides a means of transforming and matching impedances. This makes it a particularly useful device. For example, if it is used to couple a resistance load R_S to an e.m.f. of internal resistance R_0, maximum power is transmitted to R_S when R_K is so chosen that the input resistance $R_{in} = R_K{}^2/R_S$ is equal to R_0.

A short-circuited quarter-wave line has an infinite input impedance according to (130-26). Hence, if it is bridged across a transmission line, it has no effect on transmission in that line at the quarter-wave frequency. However, for any second harmonic present it is a short-circuited half-wave line, which has zero input impedance, and therefore it can be used as a *harmonic suppressor*.

Finally, if we short-circuit a short length S of line, its impedance is $iR_K \tan (2\pi S/\lambda)$, whereas, if we open-circuit it, its impedance is $-i R_K \cot (2\pi S/\lambda)$. Thus we have available a positive or a negative reactance whose magnitude may be given any desired value by proper choice of S. A *stub* line of this sort has many applications. In particular, one or more stubs may be bridged across a transmission line on which there are standing waves and adjusted in such a way that the standing waves are eliminated.

Problem 130a. Show that the complex amplitude of the e.m.f. at any point on a line is

$$\mathscr{E}_{s0} = \mathscr{E}_0 \frac{\mathbf{Z}_K}{(\mathbf{Z}_K + \mathbf{Z}_0)} \frac{e^{\Gamma s} - e^{\Gamma(2S-s)}\mathbf{T}_S}{(1 - e^{2\Gamma S}\mathbf{T}_0\mathbf{T}_S)}.$$

What are the input and output reflection coefficients in this case? Explain the signs. Ans. $-\mathbf{T}_0$, $-\mathbf{T}_S$.

Problem 130b.   Find the relation between e.m.f. and current in standing waves.   Ans. Loops of e.m.f. occur at current nodes, and vice versa.

Problem 130c.   Suppose that a line of characteristic impedance R_K is matched at the input end but is terminated at the output end by a resistance $R_S \neq R_K$. Find and plot the incomplete standing wave if R_S equals (a) $R_K/2$, (b) $2R_K$. Compare with Figs. 290 and 291.

Problem 130d.   Express (130-22) with a numerical coefficient and find the value of b/a necessary to give 600 ohms.   Express (130-23) similarly and find the value of b/a for 60 ohms.

$$\text{Ans. } R_K = 120 \log \frac{b}{a} \text{ ohm, } 148;$$

$$R_K = 60 \log \frac{b}{a} \text{ ohm, } 2.72.$$

Problem 130e.   Deduce for a line of any length the exact relation $\mathbf{Z}_K = \sqrt{\mathbf{Z}_{SC}\mathbf{Z}_{OC}}$, where $\mathbf{Z}_{SC}$ and $\mathbf{Z}_{OC}$ are the short-circuit and the open-circuit input impedances, respectively, of the given line.

Problem 130f.   A line of characteristic impedance R_K has an output termination $R_S > R_K$.   A short-circuited stub of length l is bridged across the line at a distance d from R_S, the values of l and d being such that the input impedance of the line is made equal to R_K.   Find expressions giving l/λ and d/λ, where λ is the wavelength.

$$\text{Ans. } \tan 2\pi \left(\frac{l}{\lambda}\right) = \frac{\sqrt{R_S R_K}}{R_S - R_K}, \quad \tan 2\pi \left(\frac{d}{\lambda}\right) = \sqrt{\frac{R_S}{R_K}}.$$

REFERENCES

Bleaney and Bleaney, *Electricity and Magnetism* (Oxford Univ. Press, 1965).   Pp. 236–246, 291–315.

Pierce, *Electric Oscillations and Electric Waves* (McGraw-Hill, 1920). Chap. VII–XI, XVI.

Ramo, Whinnery, and Van Duzer, *Fields and Waves in Communication Electronics* (Wiley, 1965).   Chap. 1.

Ryder, *Networks, Lines and Fields* (Prentice-Hall, 1949).   Chap. 3–6.

Terman, *Electronic and Radio Engineering* (McGraw-Hill, 1955).   Chap. 3–4.

Chapter XVI

ELECTROMAGNETIC WAVES

131. Electromagnetic Equations. The fundamental equations describing the electromagnetic field produced by charges at rest or in motion relative to the observer may be taken as (1) Gauss' law (14-4) specifying the flux of displacement through a closed surface s surrounding free charge of density ρ, (2) Gauss' law (43-3) for the flux of induction in the corresponding magnetic case, (3) Ampère's law (71-3) for the magnetic field due to a current, and (4) Faraday's law (86-5) for the electric field produced by a changing magnetic flux. In addition we have relations such as (15-3) between D and E and (43-5) between B and H.

In vector notation the four field equations take the form

$$\int_s \mathbf{D} \cdot d\mathbf{s} = \int_\tau \rho d\tau, \qquad \text{(a)} \qquad \int_s \mathbf{B} \cdot d\mathbf{s} = 0, \qquad \text{(b)}$$

$$\oint \mathbf{H} \cdot d\mathbf{l} = \int_s \mathbf{j} \cdot d\mathbf{s}, \qquad \text{(c)} \qquad \oint \mathbf{E} \cdot d\mathbf{l} = -\int_s \frac{\partial \mathbf{B}}{\partial t} \cdot d\mathbf{s}, \qquad \text{(d)}$$

where the current i in Ampère's law has been expressed in terms of the current density $\mathbf{j}$ by (67-6). In (a) and (b) the surface integral on the left is taken over a *closed* surface, whereas the surface integral on the right of (c) and (d) is taken over an *open* surface bounded by the closed curve along which the line integral on the left is evaluated.

Maxwell's great contribution to electromagnetic theory had its origin in his recognition of the fact that these laws fail to satisfy the equation of continuity. This equation states that the time rate of increase of charge inside a volume τ is equal to the excess of the rate at which charge flows into τ through the boundary surface over that at which it flows out. Physically it is equivalent to the statement that charge can neither be created nor be destroyed. For if charge is indestructible, the only way in which it can accumulate in a region τ is by more charge entering than leaving the region.

Maxwell traced the difficulty to Ampère's law, which he showed to be incomplete in the form (c). In fact, he found it necessary to add a term to the right-hand side of this equation involving the integral over s of the time rate of change of displacement.   Without this added term the electromagnetic theory of light would have been impossible.   We shall now examine the reasons which led Maxwell to modify Ampère's law, although we shall develop them from a somewhat different point of view than that adopted by him in his original investigation.

If we apply Ampère's law (c) to a surface s (Fig. 293) which is closed except for a small opening, the line integral on the left is taken over only the boundary l of the opening.   If we make the hole smaller and smaller, the periphery becomes shorter and shorter, until finally, when the surface is completely closed, the left-hand member of (c) reduces to zero.   So, for a *closed* surface (c) requires

$$\int_s \mathbf{j} \cdot d\mathbf{s} = 0. \qquad (131\text{-}1)$$

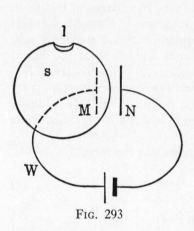

Fig. 293

In words, this relation states that the current entering through one part of s must be exactly compensated by the current leaving through other parts of the surface.   But this stringent requirement is not at all in accord with experience.   If, for instance, the surface s surrounds one plate M of a capacitor, we can certainly charge up M by a current entering s through the wire W without any compensating conduction current flowing out through the surface.   Consequently, we conclude that Ampère's law cannot be properly expressed in the form (c).

To correct Ampère's law, we will calculate the time rate of increase of charge in a volume τ from (a).   In scalar notation (art. 14) this rate of increase of charge is

$$\int_\tau \frac{\partial \rho}{\partial t}\, d\tau = \int_s \frac{\partial}{\partial t}\, (D \cos \gamma) ds.$$

Now if α is the angle which the vector $\dfrac{\partial \mathbf{D}}{\partial t}$ makes with $d\mathbf{s}$,

$$\left| \frac{\partial \mathbf{D}}{\partial t} \right| \cos \alpha = \frac{\partial}{\partial t}\, (D \cos \gamma),$$

as in (86-3), and

$$\int_s \frac{\partial}{\partial t}\, (D \cos \gamma) ds = \int_s \left| \frac{\partial \mathbf{D}}{\partial t} \right| \cos \alpha ds = \int_s \frac{\partial \mathbf{D}}{\partial t} \cdot d\mathbf{s}.$$

So

$$\int_\tau \frac{\partial \rho}{\partial t}\, d\tau = \int_s \frac{\partial \mathbf{D}}{\partial t} \cdot d\mathbf{s} \tag{131-2}$$

represents the rate at which charge accumulates inside the closed surface s.

But the excess of the rate at which charge flows into τ over that at which it leaves is $-\int \mathbf{j} \cdot d\mathbf{s}$ integrated over the closed surface s bounding τ. So, if the equation of continuity is to hold,

$$\int_s \left(\frac{\partial \mathbf{D}}{\partial t} + \mathbf{j}\right) \cdot d\mathbf{s} = 0 \tag{131-3}$$

must be valid instead of (131-1) for any closed surface. Consequently, we must replace the current density in Ampère's law by the integrand of (131-3), getting

$$\oint \mathbf{H} \cdot d\mathbf{l} = \int_s \left(\frac{\partial \mathbf{D}}{\partial t} + \mathbf{j}\right) \cdot d\mathbf{s} \tag{131-4}$$

as the complete expression for the magnetomotive force around the periphery of an open surface s.

Effectively we have added to the conduction or convection current i of art. 71 another current whose density equals the time rate of increase of displacement. Maxwell called this a *displacement current*. In part it represents a true motion of electric charges when a dielectric is present. For in this case

$$\mathbf{D} = \kappa_0 \mathbf{E} + \mathbf{P}$$

from (14-2), so that

$$\frac{\partial \mathbf{D}}{\partial t} = \kappa_0 \frac{\partial \mathbf{E}}{\partial t} + \frac{\partial \mathbf{P}}{\partial t}.$$

Now if ρ' is the charge per unit volume which suffers a displacement $\mathbf{R}$ when the medium is polarized (art. 13), $\mathbf{P} = \rho' \mathbf{R}$, and

$$\frac{\partial \mathbf{P}}{\partial t} = \rho' \frac{\partial \mathbf{R}}{\partial t}$$

represents the current passing through a unit cross section due to the velocity of the displaced charge. This is a true electric current, due, like the current in a conductor, to a flow of electricity.

It should be noted that when we take account of displacement currents as well as of conduction currents all currents flow around *closed* circuits. For (131-3) tells us that any conduction current leading into the region surrounded by a closed surface must be compensated by an equal displacement current flowing out. Thus, in the case illustrated in Fig. 293, the current passing through the wire W to the plate M of the capacitor is accompanied by a displacement current flowing through the region between the plate M and the plate N. The conduction current entering through the surface s is exactly compensated by the displacement current passing out. The net result is that the *same* current—either in the form of a conduction current or of a displacement current—flows through every cross section of the complete circuit *WMNW*.

In the case of a steady conduction current the added term in (131-4) vanishes, and in the case of slowly varying currents it is negligible except between the plates of a capacitor in the circuit. Hence, in such cases, the calculations of the magnetic field produced by a current which were made in Chapter VII have not been invalidated by Maxwell's revision of Ampère's law.

In a region in which no conduction or convection currents are present, (131-4) becomes

$$\oint \mathbf{H} \cdot d\mathbf{l} = \int_s \frac{\partial \mathbf{D}}{\partial t} \cdot d\mathbf{s}. \tag{131-5}$$

This equation states that the magnetomotive force around any closed circuit is proportional to the time rate of change of flux of displacement through the circuit, just as Faraday's law states that the induced electromotive force around a circuit is proportional to the time rate of change of flux of induction through the circuit. Why, then, is this equation not as susceptible to direct experimental verification as Faraday's law? The reason is that there exists in nature no conductor of magnetism and therefore no sensitive method of detecting a magnetomotive force. Only because metals are excellent conductors of electricity was Faraday able to detect so simply the electromotive force induced in a circuit by a varying flux of induction.

To supplement the field equations which have been under discussion we need the relation specifying the forces exerted on charge and on current by the electric and magnetic fields in which they are located. These forces are given by (7-1) and (75-3). Per unit volume the total force is

$$\mathcal{F}_\tau = \rho \mathbf{E} + \mathbf{j} \times \mathbf{B}. \tag{131-6}$$

If we denote partial differentiation with respect to the time by a dot placed over the quantity involved, we have the complete set of electromagnetic equations:

$$\int_s \mathbf{D} \cdot d\mathbf{s} = \int_\tau \rho \, d\tau, \tag{1}$$

$$\int_s \mathbf{B} \cdot d\mathbf{s} = 0, \tag{2}$$

$$\oint \mathbf{H} \cdot d\mathbf{l} = \int_s (\dot{\mathbf{D}} + \mathbf{j}) \cdot d\mathbf{s}, \tag{3}$$

$$\oint \mathbf{E} \cdot d\mathbf{l} = -\int_s \dot{\mathbf{B}} \cdot d\mathbf{s}, \tag{4}$$

$$\mathbf{D} - \kappa_0 \mathbf{E} + \mathbf{P} = \kappa_0 \kappa \mathbf{E}, \tag{5}$$

$$\mathbf{B} = \mu_0 \mathbf{H} + \mathbf{I} = \mu_0 \mu \mathbf{H}, \tag{6}$$

$$\mathscr{F}_\tau = \rho \mathbf{E} + \mathbf{j} \times \mathbf{B}. \tag{7}$$

Whereas equations (1) to (4), (7) and the relations $\mathbf{D} = \kappa_0 \mathbf{E} + \mathbf{P}$, $\mathbf{B} = \mu_0 \mathbf{H} + \mathbf{I}$ are quite general, the relation $\mathbf{D} = \kappa_0 \kappa \mathbf{E}$ holds only for isotropic dielectrics and $\mathbf{B} = \mu_0 \mu \mathbf{H}$ only for isotropic paramagnetic or diamagnetic media. The first four equations, known as the *field equations*, together with (5) and (6), suffice to determine uniquely the electric and magnetic fields produced by an arbitrarily assigned distribution of charge density ρ and current density $\mathbf{j}$. The *force equation* (7), on the other hand, specifies the force per unit volume on the charge and current present. Here, as in the field equations, ρ represents the total free charge per unit volume and $\mathbf{j}$ the current density due to that portion of the free charge which is in motion.

Problem 131. A parallel plate capacitor consists of two circular plates of radius a. It is connected to an alternating e.m.f. so that the charge is $q = q_0 \sin \omega t$. Neglecting edge effect, find the magnetic intensity between the plates in terms of the distance r from the axis. Ans. $H = \dfrac{q_0 r \omega}{2 \pi a^2} \cos \omega t$.

132. Differential Form of Field Equations.

Before we can deduce the wave equation and investigate the properties of electromagnetic waves we must express the field equations (1) to (4) of the previous article in differential form.

Equations (1) and (2) are easily transformed. Consider the small rectangular parallelepiped (Fig. 294) of dimensions Δx, Δy, Δz. The flux of displacement through the two faces perpendicular to the X axis is

$$-D_x \Delta y \Delta z + \left(D_x + \frac{\partial D_x}{\partial x} \Delta x \right) \Delta y \Delta z = \frac{\partial D_x}{\partial x} \Delta x \Delta y \Delta z.$$

Adding similar expressions for the flux through the pairs of faces perpendicular to the Y and Z axes, respectively, we have for the total outward flux

$$\left(\frac{\partial D_x}{\partial x} + \frac{\partial D_y}{\partial y} + \frac{\partial D_z}{\partial z} \right) \Delta x \Delta y \Delta z,$$

and equating this to the charge $\rho\Delta x\Delta y\Delta z$ inside the parallelepiped, we get

$$\frac{\partial D_x}{\partial x}+\frac{\partial D_y}{\partial y}+\frac{\partial D_z}{\partial z} = \rho \qquad (1')$$

for the differential form of (1).   Similarly (2) becomes

$$\frac{\partial B_x}{\partial x}+\frac{\partial B_y}{\partial y}+\frac{\partial B_z}{\partial z} = 0. \qquad (2')$$

To obtain Ampère's law in differential form we shall apply (3) to a small rectangular circuit (Fig. 295) of dimensions Δy, Δz lying in the

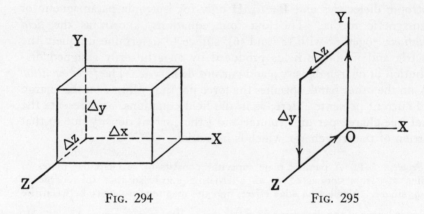

FIG. 294   FIG. 295

YZ plane.   Then, denoting the components of magnetic intensity at O by H_x, H_y, H_z,

$$H_y\Delta y + \left(H_z+\frac{\partial H_z}{\partial y}\,\Delta y\right)\Delta z - \left(H_y+\frac{\partial H_y}{\partial z}\,\Delta z\right)\Delta y - H_z\Delta z = (\dot{D}_x+j_x)\Delta y\Delta z,$$

or

$$\left(\frac{\partial H_z}{\partial y}-\frac{\partial H_y}{\partial z}\right)\Delta y\Delta z = (\dot{D}_x+j_x)\Delta y\Delta z.$$

Dividing by the area $\Delta y\Delta z$ of the circuit and writing similar expressions for the cases where the circuit lies in the ZX and XY planes,

$$\left.\begin{aligned}\frac{\partial H_z}{\partial y}-\frac{\partial H_y}{\partial z} &= (\dot{D}_x+j_x),\\[4pt]\frac{\partial H_x}{\partial z}-\frac{\partial H_z}{\partial x} &= (\dot{D}_y+j_y),\\[4pt]\frac{\partial H_y}{\partial x}-\frac{\partial H_x}{\partial y} &= (\dot{D}_z+j_z).\end{aligned}\right\} \qquad (3')$$

From Faraday's law (4) we obtain in exactly similar fashion

$$
\left.
\begin{aligned}
\frac{\partial E_z}{\partial y} - \frac{\partial E_y}{\partial z} &= -\dot{B}_x, \\[2mm]
\frac{\partial E_x}{\partial z} - \frac{\partial E_z}{\partial x} &= -\dot{B}_y, \\[2mm]
\frac{\partial E_y}{\partial x} - \frac{\partial E_x}{\partial y} &= -\dot{B}_z.
\end{aligned}
\right\} \quad (4')
$$

It may be noted that Ampère's law and Faraday's law lead to *three* scalar equations each, indicating that these laws are vector relations. The vector whose three components are given on the left-hand side of (3') is known as the *curl* of **H**. Similarly on the left-hand side of (4') we have the *curl* of **E**.

133. Electromagnetic Waves. In a homogeneous isotropic medium containing neither free charge nor current the field equations (1') to (4') of art. 132 become

$$
\frac{\partial E_x}{\partial x} + \frac{\partial E_y}{\partial y} + \frac{\partial E_z}{\partial z} = 0, \quad (1'') \qquad \frac{\partial H_x}{\partial x} + \frac{\partial H_y}{\partial y} + \frac{\partial H_z}{\partial z} = 0, \quad (2'')
$$

$$
\left.
\begin{aligned}
\frac{\partial H_z}{\partial y} - \frac{\partial H_y}{\partial z} &= \kappa_0 \kappa \dot{E}_x, \\[2mm]
\frac{\partial H_x}{\partial z} - \frac{\partial H_z}{\partial x} &= \kappa_0 \kappa \dot{E}_y, \\[2mm]
\frac{\partial H_y}{\partial x} - \frac{\partial H_x}{\partial y} &= \kappa_0 \kappa \dot{E}_z,
\end{aligned}
\right\} (3'')
\qquad
\left.
\begin{aligned}
\frac{\partial E_z}{\partial y} - \frac{\partial E_y}{\partial z} &= -\mu_0 \mu \dot{H}_x, \\[2mm]
\frac{\partial E_x}{\partial z} - \frac{\partial E_z}{\partial x} &= -\mu_0 \mu \dot{H}_y, \\[2mm]
\frac{\partial E_y}{\partial x} - \frac{\partial E_x}{\partial y} &= -\mu_0 \mu \dot{H}_z,
\end{aligned}
\right\} (4'')
$$

where we have put $\kappa_0 \kappa E$ for D and $\mu_0 \mu H$ for B.

The first step in the deduction of the wave equation consists in eliminating the components of **H** from (3'') and (4''). To accomplish this, differentiate the first of the three equations (3'') with respect to the time, getting

$$
\frac{\partial \dot{H}_z}{\partial y} - \frac{\partial \dot{H}_y}{\partial z} = \kappa_0 \kappa \ddot{E}_x.
$$

Next differentiate the second of (4'') with respect to z and the third with respect to y, getting

$$
\frac{\partial \dot{H}_y}{\partial z} = -\frac{1}{\mu_0 \mu}\left(\frac{\partial^2 E_x}{\partial z^2} - \frac{\partial^2 E_z}{\partial x \partial z}\right),
$$

$$
-\frac{\partial \dot{H}_z}{\partial y} = -\frac{1}{\mu_0 \mu}\left(\frac{\partial^2 E_x}{\partial y^2} - \frac{\partial^2 E_y}{\partial x \partial y}\right).
$$

Adding the three equations then gives, since $\kappa_0\mu_0 = 1/c^2$,

$$\frac{\partial^2 E_x}{\partial y^2} + \frac{\partial^2 E_x}{\partial z^2} - \frac{\partial}{\partial x}\left(\frac{\partial E_y}{\partial y} + \frac{\partial E_z}{\partial z}\right) = \frac{\kappa\mu}{c^2}\ddot{E}_x.$$

Using (1″) to eliminate the terms in E_y and E_z and writing similar equations in the remaining components of **E**, we have

$$\left.\begin{array}{l} \dfrac{\partial^2 E_x}{\partial x^2} + \dfrac{\partial^2 E_x}{\partial y^2} + \dfrac{\partial^2 E_x}{\partial z^2} = \dfrac{\kappa\mu}{c^2}\dfrac{\partial^2 E_x}{\partial t^2}, \\[2mm] \dfrac{\partial^2 E_y}{\partial x^2} + \dfrac{\partial^2 E_y}{\partial y^2} + \dfrac{\partial^2 E_y}{\partial z^2} = \dfrac{\kappa\mu}{c^2}\dfrac{\partial^2 E_y}{\partial t^2}, \\[2mm] \dfrac{\partial^2 E_z}{\partial x^2} + \dfrac{\partial^2 E_z}{\partial y^2} + \dfrac{\partial^2 E_z}{\partial z^2} = \dfrac{\kappa\mu}{c^2}\dfrac{\partial^2 E_z}{\partial t^2}. \end{array}\right\} \quad (133\text{-}1)$$

This set of relations is known as the *wave equation*. If we had eliminated **E** from the field equations instead of **H** we would have obtained an exactly similar set of equations in the components of **H**, namely,

$$\left.\begin{array}{l} \dfrac{\partial^2 H_x}{\partial x^2} + \dfrac{\partial^2 H_x}{\partial y^2} + \dfrac{\partial^2 H_x}{\partial z^2} = \dfrac{\kappa\mu}{c^2}\dfrac{\partial^2 H_x}{\partial t^2}, \\[2mm] \dfrac{\partial^2 H_y}{\partial x^2} + \dfrac{\partial^2 H_y}{\partial y^2} + \dfrac{\partial^2 H_y}{\partial z^2} = \dfrac{\kappa\mu}{c^2}\dfrac{\partial^2 H_y}{\partial t^2}, \\[2mm] \dfrac{\partial^2 H_z}{\partial x^2} + \dfrac{\partial^2 H_z}{\partial y^2} + \dfrac{\partial^2 H_z}{\partial z^2} = \dfrac{\kappa\mu}{c^2}\dfrac{\partial^2 H_z}{\partial t^2}. \end{array}\right\} \quad (133\text{-}2)$$

Let us consider the case where the components of **E** and **H** are functions of x and t only. Then (133-1) reduces to

$$\left.\begin{array}{l} \dfrac{\partial^2 E_x}{\partial x^2} = \dfrac{1}{v^2}\dfrac{\partial^2 E_x}{\partial t^2}, \\[2mm] \dfrac{\partial^2 E_y}{\partial x^2} = \dfrac{1}{v^2}\dfrac{\partial^2 E_y}{\partial t^2}, \\[2mm] \dfrac{\partial^2 E_z}{\partial x^2} = \dfrac{1}{v^2}\dfrac{\partial^2 E_z}{\partial t^2}, \end{array}\right\} \quad (133\text{-}3)$$

where we have put

$$v \equiv \frac{c}{\sqrt{\kappa\mu}}. \quad (133\text{-}4)$$

A similar set of equations holds for the components of **H**.

Consider the first of the three equations (133-3). Its general solution is

$$E_x = f_1\left(t - \frac{x}{v}\right) + f_2\left(t + \frac{x}{v}\right),$$

where f_1 and f_2 are arbitrary functions, as can be verified at once by substitution in the differential equation. Now if we increase t by τ and x by $v\tau$,

$$f_1\left([t+\tau]-\frac{1}{v}[x+v\tau]\right) = f_1\left(t-\frac{x}{v}\right),$$

showing that the function f_1 has the same value at the point $x+v\tau$ at the time $t+\tau$ as it has at x at the time t. Consequently, this function represents a wave advancing in the positive X direction with the *phase velocity* v. Similarly the identity

$$f_2\left([t+\tau]+\frac{1}{v}[x-v\tau]\right) = f_2\left(t+\frac{x}{v}\right),$$

shows that f_2 represents a wave traveling in the negative X direction with the same phase velocity. In both cases E_x has the same value at a given instant at all points in any plane perpendicular to the X axis. Therefore, the wave is *plane*, the wave front being infinite in extent.

If, now, we confine our attention to a plane wave moving in the positive X direction, the wave equation gives

$$E_x = f\left(t-\frac{x}{v}\right), \qquad H_x = i\left(t-\frac{x}{v}\right),$$

$$E_y = g\left(t-\frac{x}{v}\right), \qquad H_y = j\left(t-\frac{x}{v}\right),$$

$$E_z = h\left(t-\frac{x}{v}\right), \qquad H_z = k\left(t-\frac{x}{v}\right).$$

Substituting in (1″) and (2″) we find

$$\frac{\partial f}{\partial x} = 0, \qquad \frac{\partial i}{\partial x} = 0.$$

Therefore, E_x and H_x are constants in x. They are also constants in t since

$$\frac{\partial f}{\partial t} = -v\,\frac{\partial f}{\partial x}, \qquad \frac{\partial i}{\partial t} = -v\,\frac{\partial i}{\partial x}.$$

As we are interested only in the variable part of the field, and not in electrostatic and magnetostatic fields which may be superposed on the electromagnetic wave, we shall take these constants to be zero. Consequently, **E** and **H** are both at right angles to the direction of propagation. The wave, then, is transverse and in this respect has the characteristics of light.

The remaining components of **E** and **H** are not independent since they must satisfy the field equations (3″) and (4″). Denoting the derivative of a function with respect to its argument by a prime, the second and third equations of (3″), give

$$k' = v\kappa_0 \kappa\, g', \qquad j' = -v\kappa_0 \kappa\, h',$$

or

$$k = \sqrt{\frac{\kappa_0 \kappa}{\mu_0 \mu}}\, g, \qquad j = -\sqrt{\frac{\kappa_0 \kappa}{\mu_0 \mu}}\, h,$$

except for constants of integration which we have taken to be zero as before. Notice that the quantity $\sqrt{\kappa_0/\mu_0}$ can be written as $c\kappa_0$ or as $1/c\mu_0$, when convenient.

Hence we have altogether

$$\left.\begin{aligned}
E_x &= 0, & H_x &= 0, \\
E_y &= g\left(t - \frac{x}{v}\right), & H_y &= -\sqrt{\frac{\kappa_0 \kappa}{\mu_0 \mu}}\, h\left(t - \frac{x}{v}\right), \\
E_z &= h\left(t - \frac{x}{v}\right), & H_z &= \sqrt{\frac{\kappa_0 \kappa}{\mu_0 \mu}}\, g\left(t - \frac{x}{v}\right).
\end{aligned}\right\} \quad (133\text{-}5)$$

Evidently

$$\mathbf{E} \cdot \mathbf{H} = \sqrt{\frac{\kappa_0 \kappa}{\mu_0 \mu}}\{-gh + gh\} = 0.$$

Consequently, $\mathbf{E}$ and $\mathbf{H}$ lie in the wave front at right angles to each other.

We can consider that (133-5) represents two waves, each corresponding to one of the two possible states of polarization of a transverse wave. One of these waves, determined by the function $g(t - x/v)$, consists of an electric field in the Y direction and a magnetic field in the Z direction; the other, determined by the function $h(t - x/v)$, consists of an electric field in the Z direction and a magnetic field in the negative Y direction. In each wave the electric and magnetic fields are in phase and so oriented that a right-handed screw, rotated from $\mathbf{E}$ to $\mathbf{H}$ through the right angle between them, advances in the direction of propagation. As the waves corresponding to the two states of polarization are independent, we shall limit our subsequent discussion to one of them, taking

$$E_y = g\left(t - \frac{x}{v}\right), \qquad H_z = \sqrt{\frac{\kappa_0 \kappa}{\mu_0 \mu}}\, g\left(t - \frac{x}{v}\right). \quad (133\text{-}6)$$

If the wave is simple harmonic, g is a sine or cosine function and we can write

$$E_y = A \sin \omega\left(t - \frac{x}{v}\right) = A \sin(\omega t - \eta x), \qquad \eta \equiv \frac{\omega}{v}. \quad (133\text{-}7)$$

Denoting the period by P and the wave length by λ,

$$\omega(t+P) = \omega t + 2\pi, \qquad \eta(x+\lambda) = \eta x + 2\pi.$$

Consequently,

$$\omega = \frac{2\pi}{P}, \qquad \eta = \frac{2\pi}{\lambda}, \tag{133-8}$$

and we can write (133-7) in the form

$$E_y = A \sin 2\pi\left(\frac{t}{P} - \frac{x}{\lambda}\right). \tag{133-9}$$

Often it is convenient in dealing with plane waves to make use of the

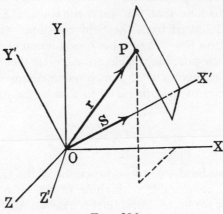

Fig. 296

wave slowness S which is defined as the reciprocal of the phase velocity v. Then $\eta = \omega S$ and (133-9) may be written

$$E_y = A \sin \omega(t - Sx). \tag{133-10}$$

Finally the last equation may be replaced by

$$E_y = Ae^{i\omega(t-Sx)}, \tag{133-11}$$

where it is understood that the imaginary part of the complex expression on the right is to be taken as representing E_y.

If the wave normal or ray does not have the direction of the X axis, we can choose a new set of axes $X'Y'Z'$ such that X' is perpendicular to the wave front, as shown in Fig. 296, and Y' is parallel to $\mathbf{E}$. Then (133-11) holds if we replace x by x' and y by y'. But if x, y, z are the coordinates relative to XYZ of a point P in the wave front,

$$x' = lx + my + nz,$$

where l, m, n are the direction cosines of OX' with respect to the original axes. Consequently,

$$E_{y'} = A\mathrm{e}^{i\omega(t-S[lx+my+nz])} = A\mathrm{e}^{i\omega(t-\mathbf{S}\cdot\mathbf{r})}, \qquad (133\text{-}12)$$

where $\mathbf{r}$ is the position vector of P and the vector wave slowness $\mathbf{S}$ is a vector of magnitude S in the direction of the wave normal. The exponent in the last expression has the advantage of being in vector form and therefore independent of the orientation of the axes to which the wave motion is referred.

Equation (133-4) shows that electromagnetic waves travel *in vacuo* with the velocity c of light. The inference that light itself is electromagnetic in character is inescapable. In addition to being transverse, electromagnetic waves possess many other characteristics of light waves. It is important to note that the wave equations (133-1) and (133-2) would not have followed from the field equations without Maxwell's revision of Ampère's law. It was his introduction of the displacement current which made possible the electromagnetic theory of light.

The index of refraction n of a material medium is defined as the ratio of the velocity of light *in vacuo* to that in the medium. Hence, from (133-4),

$$n = \frac{c}{v} = \sqrt{\kappa\mu}. \qquad (133\text{-}13)$$

Both κ and μ may be shown to be functions of the frequency, but for frequencies at all comparable with those of the visible spectrum μ is very exactly unity for all media. In this case we may write

$$n = \sqrt{\kappa}. \qquad (133\text{-}14)$$

For infra-red radiation κ should have nearly the limiting value which it assumes for steady fields. The following table illustrates the excellent agreement found for a number of gases.

	κ for Steady Fields	n^2 for Infra-Red Radiation
Air	1.000588	1.000585
H_2	1.000264	1.000277
CO_2	1.000966	1.000909
CO	1.000692	1.000670

The gamut of electromagnetic radiation with which we are familiar today extends all the way from radio waves on the long wave length end to gamma rays on the short wave length end of the spectrum. The different regions comprise roughly the following ranges of wave length (in meters):

Waves from Oscillatory Circuits	$3(10)^4$ to $(10)^{-3}$
Infra-Red Radiation	$(10)^{-2}$ to $7(10)^{-7}$
Visible Spectrum	$7(10)^{-7}$ to $4(10)^{-7}$
Ultra-Violet Radiation	$4(10)^{-7}$ to $(10)^{-8}$
X-Rays	$(10)^{-8}$ to $(10)^{-11}$
γ-Rays	$(10)^{-10}$ to $(10)^{-13}$.

All electromagnetic waves travel with the same velocity c in empty space, being distinguished from one another only by differences in wave length and frequency.

In the next article we shall see how to compute both the energy associated with an electromagnetic field and the flow of energy across a fixed surface through which electromagnetic waves are passing.

Problem 133. Standing waves are formed by two sets of progressive waves of the same amplitude and wave length traveling in opposite directions in empty space. If the progressive waves are determined by

$$E_y' = A \sin \omega\left(t - \frac{x}{c}\right), \quad E_y'' = A \sin \omega\left(t + \frac{x}{c}\right),$$

find the total fields. Comment on the positions of the nodes and loops.

Ans. $E_y = 2A \cos 2\pi\left(\frac{x}{\lambda}\right) \sin \omega t$, $\quad H_z = -2A\sqrt{\frac{\kappa_0}{\mu_0}} \sin 2\pi\left(\frac{x}{\lambda}\right) \cos \omega t$.

134. Electromagnetic Energy and Poynting Flux.

To obtain the energy equation we multiply the three equations (3′) in art. 132 by E_x, E_y, E_z, respectively, and the three equations (4′) by H_x, H_y, H_z and subtract the sum of the last three from that of the first three. If we pick out the terms containing derivatives with respect to x on the left-hand side of the resulting equation, we have

$$-E_y \frac{\partial H_z}{\partial x} + E_z \frac{\partial H_y}{\partial x} - \left(-H_y \frac{\partial E_z}{\partial x} + H_z \frac{\partial E_y}{\partial x}\right)$$

$$= -\frac{\partial}{\partial x}(E_y H_z - E_z H_y) \equiv -\frac{\partial \sigma_x}{\partial x},$$

using $\boldsymbol{\sigma}$ for the vector $\mathbf{E} \times \mathbf{H}$. Hence, the entire equation is

$$-\left(\frac{\partial \sigma_x}{\partial x} + \frac{\partial \sigma_y}{\partial y} + \frac{\partial \sigma_z}{\partial z}\right) = (\mathbf{E} \cdot \dot{\mathbf{D}} + \mathbf{H} \cdot \dot{\mathbf{B}}) + \mathbf{j} \cdot \mathbf{E}.$$

Multiplying by an element $d\tau$ of volume, replacing $\mathbf{D}$ by $\kappa_0 \kappa \mathbf{E}$ and $\mathbf{B}$ by $\mu_0 \mu \mathbf{H}$ and rearranging terms, we get

$$\mathbf{j} \cdot \mathbf{E} d\tau + \left(\frac{\partial \sigma_x}{\partial x} + \frac{\partial \sigma_y}{\partial y} + \frac{\partial \sigma_z}{\partial z}\right) d\tau = -\frac{\partial}{\partial t}\left(\frac{\kappa_0 \kappa}{2} E^2 + \frac{\mu_0 \mu}{2} H^2\right) d\tau, \quad (134\text{-}1)$$

in an isotropic medium of constant permeability.

Consider the flux of **σ** out of a volume element such as that illustrated in Fig. 297.   Putting $d\tau = dxdydz$, the net flux through the two surfaces perpendicular to the X axis is

$$-\sigma_x dydz + \left(\sigma_x + \frac{\partial \sigma_x}{\partial x} dx\right)dydz = \frac{\partial \sigma_x}{\partial x} d\tau.$$

Adding similar expressions for the other pairs of surfaces,

$$\text{Outward flux of } \boldsymbol{\sigma} = \left(\frac{\partial \sigma_x}{\partial x} + \frac{\partial \sigma_y}{\partial y} + \frac{\partial \sigma_z}{\partial z}\right)d\tau.$$

The second term on the left-hand side of (134-1), then, represents the flux of the vector **σ** out of the volume $d\tau$.   If, now, we integrate the whole equation over an arbitrary volume τ, this term will specify the

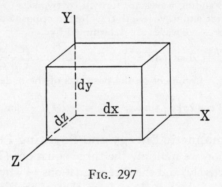

FIG. 297

flux of **σ** out of the entire volume.   This flux, however, can be expressed by the surface integral

$$\int_s \boldsymbol{\sigma} \cdot d\mathbf{s}$$

taken over the closed surface s bounding τ.   We have, then, for any volume τ

$$\int_\tau \mathbf{j} \cdot \mathbf{E} d\tau + \int_s \boldsymbol{\sigma} \cdot d\mathbf{s} = -\frac{\partial}{\partial t}\int_\tau \left(\frac{\kappa_0 \kappa}{2} E^2 + \frac{\mu_0 \mu}{2} H^2\right)d\tau. \qquad (134\text{-}2)$$

This equation is known as the *energy equation*.   We shall now investigate the meaning of the three terms which it contains.

The rate at which work is done by the electric field per unit volume is given by $\mathbf{j} \cdot \mathbf{E}$, since the electric field does work only on the moving charge which constitutes the current.   On the other hand, the magnetic field does no work, even on moving charge, since the force exerted by it is always at right angles to the direction of motion.   The total rate of doing work is, then, $\int_\tau \mathbf{j} \cdot \mathbf{E} d\tau$, which is precisely the first term on the left of (134-2).

To interpret the term on the right of (134-2) we shall consider the case where $\mathbf{E}$ and $\mathbf{H}$ vanish at all points on the boundary of τ. Then σ is zero over the surface s and (134-2) reduces to

$$\int_\tau \mathbf{j} \cdot \mathbf{E} d\tau = -\frac{\partial}{\partial t} \int_\tau \left(\frac{\kappa_0 \kappa}{2} E^2 + \frac{\mu_0 \mu}{2} H^2 \right) d\tau. \tag{134-3}$$

As the work done on the moving charges is performed at the expense of the energy of the field, the right-hand side of this equation must represent the time rate of decrease of electromagnetic energy. Therefore, we can represent the energy of the field in the volume τ by the integral

$$U = \int_\tau \left(\frac{\kappa_0 \kappa}{2} E^2 + \frac{\mu_0 \mu}{2} H^2 \right) d\tau, \tag{134-4}$$

and can assign the electric energy

$$u_E = \frac{\kappa_0 \kappa}{2} E^2 \tag{134-5}$$

and the magnetic energy

$$u_H = \frac{\mu_0 \mu}{2} H^2 \tag{134-6}$$

to each unit volume. These expressions are in accord with the electrostatic energy (21-9) and the magnetostatic energy (46-3) which we have already found it convenient to attribute to the medium through which the field extends.

We are now ready to consider the complete equation (134-2). In the previous special case there was no possibility of a flow of energy through the surface s bounding the volume τ since the field was zero at all points of this surface. In the general case, however, the law of conservation of energy reads: the rate at which the electromagnetic field does work on the charges in the volume τ plus the rate at which energy flows out in the form of radiation through the surface s bounding τ must equal the rate of decrease of electromagnetic energy in this region. Therefore, we conclude that the second term on the left of (134-2) represents the energy passing through the surface s per unit time in the form of radiation. From the form of this term it is clear that we can assign to each unit area of cross section a rate of flow of energy given by the vector

$$\sigma = (\mathbf{E} \times \mathbf{H}), \tag{134-7}$$

which is known as the *Poynting flux*. Its direction is that of the flow of energy and its magnitude specifies the quantity of energy passing through a unit cross section in a unit time. It is to be noticed that σ vanishes unless both electric and magnetic fields are present and not in the same direction. The flux of energy is perpendicular to the plane of $\mathbf{E}$ and $\mathbf{H}$ in the sense of advance of a right-handed screw rotated from the first to the second of the two vectors. It is proportional in magnitude to E, H and the sine of the angle between them.

In the case of the plane wave specified by (133-6) the electric and magnetic energies per unit volume are

$$\left.\begin{aligned}
u_E &= \frac{\kappa_0 \kappa}{2} E_y{}^2 = \frac{\kappa_0 \kappa}{2} g^2, \\[2mm]
u_H &= \frac{\mu_0 \mu}{2} H_z{}^2 = \frac{\kappa_0 \kappa}{2} g^2.
\end{aligned}\right\} \tag{134-8}$$

The energy of the wave, then, is half electric and half magnetic. The Poynting flux is

$$\sigma_x = E_y H_z = v \kappa_0 \kappa g^2 = v(u_E + u_H). \tag{134-9}$$

As this represents the energy passing through a unit cross section in a unit time, the entire energy of the wave progresses with the phase velocity v. This result is independent of direction and we have in general for plane waves

$$\sigma = vu, \tag{134-10}$$

where u is the total energy density.

Problem 134a. Calculate the energy of a spherical conductor of radius a charged with a quantity of electricity Q from (134-5) and show that the result agrees with (21-1).

Problem 134b. Calculate the energy of the solenoid of problem *89c* from (134-6) and show that the result agrees with the calculation made in problem *94*.

Problem 134c. If the earth has a downward electric field 100 volts per meter at the equator and a northward magnetic field 40 amperes per meter, what is the Poynting flux? Ans. 4000 joule/meter^2 sec eastward.

Problem 134d. Find the mean rate of flow of energy for the standing waves described in problem *133*. Ans. 0.

Problem 134e. A straight wire of resistance R carries a current i. Compute the Poynting flux through the surface and show that it accounts for the production of heat at the rate Ri^2.

135. Reflection of Electromagnetic Waves by a Perfect Conductor.

Let MN (Fig. 298) be the plane surface of a perfect conductor on which plane electromagnetic waves are incident at the angle ϕ. As the electric intensity must be zero at every instant in every part of the conductor, it is clear that the wave cannot penetrate into its interior.

Therefore, we have to consider only the incident radiation BO and the reflected radiation OC.

If we orient axes so that the Y axis is perpendicular to MN and the Z axis to the plane of incidence BOC, the vector electric intensity in the incident wave is given by the imaginary part of

$$\mathbf{E}' = \mathbf{A}'e^{i\omega(t - S[x \sin \psi - y \cos \phi])} \qquad (135\text{-}1)$$

from (133-12), where S is the wave slowness in the medium above MN. As we shall see, the angle of reflection must be equal to the angle of incidence. Therefore, the electric intensity in the reflected wave is given by the imaginary part of

$$\mathbf{E}'' = \mathbf{A}''e^{i\omega(t - S[x \sin \phi + y \cos \phi])} \qquad (135\text{-}2)$$

Everywhere on the surface of the conductor ($y=0$) the Z and X components of the resultant electric in-tensity must vanish at every instant. This requires that the exponentials in the expressions for the two waves should become identical at $y=0$. Hence the angle of reflection must be equal to the angle of incidence, as taken above. Furthermore, it requires that the Z and X components of $\mathbf{A}''$ shall be the nega-tives of the Z and X components of $\mathbf{A}'$, respectively. In the case where the radiation is polarized with the electric vector perpendicular to the plane of incidence,

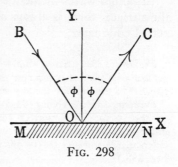

Fig. 298

$$\mathbf{A}' = k\mathbf{A}, \qquad \mathbf{A}'' = -k\mathbf{A}, \qquad (135\text{-}3)$$

and the resultant electric intensity is

$$\mathbf{E} = \mathbf{E}' + \mathbf{E}'' = 2k\mathbf{A} \sin 2\pi\left(\frac{y \cos \phi}{\lambda}\right) \cos \omega(t - Sx \sin \phi), \qquad (135\text{-}4)$$

where λ is the wave length measured along the normal to the wave front. On the other hand, in the case where the radiation is polarized with the electric vector parallel to the plane of incidence,

$$\mathbf{A}' = (i \cos \phi + j \sin \phi)A, \qquad \mathbf{A}'' = (-i \cos \phi + j \sin \phi)A, \qquad (135\text{-}5)$$

since each amplitude vector must be perpendicular to the direction of propagation. The resultant electric intensity, then, is

$$\mathbf{E} = \mathbf{E}' + \mathbf{E}'' = 2i A \cos \phi \sin 2\pi\left(\frac{y \cos \phi}{\lambda}\right) \cos \omega(t - Sx \sin \phi)$$

$$+ 2j A \sin \phi \cos 2\pi\left(\frac{y \cos \phi}{\lambda}\right) \sin \omega(t - Sx \sin \phi). \quad (135\text{-}6)$$

As the amplitude of the reflected wave has the same magnitude as that of the incident wave in both cases, all the energy is reflected. Consequently, *a perfect conductor is a perfect reflector of electromagnetic waves.*

If the region in which the waves are traveling has a permittivity κ, the free charge per unit area on the surface of the conductor is $\sigma = \kappa_0 \kappa E$ in terms of the electric intensity just outside, in accord with (15-10). In the perpendicular case, then, there is no charge on the conductor, while in the parallel case there is a charge

$$\sigma = 2\kappa_0 \kappa A \sin \phi \sin \omega(t - Sx \sin \phi), \tag{135-7}$$

which is alternately positive and negative and is greatest in magnitude at grazing incidence ($\phi = \pi/2$).

Although waves incident on a perfect conductor do not pass through the surface, there is always some penetration beyond the surface of an actual conductor.

Problem 135a. Show that when electromagnetic waves are reflected at the surface of a perfect conductor the resultant magnetic intensity at the surface is parallel to the surface for any state of polarization.

Problem 135b. Using (71-3) and (133-6), find the current per unit width on the surface of a perfect conductor on which electromagnetic waves are impinging, when the electric vector is (1) perpendicular to the plane of incidence, (2) parallel to the plane of incidence. (Take axes and angles as in Fig. 298.)

Ans. (1) $2A \sqrt{\dfrac{\kappa_0 \kappa}{\mu_0 \mu}} \cos \phi \sin \omega(t - Sx \sin \phi)$ in Z direction,

(2) $2A \sqrt{\dfrac{\kappa_0 \kappa}{\mu_0 \mu}} \sin \omega(t - Sx \sin \phi)$ in X direction.

136. Wave Guides. Returning to (135-4) and (135-6) we note that the components of electric intensity parallel to the surface of the conductor vanish not only at the surface $y = 0$ but also at the surfaces $y = k\lambda/2 \cos \phi$, where k is any positive integer. If, therefore, we place a parallel perfectly conducting plane PQ (Fig. 299) a distance $k\lambda/2 \cos \phi$ above MN, the plane waves under consideration will be reflected back and forth from the one surface to the other, advancing meanwhile in the X direction. In other words, if the distance between the two planes is a, plane waves of wave length λ will be propagated along the X axis in the region between them if, and only if, directed at an angle ϕ specified by

$$2a \cos \phi = k\lambda. \tag{136-1}$$

As unity is the smallest value which k may have and is the largest value which $\cos \phi$ may have, the longest wave length which can be transmitted in the way described is $2a$. The corresponding lowest frequency which can be transmitted is $v/2a = c/2a\sqrt{\kappa\mu}$.

Consider, now, the speed with which the wave system is propagated along the X axis. While a plane wave front of one of the constituent waves, shown by the broken line in Fig. 300, progresses a distance BC along the normal, it advances a dis-tance $AC = BC/\sin \phi$ along the X axis. Therefore, the velocity of propagation along the X axis is $v_g = v/\sin \phi$, which increases from v to infinity as ϕ decreases from $\pi/2$ to zero. Similarly, the wave length, measured along the X axis, is $\lambda_g = \lambda/\sin \phi$. These conclusions could have been reached equally well from examination of the last factor in (135-4) and in (135-6), which des-

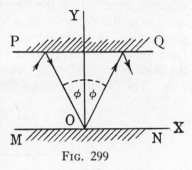

FIG. 299

cribes a wave moving in the X direction with wave slowness $S \sin \phi$ or phase velocity $v/\sin \phi$, and of wave length $2\pi/\omega S \sin \phi = \lambda/\sin \phi$.

If, now, we add to the conducting planes MN and PQ a pair of conducting planes perpendicular to the Z axis, so as to form a *wave guide* of rectangular cross section, the wave (135-4) can be transmitted

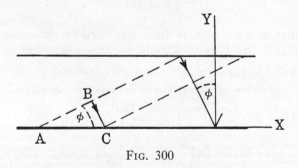

FIG. 300

since it has no component of $\mathbf{E}$ parallel to the added conducting surfaces, but the wave (135-6) fails to satisfy the boundary conditions at these surfaces.

However, there are other waves of a more general character which can be transmitted through a perfectly conducting tube of rectangular cross section. Consider, for example, the following combination of four plane waves inside such a wave guide (Fig. 301) of dimensions a_y

and a_z parallel, respectively, to the Y and Z axes:

$$\mathbf{E} = A\{jn - km\} \sin \omega(t - S[lx + my + nz])$$
$$+ \dot{A}\{jn + km\} \sin \omega(t - S[lx - my + nz])$$
$$+ A\{-jn - km\} \sin \omega(t - S[lx + my - nz])$$
$$+ A\{-jn + km\} \sin \omega(t - S[lx - my - nz]). \qquad (136\text{-}2)$$

The first trigonometrical function represents a wave traveling in a direction specified by the direction cosines, l, m, n, the second in a direction specified by the direction cosines l, $-m$, n, and so on. In each wave the vector amplitude is at right angles to the direction of propagation, as it should be. Evidently the second wave is formed from the first by reflection at a plane perpendicular to the Y axis and the third from the first by reflection at a plane perpendicular to the Z axis. The fourth is formed from the second by reflection at a plane

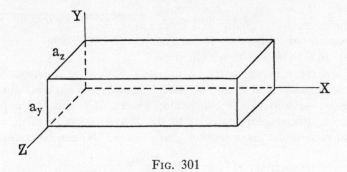

Fig. 301

perpendicular to the Z axis, or from the third by reflection at a plane perpendicular to the Y axis. Combining the sine functions, we get

$$\mathbf{E} = 4A\{-jn \cos \omega Smy \sin \omega Snz \cos \omega(t - Slx)$$
$$+ km \sin \omega Smy \cos \omega Snz \cos \omega(t - Slx)\}$$
$$= 4A\left\{ -jn \cos 2\pi\left(\frac{my}{\lambda}\right) \sin 2\pi\left(\frac{nz}{\lambda}\right) \cos \omega(t - Slx) \right.$$
$$\left. + km \sin 2\pi\left(\frac{my}{\lambda}\right) \cos 2\pi\left(\frac{nz}{\lambda}\right) \cos \omega(t - Slx) \right\}. \qquad (136\text{-}3)$$

The component of $\mathbf{E}$ tangent to the conducting planes $y = 0$ and $y = a_y$ is the Z component, and this vanishes at the surface of each plane provided $2ma_y = k_y\lambda$, where k_y is a positive integer. Similarly the component of $\mathbf{E}$ tangent to the conducting planes $z = 0$ and $z = a_z$, that is, the Y component, vanishes at the surface of each plane provided $2na_z = k_z\lambda$, where k_z is a positive integer. If these relations are satisfied, the boundary conditions of the problem are fulfilled and the composite wave can be transmitted by the guide. The electric intensity in the transmitted wave, then, is

$$
\mathbf{E} = \frac{2A\lambda}{\pi}\left\{ -j\left(\frac{k_z\pi}{a_z}\right) \cos\left(\frac{k_y\pi y}{a_y}\right) \sin\left(\frac{k_z\pi z}{a_z}\right) \cos \omega(t - Slx)\right.
$$
$$
\left. + k\left(\frac{k_y\pi}{a_y}\right) \sin\left(\frac{k_y\pi y}{a_y}\right) \cos\left(\frac{k_z\pi z}{a_z}\right) \cos \omega(t - Slx)\right\} \quad (136\text{-}4)
$$

where

$$
l^2 = 1-(m^2+n^2) = 1-\left\{\left(\frac{k_y\lambda}{2a_y}\right)^2 + \left(\frac{k_z\lambda}{2a_z}\right)^2\right\}. \quad (136\text{-}5)
$$

The *mode* of vibration is specified by the integers assigned to k_y and k_z. The cut-off wave length λ_c is the longest wave length of any stated mode which can be transmitted by the wave guide. As the largest value of m^2+n^2 is unity, the cut-off wave length is

$$
\lambda_c = \frac{1}{\sqrt{\left(\dfrac{k_y}{2a_y}\right)^2 + \left(\dfrac{k_z}{2a_z}\right)^2}}, \quad (136\text{-}6)
$$

and the corresponding cut-off frequency is

$$
\nu_c = \frac{c}{\sqrt{\kappa\mu}}\sqrt{\left(\frac{k_y}{2a_y}\right)^2 + \left(\frac{k_z}{2a_z}\right)^2}. \quad (136\text{-}7)
$$

The phase velocity along the guide is $v_g = v/l$, which may have any value between v and ∞, the latter value being attained at the cut-off wave length. Similarly, the wave length measured along the guide, called the *guide wave length*, is $\lambda_g = \lambda/l$.

Another combination of four plane waves which can be transmitted by a rectangular tube, which differs from that specified by (136-2) only in that the polarization of each constituent wave is perpendicular to that of the corresponding constituent in the earlier combination, is given by

$$
\begin{aligned}
\mathbf{E} = \ & A\{-i(m^2+n^2)+jlm+knl\} \sin \omega(t - S[lx+my+nz]) \\
& + A\{i(m^2+n^2)+jlm-knl\} \sin \omega(t - S[lx-my+nz]) \\
& + A\{i(m^2+n^2)-jlm+knl\} \sin \omega(t - S[lx+my-nz]) \\
& + A\{-i(m^2+n^2)-jlm-knl\} \sin \omega(t - S[lx-my-nz]) \\
= \ & 4A\{i(m^2+n^2) \sin \omega Smy \sin \omega Snz \sin \omega(t - Slx) \\
& -jlm \cos \omega Smy \sin \omega Snz \cos \omega(t - Slx) \\
& -knl \sin \omega Smy \cos \omega Snz \cos \omega(t - Slx)\} \\
= \ & 4A\left\{ i(m^2+n^2) \sin 2\pi\left(\frac{my}{\lambda}\right) \sin 2\pi\left(\frac{nz}{\lambda}\right) \sin \omega(t - Slx)\right. \\
& -jlm \cos 2\pi\left(\frac{my}{\lambda}\right) \sin 2\pi\left(\frac{nz}{\lambda}\right) \cos \omega(t - Slx) \\
& \left. -knl \sin 2\pi\left(\frac{my}{\lambda}\right) \cos 2\pi\left(\frac{nz}{\lambda}\right) \cos \omega(t - Slx)\right\}. \quad (136\text{-}8)
\end{aligned}
$$

In this case the boundary conditions are satisfied if $2ma_y = k_y\lambda$ and $2na_z = k_z\lambda$, as before. The electric intensity in the transmitted wave, then, is

$$\mathbf{E} = \frac{A\lambda^2}{\pi^2}\left\{\mathbf{i}\left[\left(\frac{k_y\pi}{a_y}\right)^2 + \left(\frac{k_z\pi}{a_z}\right)^2\right] \sin\left(\frac{k_y\pi y}{a_y}\right) \sin\left(\frac{k_z\pi z}{a_z}\right) \sin\omega(t - Slx)\right.$$

$$-\mathbf{j}\frac{2\pi l}{\lambda}\left(\frac{k_y\pi}{a_y}\right) \cos\left(\frac{k_y\pi y}{a_y}\right) \sin\left(\frac{k_z\pi z}{a_z}\right) \cos\omega(t - Slx)$$

$$\left. -\mathbf{k}\frac{2\pi l}{\lambda}\left(\frac{k_z\pi}{a_z}\right) \sin\left(\frac{k_y\pi y}{a_y}\right) \cos\left(\frac{k_z\pi z}{a_z}\right) \cos\omega(t - Slx)\right\},$$

$$(136\text{-}9)$$

where l is specified by (136-5). The cut-off wave length and frequency are given by (136-6) and (136-7), respectively, and the phase velocity and wave length measured along the guide are the same as before.

It should be noted that the electric field in (136-4) is entirely transverse to the axis of the tube, whereas the electric field in (136-9) has a longitudinal as well as transverse components. Since the magnetic vector associated with each constituent plane wave lies in the wave front at right angles to the electric vector, it follows that the magnetic field is entirely transverse in the second case but has a longitudinal component in the first. Therefore, the wave described by (136-4) is called a *TE* (transverse electric) wave, and that described by (136-9) a *TM* (transverse magnetic) wave. If it is desired to specify the mode by stating the values of the integers k_y and k_z, they are appended as subscripts. Thus, TM_{12} indicates a wave of type (136-9) in which $k_y = 1$, $k_z = 2$. It should be noted that (136-4) reduces to a wave like (135-4) if $k_z = 0$. But we have seen that the latter wave can be transmitted by a rectangular wave guide. Therefore, the mode of lowest order of a *TE* wave is TE_{10} or TE_{01}. On the other hand, we cannot make either k_y or k_z equal to zero in (136-9) without causing all components of the wave to vanish. So the mode of lowest order of a *TM* wave is TM_{11}.

Wave guides of the type described are particularly suitable for the transmission of *microwaves*, which have wave lengths in the centimeter range. Wave guides may be constructed with circular cross sections, but those with rectangular cross sections generally are more useful. Circular wave guides, like rectangular, transmit both *TE* and *TM* waves.

Problem 136. Find the limiting values of the width a of a wave guide of square cross section which will transmit a wave of length λ in the TE_{10} mode but not in the TE_{11} or TM_{11} modes. Ans. $\dfrac{\lambda}{2} < a < \dfrac{\lambda}{\sqrt{2}}$.

137. Reflection and Refraction of Plane Waves by Dielectrics. When light or, in fact, electromagnetic waves of any wave length strike the interface between two dielectrics, the radiation is partly reflected and partly transmitted. We shall consider separately the case where the incident radiation is polarized with the electric vector perpendicular to the plane of incidence and the case where the electric vector lies in the plane of incidence. Let *MN* (Fig. 302) be the surface separating a medium of permittivity κ_1 above from a medium of permittivity κ_2 below. The incident, reflected and refracted rays are *BO*, *OC* and *OD*, respectively, ϕ_1 being the angle of incidence and ϕ_2 the angle of refraction. Our aim is to find the ratio of the amplitude A_1'' of the reflected radiation to the amplitude A_1' of the incident radiation, and of the amplitude A_2 of the transmitted radiation to the amplitude A_1' of the incident radiation. The first of these ratios is known as the *coefficient of reflection R* and the second as the *coefficient of transmission T*. Since the energy density is proportional to the square of the amplitude, the ratio of the intensity of the reflected to that of the incident radiation, known as the *reflecting power*, is equal to the square of the coefficient of reflection. Incidentally we shall deduce Snell's law giving the relation between ϕ_2 and ϕ_1.

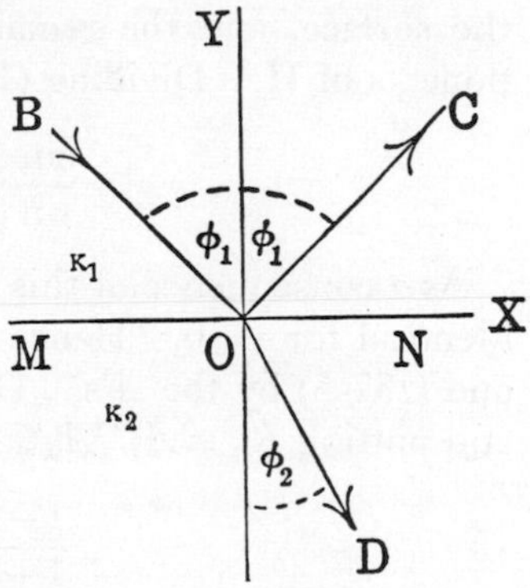

At the surface *MN* the normal component of **D** and the tangential component of **E** must be continuous, as proved in art. 14. Also, since the permeabilities

Fig. 302

are unity in the usual case, all components of **H** must be continuous. These boundary conditions have to be satisfied, then, by the three systems of waves.

Perpendicular Case. If **E** is perpendicular to the plane of incidence, we have only the component E_z. We write then

$$
\left.
\begin{aligned}
\mathbf{E}_1' &= kA_1'e^{i\omega(t-S_1[x\sin\phi_1-y\cos\phi_1])}, \\
\mathbf{E}_1'' &= kA_1''e^{i\omega(t-S_1[x\sin\phi_1+y\cos\phi_1])}, \\
\mathbf{E}_2 &= kA_2e^{i\omega(t-S_2[x\sin\phi_2-y\cos\phi_2])},
\end{aligned}
\right\} \quad (137\text{-}1)
$$

for the incident, reflected and refracted wave trains, respectively, S_1 being the wave slowness in the first medium and S_2 that in the second. In each of these expressions the electric intensity is represented by the imaginary part of the complex quantity.

The magnetic vector is perpendicular to the electric vector in the sense which makes $\mathbf{E} \times \mathbf{H}$ have the direction of propagation, as shown in art. 133. Hence, we may write

$$\left. \begin{aligned} \mathbf{H}_1' &= (-i \cos \phi_1 - j \sin \phi_1) c \kappa_0 n_1 E_1', \\ \mathbf{H}_1'' &= (i \cos \phi_1 - j \sin \phi_1) c \kappa_0 n_1 E_1'', \\ \mathbf{H}_2 &= (-i \cos \phi_2 - j \sin \phi_2) c \kappa_0 n_2 E_2, \end{aligned} \right\} \quad (137\text{-}2)$$

where we have replaced $\sqrt{\kappa}$ by the index of refraction n in accord with (133-14).

The boundary conditions, therefore, are

$$E_1' + E_1'' = E_2, \quad (137\text{-}3)$$

$$(E_1' + E_1'') n_1 \sin \phi_1 = E_2 n_2 \sin \phi_2, \quad (137\text{-}4)$$

$$(E_1' - E_1'') n_1 \cos \phi_1 = E_2 n_2 \cos \phi_2, \quad (137\text{-}5)$$

the first expressing the continuity of the tangential component of $\mathbf{E}$ at the surface, and the remaining two the continuity of the two components of $\mathbf{H}$. Dividing (137-4) by (137-3) we have *Snell's law*,

$$\frac{\sin \phi_1}{\sin \phi_2} = \frac{n_2}{n_1} = \frac{v_1}{v_2} = \frac{S_2}{S_1}. \quad (137\text{-}6)$$

As a consequence of this relation the exponentials in (137-1) become identical for $y = 0$. Hence we may replace the E's in (137-3), (137-4) and (137-5) by the A's. Dividing (137-5) by (137-4) to eliminate A_2, and putting $R_\perp \equiv A_1'' / A_1'$,

$$\frac{1 - R_\perp}{1 + R_\perp} = \frac{\sin \phi_1 \cos \phi_2}{\sin \phi_2 \cos \phi_1},$$

which gives for the coefficient of reflection

$$R_\perp = \frac{\sin \phi_2 \cos \phi_1 - \sin \phi_1 \cos \phi_2}{\sin \phi_2 \cos \phi_1 + \sin \phi_1 \cos \phi_2} = -\frac{\sin (\phi_1 - \phi_2)}{\sin (\phi_1 + \phi_2)}. \quad (137\text{-}7)$$

Similarly, if we solve for $T_\perp \equiv A_2 / A_1'$, we get for the coefficient of transmission

$$T_\perp = \frac{2 \sin \phi_2 \cos \phi_1}{\sin (\phi_1 + \phi_2)}. \quad (137\text{-}8)$$

Parallel Case. If the electric vector lies in the plane of incidence, the electric intensities in the incident, reflected and refracted waves are, respectively,

$$\left. \begin{aligned} \mathbf{E}_1' &= (i \cos \phi_1 + j \sin \phi_1) A_1' e^{i\omega(t - S_1[x \sin \phi_1 - y \cos \phi_1])}, \\ \mathbf{E}_1'' &= (-i \cos \phi_1 + j \sin \phi_1) A_1'' e^{i\omega(t - S_1[x \sin \phi_1 + y \cos \phi_1])}, \\ \mathbf{E}_2 &= (i \cos \phi_2 + j \sin \phi_2) A_2 e^{i\omega(t - S_2[x \sin \phi_2 - y \cos \phi_2])}, \end{aligned} \right\} \quad (137\text{-}9)$$

and the magnetic intensity is

$$
\left.
\begin{aligned}
\mathbf{H}_1' &= kc\kappa_0 n_1 E_1', \\
\mathbf{H}_1'' &= kc\kappa_0 n_1 E_1'', \\
\mathbf{H}_2 &= kc\kappa_0 n_2 E_2.
\end{aligned}
\right\} \quad (137\text{-}10)
$$

Equating the normal components of $\mathbf{D}$ and the tangential components of $\mathbf{E}$ and $\mathbf{H}$ on the two sides of the surface of separation, we have the boundary conditions

$$(E_1' + E_1'')n_1{}^2 \sin \phi_1 = E_2 n_2{}^2 \sin \phi_2, \qquad (137\text{-}11)$$

$$(E_1' - E_1'') \cos \phi_1 = E_2 \cos \phi_2, \qquad (137\text{-}12)$$

$$(E_1' + E_1'')n_1 = E_2 n_2, \qquad (137\text{-}13)$$

if we replace κ by n^2. The quotient of (137-11) by (137-13) leads to Snell's law again. Solving for the coefficient of reflection $R_{\parallel} \equiv A_1''/A_1'$ and the coefficient of transmission $T_{\parallel} \equiv A_2/A_1'$, we find in this case

$$R_{\parallel} = \frac{\sin \phi_1 \cos \phi_1 - \sin \phi_2 \cos \phi_2}{\sin \phi_1 \cos \phi_1 + \sin \phi_2 \cos \phi_2} = \frac{\tan (\phi_1 - \phi_2)}{\tan (\phi_1 + \phi_2)}, \qquad (137\text{-}14)$$

and

$$T_{\parallel} = \frac{2 \sin \phi_2 \cos \phi_1}{\sin (\phi_1 + \phi_2) \cos (\phi_1 - \phi_2)}. \qquad (137\text{-}15)$$

The theoretical expressions for the coefficients of reflection and of transmission for both states of polarization are well verified by experiment. In fact, Fresnel had given these relations as empirical formulas long before the advent of the electromagnetic theory of light.

It is interesting to note that of the four coefficients only $R_{\parallel}$ can vanish. This occurs when $\phi_1 + \phi_2 = \pi/2$, for then the denominator $\tan (\phi_1 + \phi_2)$ becomes infinite. Under these circumstances the reflected and refracted rays are at right angles, and all incident radiation polarized with the electric vector parallel to the plane of incidence is transmitted. If the incident radiation contains both states of polarization, the reflected radiation consists solely of electromagnetic waves polarized with the electric vector perpendicular to the plane of incidence. So by allowing unpolarized light to strike the surface of a dielectric such as glass at the proper angle, a reflected beam of polarized light may be obtained. However, on account of surface irregularities, the polarization is never complete.

The angle of incidence Φ_1 necessary to make $R_{\parallel}$ vanish is known as *Brewster's angle* or the *polarizing angle*. Making use of Snell's law, we have

$$n_1 \sin \Phi_1 = n_2 \sin \left(\frac{\pi}{2} - \Phi_1 \right),$$

or

$$\Phi_1 = \arc \tan \left(\frac{n_2}{n_1}\right). \qquad (137\text{-}16)$$

For crown glass in air $n_2/n_1 = 1.5$ and $\Phi_1 = 56°$.

Problem 137. Show that the reflecting power of glass of index of refraction n for normal incidence is $\left(\frac{n-1}{n+1}\right)^2$. What change in phase takes place on reflection? Why do $R_\perp$ and $R_\parallel$ differ in sign for normal incidence?

138. Radiation Pressure and Electromagnetic Momentum.
When electromagnetic waves impinge on matter, they exert a stress known as *radiation pressure*. To calculate this stress, we must express the force per unit volume, (7) in art. 131, in terms of the components of **E** and **H** alone. Writing down the X component of $\mathscr{F}_\tau$, we have

$$\mathscr{F}_{\tau x} = \rho E_x + (j_y B_z - j_z B_y). \qquad (138\text{-}1)$$

The charge density ρ can be eliminated by means of (1'), art. 132, and the components of the current density **j** by means of (3'), giving

$$\mathscr{F}_{\tau x} = \left\{ E_x \left(\frac{\partial D_x}{\partial x} + \frac{\partial D_y}{\partial y} + \frac{\partial D_z}{\partial z}\right) + B_z \left(\frac{\partial H_x}{\partial z} - \frac{\partial H_z}{\partial x} - \dot{D}_y\right) \right.$$
$$\left. - B_y \left(\frac{\partial H_y}{\partial x} - \frac{\partial H_x}{\partial y} - \dot{D}_z\right) \right\}. \qquad (138\text{-}2)$$

Furthermore if we multiply (2') by H_x and the second and third equations of (4') by D_z and D_y, respectively, and combine,

$$0 = \left\{ H_x \left(\frac{\partial B_x}{\partial x} + \frac{\partial B_y}{\partial y} + \frac{\partial B_z}{\partial z}\right) + D_z \left(\frac{\partial E_x}{\partial z} - \frac{\partial E_z}{\partial x} + \dot{B}_y\right) \right.$$
$$\left. - D_y \left(\frac{\partial E_y}{\partial x} - \frac{\partial E_x}{\partial y} + \dot{B}_z\right) \right\}. \qquad (138\text{-}3)$$

Adding (138-2) and (138-3), putting $D = \kappa_0 \kappa E$ and $B = \mu_0 \mu H$, and collecting terms,

$$\mathscr{F}_{\tau x} = \frac{\partial}{\partial x} \left\{ \frac{\kappa_0 \kappa}{2}(E_x^2 - E_y^2 - E_z^2) + \frac{\mu_0 \mu}{2}(H_x^2 - H_y^2 - H_z^2) \right\}$$
$$+ \frac{\partial}{\partial y} \{\kappa_0 \kappa\, E_x E_y + \mu_0 \mu\, H_x H_y\} + \frac{\partial}{\partial z} \{\kappa_0 \kappa\, E_x E_z + \mu_0 \mu\, H_x H_z\}$$
$$- \frac{\partial}{\partial t} \left\{ \frac{\kappa \mu}{c^2}(E_y H_z - E_z H_y) \right\}. \qquad (138\text{-}4)$$

Consider a small rectangular parallelepiped (Fig. 303) of matter of dimensions Δx, Δy, Δz. If we designate the stresses in the X direction on its faces by X_x, X_y, X_z, the first being a tension on the face perpendicular to the X axis and the second and third shears on the faces perpendicular respectively to the Y and Z axes, the total force in the X direction is

$$\left(\frac{\partial X_x}{\partial x}+\frac{\partial X_y}{\partial y}+\frac{\partial X_z}{\partial z}\right)\Delta x\Delta y\Delta z,$$

or

$$\frac{\partial X_x}{\partial x}+\frac{\partial X_y}{\partial y}+\frac{\partial X_z}{\partial z}$$

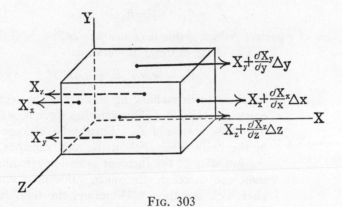

FIG. 303

per unit volume. Comparing with (138-4), we see that the electric stresses parallel to the X axis are

$$\left.\begin{array}{l} X_x = \dfrac{\kappa_0\kappa}{2}(E_x{}^2-E_y{}^2-E_z{}^2)+\dfrac{\mu_0\mu}{2}(H_x{}^2-H_y{}^2-H_z{}^2), \\[2mm] X_y = \kappa_0\kappa\,E_xE_y+\mu_0\mu\,H_xH_y, \\[2mm] X_z = \kappa_0\kappa E_xE_z+\mu_0\mu H_xH_z. \end{array}\right\} \quad (138\text{-}5)$$

In addition to this system of stresses the electromagnetic field exerts a body force the X component of which is given by the last term in (138-4). Now $(E_yH_z-E_zH_y)$ is the X component of $\mathbf{E}\times\mathbf{H}$. Thus, the body force per unit volume is

$$\mathscr{F}_\tau{}' = -\frac{\partial}{\partial t}\left(\frac{\kappa\mu}{c^2}\,\mathbf{E}\times\mathbf{H}\right) = -\frac{\partial}{\partial t}\left(\frac{\kappa\mu}{c^2}\,\boldsymbol{\sigma}\right), \quad (138\text{-}6)$$

where $\boldsymbol{\sigma}$ is the Poynting flux.

Consider a slab of matter MN (Fig. 304) perpendicular to the X axis on the left-hand face of which a steady train of electromagnetic waves impinges normally. As **E** and **H** are perpendicular to the direction of propagation, $E_x = H_x = 0$. Hence the tension is

$$X_x = -\left(\frac{\kappa_0 \kappa}{2} E^2 + \frac{\mu_0 \mu}{2} H^2\right) = -u, \qquad (138\text{-}7)$$

where u is the energy density of the radiation. As the stress is negative, it represents a pressure.

If $\bar{u}_1'$ is the mean energy density in the incident radiation, $\bar{u}_1''$ that in the reflected radiation and $\bar{u}_2$ that in the radiation which passes through the slab, the average force per unit area of the slab in the X direction due to the radiation pressure under consideration is

$$\bar{p}_r = \bar{u}_1' + \bar{u}_1'' - \bar{u}_2. \qquad (138\text{-}8)$$

In the case of a perfect reflector, this becomes $\bar{p}_r = 2\bar{u}_1'$.

The shear in the Y direction is

$$Y_x = \kappa_0 \kappa\, E_y E_x + \mu_0 \mu H_y H_x,$$

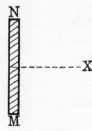

FIG. 304

obtained by interchanging x and y in the second of equations (138-5). This vanishes since $E_x = H_x = 0$. The same is true of Z_x. Finally the average value of the body force $\mathscr{F}_\tau'$ on the slab vanishes, since the intensity of the incident radiation remains constant and therefore the mean value of $\boldsymbol{\sigma}$ does not alter with the time. Therefore, the total force is found from (138-8). The predicted pressure has been verified experimentally by Nichols and Hull and by Lebedew.

Consider next a region τ containing radiation but no ρ or **j**. The force $\mathscr{F}_\tau$, then, must be zero. Therefore, if $\mathscr{F}''$ is the force on this region due to the stresses acting over its surface,

$$0 = \mathscr{F}'' - \frac{\partial}{\partial t} \int_\tau \left(\frac{\kappa \mu}{c^2}\, \boldsymbol{\sigma}\right) d\tau.$$

As the volume τ contains radiation and nothing else, the force $\mathscr{F}''$ due to the stresses on its surface must be supposed to act on the radiation in its interior. As we have

$$\mathscr{F}'' = \frac{\partial}{\partial t} \int_\tau \left(\frac{\kappa \mu}{c^2}\, \boldsymbol{\sigma}\right) d\tau, \qquad (138\text{-}9)$$

and as force is equal to time rate of increase of momentum, the radiation has an *electromagnetic momentum*

$$\mathbf{G} = \int_\tau \left(\frac{\kappa \mu}{c^2}\, \boldsymbol{\sigma}\right) d\tau. \qquad (138\text{-}10)$$

We may attribute momentum, therefore, in the amount

$$\dot{\mathbf{g}} = \frac{\kappa\mu}{c^2}\,\boldsymbol{\sigma} \tag{138-11}$$

to each unit volume of a radiation field. For plane waves the electromagnetic momentum per unit volume has the magnitude

$$g = \frac{\kappa\mu}{c^2}\,vu = \frac{u}{v} \tag{138-12}$$

from (134-10) and (133-4), equal to the energy per unit volume divided by the velocity of propagation.

To illustrate the utility of the concept of electromagnetic momentum, we shall calculate the pressure on the perfectly reflecting surface MN (Fig. 298) due to a train of electromagnetic waves incident at the angle ϕ. If v is the velocity of propagation and $g_1{}'$ the momentum per unit volume of the incident radiation, a momentum $g_1{}'v\cos\phi$ is transferred from the incident to the reflected beam per unit time by each unit area of the reflector. Consequently, the time rate of increase of electromagnetic momentum of the radiation field is $2g_1{}'v\cos^2\phi$ upward This is the force exerted by each unit area of MN on the radiation. According to the law of action and reaction, the radiation field exerts an equal and opposite force on the reflecting surface. The latter, therefore, is subject to the pressure $2g_1{}'v\cos^2\phi$. Now if $\bar{u}_1{}'$ is the mean energy density of the incident radiation, the mean pressure is

$$\bar{p}_r = 2\bar{g}_1{}'v\cos^2\phi = 2\bar{u}_1{}'\cos^2\phi \tag{138-13}$$

from (138-12). Note that equations (138-8) and (138-13) give the same result for normal incidence on a perfect reflector.

Problem 138. The earth receives 1400 joules per meter^2 per second from the sun. Calculate the maximum electric intensity and magnetic intensity in sunlight. Assuming that all the light is absorbed, compute the mean pressure at normal incidence. Ans. $1.03(10)^3$ volt/meter, 2.73 ampere/meter; $4.67(10)^{-6}$ newton/meter^2.

139. Electromagnetic Oscillators.

Although we have considered in some detail the properties of plane electromagnetic waves, we have given no attention to possible sources of electromagnetic radiation. In all cases electromagnetic waves originate in the oscillation of electric charge. The necessary vibratory motion may be produced most simply by means of the Hertzian oscillator illustrated in art. 91. Here an oscillatory discharge takes place across the gap G (Fig. 192), the charges on A and B reversing sign every half period. Essentially we have equal positive and negative charges vibrating along the line

AB with simple harmonic motion, the charge of the one sign being out of phase with that of the other by π radians. The mechanism is equivalent to an oscillating electric dipole. In our theoretical investigation of the production of electromagnetic waves we shall suppose that the oscillations are maintained at constant amplitude, so as to avoid the complications produced by damping, and shall assume that the region surrounding the oscillator is empty space.

Oscillating Electric Dipole. Consider a positive charge q oscillating with frequency $\omega/2\pi$ along the section *AB* (Fig. 305) of the *Z* axis. If a_1 is the amplitude of vibration, the displacement of the charge at any instant is

$$z_1 = a_1 \cos \omega t.$$

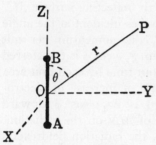

FIG. 305

The displacement of an equal negative charge vibrating with the same frequency but out of phase by π radians with the first is

$$z_2 = a_2 \cos (\omega t + \pi) = -a_2 \cos \omega t,$$

where a_2 represents the amplitude of the second charge. At any instant, then, the distance between the charges is

$$z_1 - z_2 = (a_1 + a_2) \cos \omega t,$$

and the electric moment of the dipole is

$$q(z_1 - z_2) = p_0 \cos \omega t, \qquad p_0 \equiv q(a_1 + a_2). \tag{139-1}$$

Close to the dipole the field at any instant may be treated as if static, the components of the electric intensity being given by (12-2). Consequently, at a distance r from the center of the dipole large compared with *AB*,

$$\left.\begin{aligned} E_r &= \frac{p_0 \cos \theta}{2\pi\kappa_0 r^3} \cos \omega t, \\[2mm] E_\theta &= \frac{p_0 \sin \theta}{4\pi\kappa_0 r^3} \cos \omega t. \end{aligned}\right\} \tag{139-2}$$

From (68-2) the magnetic field near the dipole is

$$\begin{aligned} H_\phi &= \frac{q}{4\pi r^2}\left(\frac{dz_1}{dt} - \frac{dz_2}{dt}\right) \sin \theta \\[2mm] &= -\frac{\omega p_0 \sin \theta}{4\pi r^2} \sin \omega t \end{aligned} \tag{139-3}$$

at right angles to the *rZ* plane, that is, in the direction of increasing azimuth ϕ measured around the *Z* axis.

As its electromagnetic field is propagated outwards from the oscillator with the velocity c, equations (139-2) and (139-3), in which we have treated the field as if it were static, are valid only in the neighborhood of the source. To obtain $\mathbf{E}$ at a distance from the oscillator, we must solve the wave equation (133-1) subject to Gauss' law (1″). The solution must reduce to (139-2) in the immediate vicinity of the oscillator if the waves are to be those produced by the mechanism which we have postulated. In fact we may consider (139-2) to represent the *boundary conditions* which our solution must satisfy.

Since the wave equation (133-1) is linear with constant coefficients, any derivative with respect to x, y, z or t of a solution is also a solution. We shall start, then, with a solution which is a function of r and t alone and build up other solutions by differentiation. As

$$r^2 = x^2 + y^2 + z^2,$$

it follows that

$$\frac{\partial}{\partial x} = \frac{\partial r}{\partial x}\frac{\partial}{\partial r} = \frac{x}{r}\frac{\partial}{\partial r},$$

$$\frac{\partial^2}{\partial x^2} = \frac{\partial}{\partial x}\left(\frac{x}{r}\frac{\partial}{\partial r}\right) = \frac{x^2}{r^2}\frac{\partial^2}{\partial r^2} - \frac{x^2}{r^3}\frac{\partial}{\partial r} + \frac{1}{r}\frac{\partial}{\partial r},$$

and similar expressions hold for $\dfrac{\partial^2}{\partial y^2}$ and $\dfrac{\partial^2}{\partial z^2}$. Consequently,

$$\frac{\partial^2}{\partial x^2} + \frac{\partial^2}{\partial y^2} + \frac{\partial^2}{\partial z^2} = \frac{\partial^2}{\partial r^2} + \frac{2}{r}\frac{\partial}{\partial r}.$$

So if we take for the dependent variable in (133-1) a function Φ_0 of r and t alone, the wave equation becomes

$$\frac{\partial^2 \Phi_0}{\partial r^2} + \frac{2}{r}\frac{\partial \Phi_0}{\partial r} = \frac{1}{c^2}\frac{\partial^2 \Phi_0}{\partial t^2},$$

since $\kappa = \mu = 1$. As all the derivatives are partial, this can be written

$$\frac{\partial^2}{\partial r^2}(r\Phi_0) = \frac{1}{c^2}\frac{\partial^2}{\partial t^2}(r\Phi_0), \tag{139-4}$$

an equation which is of precisely the same form as (133-3). Consequently, its solution is

$$\Phi_0 = \frac{1}{r}f_1\left(t - \frac{r}{c}\right) + \frac{1}{r}f_2\left(t + \frac{r}{c}\right). \tag{139-5}$$

Evidently the first term represents a spherical wave diverging from the origin and the second term one converging toward the origin. We are interested in a simple harmonic diverging wave. Therefore, we shall take

$$\Phi_0 = \frac{A_0}{r} \cos (\omega t - \eta r), \qquad \eta \equiv \frac{\omega}{c}, \qquad (139\text{-}6)$$

in the notation of (133-7).

Since Φ_0 is a solution of the wave equation,

$$\Phi_1 \equiv -\frac{\partial \Phi_0}{\partial z} = -\frac{z}{r}\frac{\partial \Phi_0}{\partial r} = -\cos \theta \frac{\partial \Phi_0}{\partial r}$$

$$= A_0 \cos \theta \left\{ \frac{1}{r^2} \cos (\omega t - \eta r) - \frac{\eta}{r} \sin (\omega t - \eta r) \right\} \qquad (139\text{-}7)$$

is also. If, then, we take for the components of **E**

$$E_x = -\frac{\partial \Phi_1}{\partial x}, \qquad E_y = -\frac{\partial \Phi_1}{\partial y}, \qquad E_z = -\frac{\partial \Phi_1}{\partial z} - \frac{1}{c^2}\frac{\partial^2 \Phi_0}{\partial t^2}, \qquad (139\text{-}8)$$

each component of the electric intensity is a solution of the wave equation.

As this procedure seems somewhat artificial at first sight, it may be illuminating to observe that the method we are following is closely analogous to that which we might pursue in obtaining the components (12-2) of the electric intensity due to a static dipole. In that case we might start with the solution

$$V_0 = \frac{A_0}{r}$$

of Laplace's equation, then differentiate with respect to z to get the potential (12-1)

$$V_1 = -\frac{\partial V_0}{\partial z} = \frac{A_0 \cos \theta}{r^2}$$

of the dipole, and finally write

$$E_x = -\frac{\partial V_1}{\partial x}, \qquad E_y = -\frac{\partial V_1}{\partial y}, \qquad E_z = -\frac{\partial V_1}{\partial z},$$

a set of equations which, of course, is exactly equivalent to (12-2). The only respects in which our procedure in obtaining (139-8) differs from that which we have outlined above for the static dipole are that we start with a solution of the wave equation, which is the generalization of Laplace's equation for electromagnetic fields, and that we have an added term in the expression (139-8) for E_z. The necessity of this added term will appear immediately.

We have yet to show that the components (139-8) of the electric intensity satisfy Gauss' law (1″). Making use of (139-7),

$$\frac{\partial E_x}{\partial x}+\frac{\partial E_y}{\partial y}+\frac{\partial E_z}{\partial z} = \frac{\partial}{\partial z}\left\{\frac{\partial^2\Phi_0}{\partial x^2}+\frac{\partial^2\Phi_0}{\partial y^2}+\frac{\partial^2\Phi_0}{\partial z^2}-\frac{1}{c^2}\frac{\partial^2\Phi_0}{\partial t^2}\right\}.$$

But, as Φ_0 is a solution of the wave equation, the expression within the braces vanishes identically. Consequently (1″) is satisfied. It is now manifest that if we had omitted the second term in the expression for E_z, the components of $\mathbf{E}$, while they would have satisfied the wave equation, would have failed to satisfy Gauss' law.

Now equation (139-8) shows that E_x, E_y and the first term in E_z are obtained from Φ_1 just as the components of the electric intensity (7-7) are obtained from the potential in an electrostatic field. So we can consider that we have the field that would be produced by the potential Φ_1 plus the electricity intensity $-\dfrac{1}{c^2}\dfrac{\partial^2\Phi_0}{\partial t^2}$ in the direction of the axis of the dipole. Consequently, with the aid of (7-8), we have

$$\left.\begin{aligned} E_r &= -\frac{\partial\Phi_1}{\partial r}-\frac{1}{c^2}\frac{\partial^2\Phi_0}{\partial t^2}\cos\theta, \\[2mm] E_\theta &= -\frac{\partial\Phi_1}{r\partial\theta}+\frac{1}{c^2}\frac{\partial^2\Phi_0}{\partial t^2}\sin\theta, \end{aligned}\right\} \tag{139-9}$$

for the components of electric intensity in the directions of increasing r and θ respectively. Making use of (139-6) and (139-7), we get explicitly

$$\left.\begin{aligned} E_r &= A_0\cos\theta\left\{\frac{2}{r^3}\cos(\omega t-\eta r)-\frac{2\eta}{r^2}\sin(\omega t-\eta r)\right\}, \\[2mm] E_\theta &= A_0\sin\theta\left\{\left(\frac{1}{r^3}-\frac{\eta^2}{r}\right)\cos(\omega t-\eta r)-\frac{\eta}{r^2}\sin(\omega t-\eta r)\right\}. \end{aligned}\right\} \tag{139-10}$$

As $\eta=2\pi/\lambda$, the terms in $1/r^3$ predominate over the others at distances from the origin small compared with the wave length. Furthermore, near the origin ηr in the argument of the trigonometrical functions represents a negligible phase angle. Consequently, we have

$$\left.\begin{aligned} E_r &= \frac{2A_0\cos\theta}{r^3}\cos\omega t, \\[2mm] E_\theta &= \frac{A_0\sin\theta}{r^3}\cos\omega t, \end{aligned}\right\} \tag{139-11}$$

in the immediate neighborhood of the oscillating dipole. So the boundary conditions (139-2) are satisfied if the constant A_0 is made equal to $p_0/4\pi\kappa_0$.

At a great distance from the origin we need retain only those terms in (139-10) involving $1/r$. Hence E_r has a negligible magnitude compared with E_θ, and, putting $2\pi/\lambda$ for η in the amplitude factor, the electric intensity consists of the component

$$E_\theta = -\frac{\pi p_0 \sin \theta}{\kappa_0 \lambda^2 r} \cos (\omega t - \eta r) \qquad (139\text{-}12)$$

alone. At this distance from the dipole a small section of the wave front is approximately plane, and the magnetic intensity is $H_\phi = \sqrt{\kappa_0/\mu_0}\, E_\theta$, from (133-6). It is convenient to combine this relation with (139-12), in the form

$$E_\theta = c\mu_0 H_\phi = -\frac{\pi p_0 \sin \theta}{\kappa_0 \lambda^2 r} \cos (\omega t - \eta r). \qquad (139\text{-}13)$$

Since H_ϕ is in a direction at right angles to the rZ plane, the lines of magnetic force are circles around the Z axis.

Both E_θ and H_ϕ are zero along the axis of the dipole on account of the factor $\sin \theta$ and are maximum in the equatorial plane. The radiation, therefore, is emitted from the dipole in greatest intensity in directions at right angles to the line of oscillation. Both fields fall off inversely with the distance r and, for a constant p_0, are inversely proportional to the square of the wave length or directly proportional to the square of the frequency. Inspection of (139-10) shows that the phase of E_θ changes by π as we pass from the vicinity of the origin to a distant point. Although the two fields are in phase at a great distance from the source, comparison of (139-2) with (139-3) shows that they differ in phase by $\pi/2$ in the neighborhood of the oscillating dipole. That the latter must be the case is clear from the fact that when the electric moment is greatest the current is zero and vice versa. The radiation emitted is polarized with E in the rZ plane and H at right angles thereto.

The Poynting flux is

$$\sigma = E_\theta H_\phi = \frac{\pi^2 c p_0^2 \sin^2 \theta}{\kappa_0 \lambda^4 r^2} \cos^2 (\omega t - \eta r) \qquad (139\text{-}14)$$

in the direction of the radius vector.

The energy radiated per unit time is obtained by integrating σ over the surface of a sphere of radius r. It is

$$\mathscr{P}_r = \int_0^\pi \sigma \cdot 2\pi r^2 \sin \theta d\theta = \frac{8\pi^3 c p_0^2}{3\kappa_0 \lambda^4} \cos^2 (\omega t - \eta r), \qquad (139\text{-}15)$$

and the mean rate of radiation is

$$\overline{\mathscr{P}}_r = \frac{4\pi^3 c p_0^2}{3\kappa_0 \lambda^4}.$$

For a given p_0 the rate of radiation is inversely proportional to the fourth power of the wave length or directly proportional to the fourth power of the frequency.

In an actual oscillator the charges which act as sources of electromagnetic radiation are not point charges as in the ideal oscillator which we have discussed. Rather we have a continuous back and forth flow of electricity between two adjacent conductors such as A and B in Fig. 306. If l is the distance between A and B

$$ql = p_0 \cos \omega t,$$

and the current i is

$$i = \frac{dq}{dt} = i_0 \sin \omega t,$$

where

$$i_0 l \equiv -\omega p_0 = -\frac{2\pi c}{\lambda} p_0.$$

In terms of the current amplitude field relation (139-13) becomes

$$E_\theta = c\mu_0 H_\phi = \frac{i_0 l \sin \theta}{2c\kappa_0 \lambda r} \cos (\omega t - \eta r), \qquad (139\text{-}17)$$

and the mean rate of radiation of energy is

$$\bar{\mathscr{P}}_r = \frac{\pi i_0^2 l^2}{3c\kappa_0 \lambda^2}. \qquad (139\text{-}18)$$

If R_o is the ohmic resistance of the oscillator, the mean rate at which energy is converted into heat is

$$\bar{\mathscr{P}}_o = \tfrac{1}{2} R_o i_0^2$$

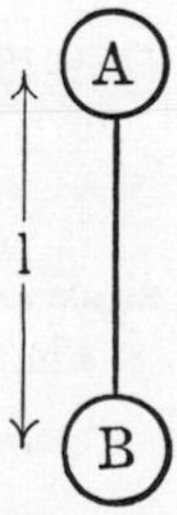

FIG. 306

from (92-8). So the total dissipation of energy per unit time is

$$\bar{\mathscr{P}} = \bar{\mathscr{P}}_o + \bar{\mathscr{P}}_r = \frac{1}{2} \Big\{ R_o + \frac{2\pi l^2}{3c\kappa_0 \lambda^2} \Big\} i_0^2.$$

The effective resistance of the oscillator, then, is increased by radiation in the amount

$$R_r = \frac{2\pi l^2}{3c\kappa_0 \lambda^2}. \qquad (139\text{-}19)$$

This is known as the *radiation resistance* of the oscillator. In numerical form it is

$$R_r = \frac{80\pi^2 l^2}{\lambda^2} \text{ ohm.} \qquad (139\text{-}20)$$

The radiation characteristics of the ordinary vertical wire antenna used in wireless communication can be determined with the aid of (139-17). In this case the antenna is divided into a number of short lengths each of which acts like an oscillating dipole. The total radiation field is then the sum of the fields due to these elementary oscillators, and the radiation resistance of the antenna can be calculated by the same methods that we have used here.

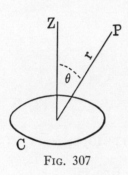

FIG. 307

Oscillating Magnetic Dipole. A circular loop of wire C (Fig. 307) in which an oscillating current $i = i_0 \cos \omega t$ is flowing constitutes an oscillating magnetic dipole. For, on account of the back and forth flow of current, the field which it produces is the same as that of an equivalent magnetic shell whose polarity is a simple harmonic function of the time. If A is the area of the circuit, the equivalent magnetic moment is $\mu_0 i A$ and the amplitude of the magnetic moment is $\mu_0 i_0 A$.

All we need do to obtain H_θ in the radiation field is to replace p_0/κ_0 by $\mu_0 i_0 A/\mu_0 = i_0 A$ in (139-12). We have then

$$H_\theta = -c\kappa_0 E_\phi = -\frac{\pi i_0 A \sin \theta}{\lambda^2 r} \cos (\omega t - \eta r), \qquad (139\text{-}21)$$

since $c\kappa_0 E_\phi$ must be the negative of H_θ for a diverging wave.

The mean rate of radiation in this case is found to be

$$\bar{\mathscr{P}}_r = \frac{4\pi^3 i_0{}^2 A^2}{3c\kappa_0 \lambda^4}. \qquad (139\text{-}22)$$

Comparing this with (139-18), we see that for the same current and wave length.

$$\frac{\text{Radiation from Magnetic Oscillator}}{\text{Radiation from Electric Oscillator}} = \left(\frac{2\pi A}{\lambda l}\right)^2. \qquad (139\text{-}23)$$

Since the linear dimensions of an oscillating dipole must be small compared with the wave length λ of the emitted radiation, a magnetic oscillator is inefficient compared with an electric oscillator of comparable size as a source of electromagnetic waves. Now open circuits operate effectively as electric oscillators, whereas closed loops have the characteristics of magnetic oscillators. Consequently, the former are used in preference to the latter for wireless antennas.

Problem 139a. An oscillator has a length 5 meters and carries a current whose r.m.s. value is 5 amperes. The frequency is 1000 kilocycles per second. Find the power radiated. Ans. 5.48 watt.

Problem 139b. What is the radiation resistance of the oscillator of problem *139a?* Ans. 0.219 ohm.

Problem 139c. Find the relative efficiency as sources of electromagnetic waves of an electric oscillator of length 5 meters and a magnetic oscillator of diameter 5 meters at a frequency 1000 kilocycles per second. Ans. 148:1.

Problem 139d. An antenna consists of a straight wire of length $\lambda/2$ parallel to the Z axis with center at the origin. The amplitude of the current along the antenna is given by $i_0 = i_{00} \cos \eta z$. Find the radiation field at a distance r from the origin great compared with the wave length λ.

$$\text{Ans. } E_\theta = c\mu_0 H_\phi = \frac{i_{00} \cos \left(\dfrac{\pi}{2} \cos \theta \right)}{2\pi c \kappa_0 r \sin \theta} \cos (\omega t - \eta r).$$

140. Graphical Representation of Electromagnetic Waves.
Since electromagnetic waves progress through empty space with the

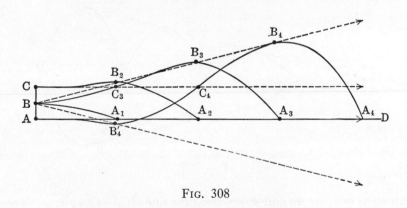

FIG. 308

velocity c, we can consider the field of an oscillating point charge to be traveling out from it radially in all directions with this velocity, the charge replenishing the field, as fast as it moves away, by the emission of new lines of force. For instance, let us consider a charge oscillating up and down along the line AC (Fig. 308) with simple harmonic motion and let us fix our attention on a line of electric force extending to the right. If we suppose the charge to be initially at rest at A, the line of force under consideration is then the straight line AD. If, now, the simple harmonic motion is imparted to the charge, the field at A moves out to A_1 with the velocity c while the charge moves up to B. The line of force is now BA_1D. Allowing another equal interval of time to elapse, A_1 has progressed to A_2 and B to B_2 while the charge has reached the upper end C of its path, and the line of force under consideration has assumed the form CB_2A_2D. The direction of motion

BB_2 of the point B of the field is horizontally to the right *relative to an observer moving with the charge*, therefore inclined upward relative to an observer who does not partake of the motion. Continuing the process we find $BC_3B_3A_3D$ and $AB_4'C_4B_4A_4D$ for successive later configurations of the line of force under consideration, the line of motion BB_4' being inclined below the horizontal on account of the downward motion of the charge on passing through B on its return to A. We have here a moving picture of an electromagnetic wave progressing to the right from the oscillating charge. The farther the wave travels from the source, the steeper and more nearly transverse it becomes. The reader can easily show that no wave is emitted in the vertical direction.

The line of force shown in the figure has exactly the configuration of a stream of water issuing from a nozzle kept pointed to the right and

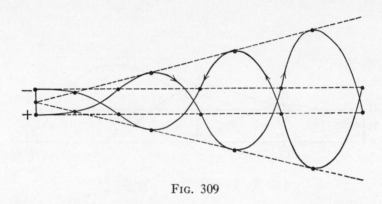

FIG. 309

caused to oscillate up and down along the line AC. The picture is not merely approximately correct, but is an *exact* representation of an electromagnetic wave. In fact the entire assembly of Maxwell's field equations, $(1'')$ to $(4'')$ of art. 133, has been shown* to be merely the kinematical equations of motion of the lines of force of the field as here represented. Had this representation been available before Oersted's discovery of the magnetic effect of a current, Ampère's law with Maxwell's addition of the displacement current, Faraday's law and the second term in the force equation could have been predicted without any appeal to experiment.

We cannot apply correctly the foregoing representation to the resultant field of an oscillating dipole since the radial velocity of propagation c applies only to the individual field of a single point charge. The waves produced by a dipole must rather be considered as the resultant

---

* Page and Adams, *Electrodynamics*, D. Van Nostrand Co., Inc., 1940.

of the two trains of waves to which the two charges give rise.   These are illustrated in Fig. 309 for a horizontal line of force extending from each charge.   Remembering that the line of force terminating on the positive charge is directed *away* from the charge on which it originates whereas that terminating on the negative charge is directed *toward* its source, it is clear from the diagram that the transverse components of the two fields reinforce each other whereas the longitudinal components are oppositely directed.   Thus, while the field is largely longitudinal close to the dipole, it is almost entirely transverse at a distance of a few wave lengths.

REFERENCES

Bleaney and Bleaney, *Electricity and Magnetism* (Oxford Univ. Press, 1965).   Chap. 10, pp. 315–326.

Corson and Lorrain, *Introduction to Electromagnetic Fields and Waves* (Freeman, 1962).   Chap. 8–9, 11–12.

Kip, *Electricity and Magnetism* (McGraw-Hill, 1962).   Chap. 12.

Ramo, Whinnery, and Van Duzer, *Fields and Waves in Communication Electronics* (Wiley, 1965).   Pp. 228–248, Chap. 6–7, pp. 420–445.

Ryder, *Networks, Lines and Fields* (Prentice-Hall, 1949).   Chap. 7–10.

Terman, *Electronic and Radio Engineering* (McGraw-Hill, 1955). Chap. 5.

Appendix A

ALTERNATIVE DEVELOPMENT OF
MAGNETIC THEORY

A1. Fundamental Relations. Although the classical theory of magnetism, including the definition of the magnetic field, was based historically on the concept of the magnetic pole, all existing evidence confirms Ampère's theory that *all* magnetic effects are due to the motion

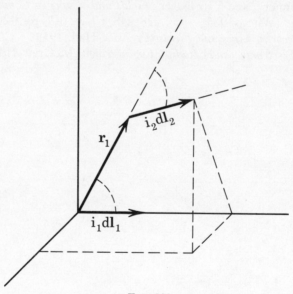

FIG. 310

of electric charge. Consequently the theory of magnetism can be developed from the observed interactions between moving charges or, more conveniently, from those between current elements.

Let us first consider the force on a current element $i_2 dl_2$ located at a distance $\mathbf{r}_1$ from a current element $i_1 dl_1$ (Fig. 310). The work of

Ampère and others shows that this force can be represented by

$$d^2\mathscr{F}_2 = \frac{\mu_0 i_2 i_1}{4\pi r_1{}^3} d\mathbf{l}_2 \times (d\mathbf{l}_1 \times \mathbf{r}_1),\tag{A1-1}$$

that is, by

$$d^2\mathscr{F}_2 = i_2 d\mathbf{l}_2 \times d\mathbf{B}_1, \qquad d\mathbf{B}_1 \equiv \frac{\mu_0 i_1 d\mathbf{l}_1 \times \mathbf{r}_1}{4\pi r_1{}^3}.\tag{A1-2}$$

Evidently $d\mathbf{B}_1$ is a vector field due to $i_1 d\mathbf{l}_1$, in terms of which the force on $i_2 d\mathbf{l}_2$ can be expressed. It is physically identical with the *magnetic induction*, as historically defined, and is therefore so designated. If $d\mathbf{B}_1$ is replaced by a finite field $\mathbf{B}_1$, the force on $i_2 d\mathbf{l}_2$ is, of course,

$$d\mathscr{F}_2 = i_2 d\mathbf{l}_2 \times \mathbf{B}_1.\tag{A1-3}$$

Since the force on $i_1 d\mathbf{l}_1$ at a distance $\mathbf{r}_2 = -\mathbf{r}_1$ from $i_2 d\mathbf{l}_2$ is represented by

$$d^2\mathscr{F}_1 = \frac{\mu_0 i_1 i_2}{4\pi r_2{}^3} d\mathbf{l}_1 \times (d\mathbf{l}_2 \times \mathbf{r}_2),\tag{A1-4}$$

we see that $d^2\mathscr{F}_1 \neq -d^2\mathscr{F}_2$, in general. Hence, the magnetic forces between current elements do not obey the law of action and reaction.

A2. Magnetic Induction of Circuits. Omitting the subscripts, we have Ampère's induction law (A1-2) in the general form

$$d\mathbf{B} = \frac{\mu_0 i d\mathbf{l} \times \mathbf{r}}{4\pi r^3},\tag{A2-1}$$

where $\mathbf{r}$ is the distance from $i d\mathbf{l}$ to the field point. The induction field due to a complete circuit is found by integrating (A2-1) around the circuit. The results for several cases can be taken directly from art. 69, since these apply to empty space where $B = \mu_0 H$. Thus, at the center of a circular coil of n turns and radius a, $B = \mu_0 n i / 2a$ perpendicular to the plane of the coil, and at any point on the axis of an infinitely long solenoid of n_l turns per unit length, $B = \mu_0 n_l i$ parallel to the axis. In particular, the components of $\mathbf{B}$ due to a small circuit of area A (Fig. 131) are

$$\left.\begin{aligned}B_R &= \frac{\mu_0 i A}{2\pi R^3} \cos \Theta, \\[2ex] B_\Theta &= \frac{\mu_0 i A}{4\pi R^3} \sin \Theta.\end{aligned}\right\}\tag{A2-2}$$

Comparison of these with (12-2) shows that (A2-2) represents a dipole type of field which can be derived from a magnetic scalar potential $\mu_0 iA \cos \Theta / 4\pi R^2$, and suggests that we call $p \equiv \mu_0 iA$ the *magnetic moment** of the circuit. Vectorially, it is directed along the positive normal to A. Then

$$
\left.\begin{aligned}
B_R &= -\frac{\partial}{\partial R}\left(\frac{p \cos \Theta}{4\pi R^2}\right) = \frac{p \cos \Theta}{2\pi R^3}, \\
B_\Theta &= -\frac{\partial}{R \partial \Theta}\left(\frac{p \cos \Theta}{4\pi R^2}\right) = \frac{p \sin \Theta}{4\pi R^3}.
\end{aligned}\right\} \tag{A2-3}
$$

As it will be much simpler to employ these and other expressions in vector form, we will digress for a brief discussion of vectors and vector operations.

A3. Vector Analysis. In art. 67 we defined the scalar product of two vectors, $\mathbf{P}$ and $\mathbf{Q}$, so that

$$
\mathbf{P}\cdot\mathbf{Q} = P_x Q_x + P_y Q_y + P_z Q_z
$$

and the vector product so that

$$
\mathbf{P}\times\mathbf{Q} = i(P_y Q_z - P_z Q_y) + j(P_z Q_x - P_x Q_z) + k(P_x Q_y - P_y Q_x).
$$

Suppose, now, we define an *operator*, called "del", by

$$
\boldsymbol{\nabla} \equiv i\,\frac{\partial}{\partial x} + j\,\frac{\partial}{\partial y} + k\,\frac{\partial}{\partial z}.
$$

Then the *divergence* of $\mathbf{Q}$ is

$$
\boldsymbol{\nabla}\cdot\mathbf{Q} = \frac{\partial Q_x}{\partial x} + \frac{\partial Q_y}{\partial y} + \frac{\partial Q_z}{\partial z}, \tag{A3-1}
$$

and the *curl* of $\mathbf{Q}$ is

$$
\boldsymbol{\nabla}\times\mathbf{Q} = i\left(\frac{\partial Q_z}{\partial y} - \frac{\partial Q_y}{\partial z}\right) + j\left(\frac{\partial Q_x}{\partial z} - \frac{\partial Q_z}{\partial x}\right) + k\left(\frac{\partial Q_y}{\partial x} - \frac{\partial Q_x}{\partial y}\right). \tag{A3-2}
$$

For example, in terms of $\boldsymbol{\nabla}$ equations (1′) and (4′) of art. 132 become simply $\boldsymbol{\nabla}\cdot\mathbf{D} = \rho$ and $\boldsymbol{\nabla}\times\mathbf{E} = -\dot{\mathbf{B}}$, respectively. Similarly, the *gradient* of a scalar function Ψ is

$$
\boldsymbol{\nabla}\Psi = i\,\frac{\partial \Psi}{\partial x} + j\,\frac{\partial \Psi}{\partial y} + k\,\frac{\partial \Psi}{\partial z}, \tag{A3-3}
$$

from which

$$
(\boldsymbol{\nabla}\Psi)\cdot d\mathbf{1} \equiv (\boldsymbol{\nabla}\Psi)\cdot(i\,dx + j\,dy + k\,dz) = d\Psi. \tag{A3-4}
$$

An example of the gradient is $\mathbf{E} = -\boldsymbol{\nabla}V$, the vector form of (7-7).

---

* This is in accord with historical usage. The designation "magnetic moment" is sometimes applied to the product iA only, the factor μ_0 being introduced elsewhere.

Although $\nabla \cdot \mathbf{Q}$, $\nabla \times \mathbf{Q}$ and $\nabla \Psi'$ have been expressed above in terms of rectangular coordinates, they may be expressed equally well in terms of spherical or cylindrical coordinates*. Thus, in spherical coordinates

$$\nabla \Psi' = \mathbf{R}_u \frac{\partial \Psi'}{\partial R} + \mathbf{\Theta}_u \frac{\partial \Psi'}{R \partial \Theta} + \mathbf{\Phi}_u \frac{\partial \Psi'}{R \sin \Theta \partial \Phi}, \tag{A3-5}$$

where $\mathbf{R}_u$, $\mathbf{\Theta}_u$ and $\mathbf{\Phi}_u$ are unit vectors in the directions of increasing R, Θ and Φ, respectively. Vector equations in which the coordinates do not appear explicitly are, in general, valid in any proper coordinate system.

There are a number of useful vector relations and identities. (See, for instance: Coffin, *Vector Analysis*.) Some of these are listed below for general reference.

$$\int_\tau \nabla \cdot \mathbf{Q} d\tau = \int_s \mathbf{Q} \cdot d\mathbf{s}. \quad \textit{Gauss' Theorem.} \tag{A3-6}$$

$$\int_s \nabla \times \mathbf{Q} \cdot d\mathbf{s} = \oint \mathbf{Q} \cdot d\mathbf{l}. \quad \textit{Stokes' Theorem.} \tag{A3-7}$$

$$\mathbf{P} \cdot \mathbf{Q} \times \mathbf{R} = \mathbf{Q} \cdot \mathbf{R} \times \mathbf{P} = \mathbf{R} \cdot \mathbf{P} \times \mathbf{Q}. \tag{A3-8}$$

$$\left.\begin{array}{l} \mathbf{P} \times (\mathbf{Q} \times \mathbf{R}) = \mathbf{Q}(\mathbf{R} \cdot \mathbf{P}) - \mathbf{R}(\mathbf{P} \cdot \mathbf{Q}), \\ \mathbf{Q} \times (\mathbf{R} \times \mathbf{P}) = \mathbf{R}(\mathbf{P} \cdot \mathbf{Q}) - \mathbf{P}(\mathbf{Q} \cdot \mathbf{R}), \\ \mathbf{R} \times (\mathbf{P} \times \mathbf{Q}) = \mathbf{P}(\mathbf{Q} \cdot \mathbf{R}) - \mathbf{Q}(\mathbf{R} \cdot \mathbf{P}). \end{array}\right\} \tag{A3-9}$$

$$\nabla \cdot \mathbf{Q} \times \mathbf{R} = \mathbf{R} \cdot \nabla \times \mathbf{Q} - \mathbf{Q} \cdot \nabla \times \mathbf{R}. \tag{A3-10}$$

$$\nabla \cdot (\Psi' \mathbf{Q}) = \Psi' \nabla \cdot \mathbf{Q} + (\nabla \Psi') \cdot \mathbf{Q}. \tag{A3-11}$$

$$\nabla \times (\Psi' \mathbf{Q}) = \Psi' \nabla \times \mathbf{Q} + (\nabla \Psi') \times \mathbf{Q}. \tag{A3-12}$$

$$\nabla \cdot \nabla \times \mathbf{R} = 0. \tag{A3-13}$$

$$\nabla \times (\nabla \times \mathbf{R}) = \nabla(\nabla \cdot \mathbf{R}) - \nabla \cdot \nabla \mathbf{R}. \tag{A3-14}$$

$$\nabla \times (\nabla \Psi') = 0. \tag{A3-15}$$

The dot and cross combination of vectors in (A3-8) is a *triple scalar product*. Similarly, the double cross combination in (A3-9) is a *triple vector product*.

A4. Circuital Form of Ampère's Law.

In art. 70 it is shown that the magnetic effects of an extended current circuit C are expressible as the sum of the effects of the elementary circuits or meshes into which

---

* Moon, P. and Spencer, D. E., *Foundations of Electrodynamics*, D. Van Nostrand Co., Inc., 1960, pp. 300–305; Schwarz, W. M., *Intermediate Electromagnetic Theory*, John Wiley & Sons, Inc., 1964, pp. 410–411.

the extended circuit can be divided by means of a conducting network. The increment of potential due to a mesh of area A is

$$\frac{\mu_0 i A \cos \Theta}{4\pi R^2} = -\frac{\mu_0 i \Omega_A}{4\pi},$$

where Ω_A is the solid angle subtended at the point P by A (Fig. 131), the minus sign indicating that Ω_A is negative when the positive side of A faces P and vice versa. Therefore, the potential function due to the extended circuit, found by summation, is simply $-\mu_0 i \Omega / 4\pi$ and the induction is given by

$$\mathbf{B} = -\boldsymbol{\nabla} \left(-\frac{\mu_0 i \Omega}{4\pi} \right) = \frac{\mu_0 i}{4\pi} \boldsymbol{\nabla}\Omega. \qquad (A4\text{-}1)$$

Here Ω is the solid angle subtended at P by the circuit C.

Let us now calculate the line integral of $\mathbf{B}$ around a closed path l. Since $(\boldsymbol{\nabla}\Omega)\cdot d\mathbf{1} = d\Omega$ from (A3-4), this is

$$\oint \mathbf{B}\cdot d\mathbf{1} = \frac{\mu_0 i}{4\pi} \oint d\Omega = \frac{\mu_0 i}{4\pi} (\Omega_f - \Omega_i),$$

where Ω_i is the initial value of Ω at some point on l and Ω_f is the final value after the loop is completed. If l does not link C, Ω is a one-valued function of position, so that $\Omega_f = \Omega_i$ and the line integral equals zero. However, if l links C (Fig. 311), Ω increases continuously around l, changing sign at some point Q. This change of sign indicates that Ω has increased by the total solid angle in space around the point, that is, by 4π. Hence $\Omega_f = \Omega_i + 4\pi$, giving

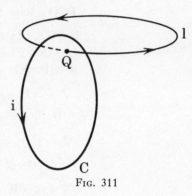

Fig. 311

$$\oint \mathbf{B}\cdot d\mathbf{1} = \mu_0 i. \qquad (A4\text{-}2)$$

This is the circuital form of Ampère's law. Evidently it applies to any number of simultaneous current linkages, provided i represents the algebraic sum of the currents linked. Also, if the currents are distributed in space with a density $\mathbf{j}$ (art. 48), the circuital relation (A4-2) assumes the more general form

$$\oint \mathbf{B}\cdot d\mathbf{1} = \mu_0 \int_s \mathbf{j}\cdot d\mathbf{s}, \qquad (A4\text{-}3)$$

where s is any surface bounded by l.

Since the addition of a constant to the potential function used in (A4-1) does not alter the value of **B**, the complete induction scalar potential V_B due to a current circuit is usually taken to be

$$V_B = -\frac{\mu_0 i}{4\pi}(\Omega + 4\pi\nu),\qquad\text{(A4-4)}$$

where Ω is the solid angle subtended at the point P and ν is an integer representing the number of times i is linked by the path along which V_B is calculated. This gives for the potential drops around the loop l above $\mu_0 i(0)$ and $\mu_0 i(1)$, respectively, as already found.

A5. Properties of the Induction. It can be shown* that a vector such as **B** is completely determined when its curl and its divergence are known. Consequently, it is important to find $\nabla \times \mathbf{B}$ and $\nabla \cdot \mathbf{B}$.

The expression for $\nabla \times \mathbf{B}$ follows at once from (A4-3) if the loop integral is transformed by means of (A3-7), so that we have

$$\int_s \nabla \times \mathbf{B} \cdot d\mathbf{s} = \mu_0 \int_s \mathbf{j} \cdot d\mathbf{s}$$

This can be true only if

$$\nabla \times \mathbf{B} = \mu_0 \mathbf{j},\qquad\text{(A5-1)}$$

since s is an arbitrary bounded surface.

In order to find $\nabla \cdot \mathbf{B}$ we require the value of $\mathbf{r}/r^3$ in Ampère's formula (A2-1). As

$$r = \sqrt{(x-x_e)^2 + (y-y_e)^2 + (z-z_e)^2},$$

where x_e, y_e, z_e are the coordinates of the current element

$$i d\mathbf{1} = i(\mathbf{i}\,dx_e + \mathbf{j}\,dy_e + \mathbf{k}\,dz_e),$$

we have

$$\nabla\left(\frac{1}{r}\right) = -\frac{\mathbf{i}(x-x_e)+\mathbf{j}(y-y_e)+\mathbf{k}(z-z_e)}{[(x-x_e)^2+(y-y_e)^2+(z-z_e)^2]^{3/2}} = -\frac{\mathbf{r}}{r^3}.$$

Hence, (A2-1) can be written

$$d\mathbf{B} = -\frac{\mu_0 i}{4\pi} d\mathbf{1} \times \nabla\left(\frac{1}{r}\right) = \frac{\mu_0 i}{4\pi}\nabla\left(\frac{1}{r}\right) \times d\mathbf{1} = \frac{\mu_0 i}{4\pi}\nabla\times\left(\frac{d\mathbf{1}}{r}\right).$$

This gives a complete circuit

$$\mathbf{B} = \frac{\mu_0 i}{4\pi}\oint \nabla\times\left(\frac{d\mathbf{1}}{r}\right) = \nabla\times\left[\frac{\mu_0 i}{4\pi}\oint\frac{d\mathbf{1}}{r}\right],$$

* Page and Adams, *Electrodynamics*, D. Van Nostrand Co., Inc., 1940, p. 61.

since ∇ does not act on x_e, y_e, z_e, the variables of integration; or

$$\mathbf{B} = \nabla \times \mathbf{A}_B, \qquad \mathbf{A}_B \equiv \frac{\mu_0 i}{4\pi} \oint \frac{d\mathbf{l}}{r}. \tag{A5-2}$$

The quantity $\mathbf{A}_B$, which has various theoretical applications, is called the induction *vector potential*. Inasmuch as $\nabla \cdot \nabla \times \mathbf{A}_B = 0$ from (A3-13), it follows that

$$\nabla \cdot \mathbf{B} = 0. \tag{A5-3}$$

This is an important result, as it can be shown to signify that $\mathbf{B}$ is *solenoidal*, that is, everywhere continuous.

Although (A5-1) and (A5-3) are conveniently derived from complete-circuit formulas, as above, they are in fact entirely general and they apply to any type of induction field.

A6. Permeable Media. So far we have dealt only with macroscopic currents and their induction fields, that is with currents and fields in regions where no magnetized materials are present. However, we know that some permeable materials can be magnetized, either permanently or temporarily, by means of external induction fields, so as to produce fields of their own. According to Ampère's theory, such fields are due to permanent intra-molecular currents. These Ampèrian currents have magnetic moments which are directed at random before the material is magnetized but which are aligned progressively during the process of magnetization. Hence, magnetic moment is distributed throughout the medium, the amount per unit volume at any position, denoted by $\mathbf{I}$,* being called the *magnetization*. This is analogous to the polarization in the electric case (art. 13).

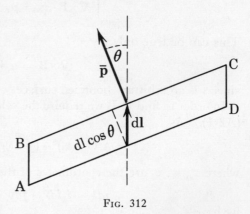

Fig. 312

In order to simplify the analysis let us suppose that the Ampèrian currents on the average have a magnitude $\bar{\imath}$ and flow in circular circuits of area $\bar{A}$. Thus, each Ampèrian circuit has a magnetic moment $\bar{p} = \mu_0 \bar{\imath} \bar{A}$. We wish to find the net current i_a due to these, which passes through a surface s bounded by a closed curve l. This surface is small on a macroscopic scale, yet large enough to span many Ampèrian

* If magnetic moment is defined without the factor μ_0 (Footnote, p. 510), the magnetization is usually denoted by $\mathbf{M}$, in which case $\mathbf{I}$ is replaced by $\mu_0\mathbf{M}$.

currents. It is evident that only those currents which actually link l can produce a net current through s. All others either do not pass through s at all, or they pass through twice, in opposite senses.

Consider an element $d\mathbf{1}$ (Fig. 312) of the curve l, together with an Ampèrian current whose magnetic moment is in the plane of the figure at an angle θ with $d\mathbf{1}$. Let $ABCD$ in the figure represent the cross section of a slanting cylinder whose bases AD and BC are each equal to $\bar{A}$. Then it is apparent that $d\mathbf{1}$ is linked by all the Ampèrian currents with moments effectively parallel to the one illustrated, provided their centers are located somewhere within the cylinder. As this is true for any azimuthal orientation of the cylinder around $d\mathbf{1}$, the total number of current linkages due to currents characterized by the angle θ must be $\bar{A}(dl \cos \theta)dn$, where dn is the total number of these currents per unit volume. The contribution to the current through s is therefore

$$d^2 i_a = i\bar{A}(dl \cos \theta)dn = \frac{1}{\mu_0}(\not{p}dn \cos \theta)dl = \frac{1}{\mu_0} d\mathbf{I} \cdot d\mathbf{1},$$

since $\not{p}dn \cos \theta$ is the incremental component of $\mathbf{I}$ in the direction of $d\mathbf{1}$. Integrating over all values of θ, we have

$$di_a = \frac{1}{\mu_0} \mathbf{I} \cdot d\mathbf{1}$$

and, finally, with the aid of (A3-7),

$$i_a = \frac{1}{\mu_0} \oint \mathbf{I} \cdot d\mathbf{1} = \frac{1}{\mu_0} \int_s \mathbf{\nabla} \times \mathbf{I} \cdot d\mathbf{s}, \qquad \text{(A6-1)}$$

for the entire surface s. In terms of the Ampèrian current density $\mathbf{j}_a$ this becomes

$$\int_s \mathbf{j}_a \cdot d\mathbf{s} = \frac{1}{\mu_0} \oint \mathbf{I} \cdot d\mathbf{1} = \frac{1}{\mu_0} \int_s \mathbf{\nabla} \times \mathbf{I} \cdot d\mathbf{s}, \qquad \text{(A6-2)}$$

which requires that

$$\mathbf{j}_a = \frac{1}{\mu_0} \mathbf{\nabla} \times \mathbf{I}. \qquad \text{(A6-3)}$$

We can now modify the circuital form of Ampère's law (A4-3) and the curl equation (A5-1) so as to make them applicable to fields in permeable media. Since they were derived for macroscopic currents, we must add $\mathbf{j}_a$ in appropriate form to $\mathbf{j}$ in each case. Thus, adding (A6-2) to the right-hand side of (A4-3), we obtain

$$\oint \mathbf{B} \cdot d\mathbf{1} = \mu_0 \int_s \mathbf{j} \cdot d\mathbf{s} + \oint \mathbf{I} \cdot d\mathbf{1},$$

that is,

$$\oint (\mathbf{B}-\mathbf{I})\cdot d\mathbf{l} = \mu_0 \int_s \mathbf{j}\cdot d\mathbf{s}.$$

If, now, we put $\mathbf{H} \equiv (\mathbf{B}-\mathbf{I})/\mu_0$, Ampère's law assumes the general form

$$\oint \mathbf{H}\cdot d\mathbf{l} = \int_s \mathbf{j}\cdot d\mathbf{s}, \qquad (A6\text{-}4)$$

where $\mathbf{H}$ is the *magnetic intensity* or the *magnetic field strength*.   Similarly, the general form of the curl equation, found either by converting the line integral in (A6-4) to a surface integral or by combining (A6-3) with (A5-1), is

$$\nabla \times \mathbf{H} = \mathbf{j}. \qquad (A6\text{-}5)$$

Since $(\mathbf{B}-\mathbf{I})$ is identical in value with its corresponding historical expression, the same is true of $\mathbf{H}$ and such derived quantities as the magnetic susceptibility $\chi \equiv I/\mu_0 H$ and the permeability $\mu \equiv B/\mu_0 H$.

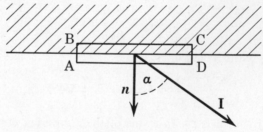

FIG. 313

In addition to the volume currents represented by $\mathbf{j}_a$, there are surface currents on the surfaces bounding the medium.   These currents are due to the uncompensated portions of the Ampèrian currents located at the surface, as indicated in Fig. 134.   Hence, their direction must be perpendicular to $\mathbf{I}$ at every point.   To find their magnitude, apply (A6-1) to a small rectangle $ABCD$ (Fig. 313) which includes a length Δl of the bounding surface and which lies in the plane determined by the outward normal unit vector n and the magnetization $\mathbf{I}$.   The sides AD and BC (of length Δl) lie on opposite sides of the surface but their separation is negligibly small.   Let k_a represent the current per unit width of surface (directed away from the reader).   Then (A6-1) gives

$$k_a \, \Delta l = \frac{1}{\mu_0} \mathbf{I} \cos \left(\frac{\pi}{2} - \alpha \right) \Delta l = \frac{1}{\mu_0} \mathbf{I} \sin \alpha \, \Delta l,$$

since the line integral is zero except along BC, and the result can be expressed vectorially as

$$k_a = \frac{1}{\mu_0} \mathbf{I} \times \mathbf{n}. \tag{A6-6}$$

Note that the surface currents exist and contribute to the magnetic field even if $\mathbf{j}_a$ vanishes, as is the case when $\mathbf{I}$ is constant throughout the medium.

The divergence equation does not require generalization for a permeable medium as (A2-1) holds for all currents, including Ampèrian. However, if we integrate (A5-3) through a volume τ which is bounded by a closed surface s, and use (A3-6), we have

$$\int_\tau \mathbf{\nabla} \cdot (\mu_0 \mathbf{H} + \mathbf{I}) d\tau = \int_s \mu_0 \mathbf{H} \cdot d\mathbf{s} + \int_\tau \mathbf{\nabla} \cdot \mathbf{I} d\tau = 0,$$

or

$$\int_s \mu_0 \mathbf{H} \cdot d\mathbf{s} = - \int_\tau \mathbf{\nabla} \cdot \mathbf{I} d\tau.$$

If this relation is compared with (14-1), which can be written

$$\int_s \kappa_0 \mathbf{E} \cdot d\mathbf{s} = - \int_\tau \mathbf{\nabla} \cdot \mathbf{P} d\tau$$

when $\sum q = 0$, it is clear that $-\mathbf{\nabla} \cdot \mathbf{I}$ plays the same role in a permeable medium as $-\mathbf{\nabla} \cdot \mathbf{P}$ in a dielectric. In accord with historical practice, it is called the *pole-strength per unit volume*. Similarly, at the surface of a permeable medium, $\mathbf{I} \cdot \mathbf{n}$ is called the *pole-strength per unit area*. Essentially, these designations provide the Ampèrian definition of pole-strength. Thus, the ends of a thin longitudinally magnetized rod of cross section S constitute poles whose strengths are IS and $-IS$, respectively.

In order to complete our discussion of the current-interaction approach to magnetism we must demonstrate that Ampère's Formula (A1-1) leads to Coulomb's Law (37-2). This can be done by calculating the force between two long thin uniformly magnetized rods, as shown in the next article.

A7. Coulomb's Law. Let us consider two long thin magnets whose cross sections are uniform but not necessarily circular. To avoid excessive use of subscripts and to be consistent with (37-2), we will distinguish quantities pertaining to one magnet from those pertaining to the other, when necessary, by prime accents. Then the magnetizations are $\mathbf{I}$, $\mathbf{I}'$ and the cross sections are S, S', respectively, the magnetizations being along the magnets and hence perpendicular to the cross sections. From (A6-2) the Ampèrian current densities vanish within the magnets, as $\mathbf{I}$ and $\mathbf{I}'$ are assumed to be constants. However, from (A6-6) there are surface current densities $k_a = \mathbf{I}/\mu_0$ and $k'_a = \mathbf{I}'/\mu_0$ which are directed *around* the cylindrical surfaces of the magnets. The end surfaces, being cross sections, are devoid of surface currents but, as explained in art. A6, they constitute poles whose positive strengths are $m \equiv IS = \mu_0 k_a S$ and $m' \equiv I'S' = \mu_0 k'_a S'$, respectively.

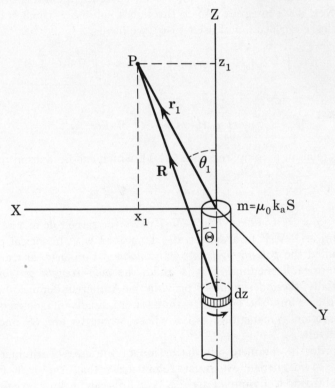

Fig. 314

We are now ready to calculate the forces on the magnets, which we suppose to be long enough to be considered infinite. It is clear that these forces are, in effect, the forces on the cylindrical current sheets formed by the surface currents. The magnets are placed so that the separation of their positive ends is large compared with the dimensions of S and S', but small compared with the separation of the negative ends.

The first step in the calculation is to find the magnetic intensity* due to the unprimed magnet. With axes and distances as shown in Fig. 314, the contribution to the field at $P(x_1, z_1)$ made by the elementary length dz of the magnet is, from (69-9),

$$d\mathbf{H}_1 - \frac{(k_a dz)S}{4\pi R^3}\left\{\mathbf{R}_u(2\cos\Theta) + \mathbf{\Theta}_u(\sin\Theta)\right\},$$

where $\mathbf{R}_u$ and $\mathbf{\Theta}_u$ are unit vectors in the directions of increasing R and Θ, respectively. This results from the fact that the element dz is equivalent to a current $k_a dz$ in a small circuit of area S. To simplify integration we substitute

$$\mathbf{R}_u = \mathbf{i}\sin\Theta + \mathbf{k}\cos\Theta,$$

$$\mathbf{\Theta}_u = \mathbf{i}\cos\Theta - \mathbf{k}\sin\Theta,$$

and then express R and Θ in terms of x and z, obtaining

$$\mathbf{H}_1 = \frac{k_a S}{4\pi}\left\{\mathbf{i}\int_{-\infty}^{0}\frac{3x_1(z_1-z)dz}{[x_1{}^2+(z_1-z)^2]^{5/2}} - \mathbf{k}\int_{-\infty}^{0}\frac{[x_1{}^2-2(z_1-z)^2]dz}{[x_1{}^2+(z_1-z)^2]^{5/2}}\right\}$$

$$= \frac{k_a S}{4\pi}\left|\frac{\mathbf{i}x_1+\mathbf{k}(z_1-z)}{[x_1{}^2+(z_1-z)^2]^{3/2}}\right|_{-\infty}^{0} = \frac{m(\mathbf{i}x_1+\mathbf{k}z_1)}{4\pi\mu_0(x_1{}^2+z_1{}^2)^{3/2}}.$$

The evaluation of the integrals is left to the reader, as they reduce easily to standard forms. Since $\mathbf{r}_1 = \mathbf{i}x_1 + \mathbf{k}z_1$, the magnetic intensity has the simple form

$$\mathbf{H}_1 = \frac{m\mathbf{r}_1}{4\pi\mu_0 r_1{}^3}, \tag{A7-1}$$

that is, it has the magnitude $m/4\pi\mu_0 r_1{}^2$ and it is directed radially away from m. This corresponds exactly to (38-2).

The next step is to locate the pole m at $P'(x_2, z_2)$, a distance $\mathbf{r}'$ from m', with axes and other distances as shown in Fig. 315. Here the cross section of m' has been exaggerated relative to that of m for clarity. First we must find the force on the elementary length dz', that is, the force on a current $k'_a dz'$ in a small circuit of area S'. From (A1-3) this is seen to be

$$d\mathscr{F}' = \oint (k'_a dz')d\mathbf{l}' \times (\mu_0\mathbf{H}_1) = \frac{m(k'_a dz')}{4\pi}\oint\frac{d\mathbf{l}'\times\mathbf{r}_1}{r_1{}^3}.$$

---

* Historically, it is customary to employ $\mathbf{H}$ rather than $\mathbf{B}$ when forces on magnets are involved.

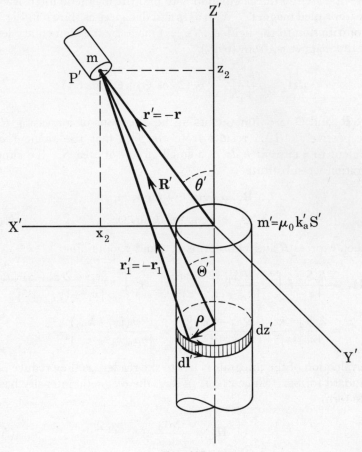

Fig. 315

As in art. 69, $\mathbf{R}' = R'(\mathbf{i} \sin \Theta' + \mathbf{k}' \cos \Theta')$, $\boldsymbol{\rho}' = \mathbf{i}'x' + \mathbf{j}'y'$ and $\mathbf{r}'_1 = -\mathbf{r}_1 = \mathbf{R}' - \boldsymbol{\rho}'$, with $r'_1 \equiv r_1$. Hence, second order terms being neglected,

$$\frac{1}{r_1{}^3} = \frac{1}{R'^3\left(1 - 2\dfrac{x'}{R'} \sin \Theta'\right)^{3/2}} = \frac{1}{R'^3}\left(1 + 3\,\frac{x'}{R'} \sin \Theta'\right)$$

and

$$d\mathscr{F}' = -\frac{m(k'_a dz')}{4\pi R'^3} \oint \left(1 + 3\,\frac{x'}{R'} \sin \Theta'\right)(d\mathbf{l}' \times \mathbf{R}' - d\mathbf{l}' \times \boldsymbol{\rho}').$$

The integration required here is exactly the same as that carried out in the derivation of (69-9), so we have at once

$$d\mathscr{F}' = -\frac{m(k'_a S')dz'}{4\pi R'^3}\left(2k'+3\frac{\sin\Theta'}{R'}j'\times\mathbf{R}'\right)$$

$$= -\frac{mm'}{4\pi\mu_0 R'^3}\{i'(3\sin\Theta'\cos\Theta'+k'(2-3\sin^2\Theta'))\}dz'.$$

In terms of x' and z' the total force on the primed magnet is given by

$$\mathscr{F}' = -\frac{mm'}{4\pi\mu_0}\left\{i'\int_{-\infty}^0\frac{3x_2(z_2-z')dz'}{[x_2{}^2+(z_2-z')^2]^{5/2}}-k'\int_{-\infty}^0\frac{[x_2{}^2-2(z_2-z')^2]dz'}{[x_2{}^2+(z_2-z')^2]^{5/2}}\right\}$$

$$= -\frac{mm'}{4\pi\mu_0}\left|\frac{i'x_2+k'(z_2-z')}{[x_2{}^2+(z_2-z')^2]^{3/2}}\right|_{-\infty}^0 = -\frac{mm'(i'x_2+k'z_2)}{4\pi\mu_0(x_2{}^2+z_2{}^2)^{3/2}}.$$

This reduces to

$$\mathscr{F}' = -\frac{mm'\mathbf{r}'}{4\pi\mu_0 r'^3} = \frac{mm'\mathbf{r}}{4\pi\mu_0 r^3},$$

since $\mathbf{r}' = -\mathbf{r}$, with $r' \equiv r$. A similar direct calculation of the force on the unprimed magnet gives

$$\mathscr{F} = -\frac{m'm\mathbf{r}}{4\pi\mu_0 r^3} = \frac{m'm\mathbf{r}'}{4\pi\mu_0 r'^3},$$

confirming the law of action and reaction for the force between two magnets. This is to be expected, in spite of (A1-1) and (A1-4), as it can be shown* that the law holds for any two complete circuits and, consequently, for the groups of Ampèrian circuits of which the magnets are composed. Thus, the force on either magnet due to the other has the magnitude $\mathscr{F} = mm'/4\pi\mu_0 r^2$, which is Coulomb's Law.†

The foregoing analysis can be extended without difficulty to the calculation of the forces on magnets of finite length and the torques on dipoles, if these are desired. In any event it is clear that the total forces on a magnet, although actually distributed throughout the magnet, *appear* to be concentrated at its poles, since these forces are simply expressed in terms of the pole-strengths and the field *at the poles*. It is this convenient property of poles that led originally to the pole concept.

REFERENCE

"The Teaching of Electricity and Magnetism at the College Level", *Am. J. of Phys.* **18**, 1–25: 69–88 (1950).

* Page and Adams, *Am. Jour. Physics* **13**, 141 (1945).

† Pole-strength sometimes is defined in such a way that the force per unit pole is **B**, rather than **H** as above. In this case Coulomb's Law assumes the form $\mathscr{F} = \mu_0 mm'/4\pi r^2$.

Appendix B

VALUES OF PHYSICAL CONSTANTS
AND ATOMIC WEIGHTS

B1. Physical Constants. In 1963 the National Academy of Sciences–National Research Council (NAS–NRC) Committee on Fundamental Constants recommended a new set of mutually consistent "best" values for the basic physical constants. (See, for example, *Physics Today*, Feb. 1964, pp. 48–49.) Some of these values, together with a few derived from them, are listed below for convenient reference. Note that particle masses are given in kilograms and also in atomic mass units, since both values are of interest. By definition, the atomic mass unit (designated by u) is exactly one-twelfth the mass of the carbon isotope C^{12}.

Velocity of light	$2.997925(10)^8$ meter/sec
Elementary charge	
Electron	$-1.60210(10)^{-19}$ coulomb
Proton	$1.60210(10)^{-19}$ coulomb
Avogadro's number	$6.02252(10)^{26}$ molecule/kg-mol
Loschmidt's number	$2.68699(10)^{25}$ molecule/meter^3
Rest mass	
Electron	$9.1091(10)^{-31}$ kg; $5.48597(10)^{-4}$ u
Proton	$1.67252(10)^{-27}$ kg; 1.00727663 u
Neutron	$1.67482(10)^{-27}$ kg; 1.0086654 u
Atomic mass unit	$1.660435(10)^{-27}$ kg
Mass ratio	
Proton/Electron	$1.8361(10)^3$
Neutron/Electron	$1.8386(10)^3$
Faraday's constant	$9.64870(10)^7$ coulomb/kg-equiv.
Planck's constant	$6.6256(10)^{-34}$ joule sec
Electron charge/mass	$-1.758796(10)^{11}$ coulomb/kg
Gas constant	$8.3143(10)^3$ joule/deg kg-mol
Gas standard volume	$2.24136(10)^1$ meter^3/kg-mol

Boltzmann's constant $1.38054(10)^{-23}$ joule/deg molecule
Gravitational constant $6.670(10)^{-11}$ newton meter^2/kg^2

B2. Atomic Weights. The presently accepted physical scale of atomic weights* is based on the choice of 12-even for the atomic weight of C^{12}. Then the atomic weight of any substance is the ratio of its atomic mass to the atomic mass unit defined in art. B1. In the case of a natural substance, which occurs as a mixture of isotopes, the observed average atomic mass is used. Thus, the atomic weight of C^{12} is 12-even but that of natural C is 12.01115. Since 12 kilograms of C^{12} and 12.01115 kilograms of natural C each constitute a kilogram-mol (art. 57), these amounts contain the same number of atoms, namely, $6.02252(10)^{26}$.

Some commonly used natural atomic weights are given below.

Aluminum	26.9815	Mercury	200.59
Bismuth	208.980	Nickel	58.71
Chlorine	35.453	Nitrogen	14.0067
Copper	63.54	Oxygen	15.9994
Gold	196.967	Silver	107.870
Hydrogen	1.00797	Sulfur	32.064
Iron	55.847	Uranium	238.03
Lead	207.19	Zinc	65.37

*Nier, A. O., *The Physics Teacher* **1** (1), 11 (Apr. 1963).

INDEX

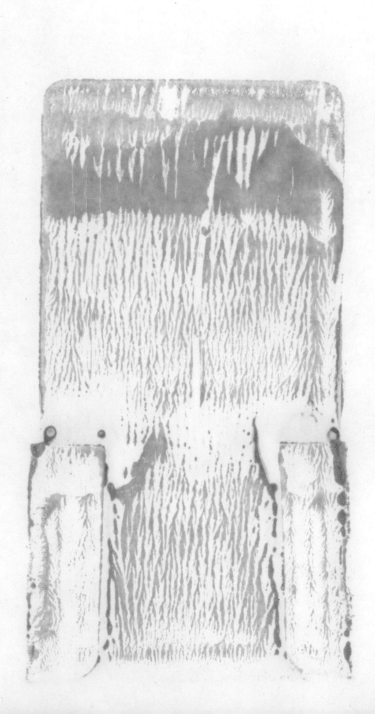